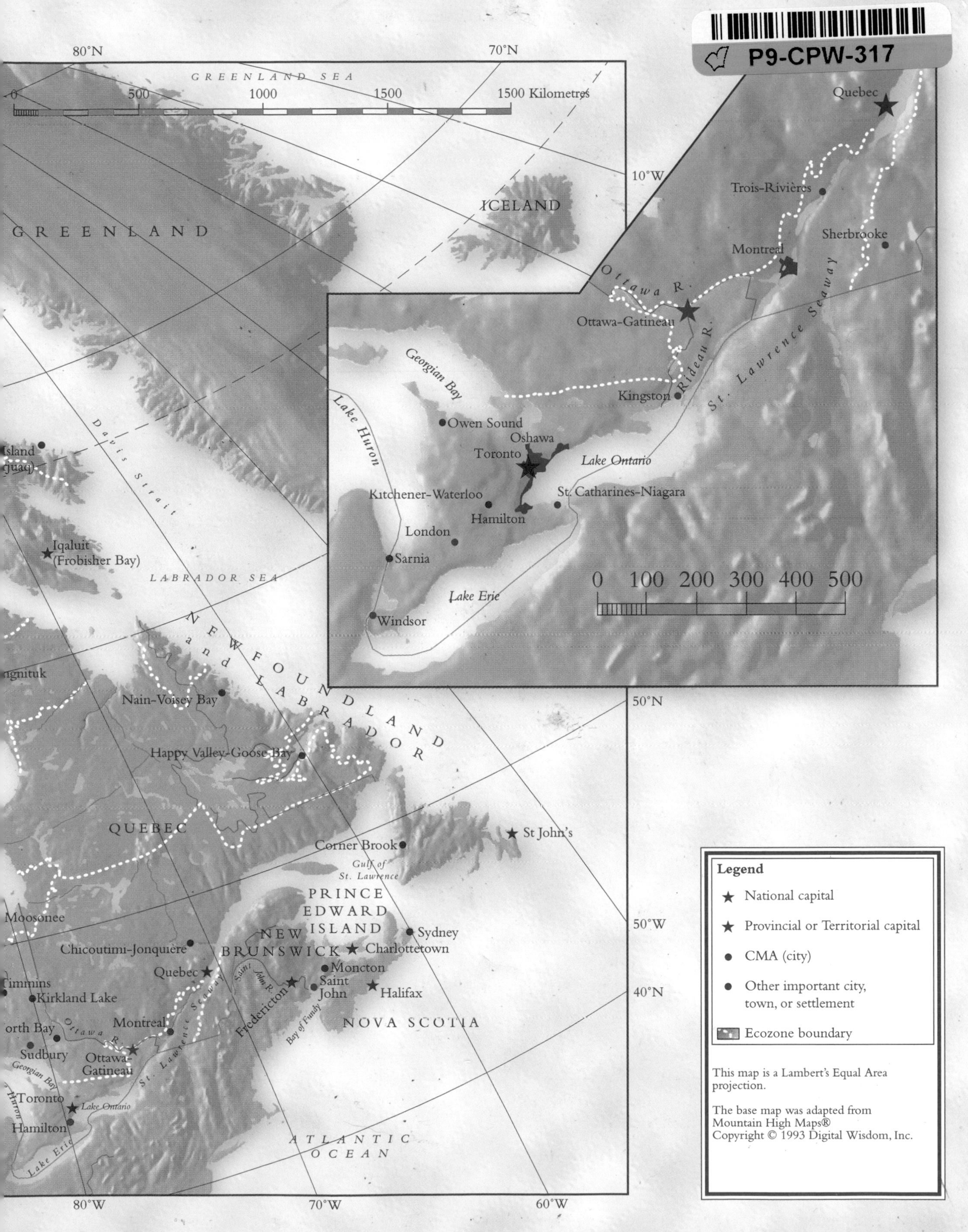

P9-CPW-317
80°N
70°N
GREENLAND SEA
0
500
1000
1500
1500 Kilometres
10°W
ICELAND
GREENLAND
Quebec
Trois-Rivières
Sherbrooke
Montreal
Ottawa R.
Ottawa-Gatineau
Rideau R.
St. Lawrence Seaway
Georgian Bay
Lake Huron
Kingston
Owen Sound
Oshawa
Toronto
Lake Ontario
Kitchener-Waterloo
St. Catharines-Niagara
Hamilton
London
Sarnia
Lake Erie
Windsor
0 100 200 300 400 500
Davis Strait
Iqaluit (Frobisher Bay)
LABRADOR SEA
NEWFOUNDLAND and LABRADOR
Nain-Voisey Bay
Happy Valley-Goose Bay
50°N
QUEBEC
St John's
Corner Brook
Gulf of St. Lawrence
PRINCE EDWARD ISLAND
NEW BRUNSWICK
Moosonee
Sydney
Chicoutimi-Jonquière
Charlottetown
Quebec
Moncton
Timmins
Kirkland Lake
Saint John
Halifax
Fredericton
Saint John R.
Bay of Fundy
NOVA SCOTIA
Montreal
Ottawa R.
North Bay
Sudbury
Ottawa-Gatineau
Georgian Bay
Toronto
Lake Ontario
Hamilton
Lake Erie
ATLANTIC OCEAN
50°W
40°N
80°W
70°W
60°W
Legend
National capital
Provincial or Territorial capital
CMA (city)
Other important city, town, or settlement
Ecozone boundary
This map is a Lambert's Equal Area projection.
The base map was adapted from Mountain High Maps® Copyright © 1993 Digital Wisdom, Inc.

Making Connections

Canada's Geography Second Edition

Bruce W. Clark **John K. Wallace** **Kim M. Earle**

Toronto

Library and Archives Canada Cataloguing in Publication

Clark, Bruce, 1948–
Making connections : Canada's Geography / Bruce Clark, John K. Wallace, Kim Earle.

ISBN 0-13-198089-0

1. Canada—Geography—Textbooks. I. Wallace, John K., 1946– II. Earle, Kim III. Title.

FC57.C527 2006 917.1 C2005-904330-X

Publisher: Susan Cox
Product Manager: Patti Henderson
Executive Editor: Elynor Kagan
Developmental Editors: Jennifer Howse, Francine Geraci
Production Editors: Milena Mazzolin, Ann Echlin
Copy Editors: Ann Echlin, Gail Copeland
Proofreaders: Anita Levin, Marg Bukta, Susan McNish
Statistics Researcher: Mary Bissell
Production Coordinator: Helen Luxton
Permissions/Photo Researcher: Sandy Cooke
Design Team: Claire Milne, Debbie Kumpf, Gerry Dunn, David Cheung
Illustrator: Deborah Crowle
Cover Design: Julia Hall

Cover Photograph: Altitude/Jourdan, François

1 2 3 4 5 TCP 10 09 08 07 06

Printed and bound in Canada

The publisher has taken every care to meet or exceed industry specifications for the manufacturing of textbooks. The spine and endpapers of this sewn book have been reinforced with special fabric for extra binding strength. The cover is a premium, polymer-reinforced material designed to provide long life and withstand rugged use. Mylar gloss lamination has been applied for further durability.

Table of Contents

Acknowledgements

The creation of *Making Connections: Canada's Geography* involved the contributions of many more people than the three whose names appear on the cover. We would like to thank the staff at Pearson Education Canada (Susan Cox, Patti Henderson, Elynor Kagan, Francine Geraci, Ann Echlin, Helen Luxton, Sandy Cooke, Debbie Kumpf, Gerry Dunn, and David Cheung) for their professionalism and dedication to the project. In particular we would like to thank Jennifer Howse and Milena Mazzolin for their unceasing commitment to make this book as good as it possibly could be and for their upbeat nature during the busiest times. We would also like to thank our partners, Laurie Wallace, June Wan, and Owen Earle for their support and for their patience during the many hours when our attention was focused on the creation of this book.

John Wallace, Bruce Clark, and Kim Earle

The publisher of this book would like to acknowledge the dedicated efforts of the team of reviewers for their important suggestions and helpful comments at the various stages of development of this textbook.

Gerald Bell
Brian Gallagher
Terrence Hourigan
Ivan Ius
Joe Maurice
Helena Pereira Raso
Pina Sacco
Louise Savella
Elizabeth A. Smith

The publisher would also like to thank the teachers who responded to survey questions for providing some very thoughtful and helpful comments and suggestions for changes to this new edition.

To the Student

Geography is much more than a collection of facts about where things are located and why they are there. Most importantly, it is a subject that connects physical and social perspectives to the study of people, places, and environments. Through the use of *Making Connections: Canada's Geography*, you will have an opportunity to extend your ability to see Canada and the world as a geographer does.

In particular you will

- learn about the physical, economic, cultural, political, and environmental systems of Canada and how they interact with each other
- examine the relationships between people and the urban, cultural, and economic environments within which they live
- study the connections that exist between Canada and the rest of the world
- consider how constant change affects Canada and the world and how change presents us with both challenges and opportunities
- learn how to make more informed judgments about the many issues that face us as Canadians
- improve your ability to use the "toolbox" that supports the geographer, such as the Internet, satellite imagery, geographic information systems (GIS), and the Global Positioning System (GPS)

A Note to Teachers and Students: How to Use This Book

Before we began this revision of *Making Connections*, we asked students and teachers to tell us what worked well in the first edition, and what they thought we should change for this edition. We have incorporated many of their comments and suggestions, and we think you will find this new edition more student- *and* teacher-friendly.

Take a moment to scan this book, beginning with the features highlighted below. They will help you to see how this book is organized and how to use it to your best advantage.

- **Unit 2, Methods of Geographic Inquiry**, is a special section that you can use as a reference tool throughout this course. It contains activities and information that will help you develop and apply key geography skills you will need to use when you are learning about the geography of Canada.

UNIT 2
Methods of Geographic Inquiry

- **Key ideas and key terms** are found at the beginning of every chapter. These features can be used as study aids for reviewing and preparing for tests. All key terms are defined in the **glossary** at the end of the book as well as within each chapter as they are introduced.

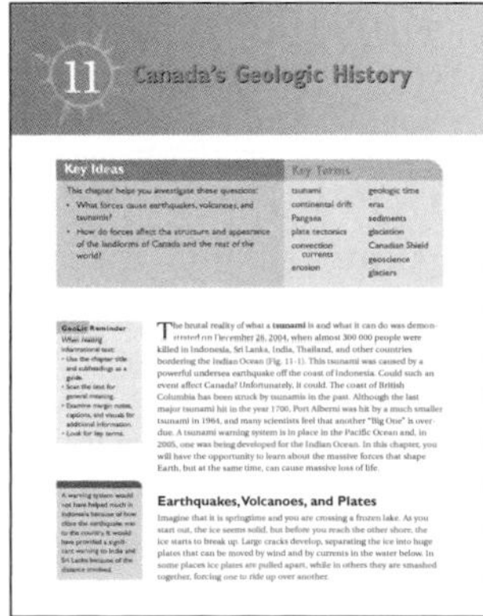
11 Canada's Geologic History

Key Ideas

Key Terms

Earthquakes, Volcanoes, and Plates

- **Visuals:** A wide variety of **maps, charts, graphs, photos, and diagrams** are included.

- **GeoLit Reminders** are new to this edition. They are designed to provide tips or suggestions to help you understand the concepts or topics in that chapter.

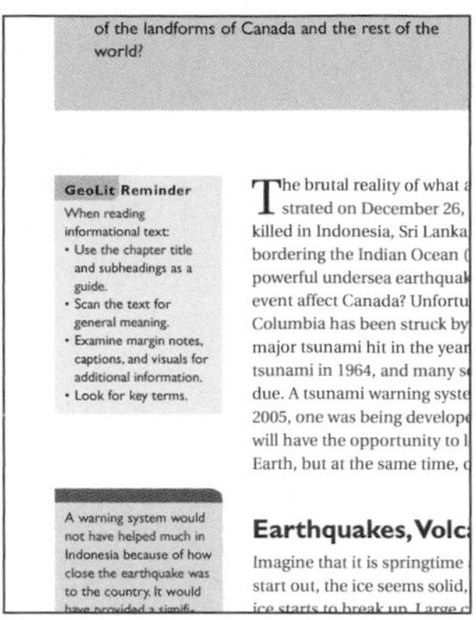

of the landforms of Canada and the rest of the world?

GeoLit Reminder

When reading informational text:
- Use the chapter title and subheadings as a guide.
- Scan the text for general meaning.
- Examine margin notes, captions, and visuals for additional information.
- Look for key terms.

- **Geographical information and topic hints** are set up as margin notes throughout each chapter.

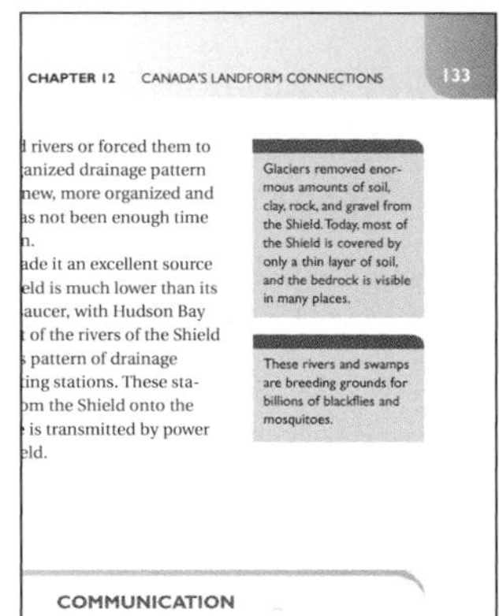

CHAPTER 12 CANADA'S LANDFORM CONNECTIONS 133

Glaciers removed enormous amounts of soil, clay, rock, and gravel from the Shield. Today, most of the Shield is covered by only a thin layer of soil, and the bedrock is visible in many places.

These rivers and swamps are breeding grounds for billions of blackflies and mosquitoes.

COMMUNICATION

- **Issues and Case Studies** present interesting aspects or viewpoints on the geography topics within a specific chapter. We provide some background information to help you understand more about each topic, and ask questions to help you uncover important aspects of opinions or facts.

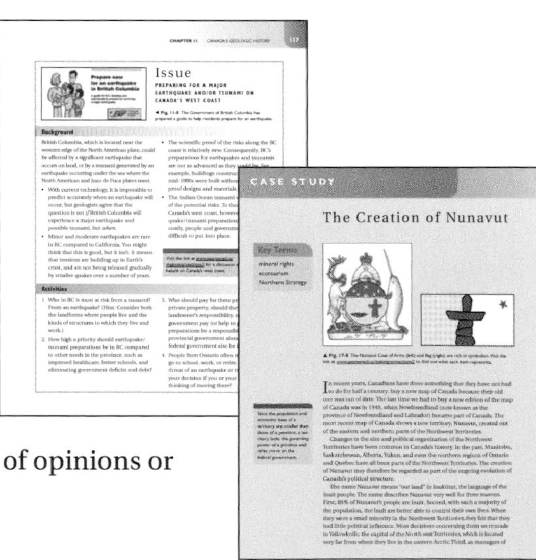

Issue

PREPARING FOR A MAJOR EARTHQUAKE AND/OR TSUNAMI ON CANADA'S WEST COAST

Background

Activities

CASE STUDY

The Creation of Nunavut

Key Terms

- **Questions and Activities** are included throughout the text and at the end of each chapter. Question blocks are divided into *four* groups according to the types of answers required:
  - *Knowledge and Understanding* questions review facts and concepts and the understanding of their meaning and significance
  - *Thinking* questions focus on the use of critical and creative thinking skills, including research; gathering information; analysing, evaluating, and synthesizing information; and inquiry, problem-solving, and decision-making
  - *Communication* questions develop the ability to convey meaning through a variety of forms including oral, written, and visual
  - *Application* questions focus on the use of knowledge and skills to make connections within and between various contexts

- **GeoCareers** present information on types of industries or specific jobs that have application to geography topics or concepts. You can research updated information on these careers by using the Internet links provided.

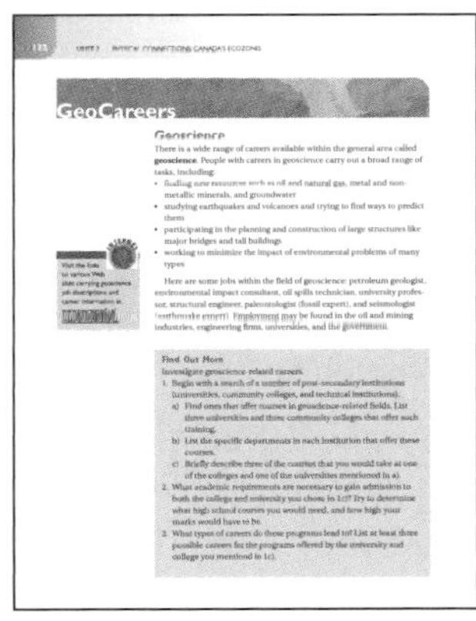

GeoCareers

Geoscience

There is a wide range of careers available within the general area called **geoscience**. People with careers in geoscience carry out a broad range of tasks, including

- studying earthquakes and volcanoes and trying to find ways to predict them
- participating in the planning and construction of large structures like major bridges and tall buildings
- working to minimize the impact of environmental problems of many types

Here are some jobs within the field of geoscience: petroleum geologist, environmental impact consultant, oil spills technician, university professor, structural engineer, paleontologist (fossil expert), and seismologist. Employment may be found in the oil and mining industries, engineering firms, universities, and the government.

Find Out More

Investigate geoscience-related careers.

1. Begin with a search of a number of post-secondary institutions (universities, community colleges, and technical institutions).
   a) Find ones that offer courses in geoscience-related fields. List three universities and three community colleges that offer such training.
   b) List the specific departments in each institution that offer these courses.
   c) Briefly describe three of the courses that you would take at one of the colleges and one of the universities mentioned in a).
2. What academic requirements are necessary to gain admission to both the college and university you chose in 1c)? Try to determine what high school courses you would need, and how high your marks would have to be.
3. What types of careers do these programs lead to? List at least three possible careers for the programs offered by the university and college you mentiond in 1c).

- **Culminating Activities** tie chapter ideas together by applying the information in an interesting and engaging case-study style format.

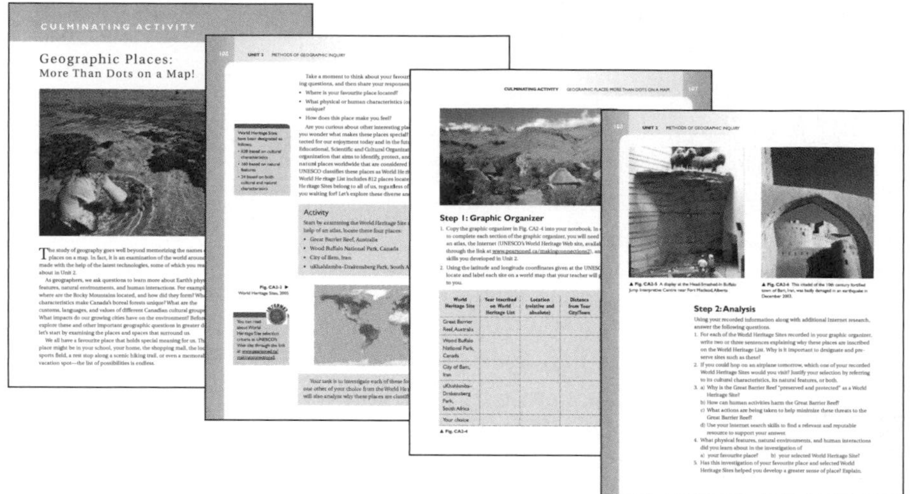

- **GIS Activities and Internet Research Activities** help to develop technology skills and are identified in the margin by GIS or Internet activity icons.

UNIT 1

Canadian Connections: An Overview

NASA scientists created this image of Earth using city lights as seen from space. Where is your community on this image? How "bright" does it appear compared to other areas of Canada and the world? What do the differences in lighting mean? What connections do you have with places in other parts of the world? If you have friends or relatives in other parts of the world, do they live in an area that is brighter or darker than where you live?

Location is just one of the ways we may be connected with other people. The ways we run our industries, what we buy and sell, our choices about how to dispose of our waste, how much pollution we produce, or whether we walk, drive, or take public transit show how we affect, and are affected by, people around the corner, or around the world. This book, and your study of Canadian geography, is all about connections—about your identity and how you relate to the world and, in particular, to our country, Canada.

1 Exploring Canada: A Study in Connections

Key Ideas

This chapter helps you investigate these questions:

- What are my connections to Canada and the world?
- How much pride do I have for Canada?
- What is Canada's position on the world stage?

Key Terms

geography

population density

geographical systems

global connections

statistical analysis

geotechnologies

mental maps

gross domestic product (GDP) per capita

absolute measure

relative measure

Human Development Index (HDI)

Gender Empowerment Measure (GEM)

Environmental Sustainability Index (ESI)

▼ **Fig. 1-1** What *connections* do you see on this satellite image of Earth? You can learn more about satellite imaging in Chapter 7.

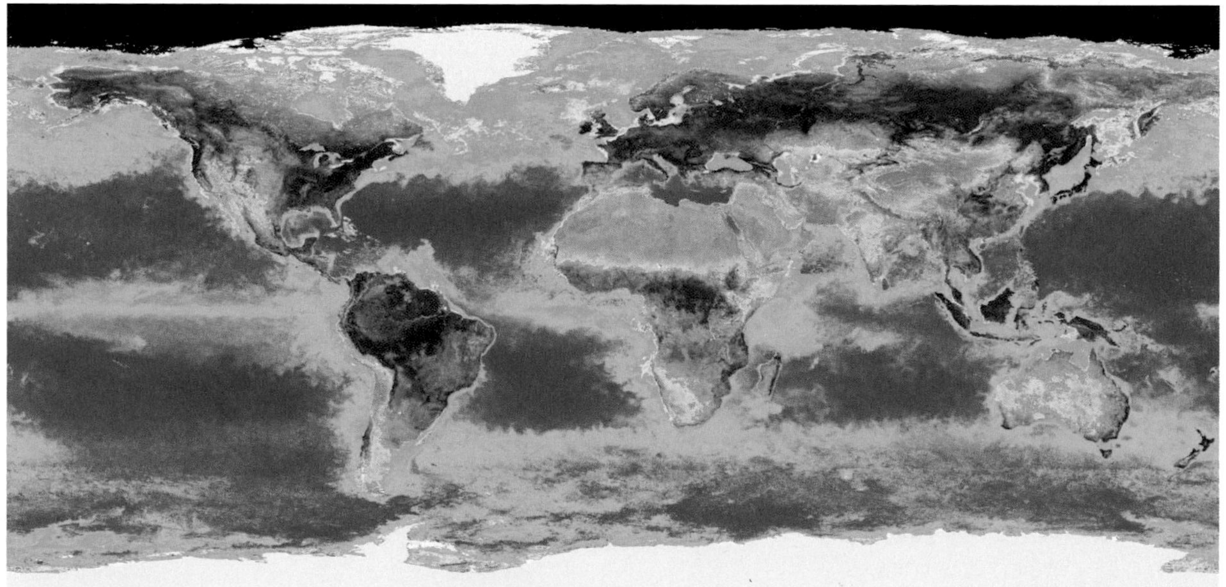

Experts say that the best way to learn **geography** is to do geography, so here goes!

Satellites have given us the opportunity to "see" Earth in an entirely different way. Fig. 1-1 is just one such image of our home. See if you can answer the following questions about this image.

1. What do you think is being shown in the image? Give specific evidence to support your answer. Here is a hint: The legend has two different but related colour scales, one for land and the other for oceans.

How did you do with this question? It was quite a challenge, considering that you were given so little help to get started. Congratulations if you were able to figure out that the image shows the density of vegetation—both on land and in the oceans. When you read the colour scales on page 4 from left to right, the colours indicate vegetation densities from the least (sometimes none) to the greatest. It may be useful to have an atlas handy as you continue to Question 2.

2. First, look at the land areas in the image.
   a) Using the atlas, name an area with no vegetation. What colour is this area in the image?
   b) Where do you find areas with very limited vegetation (yellow-brown areas)? Name one such area from each of four different continents.
   c) Where do you find areas with the most vegetation (very dark green areas)? Name one such area, again from each of four different continents.
3. Second, look at Canada.
   a) Where do you find areas with the most vegetation (very dark green areas)? What type of vegetation is found in these areas? Did you get your answer from a book or is it based on your personal experience?
   b) In what part of Canada do you find the least vegetation? What type of vegetation do you find there?
   c) Between these two **extremes**, you will find two areas of pale green. What type(s) of vegetation do you find in these areas? Why?
4. Next, look at the oceans. Again, your atlas may be of help here.
   a) What type of vegetation lives in the ocean, i.e., what is being shown here?
   b) What parts of the ocean have the least vegetation (areas of dark blue to purple)? Why might this be?

Look at the vegetation regions map of Canada in your atlas.

extremes
two things that are as different from each other as possible

c) Look closely for areas with large amounts of vegetation (areas of yellow, orange, and red). These areas tend to be related to one or more of three physical geography factors. Name these factors, and give at least three examples of each. Bonus: Explain how each of these physical factors contributes to a high density of vegetation.

5. Now we come to the "so what?" part of this exercise. Your study of Canadian geography is all about *making connections;* hence the title of this book. Now it is time to make connections starting with the information in Fig. 1-1. Describe the connection between each of the following. You may want to use your atlas to help you with these questions.
   a) What is the connection between vegetation density and high **population density**? Are you surprised by this relationship? Why or why not?
   b) What is the connection between vegetation density and low population density?
   c) Given the ocean vegetation density that you see, where would you look for the largest whale populations? Why?
   d) What is the connection between vegetation density and climate?

Population density can be calculated by dividing population by area. It is most often expressed in units of people/km^2.

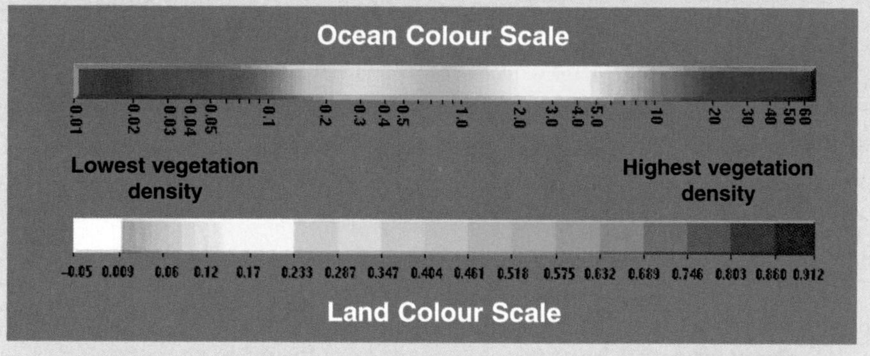

A Student's Connections

Consider the geographic connections of a Canadian student who lives in Oshawa, Ontario (Fig. 1-2).

Like all students, she has connections at a local, regional, provincial, national, and international level. Some of her connections are obvious. For example, she has ties with distant parts of Canada when she visits her sister at university in New Brunswick, or stays with her uncle and aunt on their farm in Alberta in the summer. She has regional ties because she reads the Toronto newspaper that her family buys every day and because she often goes to the Oshawa Civic Auditorium to see the Oshawa Generals play the Kingston Frontenacs in a hockey game.

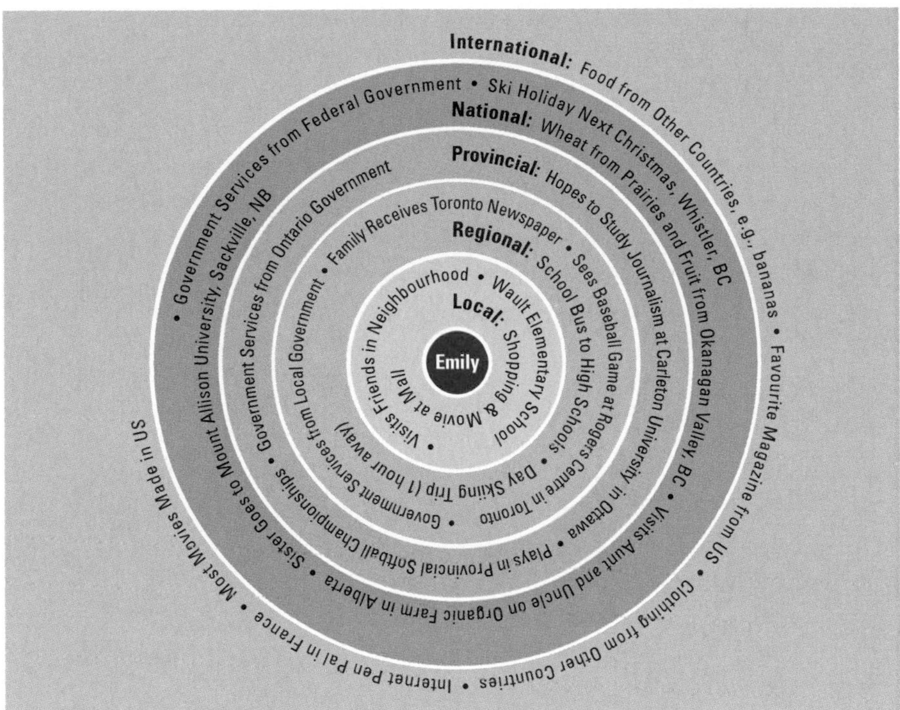

◀ **Fig. 1-2** Just like this student, every Canadian has connections at many different levels.

Other connections are less clear. For example, a close look at the labels on her clothing would reveal that some of it was made in countries such as China and India. When she broke her leg cross-country skiing last year, the money for her treatment and hospital stay came from taxpayers in the rest of Canada as well as in Ontario. Are you aware of the ways in which you are connected to the rest of the world?

Five focus areas are important to geographers in trying to understand all the connections that exist in the world.

1. *Reasons why things are located where they are.* For example, a geographer might study why the soils in one area are better for farming than those in another area, or why Tim Hortons would choose a particular location for a new restaurant.
2. ***Geographical systems** that shape our world.* For example, a geographer might want to understand better the forces that cause devastating earthquakes, or the relationship between immigration and the need for the construction of a new school.
3. *Interactions between people and the environment they live in.* For example, a geographer might want to investigate the impact of SUV ownership on climate change, or consider how better sewage treatment systems could reduce water pollution.

4. ***Global connections*** *between regions and countries.* For example, a geographer might study the impact of foreign tourism on the economy of a Caribbean island, or examine the effectiveness of the foreign aid that Canada gives to poorer nations.
5. *Special tools and skills that geographers use.* For many years, geographers have used traditional tools, such as mapping, graphing, **statistical analysis**, and aerial photography, in their work. In recent years, a host of new **geotechnologies**, such as remote sensing, GPS, and GIS, have revolutionized the field of geography.

You will have the opportunity to learn about geotechnologies in Chapters 3, 5, and 7.

INTERNET

If you would like to learn more about careers in geography, check www.pearsoned.ca/makingconnections2.

Your Connections

By using *Making Connections: Canada's Geography*, you will have a chance to learn about all these aspects of geography and to develop a better understanding of your connections. The activities that follow provide a starting point.

A MENTAL MAP OF CANADA

We use an atlas or road map to help us find the location of a place or to discover some missing information. More often, we make use of a collection of special maps that exist in our minds—what we might call our **mental maps**. These mental maps are very important since they provide the basis on which we make decisions and take actions. Some of these maps are much more complete and accurate than others. For example, your mental map of the house or apartment in which you live is going to be more precise than your mental map of New York City or New Zealand.

A very important mental map for any Canadian is that of our country.

1. Take an unlined sheet of 8½″ x 11″ paper. Turn it sideways, and then draw your mental map of Canada on it. Include any important geographic features you are aware of, such as provinces, main cities, water bodies, and land features. Do not look at someone else's map as you do this—remember, this is *your* mental map!
2. It is interesting to think about the reasons why your mental image looks like it does. Consider the features that you included. Why did you include some and leave others out? You should be able to identify at least two reasons why you are more familiar with certain parts of Canada than with others.
3. Compare your map with that of a classmate whose map seems quite different from yours. Can you determine why the differences exist?

Keep the map you have drawn. You may want to try drawing another mental map later in the course to see what you have learned.

AN INTRODUCTORY MAP OF CANADA

Develop a reference map of Canada that you can use and add to during this course. You can create this map in one of two ways: either with pencil and paper, or with GIS software. If you are doing the former, follow the instructions below. If you are using ArcView, your teacher will give you full instructions. Label the following on a blank map of Canada that your teacher will provide.

1. Provinces and territories
2. National, provincial, and territorial capitals
3. Additional cities: Vancouver, Calgary, Saskatoon, Thunder Bay, Windsor, London, Hamilton, Montreal, and Saint John
4. Lakes: each of the five Great Lakes, plus Winnipeg, Great Slave, and Great Bear
5. Rivers: Fraser, Mackenzie, Saskatchewan, St. Lawrence, and Ottawa
6. Large water bodies: Pacific Ocean, Atlantic Ocean, Arctic Ocean, Hudson Bay, the Gulf of St. Lawrence, and James Bay
7. Neighbours: the United States (including Alaska) and Greenland

This logo will tell you where a GIS exercise appears in this book.

▼ **Fig. 1-3** Saskatoon's city skyline is reflected in the South Saskatchewan River. Saskatoon is Saskatchewan's largest city and a busy hub of commerce and industry centred around technology and mining.

A CANADIAN

In the same way that we have a mental image of the map of Canada, we all have a stock of information about Canada's geography, history, and culture that shapes how we see ourselves as Canadians. Answer the following questions in your notebook. A warning, though: You may find some of them difficult.

1. What province or territory has one of the world's great stores of dinosaur bones?
2. In 2004, the CBC ran a series of television programs that asked Canadians to choose the Greatest Canadian of all time. Who was chosen for this honour?
3. Canada is the second-largest country in the world. What country is larger in area than Canada?
4. Which hockey team has won the Stanley Cup most often?
5. In 2004, Canada's foreign trade was closest to:
   a) $90 million per hour
   b) $90 million per day
   c) $90 million per week
   d) $90 million per month
   e) $90 million per year
6. Which prime minister was in power for the longest period of time?
7. Which of these materials is *not* mined in Canada?
   a) gold
   b) copper
   c) diamonds
   d) tin
   e) coal
8. What is the name of Canada's newest territory?
9. Which of these people is *not* Canadian?
   a) actor Kiefer Sutherland
   b) singer Shania Twain
   c) actor Angelina Jolie
   d) golfer Mike Weir
   e) singer Avril Lavigne

QUIZ

⑩ Which province joined Canada in 1949?

⑪ What is the name of the highest award that Canada gives for outstanding achievement and service to the country or to the world?

⑫ What is the name of the longest river in Canada?

⑬ Other than Great Britain (including Ireland) and France, what country is the origin of the greatest number of Canadian residents?

⑭ In terms of value, what is Canada's most important export **commodity**?

⑮ In what province or territory is Canada's highest mountain?

Bonus Question
(Yes, you can get more than 100% on this quiz!)

One of the celebrities mentioned in #9 is a relative of the person chosen as the Greatest Canadian (#2). Which celebrity is it, and what is their relationship?

The correct answers to this quiz can be found on page 18.

commodity
a product that is bought and sold

To learn more about Canada, go to www.pearsoned.ca/makingconnections2.

Canada on the World Stage

On what basis would you compare Canada with other countries such as Japan, Ethiopia, Argentina, or any other of the over 190 countries in the world? You could use many different types of measurements, including size, population, population density, and wealth.

Area

Canada is one of the world's largest countries. Fig. 1-4 compares the areas of the 10 largest countries in the world. It includes the areas of five other countries to give you a sense of the vastness of the 10 largest countries.

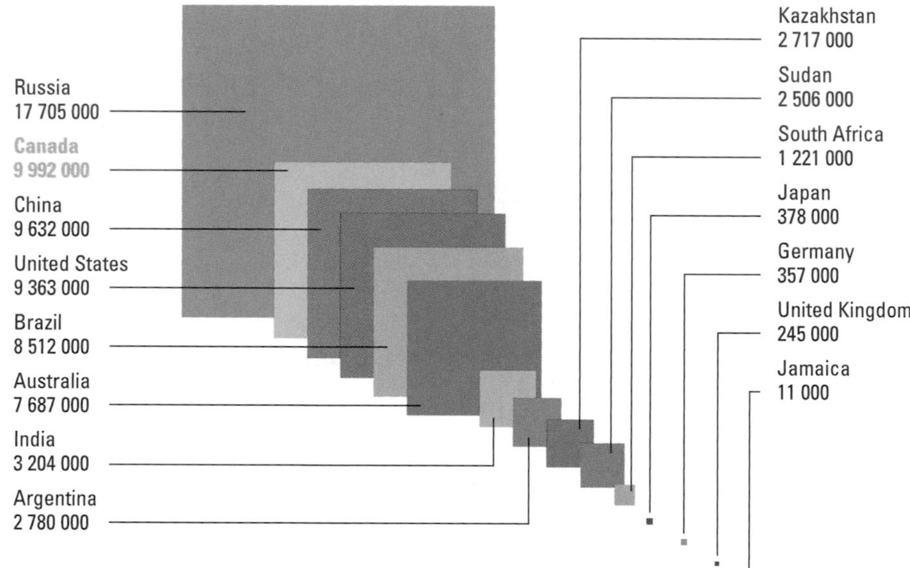

Fig. 1-4 ► The areas of the 10 largest countries in the world are listed first, followed by the areas of five other countries (in km^2).

Population

Compared to many other countries, Canada does not have that many people (Fig. 1-5). Our population of 32 000 000 in 2005 is far less than that of many countries. In fact, only one out of every 200 people in the world lives in Canada. Fig. 1-5 compares Canada with those countries with the largest populations. Keep in mind that the world's population is more than 6 billion.

Population Density

You have just seen that Canada is a very large country with a relatively small population. The relationship between a country's area and population can be shown using a simple measurement called population density. This can be calculated by dividing the country's population by its area in square kilometres. Let's calculate Canada's population density:

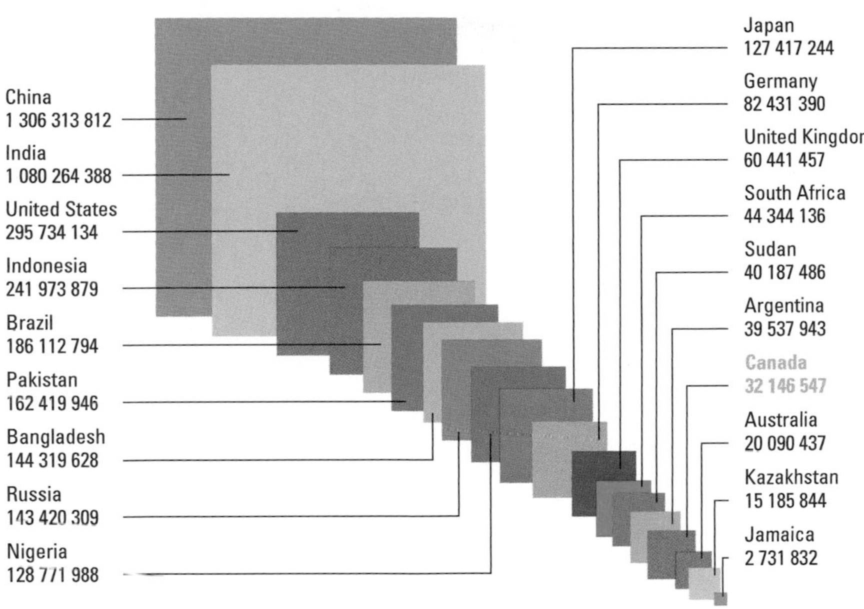

◀ **Fig. 1-5** The 10 countries with the largest populations are listed first, along with the other countries shown in Fig. 1-6. In 2005, Canada had the 35th largest population in the world.

32 000 000 people/9 992 000 km^2
= 3.2 people/km^2

This does not mean that there are three people living on each and every square kilometre of Canada. Rather, population density is just a way to express the relationship between the area and the population of a country.

Population densities vary enormously from country to country. Greenland, for example, has 0.03 people/km^2, and the Falkland Islands has 0.2 people/km^2. At the other extreme are crowded countries such as Singapore (6430 people/km^2). If we examine the population densities of the countries in Fig. 1-6, we see a smaller, but still significant, range of values.

To get a sense of what some different densities look like, examine Fig. 1-7.

Some areas in Canada have population densities of hundreds of people/km^2, while some large areas have no people.

Population Density (people/km^2), 2005

Country	Density	Country	Density
Argentina	14	Jamaica	248
Australia	3	Japan	337
Bangladesh	1002	Kazakhstan	6
Brazil	22	Nigeria	139
Canada	3	Pakistan	185
China	136	Russia	8
Germany	231	South Africa	36
India	341	Sudan	16
Indonesia	126	United Kingdom	248
		United States	31

◀ **Fig. 1-6** What do you notice about Canada's population density compared with countries that have the largest populations?

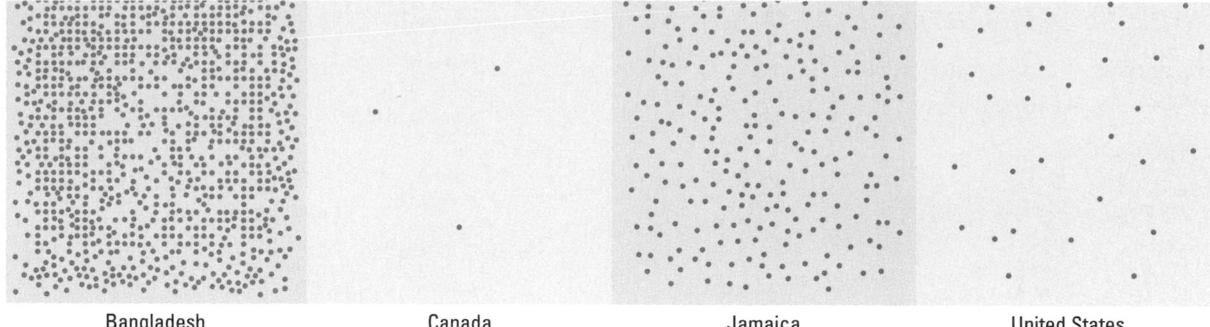

▲ **Fig. 1-7** Different population densities

Wealth

Canadians have higher average incomes than people in most other parts of the world. In fact, only seven countries (Luxembourg, the United States, Norway, Switzerland, Denmark, Ireland, and Iceland) have higher average incomes. Even Canadians with lower incomes might be considered wealthy by many people who live in Asia, Africa, or Latin America. It is not easy to measure a country's wealth in a clear and descriptive way. A commonly used measurement is **gross domestic product (GDP) per capita**. GDP is the value of all the goods and services produced in the country in a year. As such, it is a measure of the size of the entire economy. When the GDP is divided by the country's population, the result is an indication of the average wealth per person.

Per capita means per person. GDP per capita is often reported on a "purchasing power parity" (PPP) basis. This measure relates the GDP of the country to the cost of living in that country.

Many of the citizens of a country with a high GDP per capita are probably better able to afford the basics of life, namely, food, shelter, clothing, and medical care. They may also be able to afford some of the luxuries, such as cars, computers, and holidays. On the other hand, many citizens of countries with a low GDP per capita might have difficulty affording even basic needs. Of course, people live in various degrees of wealth and poverty in every country of the world, regardless of a country's GDP per capita.

GDP per capita varies enormously from country to country. A sample of the world's countries reveals the great range of GDP per capita, as well as the large gap between the richer and poorer countries (Fig. 1-8). The world average for GDP per capita (PPP) was $8800 in 2004.

These values are in US dollars. American currency is almost always used to make economic comparisons among countries.

Fig. 1-8 ▶ GDP per capita, 2004 (reported on a PPP basis).

Country GDP per Capita ($US)

Country	GDP per Capita	Country	GDP per Capita
Argentina	$12 400	Japan	$29 400
Australia	$30 700	Luxembourg	$58 900
Bangladesh	$2 000	Mexico	$9 600
Canada	$31 500	Russia	$9 800
China	$5 600	South Africa	$11 100
Egypt	$4 200	South Korea	$19 200
Ethiopia	$800	United States	$40 100
France	$28 700		

Snapshots: Canada and the Rest of the World

Geographers have many ways of measuring where Canada stands compared to other countries. This section shows how Canada ranks in several different categories.

Available Cropland

1. United States 179 million hectares
6. Australia
7. Canada 46 million hectares
8. Indonesia

Fig. 1-9 Canada ranks 7th in the world in terms of available cropland (2003).

The existence of sufficient farmland is critical to a nation's ability to feed itself or to earn money by exporting agricultural products. Note that this ranking is for the total amount of cropland in a country and does not consider the population of the country. This type of measure is called an **absolute measure**.

Number of Immigrants

1. Luxembourg
2. Australia
3. Switzerland
4. New Zealand
5. Canada

Fig. 1-10 In 2003, Canada ranked 5th in terms of percentage of foreign-born citizens in the total population.

Energy Use per Capita

1. Iceland
2. Luxembourg
3. United States

4. Canada

Fig. 1-11 Canada ranks 4th in the world in terms of energy use per capita (2004).

Energy use per capita in a country is a reliable indicator of the level of that country's economic development. This is a **relative measure**. This means that it relates the amount of energy used to the country's population.

Average Life Expectancy

1. Japan (81 years)

2. Australia, Canada, France, Iceland, Singapore, Sweden, Switzerland (tie—80 years)

Fig. 1-12 Canada is tied for 2nd in the world in terms of average life expectancy (2004).

Canadians live for an average of almost 80 years. By comparison, residents of some African countries live, on average, for less than 40 years.

Value of Foreign Trade

1. United States
7. Italy
8. Canada
9. Netherlands

Fig. 1-13 Canada ranks 8th in the world in terms of the value of foreign trade (2004).

The value of foreign trade indicates a country's level of involvement in the world economy.

Amount of Fresh Water

1. Brazil
2. Russia
3. Canada
4. China

Fig. 1-14 Canada ranks 3rd in the world in terms of fresh water availability.

A number of experts have suggested that a shortage of fresh water will be the most important factor limiting growth in the 21st century. Is this going to be a problem for Canada?

Prisoners per Capita

1. United States 715 prisoners per 100 000 people
111. Australia
112. Canada 116 prisoners per 100 000 people
113. Tanzania

Fig. 1-15 Canada ranks 112th in terms of rate of imprisonment (number of prisoners per 100 000 people, 2005).

Nobel Prize Winners

1. Iceland 3.56 Nobel Prizes per 1 000 000 people

12. Canada 0.31 Nobel Prizes per 1 000 000 people
15. Slovakia
17. Australia

Fig. 1-16 Canada ranks 12th in terms of the number of Nobel Prize winners (2005).

The Nobel Prize is the most famous and prestigious international award. It is presented for outstanding achievement in the fields of chemistry, physics, medicine, literature, and peace. More broadly, the award may be viewed as representing a nation's cultural and scientific achievements.

Educational Achievement

1. Canada 42 per 100 people
2. United States 37 per 100 people

Fig. 1-17 Canada ranks 1st in terms of the number of people with post-secondary education (2003).

Size of the Military

1. Eritrea 45.84 soldiers per 1000 people
117. Argentina
118. Canada 1.83 soldiers per 1000 people
119. Brazil

Fig. 1-18 Canada ranks 118th in terms of the size of its military (number of military personnel per 1000 people, 2004).

A country may choose to have a large military for a variety of reasons. No matter what the reason might be, the human and financial resources spent on the military are not available for other purposes.

Happiness

1. Iceland 94% (97% happy, 3% unhappy)
16. Austria
17. Canada 75%
18. Poland

Fig. 1-19 Canada ranks 17th in terms of the overall happiness of its population (2001). The lowest score was for Bulgaria at –24%.

People were asked if they were "very happy," "quite happy," "not very happy," or "not at all happy." The percentage that said that they were "not very happy" or "not at all happy" was subtracted from the percentage that said that they were "very happy" or "quite happy." The result was a measure of net happiness.

McDonald's Restaurants

1. United States 44 McDonald's restaurants per 1 000 000 people
2. New Zealand
3. Canada 36 McDonald's restaurants per 1 000 000 people
4. Australia

Fig. 1-20 Canada ranks 3rd in terms of the number of McDonald's restaurants per 1 000 000 people (2003).

Instead of using the *absolute*, or total, number of restaurants in each country, this ranking uses the *relative* number of restaurants—that is, the number of restaurants relative to each one million people in the country.

Number of Cars

1. Italy 539 cars per 1000 people
8. France
9. Canada 459 cars per 1000 people
10. Belgium

Fig. 1-21 Canada ranks 9th in terms of the number of cars per 1000 people (2002).

The private automobile is both a blessing (it gives us great freedom and mobility) and a curse (its production and operation contribute to many serious environmental problems such as global warming). Which countries have the most cars? The measure used here is a relative measure.

Human Development Index

1. Norway
2. Iceland
3. Australia
4. Luxembourg
5. Canada

Fig. 1-22 Canada ranks 5th on the HDI (2005). You can see how the HDI is calculated at www.pearsoned.ca/makingconnections2.

The **Human Development Index (HDI)** combines measures in three critical areas—*health, education,* and *wealth*—to indicate a country's level of human development. Values are from 0 to 1, with 1 being the best. In 2004, the range was from a low of 0. 273 to a high of 0.956.

Gender Empowerment Measure

1. Norway 0.928
4. Luxembourg
5. Canada 0.807
6. Sweden

Fig. 1-23 Canada ranks 5th on the GEM (2005).

The **Gender Empowerment Measure (GEM)** is an index that is designed to indicate the amount of economic and political power that a country's women have. Like the HDI, it is a number from 0 to 1. A value of 1 indicates that women have as much power as men; a value of 0 indicates that women have no power.

Environmental Sustainability Index

1. Finland 75.1
5. Iceland
6. Canada 64.4
7. Switzerland

Fig. 1-24 Canada ranks 6th on the ESI (2005). If you can't wait to study the ESI later, you can read the full report at www.pearsoned.ca/makingconnections2.

The **Environmental Sustainability Index (ESI)** predicts the ability of each of the world's countries to protect the environment in the years to come. It combines 76 separate measurements into one value per country. In Chapter 38, you will have the chance to study the ESI in more depth.

These Snapshots should give you a lot to think about when you consider the question, "What is Canada really like?" As you use *Making Connections: Canada's Geography* during this course, you will have many opportunities to learn even more about our fascinating country.

QUESTIONS

KNOWLEDGE AND UNDERSTANDING

1. a) Locate the countries listed in Fig. 1-4 in an atlas. Are these large countries found in any particular part of the world, or are they found in all parts of the world?
   b) Which countries are similar in size to Canada?
2. Give two examples of absolute measures and two of relative measures from the text.
3. In this chapter, you learned about three "indices"—the HDI, GEM, and ESI. Give two features of each index.

THINKING

4. a) Using the information from Fig. 1-8, group the countries into "wealthier" and "poorer" categories.
   b) Which country is difficult to classify? What does this country's GDP per capita indicate about the level of its economic development compared with the other countries in Fig. 1-8?
5. What is a shortcoming of GDP per capita as a measure of a country's wealth? (Hint: Think about what information the GDP per capita does not give you.)
6. In Fig. 1-9, Available Cropland, you will see that Canada and Indonesia have a similar ranking. Keep in mind that these rankings are based on the actual amount, or absolute measure, of available cropland in each country.
   a) Suggest why an absolute measure of available cropland might be useful when comparing the two countries. (Hint: Keep in mind what you have learned in Fig. 1-5 about Canada and Indonesia.)
   b) Suggest why a relative measure of available cropland in the two countries might be useful.
   c) Suggest why an absolute measure of available cropland might be misleading when comparing the two countries.

COMMUNICATION

7. You have decided to become Internet "pen pals" with a student in Indonesia who knows virtually nothing about Canada and has asked you to describe it. Based on what you have learned in this chapter, along with what you knew before, write a brief, point-form description of Canada that you could e-mail to your pen pal.

APPLICATION

8. a) Fig. 1-25 lists the 10 largest countries in the world along with five other countries. Copy this chart into your notebook and fill in the missing information. You might want to work with a partner to share the calculations. The values for China are shown. (The difference in area between China and Canada is 9 632 000 − 9 992 000 = −360 000 km^2. China's size as a percentage of Canada's size can be calculated using the formula 9 632 000/9 992 000 × 100).
   b) Add together the areas of Canada and the United States.
      i. How does this number compare with the area of Russia?
      ii. What special problems would the government of a country as large as Russia have?
      iii. In 1991, the Union of Soviet Socialist Republics (USSR) split into 15 new countries. Two of these countries are large enough to appear on the list in Fig. 1-25. Which countries are they?
   c) Divide the list into five groups based on size (very large, large, medium, small, and very small). To do this, look for natural breaks in the range of numbers. For example, there is an obvious break between Russia and all of the others. Note that the groups may or may not have the same number of countries.

d) Draw five boxes, each 3 cm x 3 cm, in your notebook. Each box represents one square kilometre.

e) Label each box with the name of one country from each group in 8 c). Make sure that you label one of the boxes "Canada."

f) Using the information in Fig. 1-6, draw in each box the number of dots needed to show the population density of the country. In Canada's box, for example, put three small dots.

g) Consider the population density represented by each box. What are the advantages and disadvantages for

i. countries with a high population density?
ii. countries with a low population density?

Country	Area (km^2)	Amount larger (+)/smaller (–) than Canada (km^2)	Percentage of Canada's size
Russia	17 705 000		
Canada	9 992 000		
China	9 632 000	–360 000	96.4
United States	9 363 000		
Brazil	8 512 000		
Australia	7 687 000		
India	3 204 000		
Argentina	2 780 000		
Kazakhstan	2 717 000		
Sudan	2 506 000		
South Africa	1 221 000		
Japan	378 000		
Germany	357 000		
United Kingdom	245 000		
Jamaica	11 000		

▲ Fig. 1-25

ANSWERS TO CANADA QUIZ (PP. 8–9)

1. The area near Drumheller, Alberta, is the place to look for dinosaur bones.
2. Tommy Douglas was the surprise selection for his role in establishing medicare in Canada, both as premier of Saskatchewan, and later as first leader of the NDP.
3. Russia is about as big as Canada and Australia combined.
4. The Montreal Canadiens have won the Stanley Cup 24 times. The Toronto Maple Leafs are second with 11 wins.
5. a) $90 million per hour.
6. William Lyon Mackenzie King was prime minister three separate times for a total of about 21 years.
7. d) Tin is not mined in Canada.
8. Nunavut became a territory on April 1, 1999. Before this date, it was part of the Northwest Territories.
9. c) Despite her French name, Angelina Jolie was born in Los Angeles.
10. Newfoundland joined Canada in 1949.
11. This award is called the Order of Canada. This award has three levels: Companion, Officer, and Member. New recipients are announced in July and December each year.
12. The Mackenzie River is 4241 km long.
13. Germany ranks behind Great Britain and France.
14. Cars, trucks, and auto parts are our most important export. In 2004, we sold more than $90 billion worth—primarily to the United States.
15. Mount Logan's elevation is 5959 m. It is located in the Yukon.

Bonus Question: Kiefer Sutherland is Tommy Douglas's grandson.

UNIT 2

Methods of Geographic Inquiry

The images on this page show some of the tools geographers use. You can use some of these tools, too! What different types of maps do you use? Have you ever used GPS in a car, on a bike, or as a jogger? In what ways could you use a topographic map of your neighbourhood? The chapters in this unit encourage you to develop your geographical skills so you can explore the world around you. Exploring often begins by asking questions—about a place's physical features, its natural environment, and how human activity affects, and is affected by, the environment. As you develop your skills in mapping, graphing, and analyzing geographic images, think about how each of these skills helps you to answer what makes a place special.

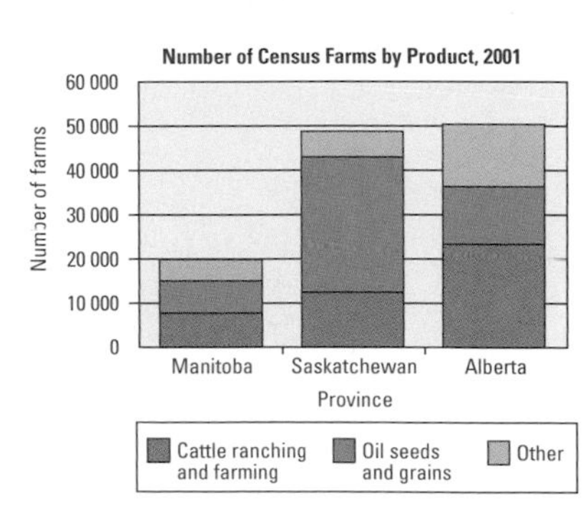

2 Maps: The Geographer's Basic Tools

Key Ideas

This chapter helps you investigate these questions:

- Why are maps considered the most basic tools for geographers?
- How can the limitations of various maps be minimized?
- How are electronic technologies revolutionizing the ways in which we use maps?

Key Terms

map
scale
small-scale map
large-scale map
general-purpose map
thematic map
topographic map
geotechnology
digital mapping

Carpenters and dentists need good tools to do their jobs properly. Geographers, too, need effective tools to do their job. One of the most important of these is the map. People have used maps for over 4500 years for exploring, determining their location and direction of travel, and describing the shape of the world. You may have consulted a map while camping, canoeing, or hiking. Perhaps, in preparing for a trip, you used a road map to plan your route. Likewise, you may have used a street map to find your way around an unfamiliar neighbourhood or city.

Maps are very useful tools. They help you visualize the shape of countries and locate important features. There are many different types of maps, and each has certain advantages. In this chapter, we will learn about map projections, the key features of maps, and how different types of maps are used.

What Is a Map?

A **map** is a representation of Earth's features drawn on a flat surface. Unlike photographs, maps cannot show you what the land actually looks like. Instead, maps use symbols and colours to represent the features of an area. For example, streets may be shown as red lines, and airports often are shown with a drawing of an airplane.

A map also simplifies the real world. Fig. 2-1 shows only a few major Canadian cities and no highways. The maker of any map must decide which features to include and which ones to ignore, depending on the map's purpose. For example, someone with a sweet tooth might want a map that includes every candy shop in town. A map that includes only those features that are needed is easy to use.

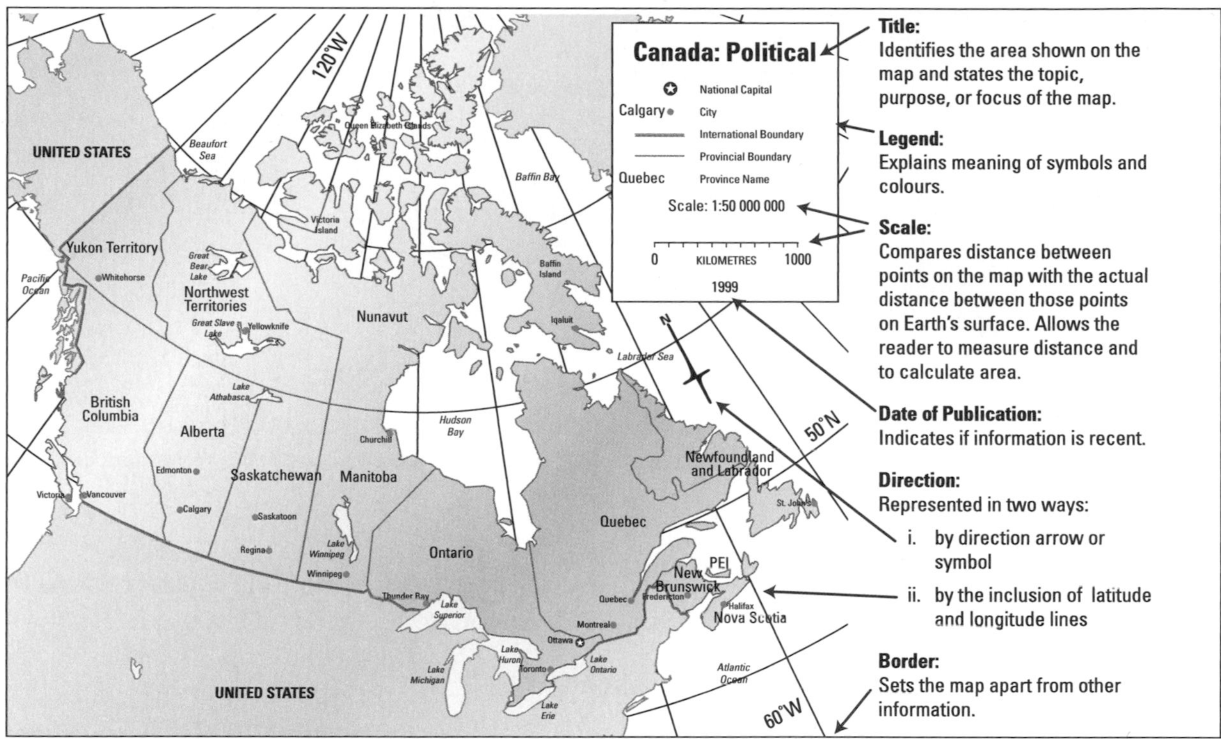

▲ **Fig. 2-1** The basic features of a map

Map Requirements

Whenever you draw a map, certain features should always be included. These features are described in Fig. 2-1. They help the map reader understand the purpose of the map.

Large- and Small-scale Maps

The **scale** of a map shows the relationship between the size of an object (e.g., a lake or a section of highway) in real life and its size as drawn on the map. Maps can be described as either large scale or small scale. A world map in your atlas might have a scale of something like 1:17 500 000. This would be an example of a **small-scale map** (Fig. 2-2). Small-scale maps show a small amount of detail in a large area. They are used to show more general information such as physical, political, or economic information. Wall maps of the world or Canada, along with road maps, are examples of small-scale maps.

> 1:50 000 means that 1 cm on the map represents 50 000 cm (or 500 m) on Earth's surface. You can learn more about map scales in Chapter 4.

On the other hand, if you wanted to create a map of your schoolyard, you would want to show many details. To do this, you would make a large-scale map with a scale of, perhaps, 1:500. **Large-scale maps** show a large amount of detail in a small area (Fig. 2-3). They are used for more detailed tasks, such as residential planning and military operations. You would also use them for hiking, because you need to be able to see considerable detail about the terrain and the location of trails.

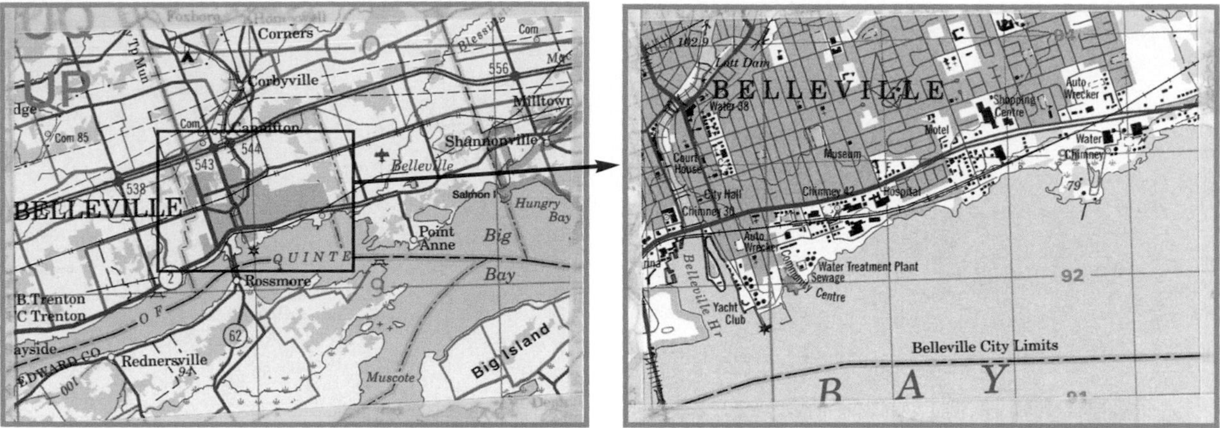

▲ **Fig. 2-2** A small-scale map 1:250 000 shows less detail of a large area.

▲ **Fig. 2-3** A large-scale map 1:50 000 shows more detail of a small area.

In general, maps with a scale of 1:250 000 or more are considered small scale. Those with a scale less than this, for example, 1:50 000 or less, are considered large scale.

Types of Maps

There are many types of maps. Some examples are political, navigational, topographic, vegetation, and weather maps. Within this vast range, we will examine only a few types. We can classify these under three broad headings: general-purpose maps, thematic maps, and topographic maps.

General-purpose Maps

General-purpose maps provide many types of information on one map. Most atlas maps, wall maps, and road maps fall into this category. Here are some features that might be shown on general-purpose maps:

- bodies of water
- roads
- railway lines
- parks
- elevations
- towns and cities
- political boundaries
- latitude and longitude
- national and provincial parks

These maps give a broad understanding of the location and features of an area. You can gain an understanding of the type of landscape, the location of urban places, and the location of major transportation routes all at once. Fig. 2-1 is an example of a general-purpose map.

Thematic Maps

If you require very specific information about a place, **thematic maps** are useful. These maps are designed to show information on one particular topic or theme. Because only one type of information is shown, thematic maps tend to be easy to understand. Study the examples in Fig. 2-4.

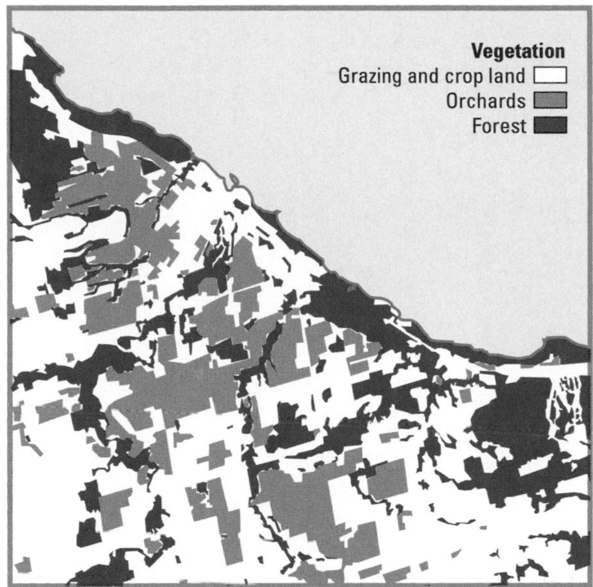

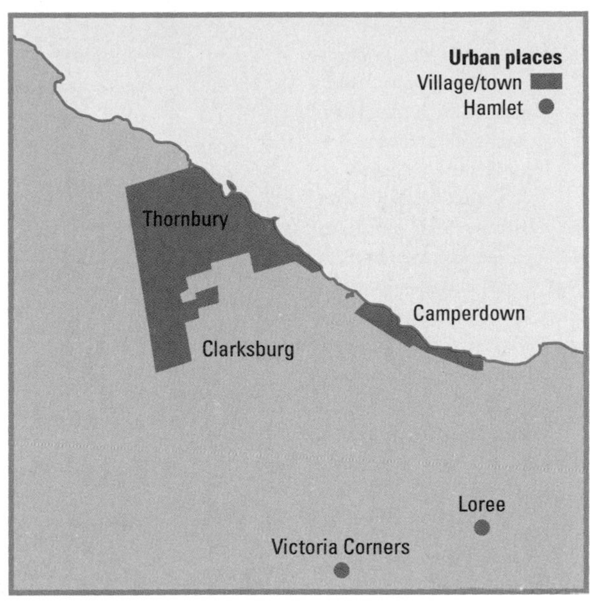

▲ **Fig. 2-4** Each of these thematic maps shows a different characteristic of the area shown in Fig. 2-6.

Topographic Maps

Topographic maps use symbols to show a variety of features (Fig. 2-5). Two very important features are contour lines, which show changes in elevation, and a grid system that is used for locating places on the map. If you want to examine the characteristics of a small area of Earth's surface in detail, these maps are useful (Fig. 2-6).

You will learn more about the grid system in Chapter 3.

Geotechnology: The Digital Map

The computer age is causing a revolution in maps and mapping. Since the first maps were created many centuries ago, they have had two characteristics in common. One is that they were printed on paper or a similar material. The other is that they were a static resource: once they were printed, it was almost impossible to make significant changes. Computer technology is changing all this. We have to realize that the "map" is the geographic data itself, and not the piece of paper on which the data appear. Maps exist in **digital** form in computer programs, in various handheld devices, or on the Internet. Users can customize the presentation of the data in the way that best meets their needs. For example, they can choose what information to include on the map, what scale to use, what map projection, colours, symbols, and so on.

digital
information that is stored on an electronic device in the form of numbers

Many types of **geotechnology** are now in use. In Chapter 3, you will learn about some of the many uses of Global Positioning Systems (GPS). In Chapter 5, you will learn how you can create maps using Geographic Information Systems (GIS) software. In *Making Connections*, you will have a number of opportunities to create GIS maps to help you with your study of Canadian geography.

Fig. 2-5 ▶
Here are some map symbols used in topographic maps. Features such as woods, orchards, and lakes are represented by coloured patterns called **area symbols**. **Line symbols** represent features that are linear in nature, such as roads, railways, and telephone lines. Features that occupy a specific point, such as buildings, bridges, and towers, are represented by **point symbols**.

FEATURES OF TOPOGRAPHIC MAPS

Physical Features

- Marsh
- River, large
- River, small
- Lake
- Wooded area

Human Features

- International boundary
- County or district boundary
- Metropolitan area boundary
- Highway interchange with number (42)
- Dual highway
- Road, hard surface, all weather, 2 lanes
- Road, loose or stabilized surface, all weather, 2 lanes
- Highway route marker (orange or red, 5)
- Railway, single track
- Bridge
- Cemetery
- Tower
- Pipeline: above ground, underground
- Telephone line
- Power transmission line
- Greenhouse
- Post office (P.)
- School
- Church
- House
- Barn
- Large building
- Navigation light
- Mine
- Gravel pit
- Quarry
- Golf course
- Campsite
- Orchard
- Vineyard

Direction and Location

- 44°30′ 80°30′ — Latitude and longitude
  Pinpoint location and convey direction.
- 31 30 — Map grid
  Locates any feature on a map.

Elevation (height above sea level)

- 10 — Contour line, with elevation
  The most important indication of elevation.
- △ 150 — Horizontal control point, with elevation
  Locations that have been measured and marked on the landscape.
- 1475↑ — Bench mark, with elevation
  Provides exact elevations of human features.
- • 2520 — Spot elevation
  Shows elevation between contour lines.

Fig. 2-6 ▶
A topographic map of the Thornbury area in the Georgian Bay region of Ontario

Scale: 1:50 000 (1 cm = 0.5 km) Contour interval: 10 m
Lora Bay
Marina
E
Arena
Water
Community Hall
Thornbury
Town Limits
Mill Pond
Sewage
D
River
Beaver
Airfield Condition Unknown
Little
Clarksburg
Clendenan Conservation Area
Grier Ck
Valley
Beaver
C
B
Indian
Brook
A
178.9
Camperdown
Delphi Point
F
181.4
H
Craigleith Prov Park
Motel
G
Blue
Mountains
J
I
439
Loree
Victoria Corners
Collingwood Tp Mun

This activity should be done at a computer that has Internet access.

DIGITAL MAPPING

In this chapter, you can learn about an easy form of **digital mapping.** Google Maps (maps.google.ca) is an Internet mapping site that is very handy for anyone who must travel to an unfamiliar area. This might involve an extended trip to another country or just running an errand to a different part of your town or city. Google Maps' capabilities are likely to expand in the future.

1. The first thing that Google Maps can do for you is create a map centred around a particular address. Go to maps.google.ca and you will see that you can enter an address in Canada or in the United States.
   a) For example, if you keyed in the Canadian prime minister's address (24 Sussex Drive, Ottawa, Ontario; the postal code is not needed), you would get a map similar to Fig. 2-7.

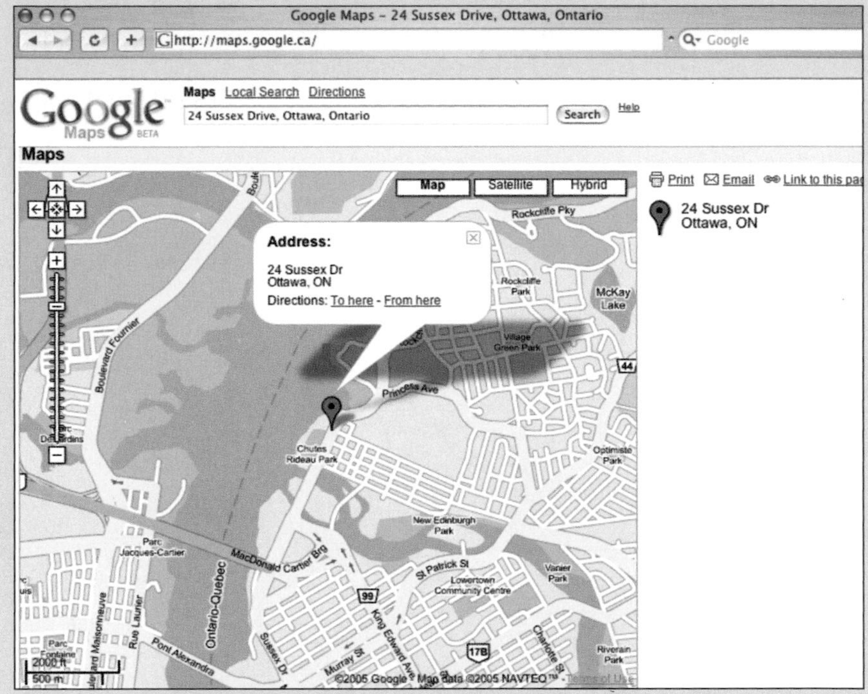

Fig. 2-7 ▶ The prime minister of Canada lives in a very attractive riverfront location in Ottawa. Note that an address search can be zoomed in or out to give more detail or show a larger area.

b) You will notice that there is a "zoom in/zoom out" tool at the left side of the map. Often this is useful because you may need more detailed local knowledge (zoom in). On the other hand, you may want to see where this location is in relation to other places. You can zoom out to do this. It is helpful to remember that as you zoom in, you are creating larger-scale maps. As you zoom out, you are creating smaller-scale maps. Try both of these options now.

c) Create a map centred on the address of your home. You can zoom in or zoom out, as necessary, so that the map will show both your school and the movie theatre nearest to where you live. Print this map if you are so instructed by your teacher.

2. Google Maps is also useful for getting driving directions between two addresses. To do this, choose the *Directions* button at the top of the Google Maps page. Next, key in the addresses of the starting and finishing points of your journey. Finally, choose *Search* and you will be given very detailed instructions to your destination (Fig. 2-8). If part of the instructions is not clear, you can click on

You will learn more about Google in Chapter 9.

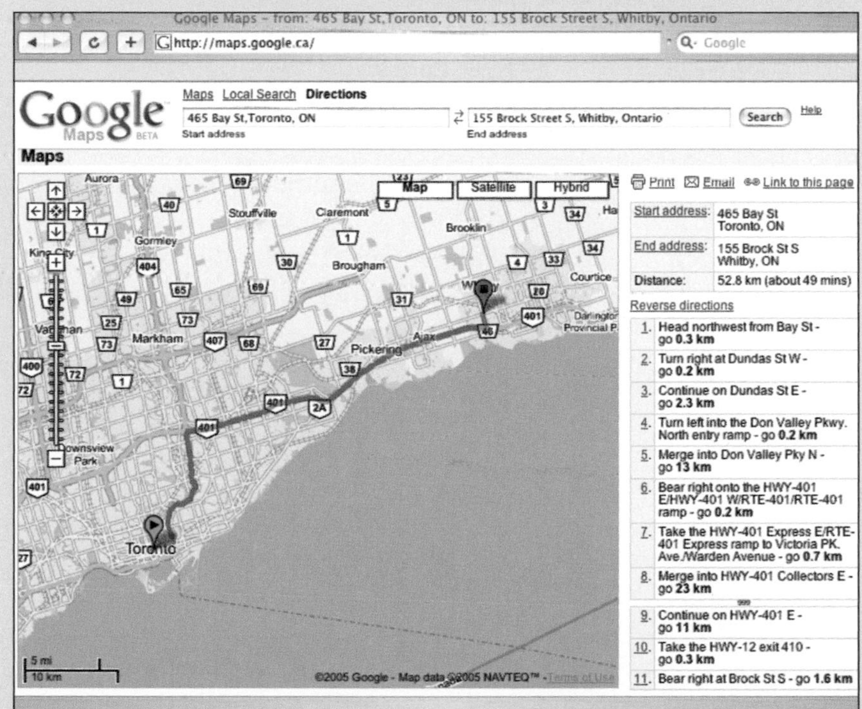

◀ **Fig. 2-8** Here are some of the instructions for a trip from downtown Toronto to downtown Whitby.

the number beside the instruction and you will get a map, with the appropriate amount of detail, to help you with this part of your journey.

a) Get directions from your home to your school. If you do not know your school's address, ask your teacher.

b) Get directions from your home to a distant location in Canada or the United States. This could be a vacation spot, the location of a major sporting event, or a college or university you might want to attend. You can search for the address of the place you want (hotel, amusement park, stadium, school, etc.) with a search engine such as Google. If you cannot find the address, you can enter the name of the city or town you are looking for, and you will get directions that will at least get you close to your desired destination. Print these instructions if your teacher tells you to.

3. List three things you can do with a map or set of directions that you create with Google Maps. (Hint: Look carefully at the screen showing the result of your search.)

4. a) Google Maps has another fascinating feature that shows the immense power of digital mapping. The maps you have been working on have *Satellite* and *Hybrid* buttons. Experiment with these and explain in your notes what each does.

   b) Why might the Satellite feature be useful?

5. a) Does Google Maps produce a general-purpose map or a thematic map?

   b) To what type of map could Google Maps best be compared?

   c) Give three advantages of a digital mapping system such as Google Maps compared to the type of map you mentioned in b).

QUESTIONS

KNOWLEDGE AND UNDERSTANDING

1. a) What is a map? Use your own words.
   b) Why are maps useful tools?
   c) How do maps help focus the reader's attention on just a few specific things?
2. What are general-purpose maps used for?
3. a) What is the purpose of thematic maps?
   b) Why are thematic maps useful?
   c) Find three examples of thematic maps in this book. Give the page reference and the theme of each map.
4. What is the purpose of a topographic map?
5. Construct a chart similar to Fig. 2-9 to compare large-scale and small-scale maps.

	Large-scale maps	Small-scale maps
Definition		
Typical Scales		
Purpose		

▲ **Fig. 2-9**

APPLICATION

6. a) List the essential features of a map.
   b) Draw a sketch map of your classroom. Make sure that all the features listed above are included on your map.
7. a) What features are found on general-purpose maps?
   b) Examine the road map in Fig. 3-2 on page 33. Which features from your answer to 7a) are shown on the road map?
   c) Describe how the features are shown on the road map.
8. Refer to Fig. 2-6.
   a) On a topographic map, what does the colour green indicate?
   b) In which direction does Indian Brook flow? How did you determine this?
   c) What features are found at the following letters?
      i. A
      ii. B
      iii. C
      iv. D
      v. E
      vi. F
   d) Consider the kinds of symbols that are used to represent features on a topographic map. Can they be understood without reference to a legend that explains them all?

3 Locating Places on a Map

Key Ideas

This chapter helps you investigate these questions:

- How are directions and locations shown on a variety of map types?
- How is geotechnology changing the way in which we find out where we are?
- What is a geomuggle, and what do I do if I don't want to be one?

Key Terms

latitude
longitude
compass point
compass rose
compass bearing
alphanumeric grid
map grid
easting
northing
prime meridian
Global Positioning System (GPS)
waypoint
telematics
geocaching

15th century
years between 1400 and 1499

Determining location is a problem that people have struggled with for centuries. Consider the Chinese sailors in the early part of the **15th century** who are thought to have made immensely long journeys, perhaps even to the coasts of Africa and the Americas. They, along with their European counterparts for more than the next three centuries, were able to determine their **latitude** with considerable accuracy, but had no practical way to determine their **longitude**. The result was that they had only a very foggy idea where they were on their voyages. Today, the specific problem in specifying location may be different. For example, your friends may say that they will meet you at the entrance to the movie theatre, but you end up standing around for quite a few minutes before you realize that you are at the exterior entrance, and they are at the theatre entrance inside the mall. But the general problem of specifying location remains. The 21st century, with its ever-expanding technology, is placing greater demands on our ability to determine location. In this chapter, you will have the opportunity to learn a variety of ways in which places can be located on a map.

Compass Points and Bearings

When giving directions, you need to know where you are and where you want to go. For example, people often use phrases such as "travel south for one kilometre, then go west when you reach the traffic lights." For these directions to work, you must know where south and west are in relation to your own position. If you were to use a map for this task, the directions "south" and "west" might be shown as **compass points** on a **compass rose** (Fig. 3-1). On maps that use lines of latitude and longitude to indicate direction, a compass rose is not necessary.

The principal points of a compass are north (N), east (E), south (S), and west (W)—the cardinal points. Halfway between these are points that combine directions to form northeast (NE), southeast (SE), southwest (SW), and northwest (NW)—the ordinal points. A further subdivision of the directions between these eight points leads to another set of points of which north-northeast (NNE) is one. This is, as you would expect, between north and northeast.

As you can easily imagine, the use of compass points soon becomes complicated and is still not very precise. Direction can be given more accurately and much more easily if **compass bearings**, measured in degrees, are used instead of compass points. Compass bearings measure the angle of a direction in relation to north, moving in a clockwise direction (Fig. 3-1). The use of compass bearings is a more accurate method for stating direction. For more precise measurements, parts of a degree can be used if needed.

By the time you get to 32 compass points, you have to deal with names like NE by N (between NE and NNE). Sailors would then subdivide each of these 32 points into 4 subpoints (for a total of 128 directions) with names like NE ¼ E.

0° and 360° are the same point on the compass.

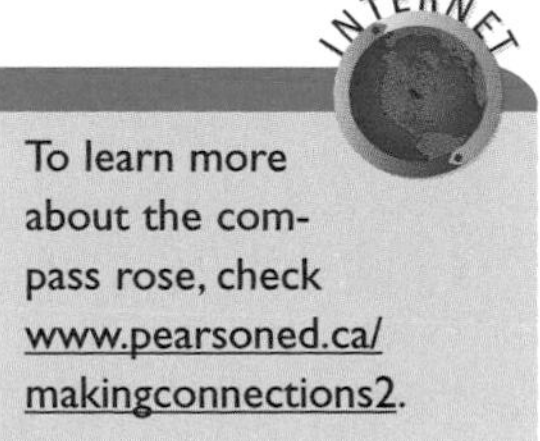

To learn more about the compass rose, check www.pearsoned.ca/makingconnections2.

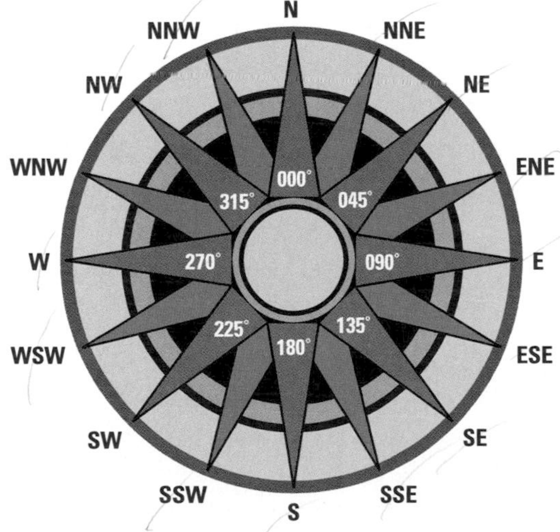

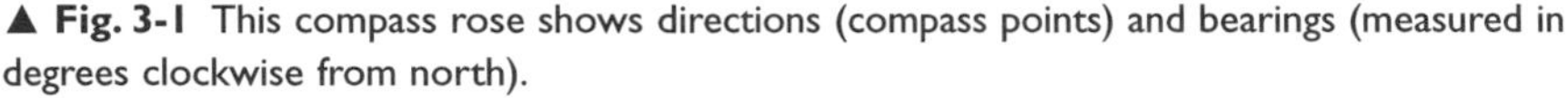
▲ **Fig. 3-1** This compass rose shows directions (compass points) and bearings (measured in degrees clockwise from north).

Grid Systems

grid
network of two sets of parallel lines that meet at right angles

The most common way to locate a place on a map is to use a **grid** system. In this chapter, we will look at three different grid systems.

Alphanumeric Grid

The **alphanumeric grid** uses letters and numerals to identify squares in a grid pattern. An alphanumeric grid is often used on road maps. Grid squares are identified by a letter along one edge of the map and a number along another (see Fig. 3-2).

Use Fig. 3-2 to answer the following questions.

1. The community of Gogama in square L13 has two symbols beside its name. What do these symbols represent?
2. In which square do you find the intersection of Highway 17 and Highway 144?
3. Which lake would you see to your south when driving the Voyageur Route between North Bay and Sturgeon Falls (N15)?
4. a) Name the town in square M15 that is named after a mineral.
   b) When measured from Sudbury, what is the closest compass point and bearing of this town? What is the compass bearing of Sudbury when measured from the town?
5. Which is larger, Britt (O14) or Sundridge (O15)?
6. Name each of the highways with the Trans-Canada symbol and list the grid location of each symbol.
7. Name each of the communities with an airport, give the grid location of each community, and indicate the type of airport.
8. a) How is the distance between two points on a road shown on the Ontario road map?
   b) Calculate the distance in kilometres between:
      i. Marten River (N15) and Latchford (M15)
      ii. Killarney (O13) and the intersection where Highway 637 meets Highway 69 (N14)
      iii. Matachewan (L14) and Dymond (L15) along Highway 65
9. There has been an accident in Temagami (M15). What is the name of the nearest community with a hospital?
10. Several minerals are mined in the Sudbury region of Ontario (N14). Identify two of the minerals by examining the map.

Hints:
1. Grid lines point N–S and E–W.
2. Use a protractor.

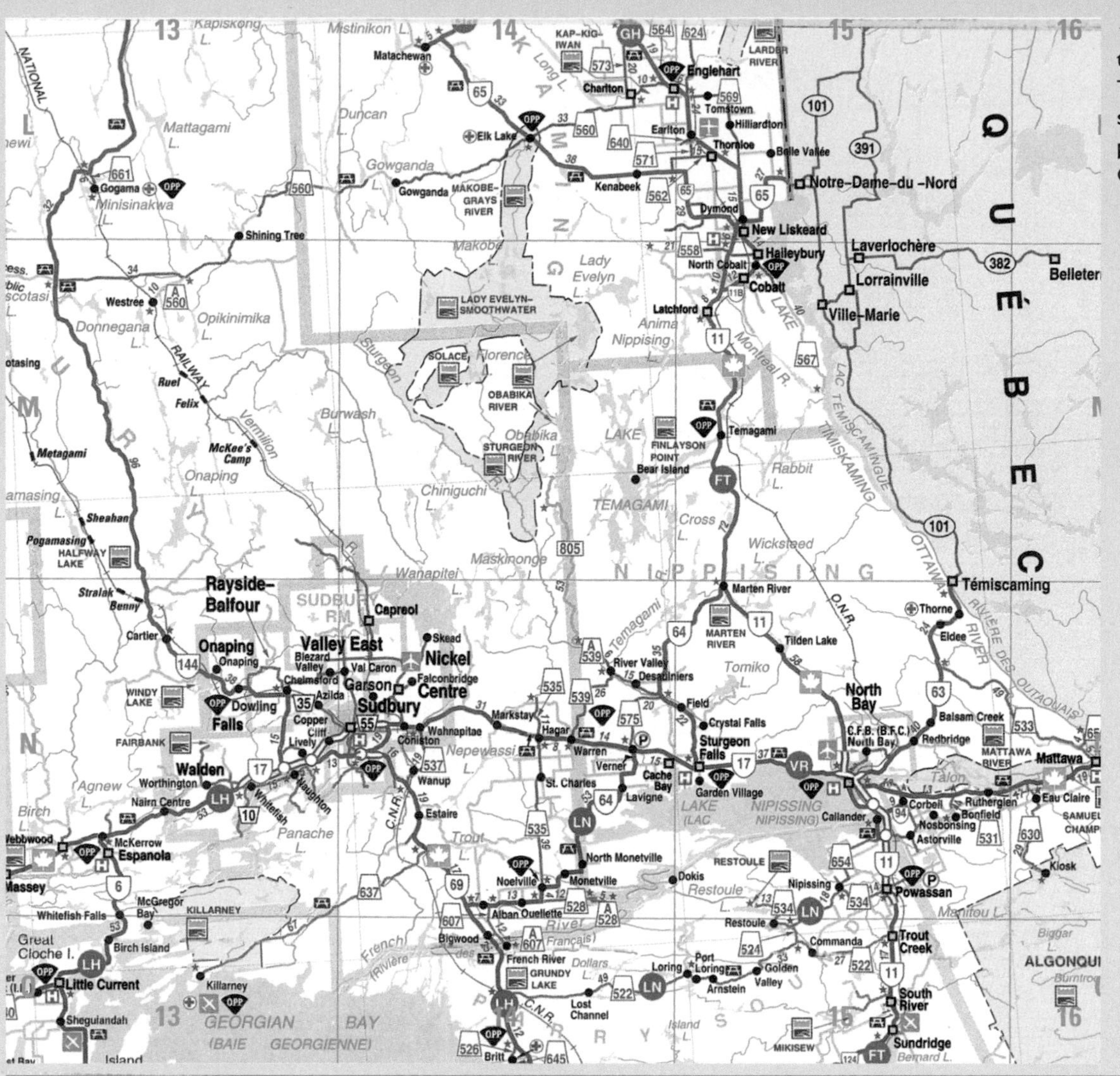

◀ **Fig. 3-2** Find the community of Temagami located in square M15 in this portion of the Ontario road map.

LEGEND *LÉGENDE*

ROAD CLASSIFICATION
CLASSIFICATION DES ROUTES

- Express Toll Route (407 ETR) — *Autoroute express à péage*
- Express Toll Route under construction — *Autoroute express à péage en construction*
- Multi-lane divided, — *À voies multiples séparées*
- Multi-lane undivided, — *À voies multiples nonséparées*
- King's highway/two-lane, hard surface — *Route principale*
- Two-lane, hard surface — *Deux voies, pavées*
- Two-lane, loose surface — *Deux voies, gravelées*
- Interchange–full/partial — *Échangeur (complet, partiel)*
- 484 Exit number — *Numéro de sortie*
- 401 King's highway number — *Numéro de route principale*
- 599 Secondary highway number — *Numéro de route secondaire*
- 803 Tertiary road number — *Numéro de route tertiaire*
- 5 County/ regional or district road, — *Chemin de comté/région/district*
- 72 148 81 53 Route number outside Ontario — *Numéro de route à l'extérieur de l'Ontario*

SETTLEMENTS BY POPULATION
LOCALITÉS ET POPULATION

Cities/towns/villages *villes/villages*

Over *plus de* 100,000	**OSHAWA**
10,000 to *à* 100,000	**Sudbury**
5,000 to *à* 10,000	**Fergus**
1,000 to *à* 5,000	**Kemptville**
Under *sous* 1,000	**Thamesville**

Communities *Communautés*

Over *plus de* 10,000	Courtice
5,000 to *à* 10,000	Elmira
1,000 to *à* 5,000	Wawa
Under *sous* 1,000	Devlin

ADMINISTRATIVE
ADMINISTRATION

- Regional Municipality/District/County Boundary — *Limites de municipalité régionale/district/comté*
- City/Town/Village — *Limites de municipalité (ville/village)*
- International boundary — *Frontière internationale*
- Province or state boundary — *Frontière provinciale ou d'état*
- Built up Area — *Agglomération*

TRAVEL AND TOURIST
VOYAGE ET TOURISME

- Railway, passenger service — *Service ferroviaire de passager*
- GO Train Station — *Gare du Réseau GO*
- Ferry Route — *Traversier*
- Major Airport *aéroport principal*
- Secondary Airport *aéroport secondaire*
- Local Airport *aéroport local*
- 26 ★ Kilometric Distance — *Distance en kilomètres*
- Trans–Canada Highway — *Route transcanadienne*
- Carpool Parking — *Parc de stationnement pour covoiturage*
- Ontario Provincial Police Detachment — *Détachement de la police provinciale de l'Ontario*
- Service Centre — *Centre de services*
- Border Crossing — *Poste frontière*
- Travel Information Centre — *Centre d'information touristique*
- Major Tourist Attraction — *Principale attraction touristique*
- National Park with camping facilities — *Parc national avec camping*
- National Park without camping facilities — *Parc national sans camping*
- Provincial Park with camping facilities — *Parc provincial avec camping*
- Provincial Park without camping facilities — *Parc provincial sans camping*
- Park Commission with camping — *Commission des parcs avec camping*
- Conservation Area with camping facilities — *Zone de protection de la nature avec camping*
- Picnic Park — *Zone de pique–nique*
- Hospital — *Hôpital*
- First aid/Nursing station — *Poste de premiers soins*

TOURIST ROUTES

- DT Deer Trail Route
- FT Frontier Trail
- GH Golden Highway
- GR Great River Road
- LH Lake Huron Circle Tour
- LN Lake Nipissing Circle Route
- VR Voyageur Route

Scale 1 : 1 600 000

Map Grid (Military Grid)

You may have noticed grids of numbered blue lines on topographic maps. This is referred to as the **map grid** or military grid. We can use the lines of this grid to locate any place on a topographic map.

The expression *"Read right up"* will help you remember which numbers go first. This means that first you read to the *right* (of the easting line) and then *up* (from the northing line).

IDENTIFYING GRID SQUARES: FOUR-DIGIT GRID REFERENCE

The numbers of the vertical grid lines increase as you go from west *to east*. As a result, they are called **easting** numbers (Fig. 3-3). The easting number refers not only to the vertical grid line, but also to the column to the right of the grid line. The numbers of the horizontal grid lines increase from south *to north* and, as you would expect, are called **northing** numbers. The northing number refers to both the horizontal grid line and the row above it. By combining the two digits from the easting and the two digits from the northing, we are able to identify a specific square on the map.

▼ **Fig. 3-3**

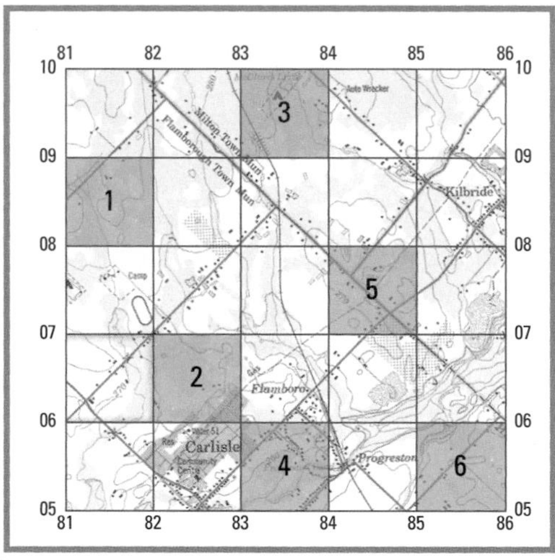

In your notebook, list the four-digit grid reference of each of the six shaded squares in Fig. 3-3.

IDENTIFYING LOCATIONS OF POINTS WITHIN GRID SQUARES: SIX-DIGIT GRID REFERENCE

There are times when we want to give a more exact location than is possible with a four-digit grid reference. For these times we can use a six-digit number. Notice in Fig. 3-4 that each side of grid square 8106 has been divided into tenths. Point A is five-tenths of the way from 81 to 82 so it is located at 815. Point A is also five-tenths of the way from 06 to 07 so it is located at 065. These numbers are combined to get a six-digit reference of 815065.

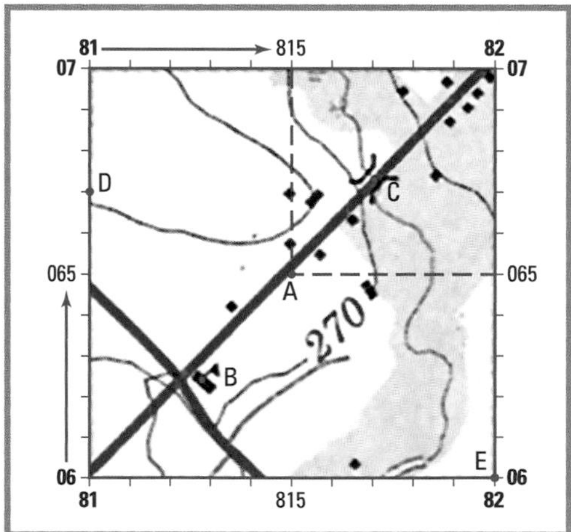

▲ **Fig. 3-4**

In your notebook, use a six-digit grid reference to identify the locations of the school at B, the bridge at C, and points D and E in Fig. 3-4.

Latitude and Longitude

A third type of grid system divides the world into a series of grid squares using lines of latitude and longitude. No matter where you are in the world, your location can be identified by a latitude and longitude "address."

If you use latitude and longitude, the geographic centre of the world is in the Gulf of Guinea, off the west coast of Africa. Check in your atlas and you will see that this is 0° latitude and 0° longitude. From here, a gridwork of lines extends north–south and east–west. This grid allows you to express the location of any place in the world in terms of where a line of latitude meets a line of longitude.

Latitude and longitude are measured as angles, with the centre of each angle at the centre of the globe (Fig. 3-5). Latitude is measured north and south from the equator, and longitude is measured east and west from the **prime meridian**.

If you think about it, you will realize that this is technically not a grid. These "squares" are not really squares, since longitude lines get closer together as you move toward either pole. When you are working with a fairly small part of the globe, however, latitude and longitude lines appear to form a grid.

meridian
name given to a line of longitude

The prime meridian was set, by international agreement, as the line of longitude passing through a famous observatory in Greenwich, a suburb of London, England. Before this time, various countries used their own "prime meridians." Of course, this practice led to considerable confusion.

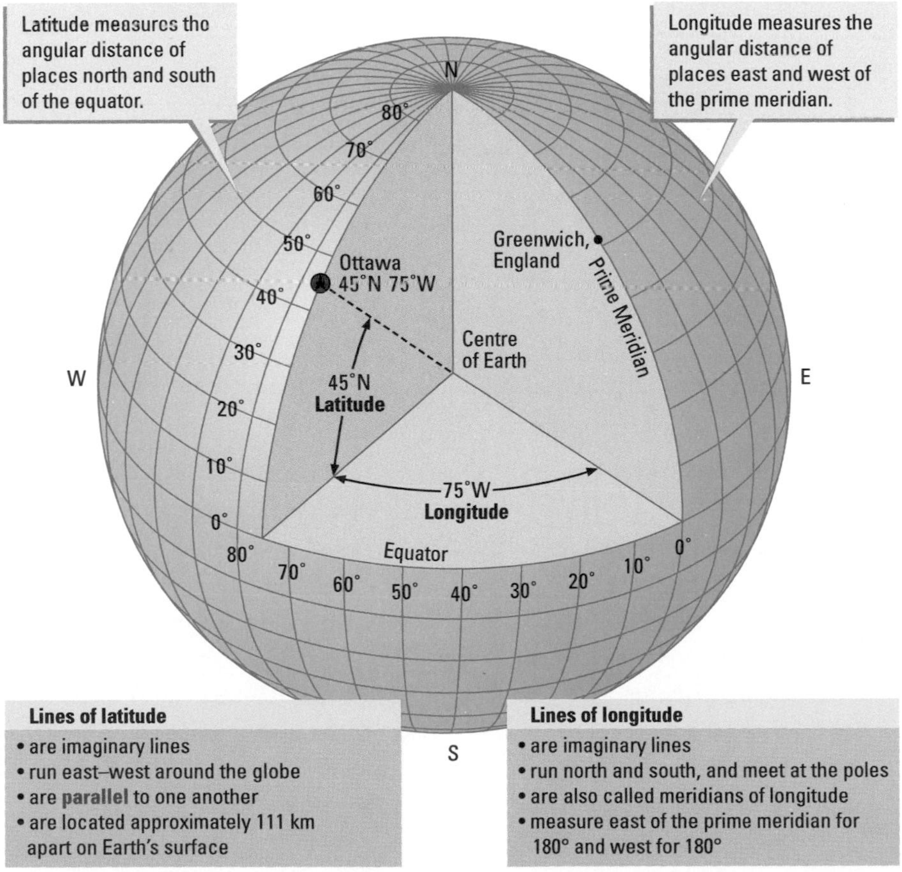

Lines of latitude
- are imaginary lines
- run east–west around the globe
- are **parallel** to one another
- are located approximately 111 km apart on Earth's surface

Lines of longitude
- are imaginary lines
- run north and south, and meet at the poles
- are also called meridians of longitude
- measure east of the prime meridian for 180° and west for 180°

parallel
name given to a line of latitude

◀ **Fig. 3-5** Latitude and longitude are much easier to understand if you can picture each as an angle measured from the centre of Earth.

gazetteer
alphabetical index of the places shown in an atlas

You will now "take a trip" around Canada to develop your skills in using latitude and longitude, and in using the **gazetteer** in an atlas. You will also learn some Canadian trivia.

1. Before you begin, check the first page of the gazetteer in your atlas to see what information it contains and how to read the information found in each entry.
2. Divide into groups of two so that you can have a friendly rivalry with a partner. See who can provide all the missing words below correctly in the least amount of time.

Your trip begins at the base of the Peace Tower located in the _____ Buildings in the city of _____ (45.5°N 75.5°W). From here you head west to Canada's nickel capital, _____ (46.5°N 81°W). You continue to travel west to the railway hub of the west, _____ (50°N 97°W). Following the Trans-Canada Highway, you arrive in a city whose name means *queen* in Latin, _____ (50.5°N 104.5°W). Your next stop is in the city famous for its western fair, called The _____ Stampede (51°N 114°W). With the hope of seeing the famous Ogopogo monster in Lake Okanagan, you spend a few days in the community of _____ (49.5°N 119.5°W). You continue to follow the Trans-Canada Highway to Vancouver, located at _____. You take the ferry to Vancouver Island to see the place where the annual bathtub race starts at _____ (49°N 124°W).

Your trip continues northward to _____, located in the Yukon at 64°N 139.5°W. Thousands of people came to this town in 1898 searching for gold. Another town famous for its gold mines is Yellowknife, located on Great Slave Lake at _____. Your next stop is known as the polar bear capital of Canada. At certain times of the year, polar bears are a tourist attraction. This city, _____, located at 58.5°N 94°W, shares the name of a famous British prime minister. You find that you really have a craving for some seafood from Atlantic Canada. You fly over Quebec to the most easterly provincial capital of _____, located at 47.5°N 52.5°W, for a serving of cod tongues. These are a rare delicacy since the cod fishery collapsed in the 1990s. After a quick flight to Halifax, located at _____, you find a restaurant that serves freshly cooked lobster with fresh bread and butter. Heading westward, you visit the largest island in the Bay of Fundy, _____, New Brunswick, located at 44.5°N 66.5°W. It is famous for its edible seaweed, called dulse. Before leaving New Brunswick you visit the Reversing Falls in _____ at 45.5°N 66°W. The centre of French Canada is _____, located at 47°N 71°W. Its old town has been declared a World Heritage Site by the United Nations. Your last stop is a visit to Canada's Museum of Civilization, located in _____ across the river from Ottawa at 45.5°N 76°W.

Geotechnology: The Impact of GPS

Picture this situation: you have just received your G1 driver's licence and are driving along a country road with your family, to visit relatives. You are driving carefully and the weather is good. Then it happens. One of your front tires blows, and your car swerves off the road and hits a large tree. The last thing you remember is the sound of breaking glass and the air bag exploding in your face. The next thing you remember are police and ambulance attendants freeing you from your wrecked car and taking everyone to the hospital. The doctors in the hospital tell you that everyone will be fine and that a prompt call for the ambulance was critically important in this outcome. You soon find out that no one actually phoned 911—rather, it was your car that called for help.

What happened was this. The car was equipped with a crash sensor. When this sensor was activated, it sent a message to the OnStar unit of your car. This unit has a built-in **Global Positioning System (GPS)** that was able to determine the exact location of the car. The OnStar unit in the car sent an emergency message to the nearest OnStar centre that there had been an accident at a particular location, serious enough to deploy

INTERNET

To learn more about GPS, check www.pearsoned.ca/makingconnections2.

OnStar was invented by General Motors but is starting to appear in some other vehicles, such as Acura and Volkswagen.

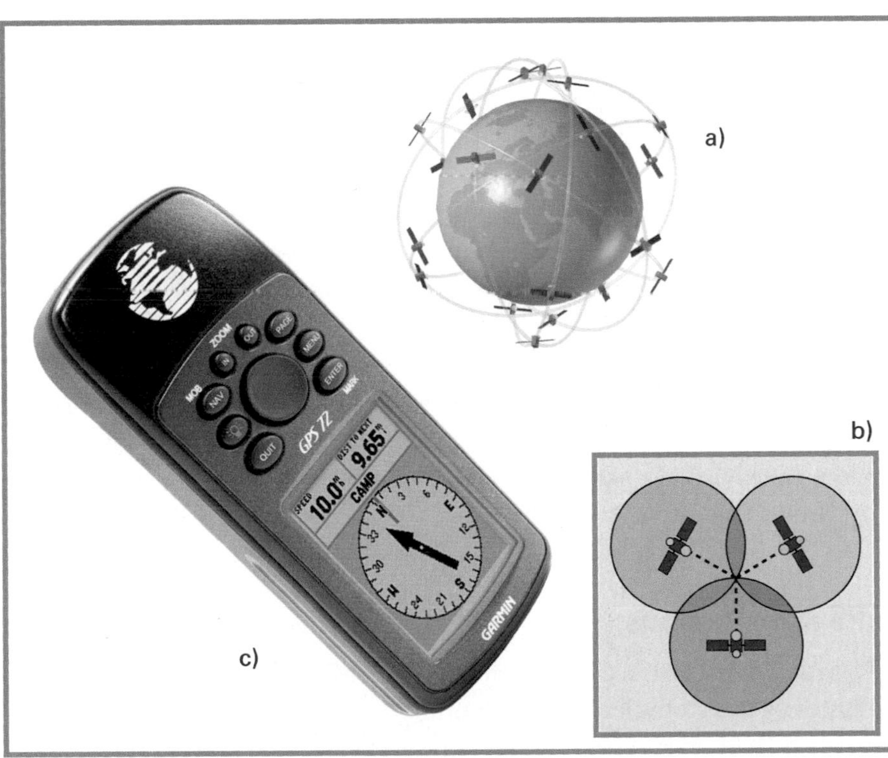

◀ **Fig. 3-6** How GPS works

a) Orbiting satellites provide navigation data around the clock. The satellites send radio signals to Earth that a GPS unit uses to calculate its latitude and longitude.

Triangulation:

b) Each satellite's signal contains the exact time it was sent.

c) A GPS unit uses this time to measure and calculate the distance of the satellite. Signals from at least three satellites are needed by a GPS unit to determine its location.

OnStar can do other things as well, such as unlock your car if you leave the keys inside, or track your car if it is stolen.

Fig. 3-7 ▶ This is a typical OnStar control unit. The left button is for making cellular calls through OnStar. The middle button connects the driver with the OnStar centre. The right button is for making an emergency contact with the OnStar centre.

air bags. A person at the OnStar centre then tried to call your car using the cellular phone that is also part of OnStar (Fig. 3-7). When no one in the car answered the call, the OnStar representative contacted the nearest emergency services and you and your family were soon on your way to the hospital.

You can learn more about how GPS works at www.pearsoned.ca/makingconnections2.

The Global Positioning System (GPS)

OnStar is just one example of the many ways in which GPS is changing the way we live. But what is GPS, and how does it work?

The Global Positioning System is a satellite-based, position-finding system operated by the United States government. The first satellite was launched in 1978, with the target number of 24 satellites being reached in 1994. Each satellite has a lifespan of about 10 years, so new satellites must be launched on a continuing basis. The satellites are placed in particular orbits so that any place on Earth is in range of at least four satellites.

Originally, the GPS was created for use by the American military. It was made available for civilian use in the mid-1980s. For many years, GPS receivers cost thousands of dollars, and only very rich individuals and companies could afford them. In recent years, as with most electronic devices, prices have dropped dramatically. Simple GPS devices now cost not much more than $100. Even the least costly GPS receiver will give you your location to within about seven metres, and often less than this. More sophisticated devices have an accuracy of less than one centimetre! The European Union is in the process of creating a similar satellite navigation system called Galileo. Galileo is being designed in such a way that it will work with the existing American GPS.

It is interesting to note that the Internet was also originally created for military use.

GPS Applications

GPS capabilities exist in a wide variety of devices. The simplest GPS unit determines and stores locations as latitude/longitude positions. In addition, they are able to store waypoints. A **waypoint** is simply a stored location that is of interest to the user. The GPS is also able to tell you the distance and direction of a waypoint from your current position.

A more complex group of devices combines GPS capability with interactive map databases. These devices show your location in relation to various landmarks. In an auto navigation system this would start with the location of streets and highways, but might include extra useful features such as the location of gas stations and hotels. A marine navigation unit combines information about water depths with port locations and facilities, lighthouses, and other marine navigation aids. An aviation system (Fig. 3-8) works in a similar fashion but would have information about airports, major highways, electrical transmission towers, etc., that would be helpful to a pilot.

In addition to units of these types that can be bought "off the shelf," GPS capabilities have also been built into many specialized units. The OnStar system is one example of this kind of GPS application. Another is used on intercity trucks. In this case, a GPS unit sends the truck's location back to the company's head office. This allows the company's management to monitor the progress of shipments. Devices that combine GPS capabilities with the ability to transmit vehicle locations to a remote receiver are called **telematic** devices.

▲ **Fig. 3-8** This is an air navigation GPS unit. It relates the plane's location, as determined by GPS, to important information needed by the pilot.

GPS Uses

GPS technology is used in a remarkable range of fields. Here are just some of them:

- Agriculture—Tractors, steered by GPS rather than people, can plough perfectly straight rows in half the time.
- Archaeology—GPS has helped archaeologists do their work much more efficiently. For example, it is used to record quickly and accurately the location of artifacts. The data collected can be used to draw quick and accurate maps of archaeological digs.

INTERNET

You can read about a variety of GPS applications at www.pearsoned.ca/makingconnections2.

- Forestry—GPS is used to plan forest cuts to ensure that the maximum amount of timber can be cut with the minimum amount of environmental damage.
- Geology—GPS is used to make precise maps of geologic features.
- Natural hazards—GPS is used in research to predict the occurrence of volcanic eruptions and earthquakes.
- Recreation—GPS technology is used, with a personal data assistant (PDA), on golf courses to indicate the distance to the hole.
- Surveying—GPS was critical in the construction of the new Hong Kong airport. The airport was built on landfill in the sea, and quick and accurate surveying was necessary to monitor the amount of **subsidence** of the fill.
- Weather forecasting—GPS units sent aloft with weather balloons give the precise location and altitude at which weather observations (temperature, air pressure, etc.) are made.

Blackberry is one brand of PDA.

subsidence
sinking due to compression

DON'T BE A GEOMUGGLE!

What, you don't know what a geomuggle is? A geomuggle is someone who has not discovered the new sport of **geocaching**. Geocaching is an active hobby based on the use of a simple handheld GPS unit. The idea is to use your GPS and maps to find a cache created by someone who has placed its location on the Internet (www.geocaching.com). There were more than 200 000 geocaches in over 200 countries in 2005. Their characteristics vary, but in simplest terms a cache is a box that contains a collection of small items and a log book (Fig. 3-9). When you find the cache, you sign the logbook and take a small item, which you replace with a comparable item. This simple theme has many variations. In some cases you have to follow a series of clues to find the cache. In other cases there may not be a real box—it may be a "virtual cache." Some caches may be very hard to find—in a remote location, or even under water.

The best way to get started with geocaching is to study the hobby's Web site. In particular, you should read over these sections: *FAQs about Geocaching* and *Guide to Finding Your First Cache.* Links to them can be found in the *Getting Started* section of the site's main page.

Finding Your First Cache

1. The best way to locate a cache in your area is to search by postal code (use the zip code box) in the upper right-hand corner of the

◀ **Fig. 3-9** A typical geocache is a waterproof container that contains instructions, a logbook, and "rewards." When you find a cache you take one reward and leave another.

main page. Chances are very good that there will be one not too distant from your school or home since, in mid-2005, there were about 3300 caches in Ontario alone. Once you have a list of caches located near you, choose your "target" based on several factors. How far away is it? Can you walk, take public transit, or will you need a ride? What terrain and difficulty ranking does it have? (You are looking for 1s or 2s for your first cache.) Does it look like an interesting cache and area to visit?

2. Learn how to operate your GPS unit well before you go.
3. Check with your teacher that you have made an appropriate cache selection. Do not go alone, and be sure to tell someone when you are leaving, where you are going, and when you will be back. Remember that the GPS unit is not telematic, so it does not tell someone else where you are. It only tells you your location. You need to be able to use the GPS unit intelligently to find your way back if you get lost.

4. Figure out what maps you will need for your search. In an urban area, or other area with many roads, you might want to use the Google Maps that are linked on the cache description page. You might want to have more than one map, each with a different scale—one with a smaller scale to get you close to the target, and the second with the largest scale possible to help you search. In a rural area, topographic maps (at least 1:50 000 scale) are best.
5. Take a small item with you to leave in the cache. Also remember to take a pen or pencil so that you can leave an entry in the cache's log. You might also want to take a camera to record your search—and success.
6. Time to become a non-geomuggle. Start your search. Remember that the GPS unit will get you within perhaps seven metres of the cache. If the cache is well hidden, you will need to do some careful, intelligent searching to find it.
7. Log your visit to the cache on www.geocaching.com. The link is on the top right corner of the cache description page.
8. Write a two- to three-paragraph description of your search for your teacher. Describe exactly what you did. Indicate which aspects of the search proved harder than you thought, and which proved easier.

Think to yourself, "If I had created this cache, where in this area would I have hidden it?"

Finding Other Caches
Once you have found your first cache you will probably want to search for others. You can increase the challenge by looking for caches that are better hidden or in more difficult terrain. You can also search for different types of caches such as multi-caches or virtual caches. You can learn about these at the Web site.

Creating Your Own Cache
The many tens of thousands of caches that exist have been created by individuals who wanted to give others the fun of a new challenge. The instructions you need to create a cache are in the section of the Web site called *How to Create a First Cache*, which is a link from the *Getting Started* section of the site's main page.

QUESTIONS

KNOWLEDGE AND UNDERSTANDING

1. How many compass points are shown in Fig. 3-1?
2. What direction is halfway between each of the following directions?
   a) NE and SW b) NE and S
   c) WSW and NNW
3. What direction is opposite each of the following directions?
   a) SW b) NNE c) ESE
4. Give the compass bearing for the following directions (compass points):
   a) N b) SSE c) NNE
5. What is the direction of the following bearings?
   a) 22.5° b) 112.5° c) 292.5°
6. a) What is GPS?
   b) What do you need to be able to use GPS?

THINKING

7. a) Briefly describe four different GPS applications.
   b) What two major advantages does GPS have? Hint: Consider the advantages that a GPS-based system has over the traditional way of finding locations.

APPLICATION

8. Use the information in Fig. 3-10 to determine the direction of each of the numbered arrows.

▼ Fig. 3-10

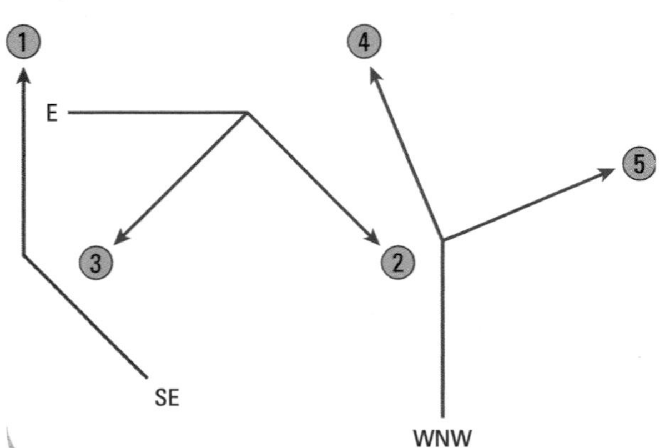

9. Using a Mercator projection in an atlas and a protractor, calculate the bearing of each of the following locations from Edmonton:
   a) Prince Albert b) Medicine Hat
   c) Kelowna d) Peace River
10. Using an atlas, draw and label the following major lines of latitude and longitude on the world map provided by your teacher.
    a) Latitude: equator, tropic of Cancer, tropic of Capricorn, Arctic Circle, Antarctic Circle
    b) Longitude: prime meridian, 180° meridian
11. a) From your atlas, determine the names of the major cities at the following locations:
    i. 47°N 52°W
    ii. 39°N 116°E
    iii. 23°S 43°W
    iv. 6°S 106°E
    b) Label each of these places on your world map.
12. a) Use your atlas to determine the location (latitude and longitude) of the following capital cities:
    i. Ottawa, Canada
    ii. Cairo, Egypt
    iii. Santiago, Chile
    iv. Wellington, New Zealand
    v. Kampala, Uganda
    b) In which hemisphere is each capital located?
13. What is the straight-line distance in kilometres between each pair of cities? Each pair is located on the same line of longitude.
    a) 20°N and 5°N
    b) 25°N and 17°S

4 Using Map Scales

Key Ideas

This chapter helps you investigate these questions:

- What is a map scale?
- How can I use map scales effectively?

Key Terms

scale

direct statement scale

line scale

representative fraction scale

Have you ever made a model of something like an airplane or a building? Every part of the model is in true proportion to the life-size object (Fig. 4-1). This reduction in size is the basic idea of scale. In Chapter 2, you saw that a map must have a scale. The **scale** shows the relationship between the distance on a map and the actual distance on Earth's surface. A small distance on the map represents a much larger distance on Earth's surface. Scale can be represented in three different ways: direct statement, line scale, and representative fraction scale.

▼ **Fig. 4-1** Every part of this model car (right) is in true proportion to the life-size object that it represents. Note that the scale of the model is 1:25. What does this mean?

Direct Statement Scale

A **direct statement scale** uses words to describe the relationship between a distance on a map and a specific distance on Earth's surface, for example, 1 cm to 10 km. This means if the distance between two towns on a map is one centimetre, the actual distance between the towns is 10 kilometres.

On the map in Fig. 4-2, the distance between *Here* and *There* is measured and found to be three centimetres. If the scale is 1 cm to 10 km, then the distance on Earth's surface is calculated as follows:

Since 1 cm = 10 km

(3 × 1) cm = (3 × 10) km

3 cm = 30 km

Therefore, the actual distance between *Here* and *There* is 30 kilometres.

A direct statement scale is also called a verbal statement.

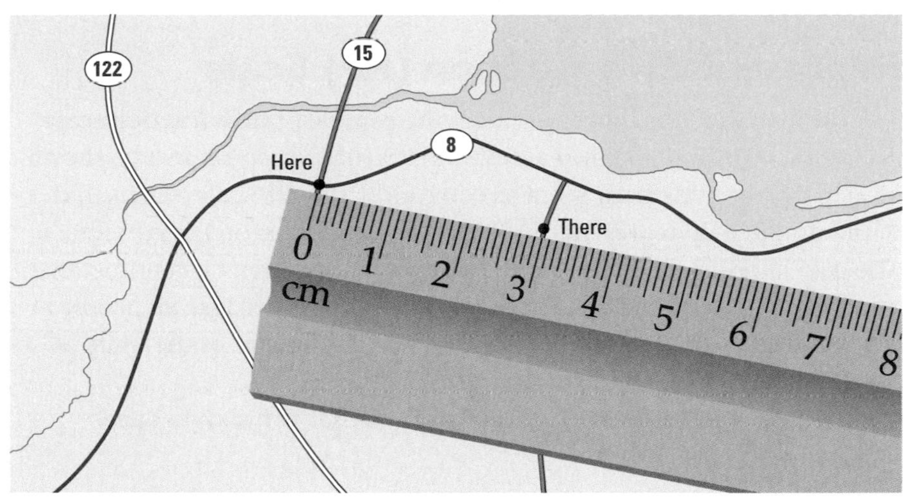

◀ **Fig. 4-2** To determine the distance on a map with a direct statement scale, measure the distance between two places. Calculate the distance using the scale.

Line Scale

A **line scale** is like a special kind of ruler that is divided into units of distance. Use a line scale to find the distance between Kingston and Cornwall, following the five steps illustrated in Fig. 4-3.

A line scale is also called a linear scale.

1

Kingston

Cornwall

Mark the locations of the two cities on the edge of a sheet of paper.

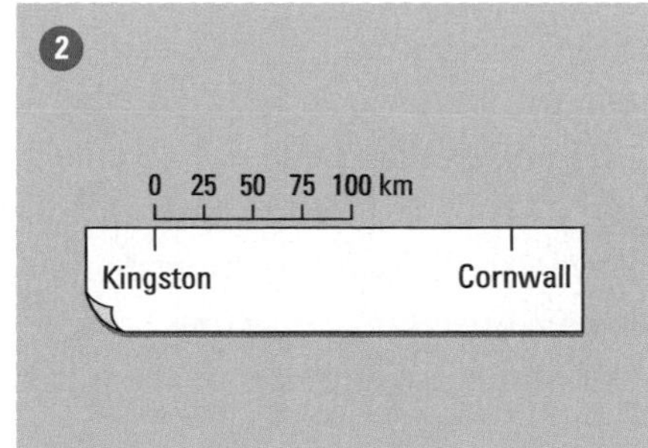

Place the edge of the paper against the line scale on the map, with the first mark at 0. ▶

◀ **Fig. 4-3** Follow these steps to find the actual distance between places using a line scale.

Fig. 4-3 *continued* ▶

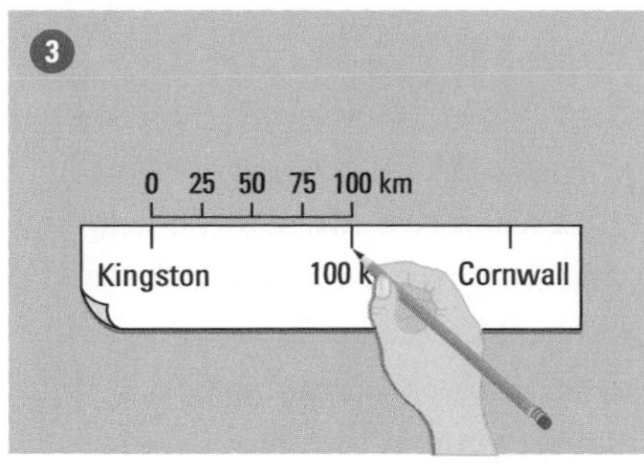

Make a mark on your paper at the right end of the scale.

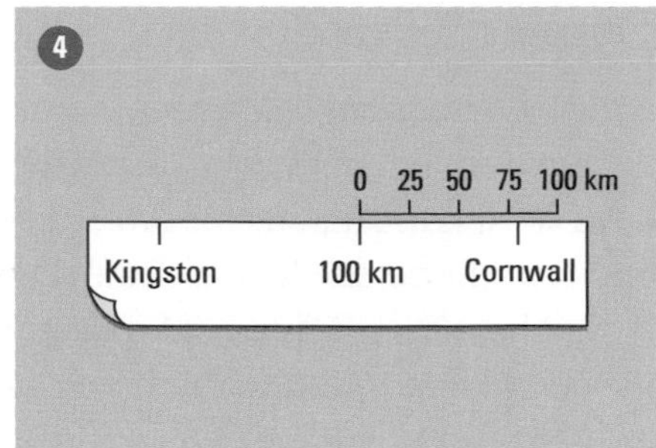

Move the mark from step three to 0 on the line scale and measure the remaining distance.

5 Calculate the total distance between Kingston and Cornwall by adding together the distances you measured (100 + 80).

The distance between Kingston and Cornwall is 180 km.

A representative fraction was used to show the scale of the model car in Fig. 4-1.

Representative Fraction (RF) Scale

The third method for showing scale is the **representative fraction scale.** An RF is a ratio and is shown as follows: 1:50 000. (It could also be shown as 1/50 000, but this form is not as common.) This RF scale means that 1 unit on the map represents 50 000 of the *same units* on Earth's surface. The user chooses the units. In Canada, this would often be centimetres, and inches in the United States. This is very useful, because all people in the world can use this scale regardless of their language or the units of measurement used in their country.

There are a few properties about this ratio that you should know:

The first term of the ratio
- is always 1
- represents the distance on the map in the units of your choice

The second term of the ratio
- represents the distance on Earth's surface
- must be in the same unit of measurement as the first term of the ratio

INTERNET

To see examples of different scales, check www.pearsoned.ca/makingconnections2.

Therefore, if the RF is 1:50 000, then 1 centimetre on the map represents 50 000 centimetres on Earth's surface.

We usually want to know distances in kilometres. To change the centimetres used in the RF into kilometres, we must know how to convert one unit of measurement into the other. Continue reading to find out how to do this.

Scale Conversion

The RF scale is practical because it can be used by everyone all over the world. It is not very useful, however, when we want to indicate an actual distance between places. For example, if the RF is 1:50 000 we know that one centimetre on the map represents 50 000 centimetres on Earth's surface. What we really want to know, however, is how many kilometres on Earth's surface are represented by one centimetre on the map. For this reason, it is important that we know how to convert from one scale to another.

Converting an RF Scale to a Direct Statement Scale

To convert an RF scale to a direct statement scale, divide the right side of the equation by 100 000, to change centimetres into kilometres.

Therefore, in order to convert a 1:50 000 RF into a direct statement, you would use the following process:

1 cm = 50 000 cm

1 cm = (50 000/100 000) km

1 cm = 0.5 km or 1 cm to 500 m

Since
1 km = 1000 m and
1 m = 100 cm,
1 km = (1000 x 100) cm
= 100 000 cm

Converting a Direct Statement Scale to an RF Scale

To convert from a direct statement scale back to an RF scale, multiply the right side of the equation by 100 000, to change kilometres into centimetres.

In order to convert the direct statement 1 cm to 2.5 km into a representative fraction, you would use the following process:

1 cm = 2.5 km

1 cm = (2.5 × 100 000) cm

1 cm = 250 000 cm or 1:250 000

When constructing a map, use the scale that is best suited to the purpose of the map. Make sure that there is a scale shown on all your maps.

QUESTIONS

KNOWLEDGE AND UNDERSTANDING

1. In your own words, what is an RF scale?
2. a) What does 1:250 000 mean?
   b) What does 1:3 000 000 mean?

APPLICATION

3. a) What does 1 cm to 0.5 km mean?
   b) Use this scale to recalculate the distance, in both kilometres and metres, between *Here* and *There* in Fig. 4-2.
4. The direct statement scale of a map is 1 cm to 35 km. If the map distance between points A and B is 9 cm, what is the actual distance?
5. The direct statement scale of a map is 1 cm to 250 km. If two places are 17 cm apart on the map, what is the actual distance between them?
6. Using the scale of 1 cm to 30 km, calculate the road distances between towns X and Y in Fig. 4-4.

▼ **Fig. 4-4**

a) 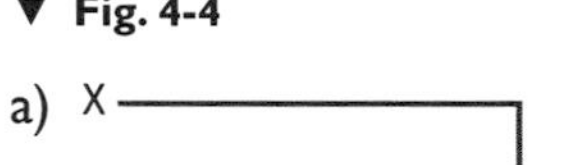

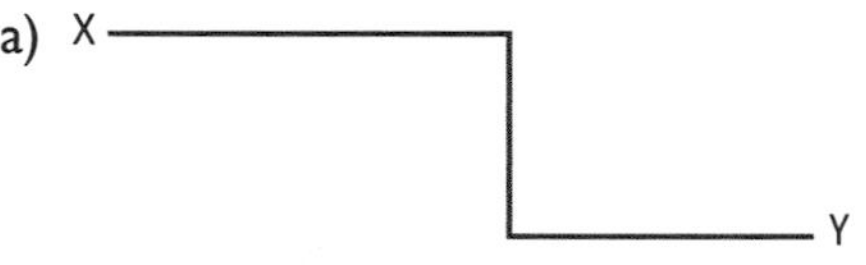

b) 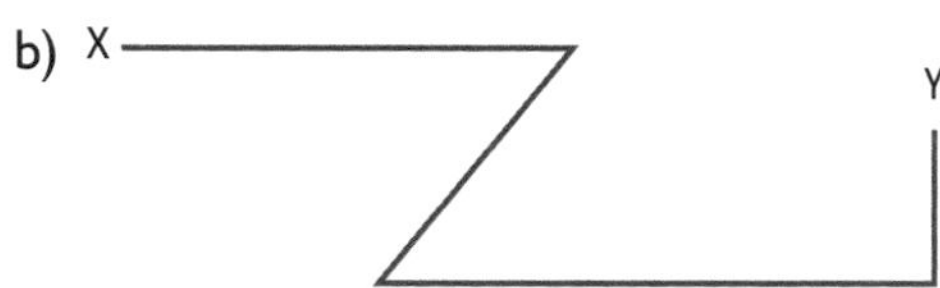

c) 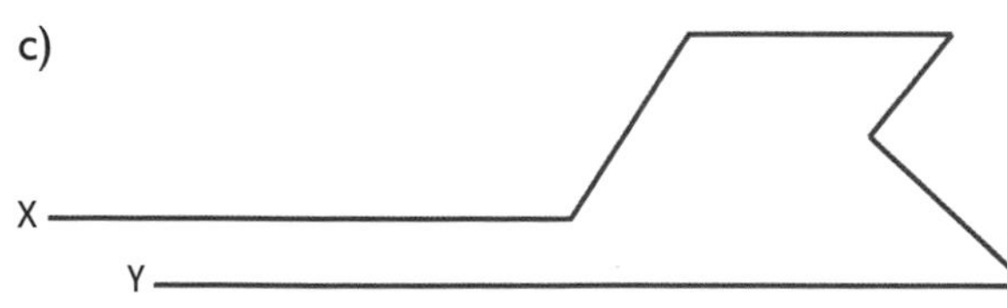

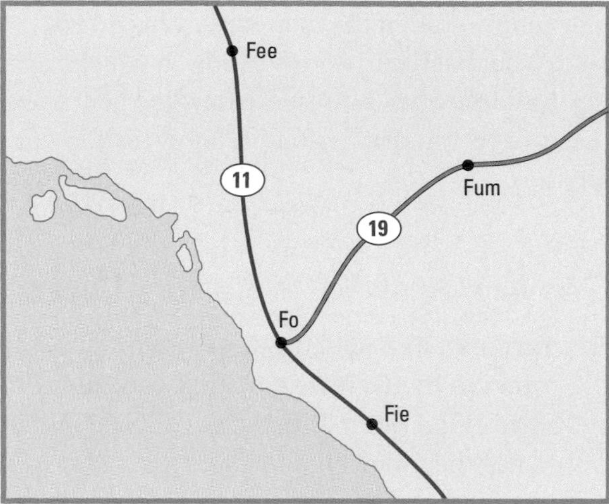

▲ **Fig. 4-5** The scale of this map is 1 cm to 12 km.

7. Refer to Fig. 4-5 to calculate the road distance between *Fee* and *Fie* and between *Fo* and *Fum*.
8. Here is a list of distances between Canadian cities. Draw straight lines in your notebook to show how each distance would appear on a map. Use a scale of 1 cm to 100 km.
   a) Calgary to Edmonton 299 km
   b) Fredericton to Montreal 834 km
   c) Regina to Winnipeg 571 km
9. a) In an atlas, find a map of a part of Canada that has a line scale.
   b) Use the line scale method to calculate the actual distance between two cities on that map.
   c) Select another pair of cities and repeat the activity.
10. Convert the following representative fractions to direct statements.
    a) 1:250 000
    b) 1:1 500 000
    c) 1:63 000 000

11. Use an atlas to find the straight-line distance between the locations listed below. Use the direct statement scale found in the atlas. (Answers will vary slightly depending on the atlas.)
    a) Wiarton, Ontario (in the Bruce Peninsula) and Port Dover, Ontario (on Lake Erie)
    b) Gananoque, Ontario (near Kingston on the St. Lawrence River) and Aylmer, Quebec (near Ottawa on the Ottawa River)
    c) Sault Ste. Marie, Ontario (between Lake Superior and Lake Huron) and Timmins, Ontario (northeast of Sault Ste. Marie)
12. Find the maps in your atlas that show the following pairs of cities. Measure the straight-line distances between the two cities. Use the RF scale shown on the map to calculate the distance in kilometres.
    a) London, England, and Rome, Italy (map of Europe)
    b) Havana, Cuba, and Miami, Florida (map of the Caribbean)
    c) Prince Rupert and Bella Coola, British Columbia (map of western Canada)
    d) Yarmouth, Nova Scotia, and Bathurst, New Brunswick (map of eastern Canada)
13. Convert the following direct statement scales to RF scales.
    a) 1 cm to 5 km
    b) 1 cm to 25 km
    c) 1 cm to 160 km
14. The line scale on a map indicates that 4 cm represents 20 km. What is the RF?
15. The line scale on a map indicates that 1.5 cm represents 50 km. What is the RF?

5 A Revolution in Geography: GIS

Key Ideas

This chapter helps you investigate these questions:

- How is GIS technology currently used in Canada?
- How could you use GIS technology to benefit your personal life?

Key Terms

geographic information systems (GIS)
base map
database
geospatial
ArcView
graduated colour map
geomatics

We take maps for granted because they are such an everyday part of our lives. Just think about the last time you used a map. Perhaps it was while reading the newspaper, watching television, working on a computer, or taking a trip. Look at the relatively simple maps on the inside covers of this book. Imagine how difficult it would be to convey to someone the information on these maps by using only words!

Maps of various kinds have been used for thousands of years. Fig. 5-1 shows part of Canada on a map that was made more than 300 years ago.

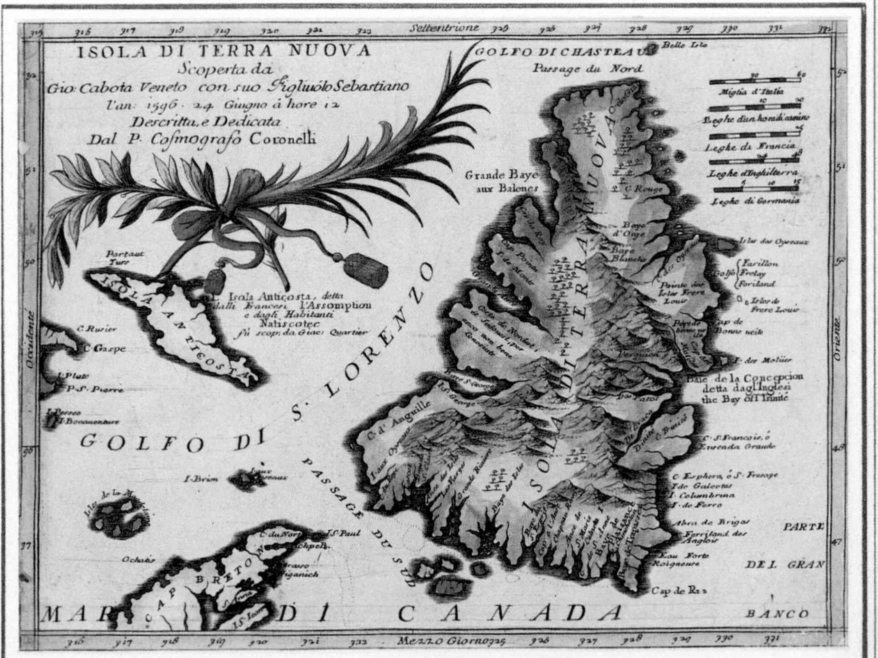

Fig. 5-1 ▶ This map, made in 1696, shows an area that is now part of Canada. Can you tell what part of Canada this is? Compare it with a current map of the same area. Why are there so many differences?

This map, created by an Italian cartographer named Coronelli, is considered a work of art. Its purpose, however, was exactly the same as that of modern maps—to show information in a graphic way about the location of places and things and the relationships that exist among them.

Geographic information systems, more commonly known as **GIS**, is a new mapping technology that has **revolutionized** map-making and map analysis. In this chapter, you will learn how GIS produces "dynamic maps." These are maps that you can make on a computer by stacking "layers" of specific geographical, or spatial, information (Fig. 5-2). You can remove or add layers of information to adapt the map to a particular purpose or to analyze the relationship between different pieces of spatial information. GIS also has the capability of producing three-dimensional maps, graphs, and diagrams. It can calculate the area of a region depicted on a map. It can create perspective views similar to photographs in which the angle of the sun is set for a specific time and date. Then, if you wish, you can send GIS maps, graphs, and diagrams over the Internet to others who may use them to do research or to solve problems.

revolutionize
change dramatically and quickly

How GIS Is Used

Purposes of GIS

GIS has three main purposes:

1. to link geographic location (where things are) to descriptive information (what things are), e.g., linking a specific address to a specific person.
2. to create maps with many different pieces of spatial information arranged in layers on top of one another. The layers can be **manipulated** to show how the data may be interrelated.
3. to help users analyze spatial information. GIS can manipulate spatial data to help users answer important questions or reach conclusions about geographical issues. The recombined data can create new sets of geographical information (data sets).

manipulate
handle or use, especially with skill

GIS is used in many aspects of day-to-day life, without our even realizing it. Here are some uses that may have an impact on your life:

- getting 911 emergency services to your home as quickly as possible
- planning water and sewage services for a new residential area
- deciding if there are enough children of the right age in an area to justify building a new school
- ensuring that the pizza you ordered gets to your home within the promised time
- illustrating the movement of air masses in the atmosphere to understand **critical** problems such as global warming

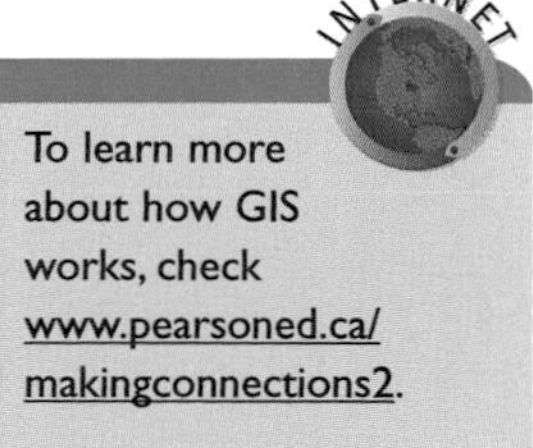

To learn more about how GIS works, check www.pearsoned.ca/makingconnections2.

critical
vitally important

How GIS Programs Work

GIS computer programs are relatively new in the study of geography. This is how these programs work.

1. Imagine that you have a **base map.** Then imagine overlaying one or more transparent layers, each with specific data, onto the base map (Fig. 5-2). For example, you might want to draw a map that combines information about road patterns (layer #1), the location of high schools (layer #2), and the pattern of district boundaries (layer #4). This is easily done with GIS.
2. GIS combines the features of a **database** program (Fig. 5-3) with those of a drawing program (Fig. 5-4). The database program contains **geospatial** data, that is, information about items that can be located on Earth's surface (e.g., by their latitude and longitude).

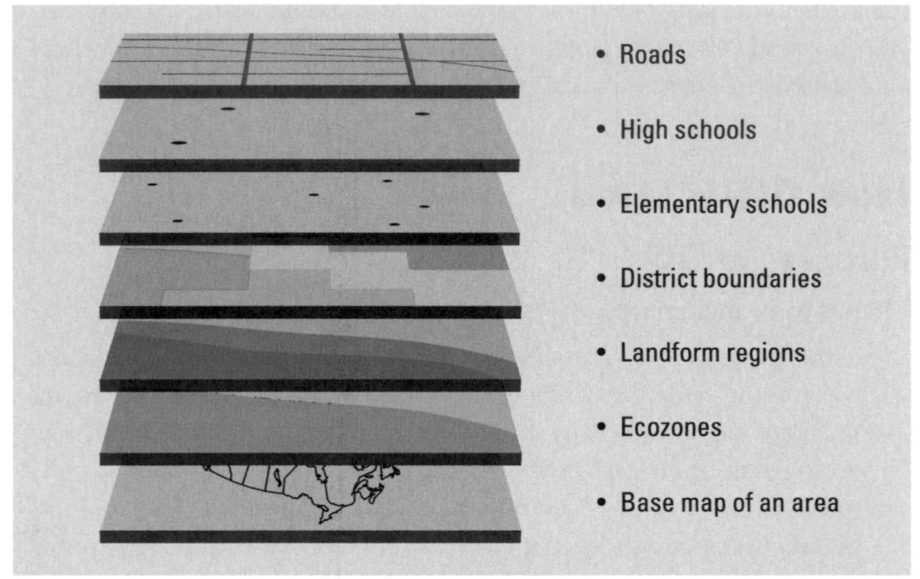

Fig. 5-2 ► You create a GIS map by adding layers, each with a different type of information, over a base map to create a stack of information. The information in a particular layer may be changed to update the map, or a layer may be omitted altogether, depending on the use of the map. You control the amount of information that you want to see at any given time.

Fig. 5-3 ► A GIS map combines the capabilities of a database, containing information such as this, with those of a dynamic map-drawing program.

Ecozone	Total Area (km²)	Land Area (km²)	Water Area (km²)	Population	Dominant Cover
Taiga Cordillera	245 865	245 505	360	360	Coniferous forest
Boreal Cordillera	432 128	427 208	4 920	16 000	Coniferous forest
Montane Cordillera	461 198	448 145	13 053	452 000	Coniferous forest
Arctic Cordillera	239 216	219 499	19 717	1 000	Perennial snow/ice
Northern Arctic	1 433 362	1 283 915	149 447	16 000	Barren lands
Southern Arctic	775 734	716 385	59 349	10 000	Arctic/alpine tundra
Atlantic Maritime	196 449	176 677	19 772	2 510 000	Mixed forest
Pacific Maritime	195 554	181 749	13 805	2 504 000	Coniferous forest
Hudson Plains	350 318	341 322	8 996	10 000	Transitional forest
Taiga Plains	563 241	496 380	66 861	21 000	Coniferous forest
Taiga Shield	1 268 623	1 156 110	112 513	34 000	Transitional forest
Prairie	440 537	432 108	8 429	3 851 000	Agricultural cropland
Boreal Shield	1 773 894	1 609 776	164 118	1 695 000	Coniferous forest
Boreal Plains	656 970	599 139	57 831	708 000	Coniferous forest
Mixedwood Plains	113 431	57 422	56 009	14 016 000	Agricultural cropland

Suppose you want to draw a map to show Canada's population density by ecozone. GIS creates the base map showing the ecozones (Fig. 5-4). Then it uses the information in the database (Fig. 5-3) to calculate the population density of each ecozone. Finally, it shades in the ecozones according to the categories you have created (Fig. 5-5). Imagine how long this would take if you had to do all the map-drawing, calculations, and shading by hand! Then think how you would feel if your teacher asked you to change from five categories of population density to four. With a GIS program, this change would take only a few seconds.

◀ **Fig. 5-4** An example of a base map created by a GIS program. Red lines indicate ecozone boundaries. You will learn more about ecozones in Chapter 15.

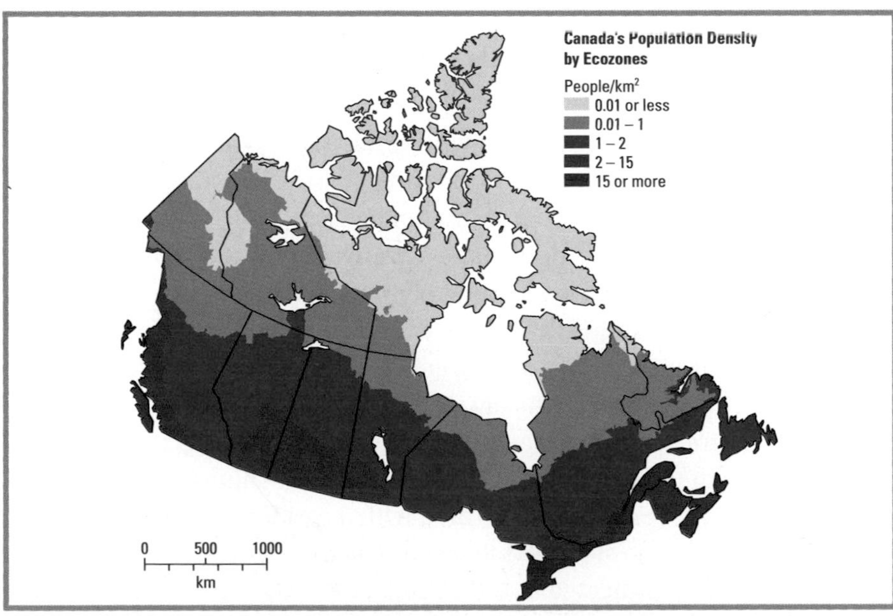

◀ **Fig. 5-5** This map of ecozone population densities was created using a GIS program.

What You Need to Work with GIS

- a powerful computer system with a printer
- GIS mapping software
- specially created computerized base maps
- the data that you wish to analyze and map
- and what is most important, an intelligent and creative person who wants to analyze and display something—YOU!

Using GIS in *Making Connections*

▲ **Fig. 5-6** This logo indicates a GIS exercise in this book.

There are many different GIS programs on the market. Most work in a similar fashion although many are very complicated programs designed for expert use. In this book, you will learn about a GIS program called **ArcView** from ESRI Canada. Your teacher will give you instructions for the six ArcView activities in this book as you need them. These activities are indicated by a special logo (Fig. 5-6).

In ArcView, the file that you create is referred to as a "project." Creating a map with ArcView consists of three major steps. The first and last steps are the same for all projects. The second step will vary because the information you put on each map will be different.

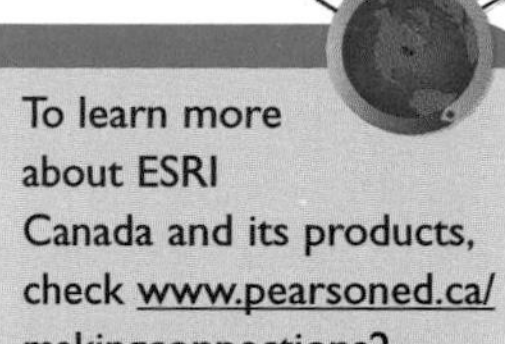

To learn more about ESRI Canada and its products, check www.pearsoned.ca/makingconnections2.

Step #1: You create a project and set up a base map to work on.
Step #2: You analyze the data and decide what layers you will put on your map and how you want to display this data.
Step #3: You assemble all the elements of your map.

Tools You Can Use in Step #2

To do the ArcView activities that are part of this book (Fig. 5-7), you will need to use the following tools.

Full instructions for doing ArcView activities will be given to you by your teacher.

1. *Identifying*: Features (cities, provinces, lakes, etc.) on ArcView maps usually have a great deal of information associated with them. When you click on a feature, this information is displayed.
2. *Labelling*: When you click the label command, it automatically adds the name of a highlighted feature to your map.
3. *Charting*: The chart feature allows you to create charts, such as pie or bar graphs, from the data with which you are working. The charts you make will appear automatically in the correct locations on your map.
4. *Graduated Colour Mapping*: In a **graduated colour map** layer, different shades of the same colour indicate different values of the same measurement. For example, an area with a certain population density is indicated by one shade, while an area with a higher population density may be indicated by a darker shade of the same colour.

5. *Single-Symbol Mapping*: A single-symbol map layer shows one feature such as the location of cities or the location of rivers. The two layers may be combined to create a map showing the relationship between the location of cities and rivers. You may use symbols found on traditional maps, e.g., a miniature black tent for a campsite or two parallel red lines for a dual highway. In addition, single-symbol and graduated colour layers can be combined; for example, you might choose to show major cities (single symbol) on your map of population density (graduated colour).
6. *Zooming*: You may want to look at a small area on your map in greater detail, or show only part of a map on your screen. With ArcView, you can zoom in to enlarge part of your map and display it at a larger scale.
7. *Querying*: The **query** tool allows you to ask questions about your data. For example, suppose you have a database of cities in Canada. You can use the query tool to find out which cities have populations over 100 000.
8. *Measuring*: This tool allows you to determine, very quickly, the distance between any two places.

query
ask a question

ArcView Activities

Chapter	Project	Tools used
1	An introductory map of Canada	Identifying Labelling
15	Population density in each ecozone	Graduated colour mapping
25	Forest coverage in each ecozone	Charting
33	Canada's foreign aid (2 maps)	Graduated colour mapping
34	Location of North American auto-assembly plants (2 maps)	Single-symbol mapping Zooming Querying
37	World production of carbon dioxide and Kyoto Conference targets (2 maps)	Graduated colour mapping Querying

◀ **Fig. 5-7** These are the ArcView activities you can do in this book.

GeoCareers

Geomatics

Geomatics is known as geospatial **technology** in the United States.

Geomatics is the term used in Canada to describe the science and technology of gathering, analyzing, and manipulating geographic (geospatial) information. It includes such fields as remote sensing, computer mapping, global positioning systems (GPS), and geographic information systems (GIS). If you have found this chapter interesting, you might consider a career in geomatics.

Jobs in geomatics include geographer, surveying and mapping technician, remote sensing scientist, and civil engineering technician. Geomatics technology and skills are also used in such fields as archaeology, medicine, forestry, and astronomy. Employment may be found in the natural resources industry, in land management companies and engineering firms, and in government.

INTERNET

The National Occupational Classification carries an extensive list of job descriptions. To learn more, go to www.pearsoned.ca/makingconnections2.

Find Out More

Conduct a career search of the geomatics (geospatial technolology) industry.

1. Begin with a search of post-secondary institutions (universities, community colleges, and technical institutions).
   a) List three institutions in Canada and two institutions in other countries that offer geomatics courses.
   b) Select one institution from part a) and list the academic requirements necessary to gain admission.
   c) Name one specific department in the institution you selected in part b) that offers courses in geomatics. Describe these courses.
2. Select one university and one community college. What academic requirements must be met to gain admission to each one? What high school courses and what marks do you need to meet these requirements?
3. What types of careers or jobs do these programs lead to? List at least three for both the college and university programs in Question 2.
4. What salary levels do these jobs offer?
5. Find at least one profile or resumé of a person who has graduated in geomatics, and write a summary of that person's experiences.
6. What aspect of this field might interest you as a potential career? Explain your answer.

In Closing...

GIS is a revolutionary technology that is changing the way we analyze and present geographic information. In this chapter, and in your Canadian Geography course, you will have only scratched the surface of this exciting field. GIS is also becoming increasingly important in your day-to-day life. Who knows? Since GIS is such a fast-growing field, you may even end up working in it when you finish your schooling.

QUESTIONS

KNOWLEDGE AND UNDERSTANDING

1. Using the glossary, define the term "geographic information systems" (GIS).
2. a) How is a GIS map created?
   b) How can the layers of a GIS map be manipulated?
3. "GIS is used in many aspects of day-to-day life." Describe three.
4. a) GIS has three major purposes. What are they?
   b) "GIS combines the features of a database program with those of a drawing program." Demonstrate.
   c) What do you need to use GIS?

APPLICATION

5. a) In your own words, briefly explain the eight tools used in ArcView.
   b) Complete the GIS activity "An Introductory Map of Canada" found on page 7 of this textbook. Your teacher will provide you with full instructions.
   c) Now that you have actually used some of the ArcView tools, go back and refine the explanations you gave in Question 5 a).

6 Aerial Photos: The View from Above

Key Ideas

This chapter helps you investigate this question:

- In what ways are aerial photographs an essential tool in geographical research and study?

Key Terms

aerial photo

stereo pair

The first aerial photographs were taken in the 1850s from cameras attached to kites. Later in the century, photographs were taken from hot-air balloons. Although these early photographs were very crude, they did point out the **potential** usefulness of photographs taken from a great height.

potential
possibility for development in the future

New techniques have tremendously improved the quality of aerial photographs. Aerial photographs are used to study such things as farm size, crop plantings, soil erosion, and the flow of traffic in cities. They are useful in archaeological studies, meteorological observations, and even crime detection. Today, aerial photographs are an essential tool in geographical research and study.

What Is a Stereo Pair?

Stereo pair images may also be taken by satellites.

Although a single **aerial photo** can be useful in the study of a geographical feature or area, the use of a **stereo pair** of photographs is more helpful. The vertical aerial photographs are taken from an aircraft, in rapid succession, by a high-speed camera looking directly down at the ground. The camera is set so that the images overlap from photo to photo. Fig. 6-1 shows how this is done. As you can see, the same area is photographed from a slightly different position in the sky. Any two overlapping aerial photos is a stereo pair.

A stereo pair image is similar to the way your eyes see objects—from two slightly different positions.

When you look at a map, you see its features in two dimensions, that is, you see length and width. When you position a stereo pair properly and view the photos through an instrument called a stereoscope, your brain sees images in three dimensions: length, width, and height. While the height of cliffs, trees, and buildings is **exaggerated**, this extra dimension allows you to see much more than is possible with a single photograph. With the use of a stereo pair, you can learn a great deal about a place without ever having to visit it.

exaggerated
made to appear larger than they actually are

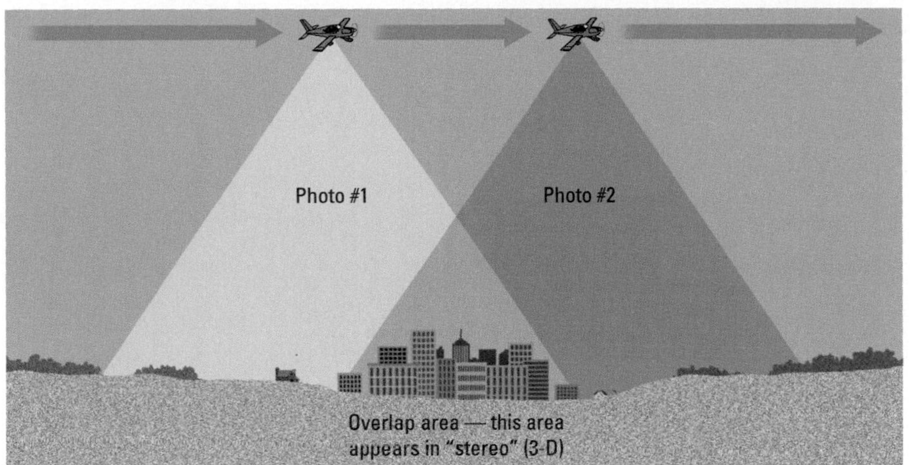

◀ **Fig. 6-1** An illustration of how a stereo pair is created by two overlapping vertical aerial photographs. The same area is photographed from two slightly different positions.

Fig. 6-2 shows a stereo pair of photographs of part of downtown Toronto. What can we learn about Toronto from these photographs? The letters A to M on the stereo pair will allow you to locate items referred to in the analysis that follows. On a piece of clear **acetate**, make an overlay map of this area. Place the acetate over the stereo pair. Use the photo on the right for all your tracings. View the stereo pair through a stereoscope to help you determine the answers to the questions in the following exercises.

Use different colours, symbols, or both to show different land uses.

acetate
clear plastic on which you draw with special pens

Commercial Land Use

The southern part of Toronto's Central Business District (CBD) is shown in the photographs. The CBD includes many of the city's most important commercial land uses, namely, the major office buildings and shopping areas.

OFFICE BUILDINGS

1. On your acetate, trace the part of the CBD that is bordered by the tallest buildings.
2. Canada's four tallest buildings are found near the corner of King Street and Bay Street (A). They are First Canadian Place (Bank of Montreal) on the northwest corner, Toronto-Dominion Centre (TD Bank) on the southwest corner, Scotia Plaza (Scotiabank) on the northeast corner, and Commerce Court (Canadian Imperial Bank of Commerce) on the southeast corner. Which of these buildings appears to be the tallest in the stereo pair? Does it appear to be a light or dark colour? Why are the buildings built so high in this part of the city?

▼ Fig. 6-2 A stereo pair of downtown Toronto

3. The Toronto Stock Exchange is located in First Canadian Place. What types of related businesses will you find in the tall office buildings nearby? Why do they locate in the financial district? What types of businesses have the wealth to build tall buildings?

SHOPPING

4. In the past, Yonge Street was the most important shopping street in downtown Toronto. Now, however, many stores have moved off the street and into downtown malls or underground walkways. The focus of shopping is the Eaton Centre (B), a multi-level shopping mall with almost 300 stores. Give one advantage and one disadvantage of this type of development.
5. It is possible to walk from just north of the Eaton Centre to Union Station (F) without going outside. This "underground city" is a series of shopping malls and walkways under the large office towers of the CBD. What are the positive and negative aspects of such a design?

The stock exchange is a place where people (like you, if you have the money) can buy shares in companies.

See the map of Toronto's CBD in Chapter 21.

Transportation Land Use

Much of the transportation land use in this area is directly related to commercial activities. Every weekday, hundreds of thousands of people travel to the CBD to go to work or to shop. Most of them travel by public transit or car.

What other methods of transportation might people use?

PUBLIC TRANSIT

1. a) The most important part of the downtown public transit system is the subway. The subway runs north–south on Yonge Street (C) and then loops at Front Street (E) to travel north–south on University Avenue (D). Why do you think this particular route was chosen for the subway? Don't forget that Union Station (F) on Front Street is the meeting point of the subway system and the GO train, a commuter railway system. What effect do the subway lines appear to have had on the growth of Toronto?
   b) Show the subway routes on your tracing.
2. The other part of the public transit system consists of a fleet of buses and streetcars. Can you suggest where three north–south and three east–west routes might be? Give two reasons why there are no subway lines along these streets.

STREETS AND ROADS

Two types of roads are shown in the stereo pair: an expressway and city streets.

3. a) Show the expressway on your tracing.
   b) What is the purpose of an expressway? In what directions does the expressway run from the downtown area?
4. What pattern is formed by the city streets? Is this pattern found where you live? How else can a city's streets be arranged?

PARKING LOTS

Because many thousands of cars enter the CBD each day, parking facilities are very important.

5. a) On your tracing, carefully draw and label all the parking lots you can see.
   b) Describe the location of parking lots in relation to high-density developments in the CBD. Why are parking lots found in these locations?
   c) Why might these parking lots be temporary land uses only? Where might new parking lots appear?
   d) In what other way do you think parking is provided that is not visible on these aerial photographs?

RAILWAYS

6. Freight handling once took place in the area on the photo indicated by the dotted line. It now takes place outside the CBD in suburban locations. Why? Which parts of the railway lands have been redeveloped? Why?
7. On your tracing, show the location of Union Station (F), the transportation hub, on Front Street. Why is this a convenient location?
8. The GO train, a commuter railway, runs along the lakeshore tracks to Union Station. About 180 trains carry some 150 000 commuters every weekday. Show the GO train route on your tracing.

A commuter train is designed to take people to and from work.

AIRPORT

9. a) Show the location of the Toronto Island Airport on your tracing. How do people get to the airport?
   b) This is not the main airport in the Greater Toronto Area. Its runways are too short for large jets. What kinds of planes would use the island airport? State one advantage and one disadvantage of having an airport near the downtown area.

Public Buildings

1. Locate Toronto City Hall (G) and show it on your tracing. Describe the shape of this structure. The open space in front of the city hall is used for concerts and special events. Locate this area. In summer, seating is provided around a pond that becomes a skating rink in winter.
2. Many hospitals are located along University Avenue. The Hospital for Sick Children (H) has a special feature on its roof. Identify this feature, and show the hospital on your tracing.

Recreational Land Use

1. On your tracing, locate some of the recreational land use in the downtown area. Include the following:
   a) yacht clubs and marinas
   b) city parks
   c) Rogers Centre (I)
   d) CN Tower (J)
   e) Roy Thomson Hall (K)
   f) Railway Museum (L)
   g) Air Canada Centre (M)
2. Put a suitable title and legend on your map.

In Closing...

In these activities, we have only begun to describe and analyze the uses of aerial photographs. As you continue your study of geography, you will discover more uses for this valuable tool.

QUESTIONS

KNOWLEDGE AND UNDERSTANDING

1. a) When were aerial photographs first taken?
   b) How were the cameras carried high above the ground to take these early aerial photographs?
2. What types of things are aerial photographs now used to study?
3. a) What is a stereo pair?
   b) Using a diagram, demonstrate how a stereo pair allows the viewer to see images in three dimensions.

APPLICATION

4. (This question will be a true test of your ability to interpret aerial photographs.) In what season and at what time of day was the stereo pair in Fig. 6-2 taken? Give evidence to support your answer.

7 Satellite Imagery: The View from Space

Key Ideas

This chapter helps you investigate these questions:

- How does satellite imagery contribute to our knowledge of Canada?
- How does satellite imagery affect your life?

Key Terms

satellite
remote sensing
geostationary orbit
near-polar orbit
radar
false colours

When you watch a weather report on television, you often see a **satellite** image that shows approaching weather systems (Fig. 7-6). We have become so accustomed to seeing images like this that we take them for granted. The use of satellites to view Earth, however, is a relatively new technology. When your grandparents were your age, they could have seen the image in Fig. 7-1 only in their imagination. It was taken by a satellite orbiting high above the border between Alberta and Montana.

Fig. 7-1 ▶ In some places, the boundary between Canada and the United States can be seen from space even though it is not marked on the ground in any way.

The 49th parallel, the border between Canada and the United States, can be seen clearly because the land-use patterns are different in each country. In Canada, most of the land is used for grazing cattle, but south of the border, grain crops are grown in smaller rectangular fields.

The technology for studying Earth by using images and photographs taken from above Earth's surface is called **remote sensing**. There are two types of remote sensing. One type uses photographs taken from aircraft. The other type uses electronic images of Earth's surface taken from satellites. Satellite images cover very large areas but show less detail than aerial photographs. Aerial photographs cover smaller areas but show greater detail. By combining information from these two types of remote sensing, geographers can learn about an area without actually visiting it. In fact, they can make observations that wouldn't be possible even if they did visit the area!

Satellites and Their Orbits

Satellites are placed in two kinds of orbits around Earth. Weather and communications satellites are in **geostationary orbit** 36 000 km above the equator. This means that they stay over the same spot on Earth's surface. They remain over the same spot because they are rotating at the same speed as Earth. From this position, weather satellites provide almost continuous observation of changing weather, and communications satellites provide continuous TV, telephone, and data transmission.

The best locations for satellites in geostationary orbit are being taken by companies in developed countries. This is a concern to developing countries, such as China, India, and Brazil, because all the good locations will have been taken when they are ready to launch their own satellites.

Other satellites do not rotate with Earth, but follow a fixed north–south or **near-polar orbit** as Earth rotates below them. They are therefore able to make images of a different part of Earth with each orbit. The combination of a satellite's orbit and Earth's rotation allows complete coverage of Earth's surface over a period of time known as the orbit cycle. The satellite passes over a particular point on Earth at the same time during each orbit cycle.

Since the 1960s, different types of satellites have been launched to collect information about Earth's surface. The United States has developed Landsat (Land Satellite), Europe has developed SPOT (*Satellite Probatoire pour l'Observation de la Terre)*, and Canada has developed RADARSAT satellites.

Landsat

Landsat produces images only during the day because it uses sunlight and heat reflected from Earth's surface. Sunlight, or visible radiation, allows the satellite to "see" such features as coastal and river erosion, snow accumulation and melt, human and agricultural land use, deforestation, and drought areas. Heat, or infrared radiation, is detected by satellite sensors from sources such as old and new lava flows, volcanic eruptions, and forest fires. Landsat's infrared sensing is very useful in determining the health of crops and forests.

INTERNET

To learn more about Landsat satellites, go to www.pearsoned.ca/makingconnections2.

The SPOT Image Corporation is owned by governments and private companies in France, Sweden, and Belgium.

INTERNET

To learn more about SPOT satellites, go to www.pearsoned.ca/makingconnections2.

3-D (three-dimensional)
showing width, length, and depth

SPOT

SPOT, like Landsat, operates only during daylight hours (Fig. 7-2). SPOT's images are used in such fields as cartography, defence, urban planning, environmental studies, and disaster management. SPOT also produces **3-D** images that are especially useful for studying geological features and for developing flight and landing simulations for airline pilots.

▼ **Fig. 7-2** A SPOT image of Ottawa

Canada's RADARSAT

For more information about RADARSAT, go to www.pearsoned.ca/makingconnections2.

Canada's early involvement with remote sensing is not surprising. We have a vast country to study, and remote sensing is an efficient and relatively inexpensive way to gather information. Furthermore, remote sensing provides us with a continuous record of any changes that are occurring on the face of the land.

In 1995, RADARSAT-1 was launched. Thanks to improvements in its software, Canada's first advanced Earth-observation satellite was still operational in 2005, and may continue to operate after the launch of RADARSAT-2. RADARSAT monitors environmental change and provides information for resource development. RADARSAT-2 has a launch date in late 2006 and a mission duration of at least seven years. Like its predecessor, RADARSAT-2 will orbit Earth 14 times per day at an altitude of about 800 kilometres. This allows complete coverage of Canada in only three days. RADARSAT-2, however, produces higher-quality images that allow the production of topographic maps at a scale of 1:20 000. The images from RADARSAT-2 have applications in the following areas:

- Agriculture: for identifying crops, determining crop health, and estimating acreage
- Marine surveillance: for detecting ships, illegal fishing vessels, and illegal **bilge** dumping
- **Monitoring** sea ice: to assess melting rate, to detect icebergs, and to determine safe shipping routes
- Disaster management: to predict floods, monitor oil spills, and determine damage
- Defence: for enemy ground surveillance and target detection

bilge
bottom of a ship in which dirty, oily water collects. It is illegal to pump out bilge water at sea because the oily water pollutes the ocean.

monitor
observe on a regular basis in order to keep a record of any changes taking place

RADARSAT records reflected **radar** signals, or microwaves, that it has sent to Earth's surface. Unlike Landsat and SPOT, which record images only during daylight hours, RADARSAT operates 24 hours a day because it does not rely on sunlight to make its images.

The radar beam can move to examine features of Earth from different angles (Fig. 7-3). This allows the production of digital 3-D models of Earth's surface. RADARSAT can also view Earth's surface under any weather conditions because its signals can penetrate cloud, rain, and fog.

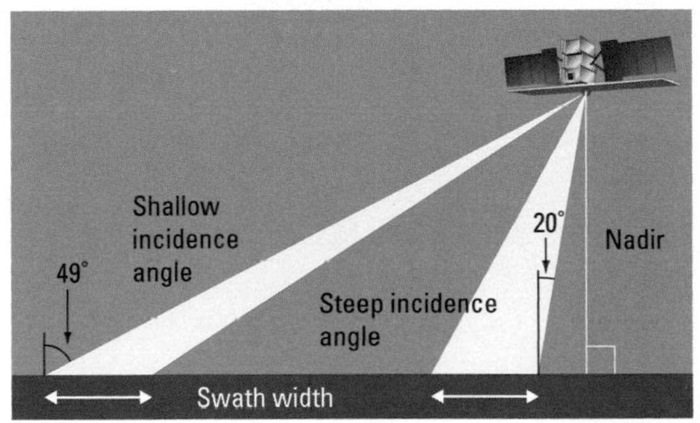

◀ **Fig. 7-3** RADARSAT satellites are very flexible because the swath width, resolution, and angle of the beam can be changed. (A swath is the area on Earth's surface covered by the radar beam.) The radar signals are electronically programmed to use any of seven different beam modes. The beam modes vary in width of swath, that is, they can cover areas on Earth's surface from 50 to 500 kilometres wide. They also vary in resolution.

How Satellites Collect Information

As satellites orbit Earth, they collect data that are sent back to Earth for analysis (Fig. 7-4). The data from these satellites are received by ground stations around the world. Canada has two such stations: one in Gatineau, Quebec, and the other in Prince Albert, Saskatchewan. The Canadian Centre for Remote Sensing (CCRS) in Ottawa receives data from eight satellites, including Landsat, SPOT, and RADARSAT. Canada has been receiving satellite images since 1972 and has become a world leader in the field. Over the years, Canadian companies have used their experience in satellite imaging to design and build receiving stations and satellites for several other countries around the world.

In order to make Earth's different features and geographical patterns more visible, scientists add **false colours** to the Landsat and SPOT satellite images. They are called "false" because they are not the colours you would actually see from space. Although it takes years of training to fully interpret such images, you can gain some understanding about Earth's surface from satellite images by following this basic guide for the images in this chapter:

- shades of red indicate different types of growing vegetation (crops, forests, grasslands)
- shades of blue-green to grey indicate areas where little vegetation is growing (urban areas, bare soil)
- shades of blue to black indicate shallow to deep water

Features as small as cars are visible in some images. It is rumoured that top-secret military satellites are able to pick up the print in a newspaper.

INTERNET

To examine satellite images and aerial photographs from around the world, check www.pearsoned.ca/makingconnections2.

Be aware: Both urban areas and rural areas with little vegetation appear as a blue-green colour.

Fig. 7-4 ▶ Satellites with a north–south orbit fly over the same location at regular **intervals**. The transfer and processing of satellite data is a complex task involving several steps that are shown below.

interval
period of time between two events

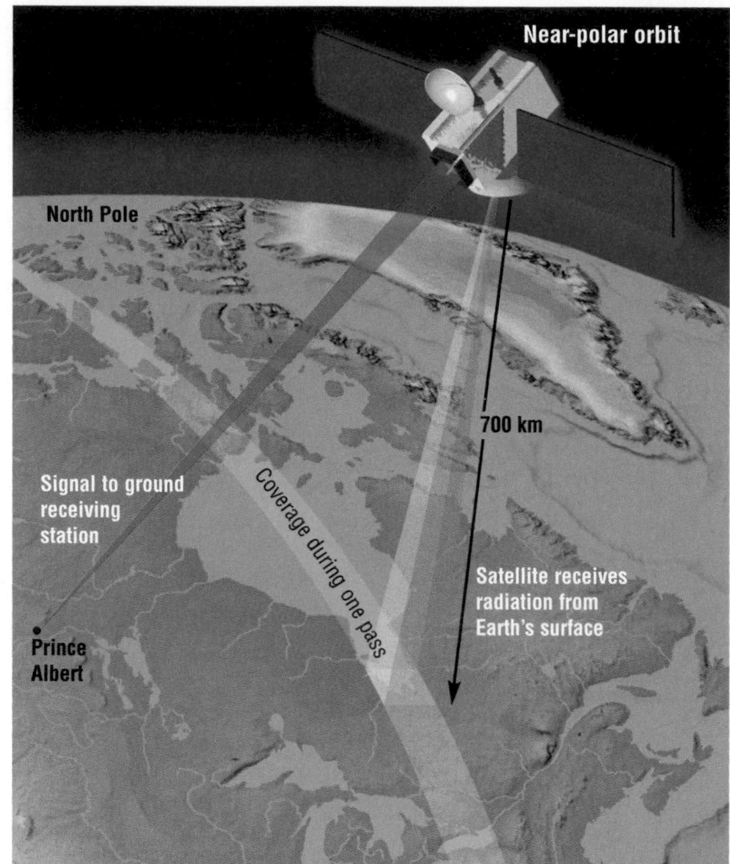

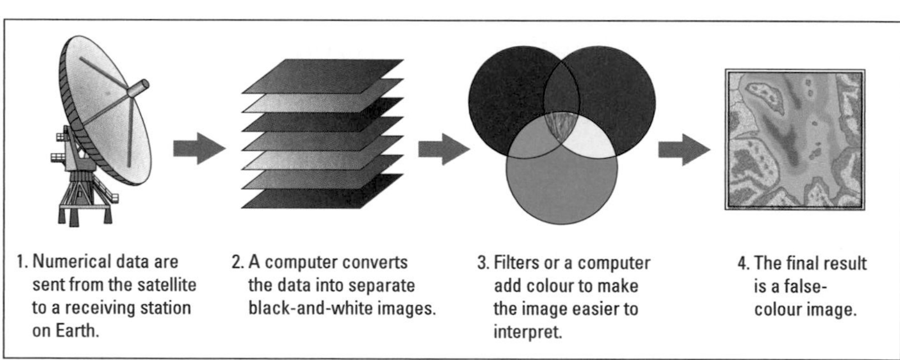

Uses of Remote Sensing

In the spring of 1997, one of Canada's worst natural disasters occurred in southern Manitoba. The Red River flooded its banks as a result of heavy winter snows that melted rapidly. RADARSAT-1 images helped officials determine when and where the flood waters would peak. This information was very helpful in evacuating citizens and in pinpointing locations where dikes had to be built.

After the devastating tsunami in South Asia on December 26, 2004, RADARSAT-1 provided imagery of the region to support relief efforts (Fig. 7-5). The archived RADARSAT-1 images from previous years provided information on transportation routes, hospitals, and central distribution points to help direct relief and rescue efforts. RADARSAT images also helped find and assess damage, determine the extent of the destruction, and locate standing water where malaria-carrying mosquitoes could breed.

▼ **Fig. 7-5** Two images of the same area in Indonesia before and after the tsunami of December 26, 2004.

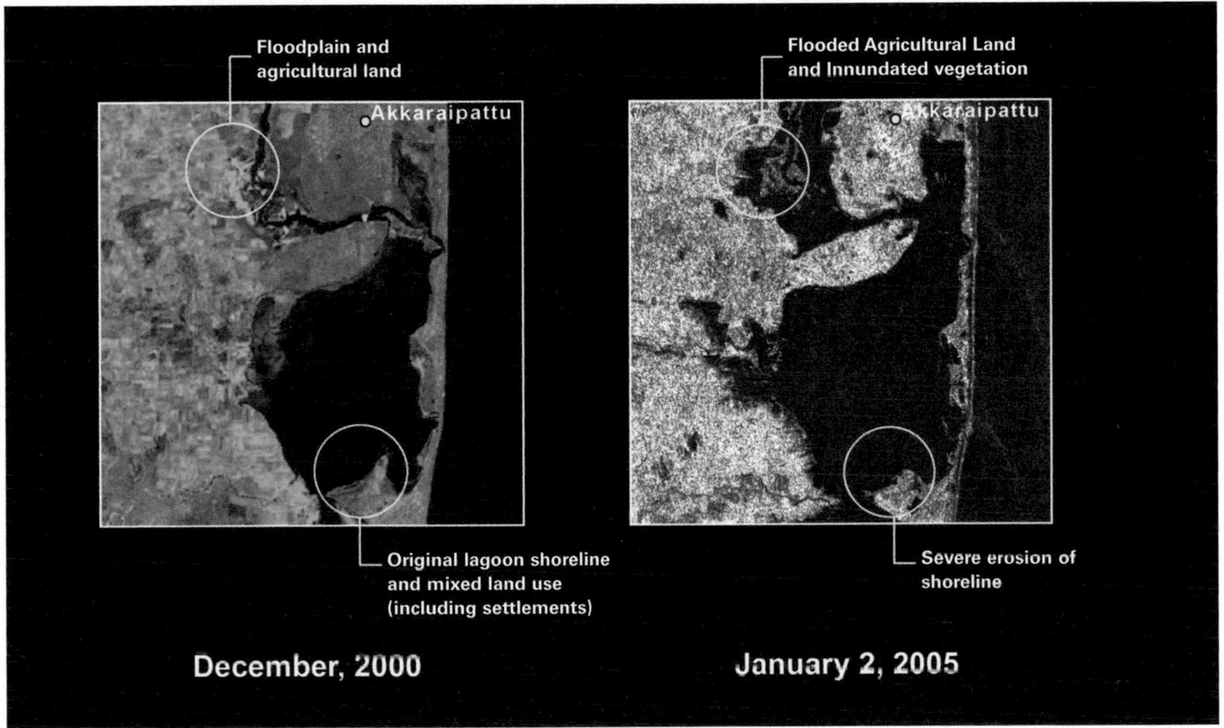

We can do a great deal with the data collected through remote sensing. The information helps us in the following ways:

- to study weather and climate, e.g., to follow the development and movement of storms
- to manage agriculture, e.g., to examine different crops, growth stages, and crop damage from pests and drought, and to predict **yields**
- to classify land cover and manage forests, e.g., to take **forest inventory**, monitor cutting, and assess fire damage
- to make maps and keep them up to date, e.g., to determine legal boundaries, to monitor urban expansion, and to aid in managing natural resources

yield
amount of crop produced

forest inventory
map and related statistics that outline stands of trees of similar type and age

- for geology and mineral exploration, e.g., to relate faults and folds to mineral deposits
- to map sea ice patterns in order to plan safe shipping routes and protect offshore oil platforms
- to monitor the environment, e.g., to track the location and effects of pollution, and to study wildlife habitat
- to monitor the oceans and coastal regions, e.g., to assess fish stocks and biological activity, oil spills, and shipping
- to analyze water resources, e.g., to map and monitor floods, determine snow thickness, and map drainage basins
- to study the impact of geologic events, such as earthquakes, volcanic eruptions, mud slides, and tsunamis

The collected data are stored and managed using geographical information systems, discussed in Chapter 5.

QUESTIONS

KNOWLEDGE AND UNDERSTANDING

1. Define the term "remote sensing."
2. Why are some satellites in geostationary orbits while others are in north–south orbits? What is the advantage of each? Give examples of each type.
3. a) What are false colours?
   b) Describe the process by which a false-colour image is produced.
   c) Explain the advantage of using false colours rather than real colours in a satellite image.
4. List five important ways that remote sensing information can be used in the study of Earth.

THINKING

5. Why would RADARSAT images be useful to Fisheries and Oceans Canada, the Canadian Coast Guard, and National Defence?
6. Satellite images provide information that may be used for many purposes, including commercial and political intelligence.
   a) How might a Canadian grain-marketing company use Landsat images that show the wheat-growing areas in other grain-producing countries?
   b) Food production in different countries can be predicted by studying the size of agricultural regions, the impact of drought, disease, or pests, and the expected crop yield. How might an organization such as the United Nations Food and Agricultural Organization use this information?

Using Satellite Images

Let's examine some satellite images to see how they are used for

- predicting weather
- making maps

Weather Forecasting

Many of us listen to or watch weather forecasts almost every day. These forecasts provide information on temperature, cloud cover, precipitation, winds, and storms. Forecasting weather accurately is a very difficult task because so many factors make up the weather and many tend to change very rapidly. The task is becoming easier, however, because satellites provide almost continuous coverage of Earth's surface.

The satellite image in Fig. 7-6 shows the southeastern United States and the Gulf of Mexico.

a) What weather does this image show?

b) Why are satellite images more useful than local weather radar in this case?

c) What is the location of the storm?

d) What information could be gained by comparing this image with one taken a few hours earlier?

◄ **Fig. 7-6**

Map-Making

Satellite images, like aerial photographs, may be used to draw maps. Using the satellite image of Southern Ontario (Fig. 7-7) and an atlas map of the same region, complete the following activity.

▼ **Fig. 7-7** Southern Ontario. The false colours in this Landsat image tell us the following:

- dark red or brown indicates dense forest or coniferous trees or both
- light red indicates hardwood forest
- pink indicates agricultural crops
- light blue indicates sparse vegetation, soil, and urban areas
- dark blue indicates water

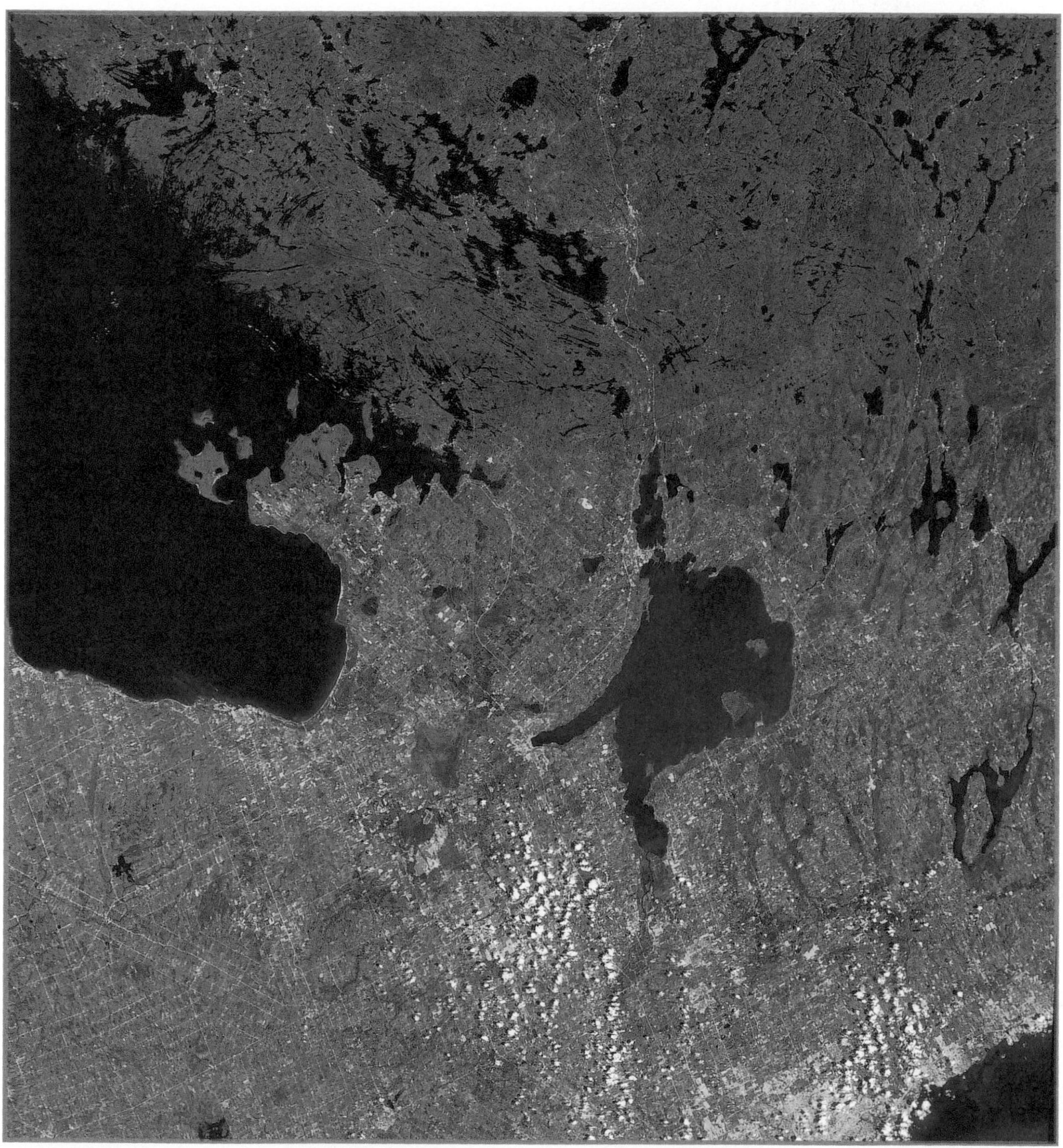

1. Compare this satellite image with your atlas map. What things can you see
   a) on both maps?
   b) only on the atlas map?
   c) only on the satellite image?

2. On a piece of clear acetate placed over the satellite image,
   a) draw the border of the satellite image
   b) trace the shorelines of all the lakes
   c) draw the rivers that you can see
   d) label the lakes and rivers

3. Locate and label the following on your acetate map:
   a) the boundary of the urban areas surrounding Toronto
   b) the communities of Barrie and Orillia
   c) Highway 11, north of Orillia (Hint: Settlement often occurs along major highways.)

4. a) On your map, draw and shade in the areas that appear as dark red or brown on the satellite image.
   b) What do these colours represent?
   c) Densely forested areas are frequently found in river valleys. What do the river valleys look like in this image?
   d) During the last ice age, glaciers shaped the landscape as they moved over this region. By observing the shapes of the lakes northeast of Lake Simcoe and the river valleys between Lake Simcoe and Lake Scugog, determine the direction in which the glaciers moved.

5. On this image, the Canadian Shield is covered by dense forest, but the Great Lakes Lowlands are primarily agricultural land with some hardwood and coniferous forests.
   a) Trace the boundary between the Canadian Shield and the Great Lakes Lowlands. (Refer to an atlas as well as the image if you are not sure where the boundary may be located.)
   b) How can you tell where this boundary is located?
   c) What might cause the different patterns and colours that you see?

8 Graph It!

Key Ideas

This chapter helps you investigate these questions:
- How do graphs help us see relationships and patterns in numerical data?
- What type of graph is best suited for the kind of data I have?

Key Terms

stacked bar graph
x/y scattergraph
pie graph
proportional area graph
spreadsheet

INTERNET

You can see more of Doria's graphs through the link at www.pearsoned.ca/makingconnections2.

Graphs can be extremely useful in helping us to see relationships and patterns. In Fig. 8-1, Brazilian artist Icaro Doria has taken the flags of China and the European Union and used the areas of the various colours on each flag to represent numerical quantities related to the country's people, economy, or problems. These "graphs" are not meant to be mathematically exact since the amount of each colour on the flag was not adjusted to the quantity being shown—they are only meant to make a point about the country.

▼ **Fig. 8-1(a) and (b)** What messages do these graphs convey?

a)

■ Working 14-year-olds
■ Studying 14-year-olds
China

b)

■ Oil consumption
■ Oil production
European Union

Any time you create a graph, your goal should be to present a particular set of numerical information in the most clear and understandable manner (Fig. 8-2). In earlier grades, you probably learned to create two simple types of graphs: bar and line graphs. Your teacher may want to review these with you. In this chapter, you will learn how to create more complicated graphs, how to use the graphing features of a spreadsheet program, and how to avoid some of the pitfalls of graphing.

Title
- clearly reflects the topic
- printed neatly and underlined or highlighted in some way
- located at top of page

Legend
- accurate labels and symbols
- positioned in an appropriate area
- well constructed

Labels
- axes and other features labelled
- printed neatly and aligned properly
- spelled accurately

Appearance
- all information accurately drawn and labelled
- colour used where appropriate

◄ **Fig. 8-2** Unlike Doria's conceptual flag graphs, you will be creating more formal, traditional graphs. This *graphing requirements checklist* will help you do a good job.

Stacked Bar Graph

A **stacked bar graph** is very much like a simple bar graph, with one important difference. While each bar in a simple bar graph represents one value, a stacked bar can be used to represent several closely related values. The information in Fig. 8-3, for example, shows the number of farms in three different types of farming operations.

Number of Census Farms by Product, 2001

	Cattle ranching and farming	Oil seeds and grains	Other	Total number of farms
Manitoba	7 544	7 358	4 916	19 818
Saskatchewan	12 294	30 842	5 854	48 990
Alberta	23 301	13 133	14 146	50 580

▲ **Fig. 8-3** The number of farms in three different types of farming operations in the three prairie provinces. These data are shown in the stacked bar graphs in Fig. 8-4.

A stacked bar graph is similar to a simple bar graph in that it can have either horizontal or vertical bars. Fig. 8-4 is a vertical stacked bar graph that used the data presented in Fig. 8-3. The X-axis (horizontal) shows the categories (provinces). The Y-axis (vertical) shows the numerical values (number of farms).

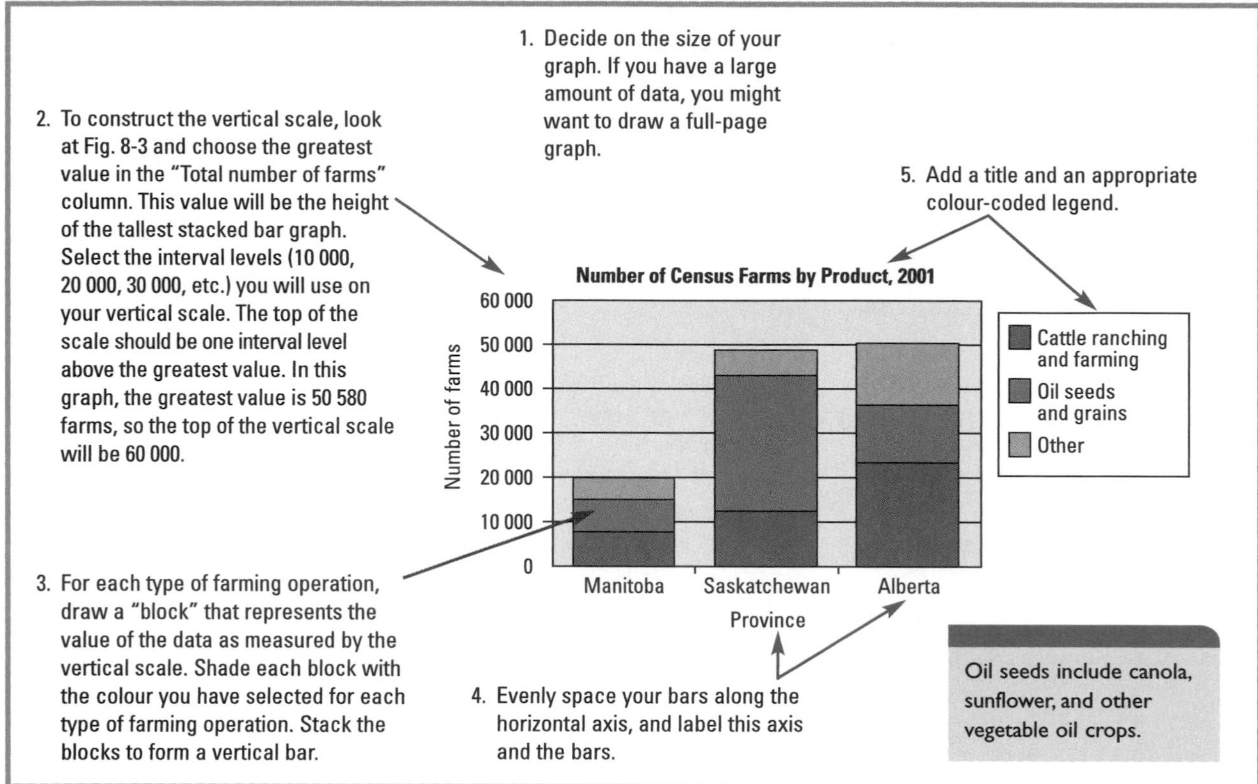

▲ **Fig. 8-4** A stacked bar graph is only slightly more complicated to draw than a simple bar graph.

X/Y Scattergraph

An **x/y scattergraph** is a very simple and useful way of showing the relationship between two sets of data. For example, you could use a scattergraph to illustrate whether there is a relationship between the level of people's education and their salary, or whether there is a relationship between people's age and how often they exercise.

We might wonder if there is a relationship between the ability to read and the number of children born in a country, but without a lengthy examination of the data in Fig. 8-5, it is difficult to tell. However, just a quick look at a scattergraph (Fig. 8-6) produced from the same information shows that there is a clear relationship between the two sets of data.

One question that is often asked about scattergraphs is which variable to put on each axis. A scattergraph is like a line graph in that there is often an **independent variable** that goes on the horizontal axis and a **dependent variable** that goes on the vertical axis. By this we mean that the dependent variable is caused or influenced by the independent variable. In this case, it is reasonable to think that higher literacy rates tend to result in smaller families because people have more access to information about family planning. In some cases, there is no obvious independent/dependent relationship; consequently, it does not matter which axis you place your information on.

▼ **Fig. 8-5** The information in this table is shown on the x/y scattergraph in Fig. 8-6.

Country	Adult Literacy Rate (%)	Total Fertility Rate
A	60	3.4
B	36	5.9
C	31	7.3
D	78	5.4
E	83	2.4
F	85	4.4
G	99	1.6
H	90	3.1
I	66	4.6
J	96	2.7
K	91	1.8
L	32	6.9
M	20	6.9

▼ **Fig. 8-6** Adult literacy rate is the percentage of the adult population that can read and write. Total fertility is the average number of children born to a woman in her lifetime.

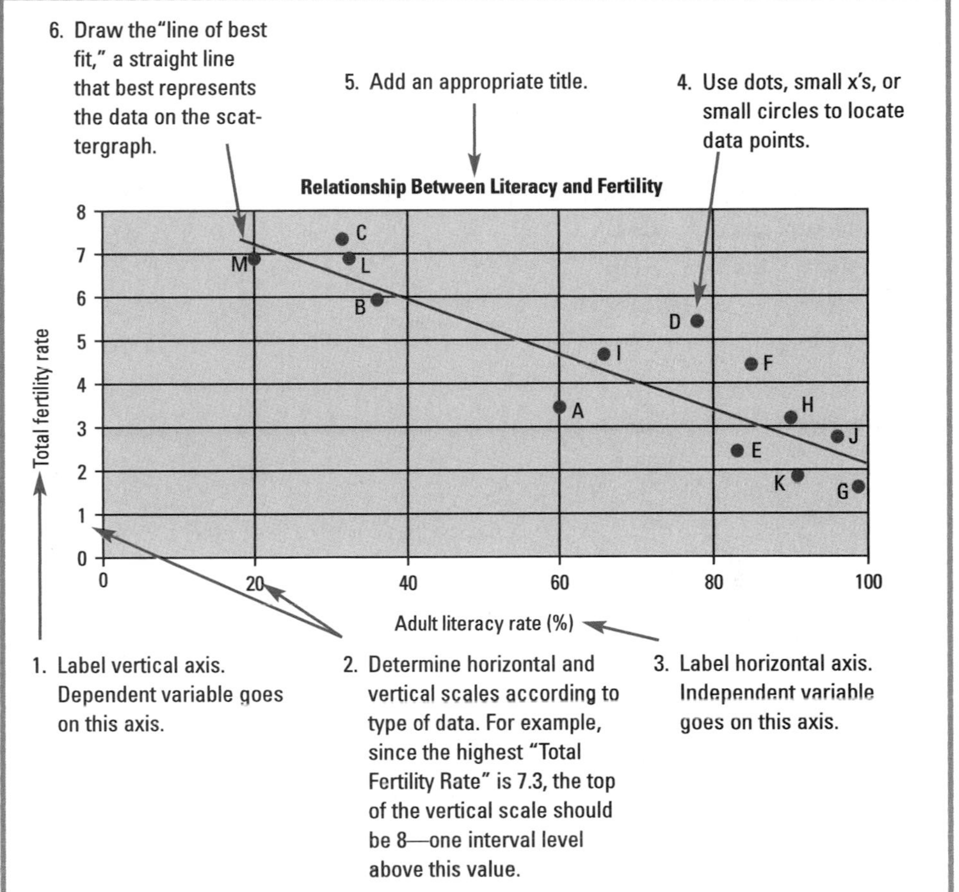

Pie Graphs

Pie graphs are frequently used in newspapers, magazines, and on television news shows because they are very easy to understand and quickly give the viewer a sense of the information being presented. They are not very difficult to draw as long as you remember a few things from math class, such as how to use a protractor and how many degrees there are in a circle. Compare the data in Fig. 8-7 with the pie graph produced from these data (Fig. 8-8). Clearly, the graph makes the information much easier to understand.

Since a pie graph shows values that are part of a whole, you could use it to show such things as how many students in your school are in each grade or what percentage of the day you spend sleeping, eating, studying, and so on.

▼ **Fig. 8-7** This information is shown on the pie graph in Fig. 8-8.

Area of National Parks (km2)

Territories	106 881
Prairie Provinces	61 842
British Columbia	6 302
Atlantic Canada	4 141
Central Canada	3 106
Total	182 272

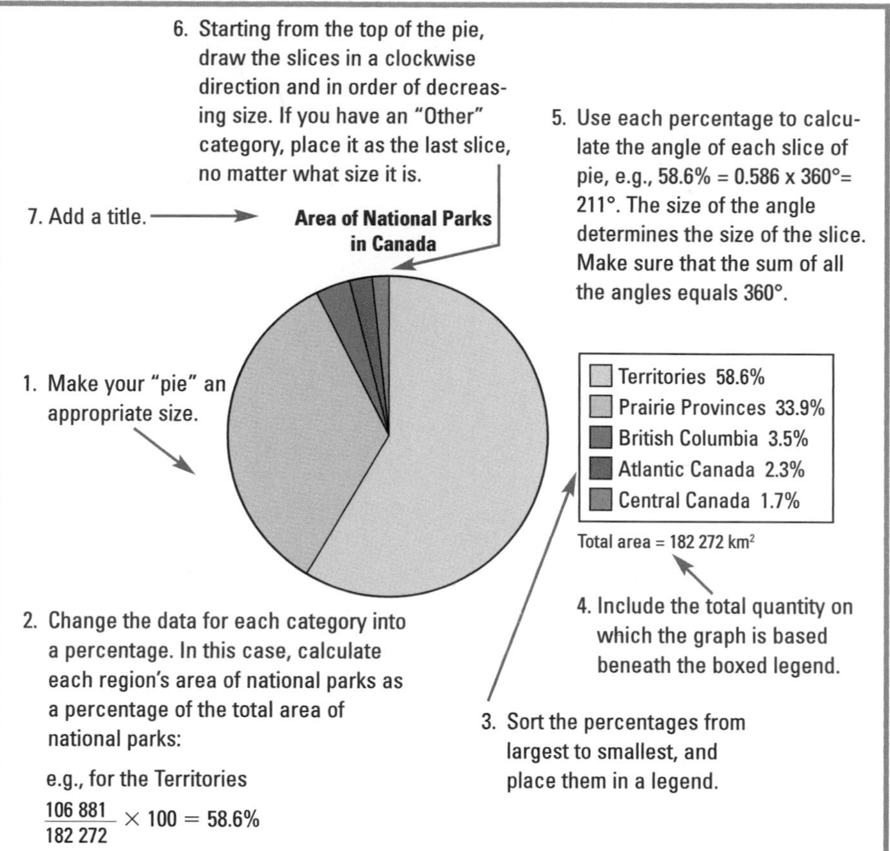

Fig. 8-8 ▶ A pie graph can show a great deal of information very simply.

Proportional Area Graphs

Sometimes when creating a graph, we may want to use shapes or symbols to represent the numerical data. Fig. 8-9 shows the number of unemployed workers in each province in April 2004. This information is graphed in Fig. 8-10, through the use of circles that are **proportional** to the numbers in the chart.

proportional sized in relation to numerical quantities

Although **proportional area graphs** are constructed in many shapes, circles are the shapes most frequently used. Proportional area graphs that use circles or squares are also the easiest to create. They are often combined with pie graphs to show not only the amount of something, but also how this amount is divided. For example, you might draw two proportional circles, one to show how much money you spend in one year, and the other, somewhat larger, to show how much Bill Gates, one of the richest people in the world, spends. You could then use the proportional circles to create pie graphs to compare how much you and Bill Gates spend on clothes, entertainment, etc.

Number of Unemployed, April 2004

Newfoundland and Labrador	49 800
Prince Edward Island	12 700
Nova Scotia	45 800
New Brunswick	47 100
Quebec	388 200
Ontario	448 200
Manitoba	28 500
Saskatchewan	31 000
Alberta	107 800
British Columbia	181 500

◀ **Fig. 8-9** These data are shown by the circles that appear in the proportional area graph in Fig. 8-10.

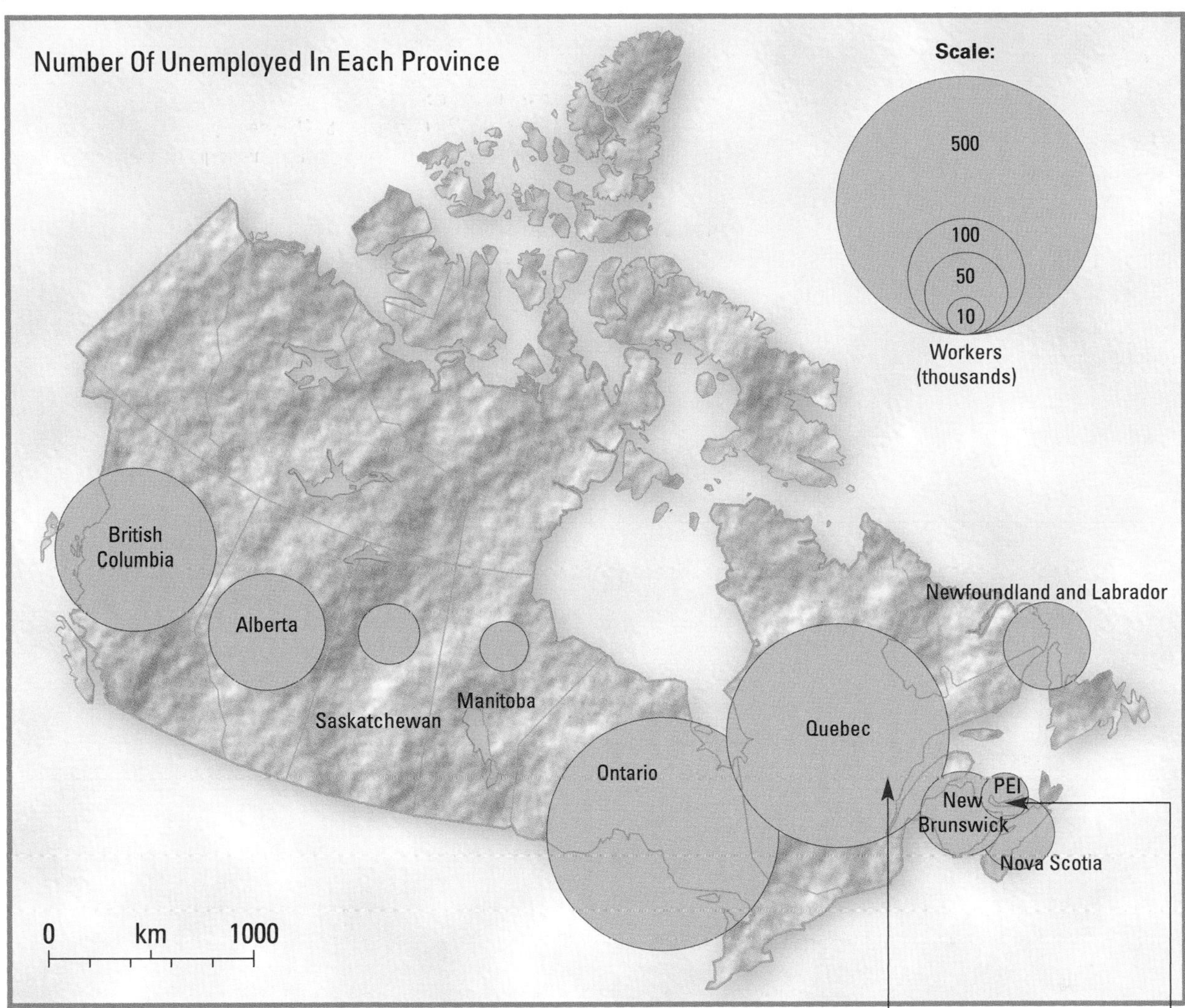

▲ **Fig. 8-10**
Proportional area graphs effectively show comparisons between data related to particular areas on a map.

1. Using Manitoba and Ontario as examples, calculate the radii of the circles like this:

Number of Unemployed

Manitoba	*Ontario*
28 500	448 200

Since the area of a circle equals πr^2,

$\pi r^2 = 28\ 500$	$\pi r^2 = 448\ 200$

Divide each side of the equation by π (3.14)

$r^2 = 9076$	$r^2 = 142\ 739$

Take the square root of each side

$r \approx 95$	$r \approx 338$

Your circles should have radii that are proportional to these numbers. You may have to divide or multiply these numbers to create circles that are of an appropriate size to fit the space available. Be sure to multiply or divide each radius by the same number for all the provinces! For example, you could divide each radius by 15, which would give you a radius for Manitoba of about 6 mm and for Ontario of about 25 mm.

2. Place each circle on a map and position each so that the area it represents is obvious.
3. Circles may overlap, but remember to place smaller circles on top.
4. Add an appropriate legend and title.

1. Examine the four tables of data in Fig. 8-11 on this page and the next page.
   a) Draw a different type of graph to represent each table of data. Choose a graph from the four different types presented in this chapter that suits the characteristics of the data.
   b) Explain why you chose the particular type of graph for each set of data.

▼ **Fig. 8-11**

A) Canadian Aboriginal Population, 2001

Ages 0–19	416 940
Ages 20–64	519 680
Ages 65+	39 680

B) Area and Population of Census Metropolitan Areas in Canada, 2001

	Area (km^2)	Population (thousands)
Calgary	5083	951
Chicoutimi–Jonquière	1723	155
Edmonton	9536	938
Halifax	2508	359
Hamilton	1358	662
Kitchener	824	414
London	2105	433
Montreal	4024	3426
Oshawa	894	296
Ottawa–Hull	5686	1064
Quebec	3150	683
Regina	3422	193
Saint John	3509	123
St. Catharines–Niagara	1400	377
St. John's	790	173
Saskatoon	5322	226
Sherbrooke	979	154
Sudbury	2612	157
Thunder Bay	2295	122
Toronto	5868	4683
Trois-Rivières	872	138
Vancouver	2821	1987
Victoria	633	312
Windsor	862	308
Winnipeg	4078	671

C) Canadian Population Projections, 2001–2026 (thousands)

2001	31 002
2006	32 229
2011	33 362
2016	34 320
2021	35 382
2026	36 191

D) Sources of Immigrants to Canada, 1963–2003

	1963	1983	2003
Asia	3 912	13 998	132 599
Europe	68 896	24 370	37 547
Other Countries	20 343	28 009	51 256

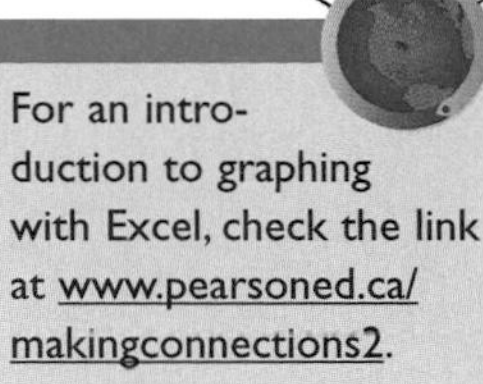

For an introduction to graphing with Excel, check the link at www.pearsoned.ca/makingconnections2.

Using a Spreadsheet

Figures 8-4, 8-6, 8-8, and 8-10 can be created using a **spreadsheet** program such as Microsoft Excel, Quattro Pro, or AppleWorks, which is a program used in many schools. With this type of program, you will be able to draw most of the simple graphs you need. To produce complex graphs, you can use more **sophisticated** spreadsheet programs such as Excel. Creating graphs on a spreadsheet has several advantages.

sophisticated advanced

- It can be much faster than drawing graphs by hand. This is particularly the case when the data are already in a computer file, or if you have to create several graphs with similar formats.
- You can produce more sophisticated, professional-looking graphs.
- Graphs produced by a spreadsheet can be moved easily to another computer program that you might be using to write a research paper or create a presentation. They can also be moved easily to an Internet Web page.

Computerized graphing can be very useful. Here are some hints to help you do the best job possible.

- Do not overuse all the features that a spreadsheet program offers you. Remember that you are trying to communicate ideas to your reader, and a complex graph or three-dimensional effects may only make your graph harder to understand.
- The program will automatically do a lot of tasks for you, e.g., label axes, choose symbols, and set scales. You may find that you can achieve a

more effective result by doing these things yourself. Experiment with the controls to achieve exactly what you want.

In fact, you may have to move data around to be able to graph them.

- The arrangement of the data on the spreadsheet will affect the look of your graph. You may want to re-sort the data on the spreadsheet or rearrange the order of the spreadsheet's columns before you start to graph.

Bias in Graphing

biased
distorted or prejudiced

The purpose of a graph is to provide a visual impression that makes the information in the graph easier to understand. A graph, however, is only as good as the skill of the person who constructs it. If a graph is constructed improperly, the reader may reach incorrect conclusions. The graph is then said to be **biased** in some way. For example:

1. *Use of a limited time scale that excludes important trends:*
   a) Examine the time period 2000–2002 in Fig. 8-12. What is happening to the price of a barrel of crude oil?
   b) Now examine the period 2002–2005. What is happening to the price of a barrel of crude oil?
   c) If you were given only the information from 2000–2002, what important trend would you miss?

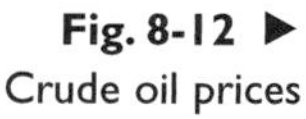

Fig. 8-12 ▶ Crude oil prices

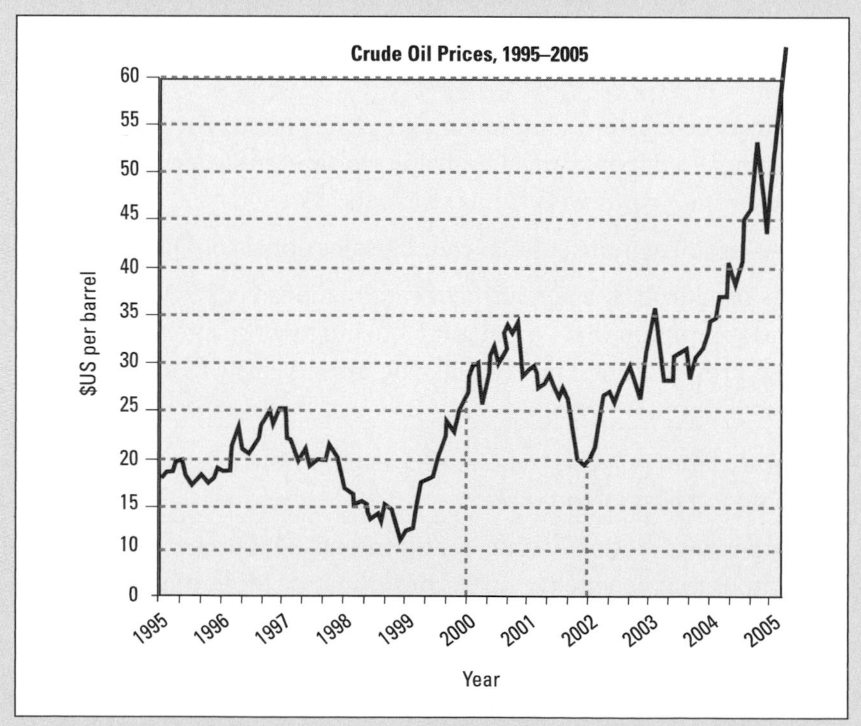

2. *Use of an inappropriate scale:*
   In the seven years between 1996 and 2002, exports of Canadian cultural goods increased considerably (Fig. 8-13).
   a) What was the dollar value of the increase?
   b) What was the percentage increase in these exports?
   c) Which figure, a) or b), gives the most accurate impression of the increase in exports of Canadian cultural goods? Explain.

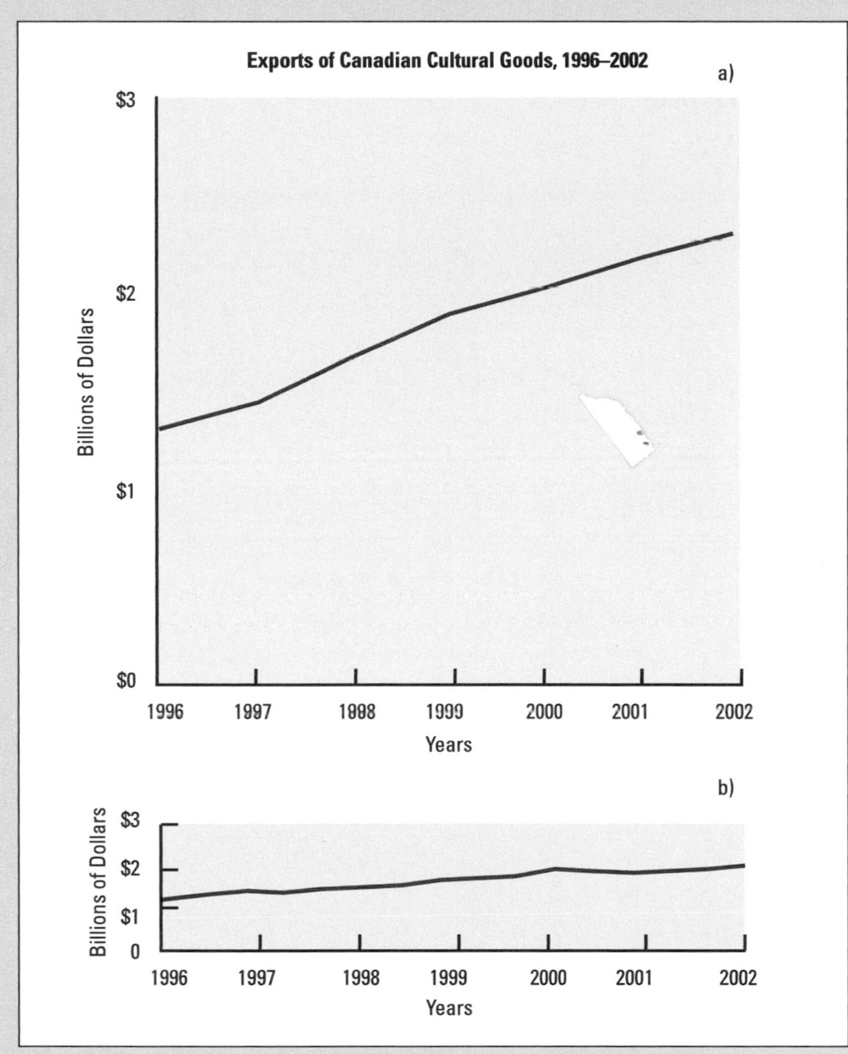

◀ **Fig. 8-13** Canadian exports of cultural goods (books, magazines, newspaper, films, videos/DVDs, music, TV programs, and artwork)

QUESTIONS

THINKING

1. a) Describe the general characteristics that any graph must have to do its job successfully.
   b) Choose any graph in Chapter 8 and describe how it meets these requirements.
2. How can Icaro Doria's approach to graphing (Fig. 8-1a and b) be applied successfully to other flags or to other graphical representations?
   a) Work with the flag of Canada first. What quantities could the areas of red and white on our flag represent (with at least some mathematical accuracy)?
   b) Now work with the flag of another country. Approximately what quantities could the areas of the various colours represent?
   c) Can Doria's approach to graphing be applied to other kinds of designs? Choose another image, such as a company logo or advertisement, that uses two to six colours. What could the area of each colour represent?

9 Cruising the Information Superhighway

Key Ideas

This chapter helps you investigate these questions:

- How can I use the Internet for research in the most effective way possible?
- What are fact, opinion, and bias, and how do they affect my research?

Key Terms

Internet
World Wide Web (WWW)
Web pages
search engine
Google
hit
bias

The **Internet** is such an accepted part of our lives that it is hard to believe that only a few years ago it did not even exist. The "parent" of the Internet was created in the 1970s to provide a means of communication for the United States government and military in the event of a nuclear war. The scientists who created it would never have guessed that a quarter of a century later you would be using it to do research for your Geography course, let alone to watch new music videos. In this chapter, you will have a chance to improve your ability to use the Internet as a research tool.

◀ **Fig. 9-1** Could this be you?

The biggest problem in using the **World Wide Web (WWW)**—an international network of Internet sites—is finding the **Web pages** that you want among the billions that exist. Let's assume that your family has decided to take an ocean kayaking holiday in Canada's newest territory, Nunavut. Few places in the world are as unspoiled as Nunavut and offer so many opportunities for adventure tourism activities such as hiking, ocean kayaking, and whale watching. Your job is to do preliminary research on what is available for your holiday and on whom you can contact to make arrangements for your trip. Where do you start? This is where a **search engine** is useful. A search engine is a system that is designed to help you find Web sites on the subject of your choice. There are many search engines, but one of the most popular is **Google**.

The total number of hits that appears for your search may vary (as will other totals in this chapter) as new Web sites are developed and others disappear.

Using Google

To search with Google, enter the terms you are looking for and click on the *Search* button. For example, if you enter the words *Nunavut tourism* you will find a total of about 193 000 matches or **hits**! This means that 193 000 pages contained both these words. The question becomes how to narrow your search in some way.

technique
method of doing something

Many **techniques** can help to narrow your search. The best way is to refine your search terms by adding another word that will reduce the number of hits. Because you are interested in adventure tourism, you could add the term *adventure* to your search. Had you searched for *Nunavut tourism adventure* at the time this book was written, you would have found about 20 100 hits (Fig. 9-2).

Fig. 9-2 ▶

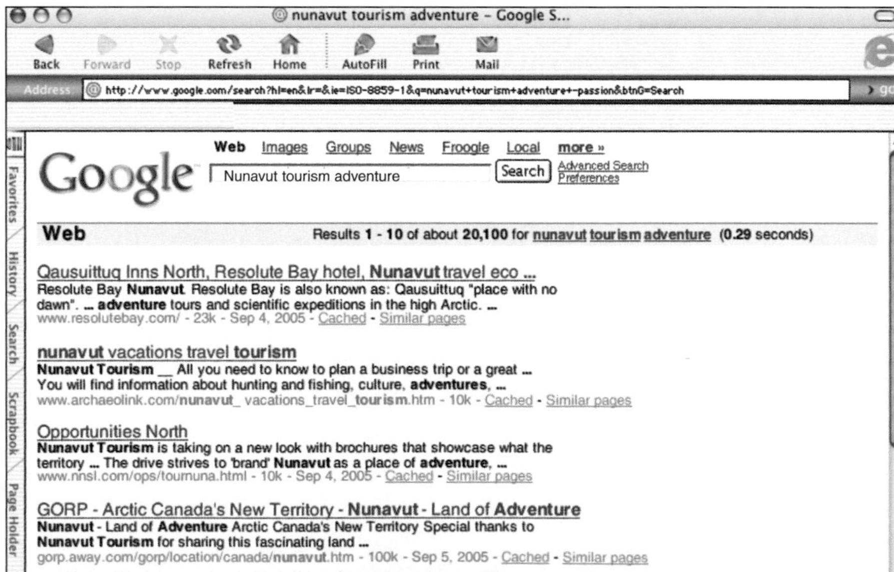

Can you do better? Yes, by clicking on the *Advanced Search* feature (Fig. 9-3), near the top of the Google search page. The Advanced Search page has a number of features that will make your search more effective.

- Searching for *Nunavut "adventure tourism"* (with quotation marks around *adventure tourism*) will allow you to find all pages that have the word *Nunavut* along with the exact phrase *adventure tourism*, rather than the words *adventure* and *tourism* separately. This results in only 846 hits.
- You can further narrow your search to find only pages written in English. In this case, this action eliminated fewer than 60 hits. If you were doing a search on tourism in France, limiting your search to English sites would be a big help.
- You are getting there, but you can focus your search even more by adding the search terms *ocean* and *kayaking*, as this is your main interest. This will yield a much smaller number of hits.
- You can also specify a date range for your search. For example, if you knew that you were looking for a relatively new adventure tourism company in Nunavut, you could limit your search to the last year and eliminate many hits.
- Remember that Google, like most search engines, sorts the Web pages it finds. What you will find is that the pages listed first are the strongest

INTERNET

The Advanced Search page has many other features that may occasionally prove useful. You should experiment with these when you have time. A good starting place is the link at www.pearsoned.ca/makingconnections2.

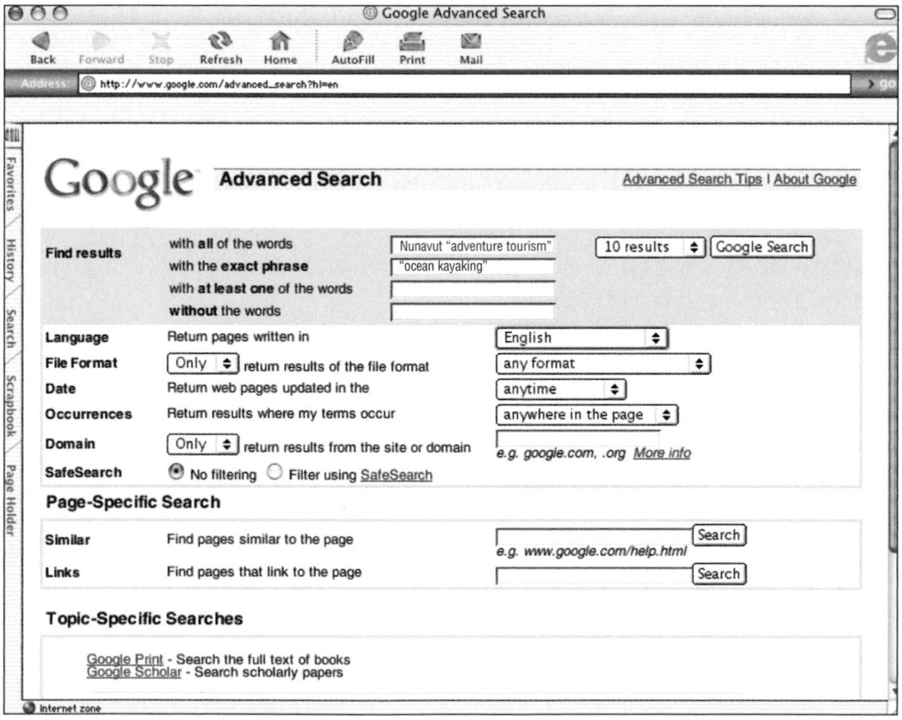

◀ **Fig. 9-3**

match to the search terms that you have provided. At this point, you can start scanning the list of sites and visiting any that appear likely to have useful information for planning your vacation.

Hints for Understanding and Using Google

- The success of your search is directly dependent on the specific search terms that you choose. If you search for *travel in the north* when you want to find information on Nunavut adventure tourism, Google will find pages about travelling on the north island of New Zealand and train journeys in northern China.

Note that Google does not look for words like *the* and *in* unless your search phrase contains them.

- The order of the search terms matters. While the searches for *Nunavut tourism* and *tourism Nunavut* may return the same number of matches, they will not be in the same order. Think about which term is most important to you and list it first.
- Google is not case-sensitive. This means you can search for *nUnAvUt ToUrIsM* if you wish. (Although why you would do this is an entirely reasonable question to ask!)

INTERNET

Find out how to access Google Scholar at www.pearsoned.ca/makingconnections2.

- Google incorporates a type of searching called "stemming." This means that it automatically looks for words similar to those that you have entered. For example, if you enter *tourism*, the program will also look for words like *tour*, *tourist*, and *touring*.

scholar
well-educated person

- In 2004, Google introduced a more specialized, academic search engine called Google **Scholar** (GS). GS looks only for Web sites that include scholarly materials, such as articles from professional journals and those published by universities. Therefore, the material you find is likely to be more reliable (and more specialized) than that found by the regular Google search engine. Unlike the regular Google, GS will also identify books and printed articles that meet your search criteria. However, you would have to go to a large library to find these, since they are not available on-line.

  Whether such academic material will be of help to you depends on what you are looking for. For example, a search of GS for *Nunavut tourism* yielded 409 hits (Fig 9-4). The sites found by GS might not be very useful for planning a holiday in Nunavut. Rather, they would tend to be related to the study of tourism there. You may find that Google Scholar proves increasingly valuable as your studies progress in senior high school and beyond.

A Google Scholar search is likely to find a much smaller number of hits than a general Google search. For example, a Google search for *diamond mining Canada* yielded 1 330 000 hits, while a Google Scholar search found only 7600 hits. Why is this difference not surprising?

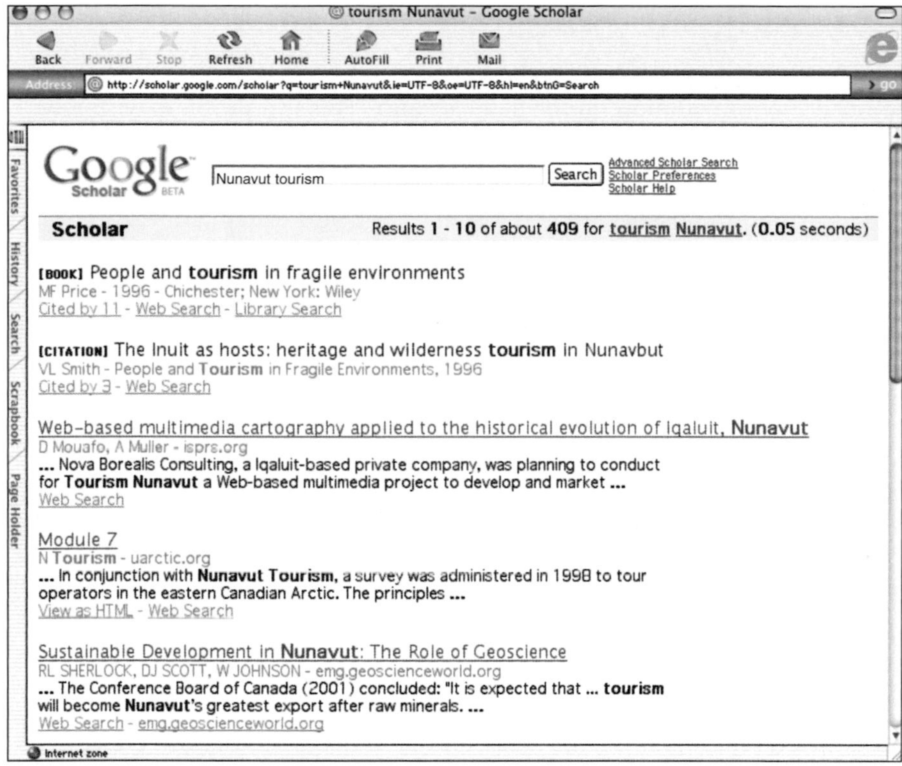

◀ **Fig. 9-4**

What to Do if You Are Not Sure Which Search Terms to Use

There will be times when you know what information you are looking for, but are not sure of which search terms to use to find it. Google has a feature that you can apply in this situation. Go to the Google Directory (directory.google.com) and search for information by working your way through a hierarchy of categories. For example, to find pages about adventure tourism in Nunavut, you might start by going to *Travel* under *Recreation*. On the next page, you could go to *Destinations* and then (on the next page) to *North America* and then *Canada*. On the page where you now find yourself, there are a number of Web sites listed that might help you find what you are looking for.

Of course you do not need to use Google. You might decide to use another search engine—new, more powerful ones are being developed all the time. Whatever search engine you choose, experiment with it until you are comfortable using its features. This will save you a great deal of time and allow you to get more from the Internet.

Other popular search engines include Alta Vista, Ask Jeeves, Lycos, and Yahoo. Metasearch engines, such as Dogpile, Mamma, and WebCrawler, make it possible to use several search engines at one time.

Assessing the Value of Web Pages

Let's assume that you find a Web page on your research topic. How do you know if the information on the page is valid? This is a problem with any information source that you might use. You must always be aware of the **bias** of those who created it. There is, however, an added problem with the information posted on the Internet. When you watch a news program on television, you know that a lot of time and money went into producing it. You realize that recognized experts in the field were likely involved in creating and reviewing the program's content. Finally, if you are offended by the show's content, you can complain to a supervising agency like the Canadian Radio-Television Commission (CRTC).

This is not the case with the Internet. It is neither difficult nor expensive to post a Web page. Anyone may post any information or personal opinion they wish without a thought about its accuracy, or whether someone reading the page will be offended. There is also no agency that hears complaints about material on the Internet.

INTERNET

You will find helpful criteria for evaluating Internet resources at www.pearsoned.ca/makingconnections2.

Many people have said that this is one of the Internet's best features because it allows ordinary people to express their ideas to the world. On the other hand, the freedom of the Internet also means that people can create Web pages that include the most controversial (and even silly) ideas. As an Internet user, you must be aware of this and be prepared to view everything that you see very critically.

Fact and Opinion

▲ **Fig. 9-5** Bjørn Lomborg's book on environmentalism stirred controversy because it failed to distinguish between fact and opinion. Who do you think bears the greatest responsibility for determining the validity of information—the author, the publisher, or the reader? Explain your answer.

In 2001, Bjørn Lomborg's book, *The Skeptical Environmentalist*, was published in English (it had been published previously in Danish). To say that his book caused a stir would be a huge understatement. Lomborg wrote that environmentalists had been falsely claiming that the world was in a desperate state. He set out to prove, among other things, that pollution was being reduced in the world; we were not running out of energy; large-scale species extinction was not happening; global warming was not occurring; and poverty in the world was being reduced.

The prestigious *Economist* magazine described Lomborg's book as "a triumph." A major British newspaper, *The Daily Telegraph*, said that *The Skeptical Environmentalist* was "probably the most important book on the environment ever written."

On the other side of the debate, a complaint from two scientists to the Danish Committees on Scientific Dishonesty stated, "In our experience, we have never seen the immediate and uniformly hostile rejection of a published work by so many senior scientists." A writer in the magazine *Scientific American* said, "The problem with Lomborg's conclusion is that the scientists themselves **disavow** it."

disavow
reject

Were all these comments being made about the same book? Indeed they were, and they point out how careful you must be to separate *fact* from *opinion*. For example, it is a fact that at midday on a clear day the sun is at its brightest and the sky appears bluest. It is opinion that

- the sun is too bright
- the sky is a beautiful shade of blue
- the tan I get will make me look healthier and more attractive

A fact is something that can be proven to be true. Everything else is opinion. Some opinions are likely true, because there is evidence to support them. For example, the link between smoking and lung cancer has been suggested by many scientific studies. We should be less sure of opinions when there is little evidence to support them. For example, there is little solid evidence that aliens have visited Earth. Alien visits to Earth may turn out to be true, but we need much more proof to accept this claim as a fact. When you do research on the Internet (and using other sources), you will run into some facts and a great many opinions. You have to be able to separate one from the other. Weighing opinions is a still greater challenge—you must decide how likely it is that an opinion is valid.

Citing Your Electronic Sources

As with any other research that you do, you must tell your reader where you found the information that you have included in your project or essay. In general, the purpose of a **citation** is to give the reader enough information to find your source.

citation
acknowledgement of a source used in writing or research

Assume that you are doing research on new national parks in Canada and want to cite a useful article that you found. You would do it like this:

Ljungren, D. (2002). Canada to create 10 enormous new parks. Retrieved July 28, 2005, from http://www.planetark.com/dailynewsstory.cfm/newsid/18070/story.htm

Often, Web pages do not list authors or dates of publication. In such a case, your citation would look like this:

Plans for Ten New Canada Parks Met with Skepticism (n.d.). Retrieved July 28, 2005, from http://news.nationalgeographic.com/news/2002/10/1010_021010_canadaparks_2.html

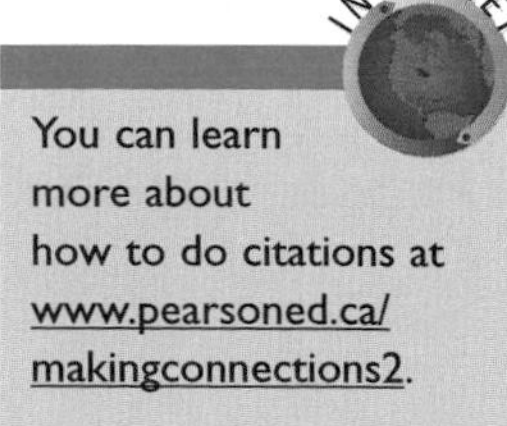

You can learn more about how to do citations at www.pearsoned.ca/makingconnections2.

QUESTIONS

KNOWLEDGE AND UNDERSTANDING

1. What is the World Wide Web, and why is it useful for doing research?
2. a) What is a search engine?
   b) Besides Google, name three other search engines.

THINKING

3. For what types of topics would a Google Scholar search be more useful than a regular Google search?
4. a) Define each of these terms: fact, opinion, bias.
   b) Explain why you must be aware of fact, opinion, and bias when you do research.
   c) Detecting bias is a challenge when you are reading. It is also a challenge when you are writing. Why might you have more difficulty detecting bias in your own writing?

APPLICATION

5. a) Choose one of the following topics or a topic given to you by your teacher for the subject of an Internet search.

Topics for Internet Search

- diamond mining in Canada
- pollution of the Great Lakes in Canada
- aquaculture in Canada
- Hibernia oil project
- Canadian foreign aid
- summer theatre in Canada
- new golf courses in Canada
- cheese making in Canada
- archaeology projects in Canada
- rock-climbing courses
- GIS job prospects
- paper recycling

   b) Conduct an Internet search for your topic using Google.
6. Choose one of the Web pages you found and comment on its bias by answering the following questions. Be sure to include the Web site address in your notes.
   a) Who created the page?
   b) What was the purpose of the page?
   c) Did the page attempt to provide a balanced approach to the topic?

10 The GeoLit Kit: What's in It for You?

Key Ideas

This chapter helps you investigate this question:

- How can improving your reading, writing, and oral skills help you communicate geographic information more effectively?

Key Terms

literacy

▼ Fig. 10-1

▼ Fig. 10-2

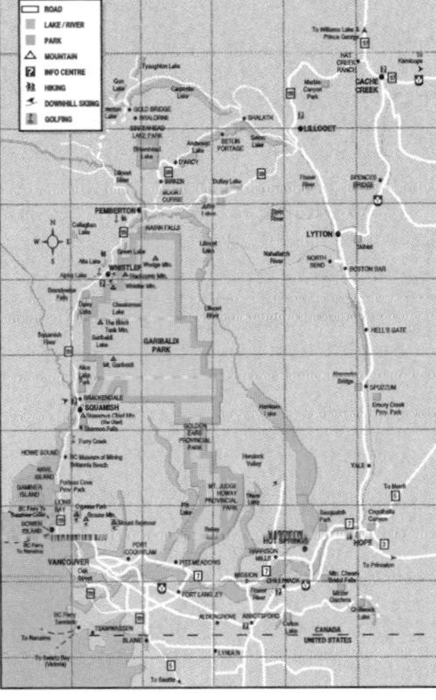

▼ Fig. 10-3

Vancouver-Whistler Wins 2010 Olympics

CBC SPORTS ONLINE - Canada's Olympic dreams have come true.

"The International Olympic Committee has the honour of announcing that the 21st Olympic Winter Games in 2010 are awarded to the city of Vancouver," International Olympic Committee president Jacques Rogge announced Wednesday in Prague, Czech Republic.

Vancouver-Whistler narrowly beat Pyeongchang, South Korea 56 votes to 53 on the second ballot of IOC voting.

"Absolutely incredible. Well I always thought it was going to tough," said bid chief John Furlong.

"We were saying all along it was going to be a close race...We are going to party all night, it's Canada's week and we're so proud."

Canada's IOC delegation in Prague, as well as thousands of supporters at GM Place in Vancouver and at Whistler village went wild, roaring with delight for several minutes when the announcement was made.

Canada will be hosting the Olympics for the third time. Calgary hosted the Winter Games in 1988 and Montreal hosted the 1976 Summer Games.

This is the second time that Vancouver-Whistler has made a pitch to host the Winter Games. The region, which was known as Vancouver-Garibaldi then, also made a bid to host the 1976 Winter Games, but lost.

The Olympic race came down to Vancouver-Whistler and Pyeongchang after Salzburg, Austria was eliminated after the first round of voting. Although Vancouver was the pre-vote favourite, the final results were much closer than many observers expected.

Pyeongchang received 51 votes on the first ballot, Vancouver-Whistler got 40 and Salzburg 16.

"I'm very nervous," said Vancouver bid chief John Furlong after the first ballot. "As we said all along there are three great bids, three great cities, anything could happen."

Furlong said he wasn't surprised that Pyeongchang, not Salzburg made it to the second ballot.

"(Pyeongchang) has a great bid, they're very passionate, very driven," he said. "They have a profound belief that they can bring winter sports to this country."

Salzburg's support appeared to migrate to Vancouver as it narrowly beat the Korean city by three votes on the second, and final, ballot.

"What I was hearing all around that was Vancouver was going to win the first round," said Canadian IOC delegate Paul Henderson.

"I wasn't shocked at Salzburg because there was a very strong movement to put 2012 in Europe and also there was a very strong movement in some countries not to go to New York. I thought Vancouver would be a slam-dunk and it wasn't."

"It's always a tough competition. We knew that it was to be tight," said Prime Minister Jean Chretien, who was on hand to help Canada's pitch.

"Anyway, we won."

Wayne Gretzky, also in Prague, credited a former Edmonton Oiler teammate for putting Vancouver over the top.

"As Jari Kurri, who is now an IOC member told me, he was the 54th vote," joked Gretzky. "I feel like I'm always feeding him the puck."

Vancouver-Whistler's victory likely puts an end to Toronto's hopes for hosting the 2012 Summer Games. Toronto lost bids to host the 1996 and 2008 Summer Games and had been planning another bid. But, the IOC won't put the Olympics in the same country in back-to-back Games.

A number of the world's greatest cities, including New York, Paris, London, Madrid and Moscow, are already vying for the 2012 Games.

"I would have loved to see my city (Toronto) get the Games but I don't think it's in the cards," said Henderson, who also led one of Toronto's bids.

"Now we can all have a good time in Vancouver."

Question: What do the items in Figs. 10-1 through 10-4 all have in common?

Answer: The photograph, map, news article, and graph are all ways to show geographic information in different formats. Such items can be interesting to look at or read. They can give you new ideas to think about and discuss. If you want to be able to interpret geographic information and communicate your ideas effectively, you will want to develop your literacy skills.

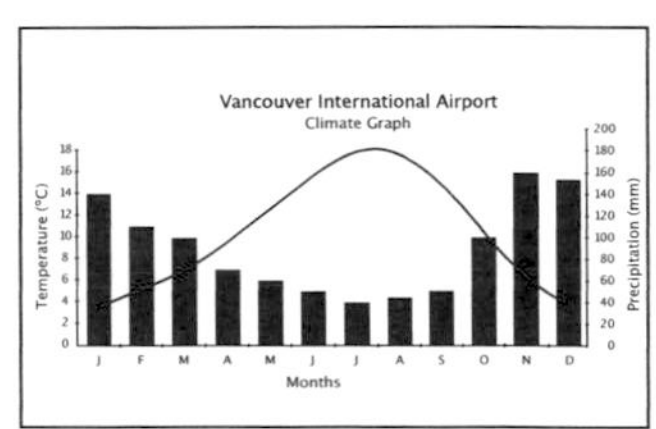

▲ Fig. 10-4

What is **literacy**? Strictly speaking, it is a person's ability to read and write. We can expand this definition to include a person's ability to communicate ideas through active listening, speaking, and making presentations. The ABC Canada Literacy Foundation defines literacy as the ability to understand and

INTERNET

Check out the ABC Canada Literacy Foundation through the link at www.pearsoned.ca/makingconnections2.

INTERNET

Learn more about the Literacy Decade through the link at www.pearsoned.ca/makingconnections2.

GeoLit Reminder

The GeoLit Reminders that appear in the margins throughout this book will assist in developing and applying your literacy skills.

use printed information in daily activities at home, at work, and in the community to achieve personal goals and realize individual potential.

When geographers and others study the world's countries, they use literacy as an indicator of a population's level of education and, indirectly, its economic and social development. For example, Canada, which ranks as one of the world's most economically and socially developed countries, has a literacy rate of 97%. Japan, whose literacy rate is even higher (99% of Japanese can read and write), also has a well-developed economy and social system. By comparison, Nepal—a poor, developing country—has a literacy rate of 47%, meaning that less than half the population can read and write. Because of these differences, the United Nations has launched a Literacy Decade (2003–2012) with the goal of improving literacy rates worldwide, giving more people the tools they need to function in an increasingly interconnected world.

Have you ever read a piece of writing and not fully understood what it meant? Have you ever been unsure where to look in a textbook in order to answer a question? This chapter gives some strategies to help improve your reading, writing, and oral skills and make you a more effective communicator—in your Geography course and beyond. These are skills that everyone has to practise and use all the time. Let's think of this chapter as a "GeoLit Kit" that you can use while reading this textbook and also apply in your other courses.

Reading—More Than Words on a Page

What Is It?

Of course, textbooks are not our only source of information. We can divide information resources into two basic categories: *written text* and *visual text*. Think of the many different types of written information that you read every day—for example, a street sign, a bus schedule, or a magazine article about your favourite singer. Visual text communicates information largely through images such as photographs, maps, or the floor plan of your local mall.

▼ **Fig. 10-5** Examples of written and visual text

Written text
Informational:
textbooks
encyclopedias
written captions under photographs, charts, or graphs
Literary:
novels
song lyrics
plays
Visual text
photographs
videos/DVDs
cartoons

Take a few minutes to brainstorm some examples of written text and visual text. Record your answers under these two headings in your notebook. Once you have finished, share your lists with a partner. Fig. 10-5 will get you started.

Written and visual texts provide important information that we use every day. But how can we use them more effectively to gather information, gain a more thorough understanding of a particular topic, develop new ideas, and expand our vocabulary?

Let's begin with reading skills.

What to Do?

Reading for the purpose of gathering information—and understanding and applying what you have read—is sometimes a challenge. Here are a few strategies to make you a more effective reader.

STEP #1—BEFORE YOU READ

When you are faced with a passage of written text, don't just jump right in and begin reading. Take a few minutes to skim the entire passage and then ask yourself the following quick questions:

- What type of written text is this—informational or literary?
- How does the layout of the text convey what it is about? For example, scanning the title, headings, subheadings, and visuals will give you an idea of the content.
- What do you already know about this topic?
- What do you think is the general meaning or purpose of the information in this text?

STEP #2—WHILE YOU ARE READING

Now that you have an overall idea about the written text, review the question that you need to answer or the task you need to perform. Keep this question in mind (or write it down in the margin of your notebook) and use the following strategies as you carefully read the text a second time. (Important: Re-read any part of the text that is unclear, and ask your teacher for help, if necessary.)

- Identify the main idea (thesis) of the text.
- Relate what you already know about this topic to the information in the text.
- Identify key words and terms. (Hint: These sometimes appear in italics or bold type.) Record them in your notebook as a vocabulary list.
- Examine the visuals, maps, graphs, charts, colour schemes, or symbols to help you understand the written text (see Fig. 10-6).
- Use relevant subheadings and point-form notes to organize and record the text's main ideas in your notebook.
- Summarize the main ideas by identifying the topic sentence of each paragraph. The topic sentence tells you what the paragraph is about. The remaining sentences develop the idea found in the topic sentence.
- Consult the table of contents, index, or glossary for additional information.
- Compare the information in the text with other sources or your own experiences.
- Using the information in the text, draw conclusions that explain your thoughts or justify your stance on the question you were assigned.

▼ **Fig. 10-6** Hints for reading visual text

Hints for Reading Visual Text

- What type of visual text is this? What is its purpose?
- What comes to mind when you first look at it?
- Use the title, labels, symbols, colour scheme, and caption to understand the meaning of the visual.
- State the main idea of the visual, giving evidence to support your summary.
- Make a note of anything that you think might be missing or inaccurate about the visual (for example, the labelling on a graph or map), as well as any additional questions or information that would help you understand it.

STEP #3—WHEN YOU HAVE FINISHED READING

Once you have finished reading, use these strategies to check your understanding:

- Explain the main idea of the written text, referring to the materials you developed in Step #2.
- Think about the importance of the information. Why was this text written? Who is the intended audience?
- Evaluate the writer's point of view. Does the text state fact or opinion? In what ways might it be biased? Have any points of view not been included?
- Does this information alter what you already thought about the topic? What other questions should you ask?
- Communicate your understanding of the text in writing, by discussing it with a partner or group, or by completing point-form notes, a summary, a graphic organizer, or other visual to represent the main ideas.

How to Use Your Reading Strategies

Now use your reading skills on the following visual and written text items. Remember to refer to the reading strategies listed above.

Task #1—Reading a photograph: Examine the photograph in Fig. 10-7 and complete the following questions.

a) Jot down your thoughts as you look at the photograph.

b) What information does this photograph convey? Record your observations in point form in your notebook.

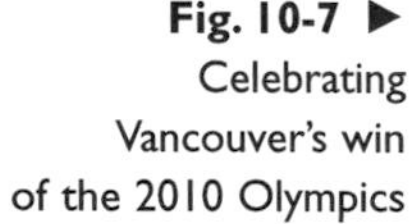

Fig. 10-7 ▶ Celebrating Vancouver's win of the 2010 Olympics

Vancouver-Whistler Wins 2010 Olympics

CBC SPORTS ONLINE - Canada's Olympic dreams have come true.

"The International Olympic Committee has the honour of announcing that the 21st Olympic Winter Games in 2010 are awarded to the city of Vancouver," International Olympic Committee president Jacques Rogge announced Wednesday in Prague, Czech Republic.

Vancouver-Whistler narrowly beat Pyeongchang, South Korea 56 votes to 53 on the second ballot of IOC voting.

"Absolutely incredible. Well I always thought it was going to be tough," said bid chief John Furlong.

"We were saying all along it was going to be a close race...We are going to party all night, it's Canada's week and we're so proud."

Canada's IOC delegation in Prague, as well as thousands of supporters at GM Place in Vancouver and at Whistler village went wild, roaring with delight for several minutes when the announcement was made.

Canada will be hosting the Olympics for the third time. Calgary hosted the Winter Games in 1988 and Montreal hosted the 1976 Summer Games.

This is the second time that Vancouver-Whistler has made a pitch to host the Winter Games. The region, which was known as Vancouver-Garibaldi then, also made a bid to host the 1976 Winter Games, but lost.

The Olympic race came down to Vancouver-Whistler and Pyeongchang after Salzburg, Austria was eliminated after the first round of voting. Although Vancouver was the pre-vote favourite, the final results were much closer than many observers expected.

Pyeongchang received 51 votes on the first ballot, Vancouver-Whistler got 40 and Salzburg 16.

"I'm very nervous," said Vancouver bid chief John Furlong after the first ballot. "As we said all along there are three great bids, three great cities, anything could happen."

Furlong said he wasn't surprised that Pyeongchang, not Salzburg made it to the second ballot.

"(Pyeongchang) has a great bid, they're very passionate, very driven," he said. "They have a profound belief that they can bring winter sports to this country."

Salzburg's support appeared to migrate to Vancouver as it narrowly beat the Korean city by three votes on the second, and final, ballot.

"What I was hearing all around was that Vancouver was going to win the first round," said Canadian IOC delegate Paul Henderson.

"I wasn't shocked at Salzburg because there was a very strong movement to put 2012 in Europe and also there was a very strong movement in some countries not to go to New York. I thought Vancouver would be a slam-dunk and it wasn't."

"It's always a tough competition. We knew that it was going to be tight," said Prime Minister Jean Chretien, who was on hand to help Canada's pitch.

"Anyway, we won."

Wayne Gretzky, also in Prague, credited a former Edmonton Oiler teammate for putting Vancouver over the top.

"As Jari Kurri, who is now an IOC member told me, he was the 54th vote," joked Gretzky. "I feel like I'm always feeding him the puck."

Vancouver-Whistler's victory likely puts an end to Toronto's hopes for hosting the 2012 Summer Games. Toronto lost bids to host the 1996 and 2008 Summer Games and had been planning another bid. But, the IOC won't put the Olympics in the same country in back-to-back Games.

A number of the world's greatest cities, including New York, Paris, London, Madrid and Moscow, are already vying for the 2012 Games.

"I would have loved to see my city (Toronto) get the Games, but I don't think it's in the cards," said Henderson, who also led one of Toronto's bids.

"Now we can all have a good time in Vancouver."

▲ **Fig. 10-8**

c) Create three questions that you need to ask in order to gather more information about this photograph.

d) Give this photograph an appropriate title. Share your title with a partner and explain why you chose it.

Task #2—Reading a written text: Read the article in Fig. 10-8. While reading, summarize the article in point form, record any unfamiliar words in your notebook, and then answer the following questions.

a) What kind of article is this? Why was it written?

b) What is the writer's point of view? Is it based on fact or opinion? Explain your answer.

c) Does the article appear to be biased in any way? Explain.

d) What questions would you like to have answered in order to understand the article better?

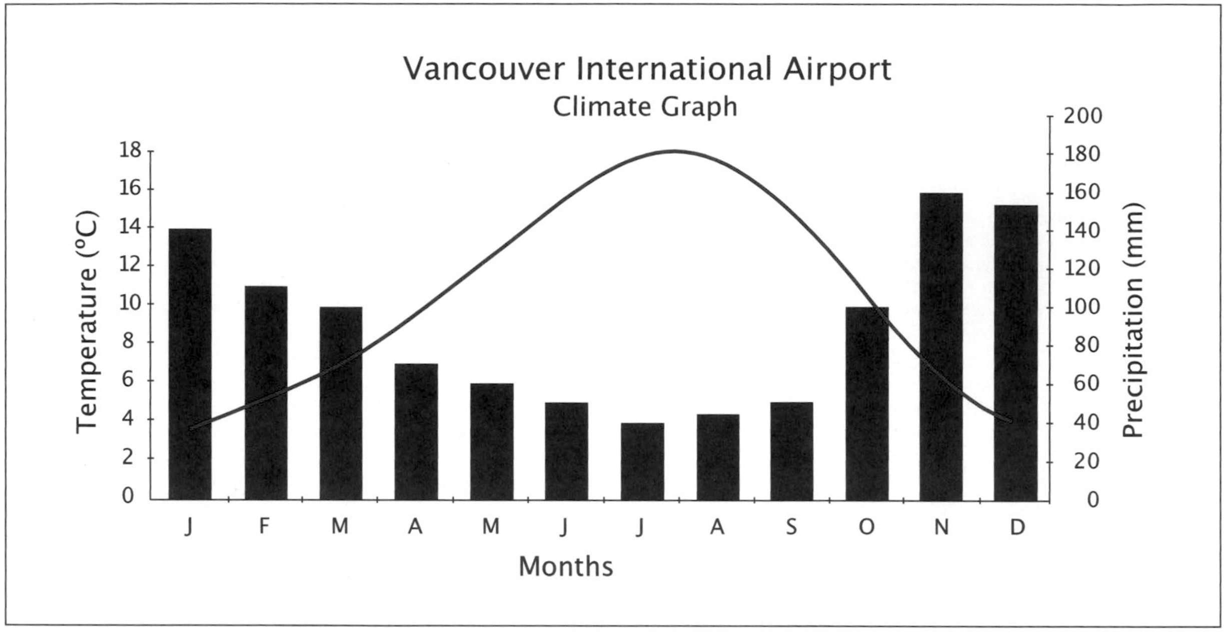

▲ **Fig. 10-9** Climate graph for Vancouver

Task #3—Reading a graph: Examine the climate graph in Fig. 10-9 and answer the questions below in your notebook. Remember to look at the labels, colour scheme, and overall patterns in the graph.

a) What two types of graph are combined to show Vancouver's climate?

b) What information does each type of graph show?

c) What units of measurement are used in each?

d) Describe the precipitation pattern for Vancouver.

e) Describe the temperature pattern for Vancouver.

f) Using information from this climate graph, would you say that February is the best month to host the Winter Olympics in Vancouver?

Task #4—Reading a map: Examine the map in Fig. 10-10 and answer the following questions in your notebook. Remember to look at the legend, symbols, colour scheme, scale, direction arrow, and human and physical features on the map.

a) What is the purpose of this map?

b) List some of the human and physical features on this map.

c) Locate the Sea to Sky Highway.

   i. What highway number is it given?

   ii. Which direction is Whistler from Vancouver?

   iii. How would you describe the route of this highway?

   iv. Using the climate graph (Fig. 10-9) and the map (Fig. 10-10), what transportation challenges do you think the Olympic organizers will need to address *before* and *during* the 2010 Vancouver–Whistler Winter Olympics?

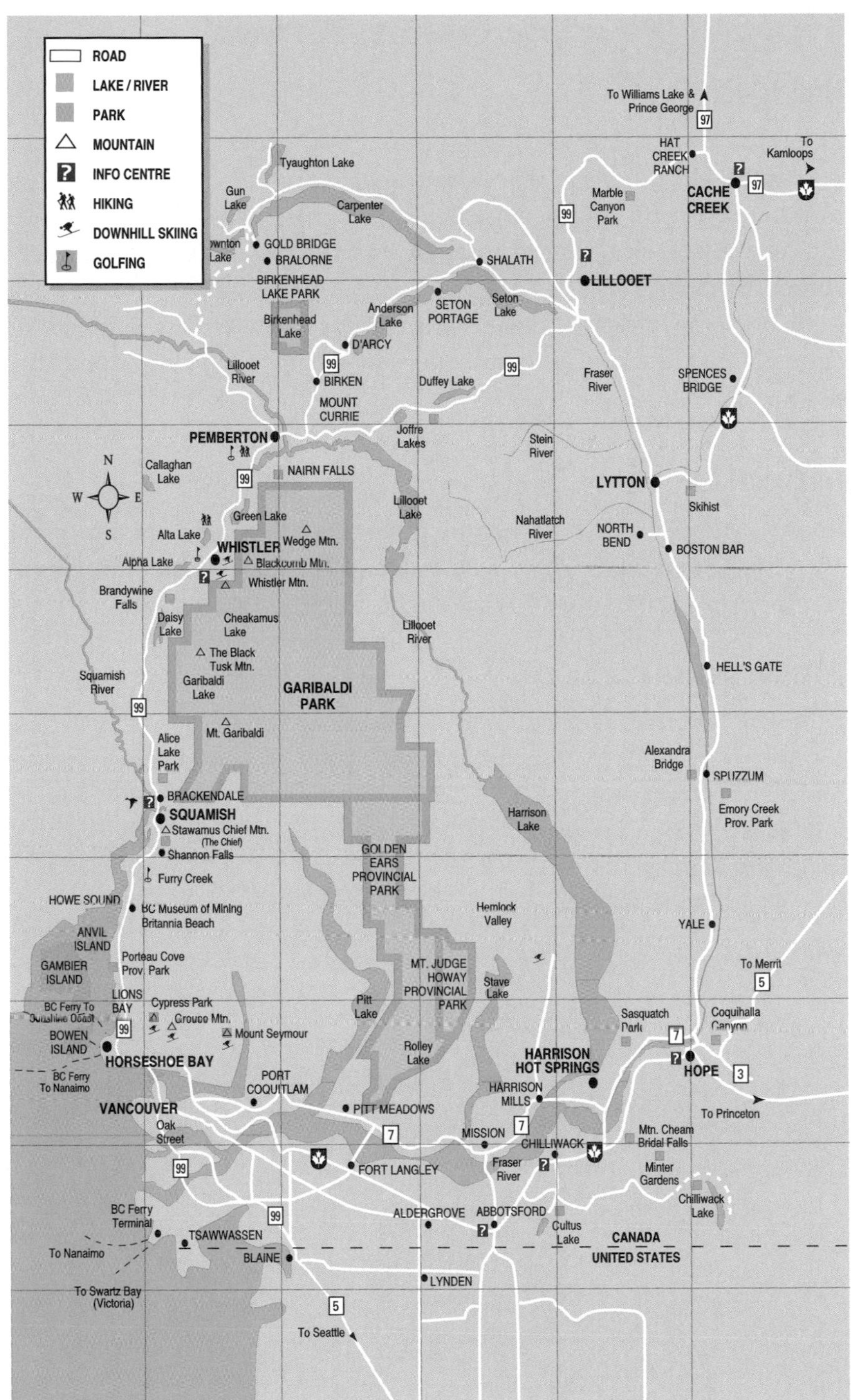

▲ **Fig. 10-10** One purpose of this map is to show Highway 99, known as the Sea to Sky Highway. What other purposes does this map fulfill?

Writing—"Practice Makes Perfect"

What Is It?

Ever hear the saying "practice makes perfect"? This saying also applies to writing skills—the more you practise writing, the better your writing becomes. But, as with reading, in order to become an effective writer, you need to use certain strategies in completing writing tasks in Geography and other subjects.

Think of all the different kinds of writing that you use every day, both in school and outside school. The web diagram in Fig. 10-11 shows some of these formats.

What to Do?

You may be surprised to learn that the different writing formats shown in Fig. 10-11 all use the same three-step process. The formats differ from one another only in the amount of detail they present.

STEP #1—GENERATE IDEAS

Ask yourself, "Where do I need to start with this writing task?" First, review the instructions for your assignment. Then, to help plan your writing, answer the following questions. This first step is important because it will enable you to convey your ideas and your supporting information clearly to the reader.

- What type of writing format are you going to use (brochure, poem, etc.)?
- What is the purpose of this writing?

Fig. 10-11 ▶ When and how might you use each of these writing formats?

- Who are your readers or audience?
- What main ideas do you need to include? (Brainstorm a list.)
- What background information does the reader need to know?
- What supporting information do you need to include?
- Do you need to include any additional information, such as visuals or bibliographic references?

STEP #2—DEVELOP AND ORGANIZE IDEAS

Now that you have outlined the ideas you want to include in your particular writing format, the next step is to establish a framework to organize and further explain your ideas to the reader. The following strategies will help you do just that. The use of graphic organizers, such as flow charts, web diagrams, **Venn diagrams**, and mental maps, will also help.

Venn diagram
diagram that uses overlapping circles to show relationships among categories

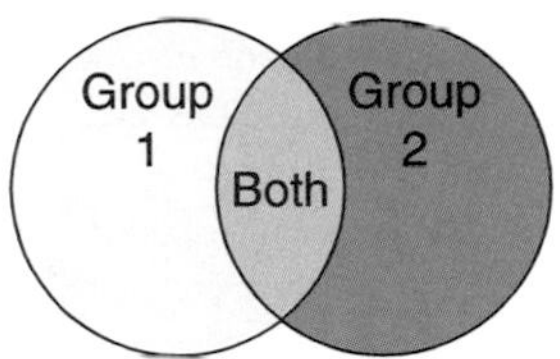

- Sort brainstormed ideas and gathered information based on their similarities and differences.
- Group related ideas and information under subheadings.
- State your main ideas in an introductory paragraph.
- Support the main topic and subtopics with gathered information. Do further research, if necessary.
- Expand your ideas, giving specific examples to strengthen your points. Allow one main idea (your topic sentence) per paragraph. Each paragraph should have at least three supporting sentences.
- Summarize your main ideas in a concluding paragraph. You may refer back to your introduction, using different wording.

STEP #3—REVISE AND EDIT

Reviewing your written work is a final, yet important, step in effective writing. Use the following questions to double-check that your writing answers the question or assignment, stays on topic, and is clearly communicated. Getting a partner to review your work may also be helpful.

- Does your writing answer the question or assigned task?
- Do your introduction and conclusion give the reader a clear overview and summary of your ideas and information?
- Are your ideas and information logically connected, and do they remain on topic?
- Are your ideas supported with reasons and relevant examples or facts?
- Are your ideas and information clearly communicated to the reader through correct spelling, grammar, and punctuation?
- Have you included all bibliographic references in proper form?

How to Use Your Writing Strategies

Now use your writing skills to complete the following task. You will need your answers to Tasks #1 through #4. Remember to refer to the writing strategies discussed above. They will serve as helpful reminders.

Task #5—Writing a summary: As a voting member of the International Olympic Committee, write a one-paragraph explanation of your decision on the 2010 Vancouver–Whistler Olympic bid. Did you support or reject this bid? (You can choose either side.) Explain your position.

Refer to your point-form notes from Task #2. You may need to reread the entire article (Fig. 10-8) or parts of it to gather extra supporting information and ideas. Refer also to the climate graph (Fig. 10-9) and the map (Fig. 10-10) for additional information.

You may choose to organize your points in a **T-chart** with "Pros" and "Cons" as the column headings. Use these points to develop your paragraph. Remember to proofread your work once it is written. Working with a partner, revise and edit each other's paragraphs.

T-chart
two-column graphic organizer that lists two facets of a topic to compare advantages and disadvantages, facts versus opinions, etc.

Facts	Opinions

Oral Communication—Conquering Stage Fright

What Is It?

Your geographic literacy skills would not be complete without effective oral communication skills. Oral skills—listening, speaking, and giving presentations—are used regularly in the classroom and include sharing ideas with partners, participating in class debates, and presenting information to peers.

You can use your listening and speaking skills to improve your reading and writing skills. To expand your vocabulary, listen to the expressions others use. When discussing a written or visual text, talk with others about the main ideas to clarify meaning and understanding. Review your written ideas with others to verify that you have conveyed them clearly.

You may not be completely comfortable sharing your ideas orally with others. The following strategies will strengthen your oral communication skills and therefore ease your "stage fright."

What to Do?

As with writing, the more you practise oral communication, the more effective and confident a speaker you will become. Working with a partner, sharing your ideas in small group activities, and participating in class discussions and presentations are great ways to improve your oral skills.

By following the instructions for the assigned task and the strategies outlined below, you will be on the path to becoming a more effective oral communicator.

STEP #1—BEFORE COMMUNICATING

- Ask the teacher for clarification if you do not fully understand the task
- Be sure you know the purpose of the presentation and who your audience will be.
- Think about the question, discussion topic, or reading that was assigned.
- Share your ideas with a partner to gain a better understanding of the question or information.
- Re-read necessary information for the assigned task or discussion.
- Decide on the main ideas and main points of information.
- Plan how to present the information to the target audience.
- Write a script or point-form notes of the main information or ideas on cue cards. With practice, you can decide which approach works best for you.
- Rehearse the entire presentation with other members of the group. Help each person with his or her part.
- Practise your part of the presentation in front of a mirror or family members to learn the material and gain confidence in your presentation.

STEP #2—MAKING PRESENTATIONS

- Explain the main ideas and information to the class in a logical format with an introduction, middle, and conclusion.
- Use appropriate and relevant visuals as support.
- Share the speaking roles if presenting in a group.
- Respond to questions posed by the audience with ideas and information that you can support with evidence.
- During your presentation, remember to speak slowly and clearly and make eye contact with your audience. (Do not read your notes word for word!) If appropriate, be prepared to move around as you speak.
- Afterward, reflect on your presentation. Which aspects were successful? Which parts needed improvement? Do you need to improve the content of your presentation or the way in which you presented your material? What improvement will you focus on in your next oral presentation?

STEP #3—BE AN ACTIVE LISTENER

- Record the presented information or ideas in point form.
- Paraphrase the presenter's statements.
- Ask specific questions to clarify the information presented.

GeoLit Reminder

Remember... be a respectful communicator:

- Participate to the best of your ability.
- Take turns speaking.
- Do not interrupt the speaker.
- Maintain eye contact with others.
- Use encouraging facial expressions.
- Avoid sarcasm and "put-downs."
- Be open-minded to new ideas.
- Express your opinion politely (e.g., "Personally, I think that...").
- Use respectful phrases when disagreeing with others (e.g., "I disagree with ___ because...").

INTERNET

Go to the 2010 Vancouver–Whistler official Web site through the link at www.pearsoned.ca/makingconnections2.

How to Use Your Oral Communication Skills

Now that you have practised using your reading and writing skills, it's time to apply your oral communication skills to the topic of the 2010 Vancouver–Whistler Olympics. (You may need to re-examine the article, climate graph, and map in Figs. 10-8, 10-9, and 10-10.) Remember to refer to the oral communication strategies discussed above. They are helpful reminders.

Task #6—Expressing your opinion: Working individually, plan a one- to two-minute oral response to the question, "Do you agree or disagree that the 2010 Winter Olympics will benefit Vancouver and Whistler?" Justify your stance by using your answers from Tasks #1 through #5. Gather any additional information you need to prepare your oral response. Once you have gathered and organized the information you wish to present, rehearse your oral presentation.

Next, present your response to a small group (three or four classmates). When all the group members have presented, discuss in your group the pros and cons of the 2010 Winter Olympics in Vancouver–Whistler. Decide on your group's stance regarding these Olympic Games—for example, do all of you agree or disagree (or are you somewhere in between?) that the Winter Olympics will benefit Vancouver and Whistler?

Using complete sentences, record your group's stance and one or two supporting points. Select one member of the group to share this statement orally with the class.

Remember your active listening skills as well as your respectful communication manners!

▼ **Fig. 10-12**

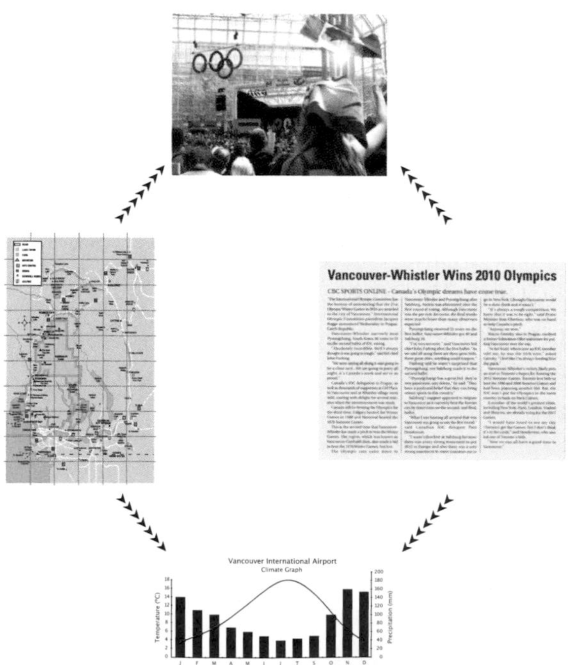

In Closing...

By completing the tasks presented in this chapter, you have developed, applied, and practised your literacy skills. You may have noticed that these skills began to overlap as you completed the assigned tasks (Fig. 10-12). For example, visual and written texts provided information for your written task. Your writing was then shared orally with a partner, who applied listening skills. All skills were combined during your presentation to the class.

The main purpose of using your reading, writing, and oral communication skills is to increase your understanding of content and to be able to convey your ideas effectively to others. It is good to know, also, that these literacy skills are transferable to other geographic topics, events, and issues that will be explored throughout this textbook.

Geographic Places:
More Than Dots on a Map!

▲ **Fig. CA2-1** Exploring the Great Barrier Reef, Australia, at low tide

The study of geography goes well beyond memorizing the names of places on a map. In fact, it is an examination of the world around us made with the help of the latest technologies, some of which you read about in Unit 2.

As geographers, we ask questions to learn more about Earth's physical features, natural environments, and human interactions. For example, where are the Rocky Mountains located, and how did they form? What characteristics make Canada's boreal forests unique? What are the customs, languages, and values of different Canadian cultural groups? What impacts do our growing cities have on the environment? Before we explore these and other important geographic questions in greater detail, let's start by examining the places and spaces that surround us.

We all have a favourite place that holds special meaning for us. This place might be in your school, your home, the shopping mall, the local sports field, a rest stop along a scenic hiking trail, or even a memorable vacation spot—the list of possibilities is endless.

Take a moment to think about your favourite place. Answer the following questions, and then share your responses with a classmate.

- Where is your favourite place located?
- What physical or human characteristics (or both) make this place unique?
- How does this place make you feel?

Are you curious about other interesting places around the world? Do you wonder what makes these places special? How are such places protected for our enjoyment today and in the future? The United Nations Educational, Scientific and Cultural Organization (UNESCO) is a global organization that aims to identify, protect, and preserve cultural and natural places worldwide that are considered important to humanity. UNESCO classifies these places as World Heritage Sites. Currently, the World Heritage List includes 812 places located in 137 countries. World Heritage Sites belong to all of us, regardless of where we live. So, what are you waiting for? Let's explore these diverse and unique places in the world!

World Heritage Sites have been designated as follows:

- 628 based on cultural characteristics
- 160 based on natural features
- 24 based on both cultural and natural characteristics

Activity

Start by examining the World Heritage Site map (Fig.CA2- 2). With the help of an atlas, locate these four places:

- Great Barrier Reef, Australia
- Wood Buffalo National Park, Canada
- City of Bam, Iran
- uKhahlamba–Drakensberg Park, South Africa

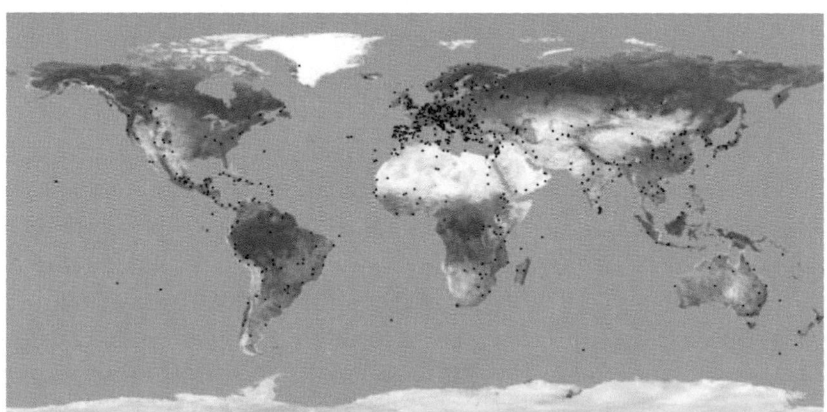

Fig. CA2-2 ▶ World Heritage Sites, 2005

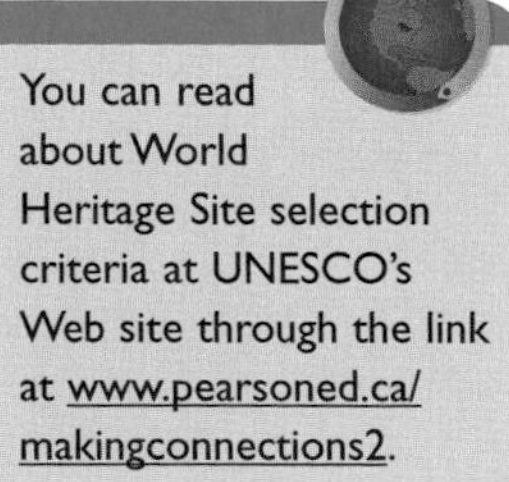

You can read about World Heritage Site selection criteria at UNESCO's Web site through the link at www.pearsoned.ca/makingconnections2.

Your task is to investigate each of these four World Heritage Sites and one other of your choice from the World Heritage Sites in Canada. You will also analyze why these places are classified as World Heritage Sites.

◀ **Fig. CA2-3** The "Giant's Castle" and tourist camps at uKhahlamba–Drakensberg Park, South Africa

Step 1: Graphic Organizer

1. Copy the graphic organizer in Fig. CA2-4 into your notebook. In order to complete each section of the graphic organizer, you will need to use an atlas, the Internet (UNESCO's World Heritage Web site, available through the link at www.pearsoned.ca/makingconnections2), and the skills you developed in Unit 2.
2. Using the latitude and longitude coordinates given at the UNESCO site, locate and label each site on a world map that your teacher will give to you.

INTERNET

To calculate your distance to the selected World Heritage Sites, check out the Web link at www.pearsoned.ca/makingconnections2.

World Heritage Site	Year Inscribed on World Heritage List	Location (relative and absolute)	Distance from Your City/Town	Cultural Characteristics	Physical Features
Great Barrier Reef, Australia					
Wood Buffalo National Park, Canada					
City of Bam, Iran					
uKhahlamba–Drakensberg Park, South Africa					
Your choice					

▲ **Fig. CA2-4**

▲ **Fig. CA2-5** A display at the Head-Smashed-In Buffalo Jump Interpretive Centre near Fort Macleod, Alberta

▲ **Fig. CA2-6** This citadel of the 10th century fortified town of Bam, Iran, was badly damaged in an earthquake in December 2003.

Step 2: Analysis

Using your recorded information along with additional Internet research, answer the following questions.

1. For each of the World Heritage Sites recorded in your graphic organizer, write two or three sentences explaining why these places are inscribed on the World Heritage List. Why is it important to designate and preserve sites such as these?
2. If you could hop on an airplane tomorrow, which one of your recorded World Heritage Sites would you visit? Justify your selection by referring to its cultural characteristics, its natural features, or both.
3. a) Why is the Great Barrier Reef "preserved and protected" as a World Heritage Site?
   b) How can human activities harm the Great Barrier Reef?
   c) What actions are being taken to help minimize these threats to the Great Barrier Reef?
   d) Use your Internet search skills to find a relevant and reputable resource to support your answer.
4. What physical features, natural environments, and human interactions did you learn about in the investigation of
   a) your favourite place? b) your selected World Heritage Site?
5. Has this investigation of your favourite place and selected World Heritage Sites helped you develop a greater sense of place? Explain.

UNIT 3

Physical Connections: Canada's Ecozones

Do you live near mountains, or lakes, or oceans? What trees and other vegetation grow well in your area? How much rain or snow do you have annually? Whether you live in a large urban area, a resource-based town, a small rural community, or on a farm, the characteristics of the land you live on affect you in a variety of ways—from the type of outdoor clothing you need in February, to the employment opportunities in your community, to the recreational activities available to you. As you complete the activities in this chapter, consider the ways in which your region is similar to (or different from) other regions in the country. If you were an artist or a writer, how would you represent your region?

11 Canada's Geologic History

Key Ideas

This chapter helps you investigate these questions:

- What forces cause earthquakes, volcanoes, and tsunamis?
- How do forces affect the structure and appearance of the landforms of Canada and the rest of the world?

Key Terms

tsunami
continental drift
Pangaea
plate tectonics
convection currents
erosion
geologic time
eras
sediments
glaciation
Canadian Shield
geoscience
glaciers

GeoLit Reminder

When reading informational text:

- Use the chapter title and subheadings as a guide.
- Scan the text for general meaning.
- Examine margin notes, captions, and visuals for additional information.
- Look for key terms.

The brutal reality of what a **tsunami** is and what it can do was demonstrated on December 26, 2004, when almost 300 000 people were killed in Indonesia, Sri Lanka, India, Thailand, and other countries bordering the Indian Ocean (Fig. 11-1). This tsunami was caused by a powerful undersea earthquake off the coast of Indonesia. Could such an event affect Canada? Unfortunately, it could. The coast of British Columbia has been struck by tsunamis in the past. Although the last major tsunami hit in the year 1700, Port Alberni was hit by a much smaller tsunami in 1964, and many scientists feel that another "Big One" is overdue. A tsunami warning system is in place in the Pacific Ocean and, in 2005, one was being developed for the Indian Ocean. In this chapter, you will have the opportunity to learn about the massive forces that shape Earth, but at the same time, can cause massive loss of life.

A warning system would not have helped much in Indonesia because of how close the earthquake was to the country. It would have provided a significant warning to India and Sri Lanka because of the distance involved.

Earthquakes, Volcanoes, and Plates

Imagine that it is springtime and you are crossing a frozen lake. As you start out, the ice seems solid, but before you reach the other shore, the ice starts to break up. Large cracks develop, separating the ice into huge plates that can be moved by wind and by currents in the water below. In some places ice plates are pulled apart, while in others they are smashed together, forcing one to ride up over another.

▲ **Fig. 11-1** In 2004, one of the most powerful earthquakes ever recorded generated a tsunami that killed about 300 000 people in Indonesia, Sri Lanka, and neighbouring countries. These flattened houses in Acheh province, Indonesia, show the impact of the tsunami.

What does this have to do with the study of geology? The structure of Earth is similar to that of a frozen lake. Both have individual plates of solid material that float on a liquid. There are three important differences, though:

1. Earth's plates are made of rock, not ice.
2. Beneath Earth's surface, the liquid is rock, not water—but a very dense, thick, liquid rock—sort of like pancake syrup that has been kept in the freezer.
3. Finally, most of the movement of the ice plates on the lake is caused by the wind, but the movement of Earth's plates is due to heat currents that start in the very centre of Earth.

The movement of Earth's plates is responsible for about 30 000 earthquakes each year that are strong enough to be felt. If one of these earthquakes occurs under the sea, and has a high enough **magnitude**, it can cause a tsunami, a powerful wave that can rise to 10 metres or more when it reaches shallow water near shore. Earthquakes, along with volcanic **eruptions**, do not occur randomly (Fig. 11-2). They occur where there is movement of the plates that make up Earth's rigid crust. You can learn more about the relationship between earthquakes/volcanoes and plates if you complete the activity on the next page.

magnitude
amount of energy of an earthquake measured by the Richter scale on a scale from 1 (small) to 9 (very large)

eruption
ejection of lava from an active volcano

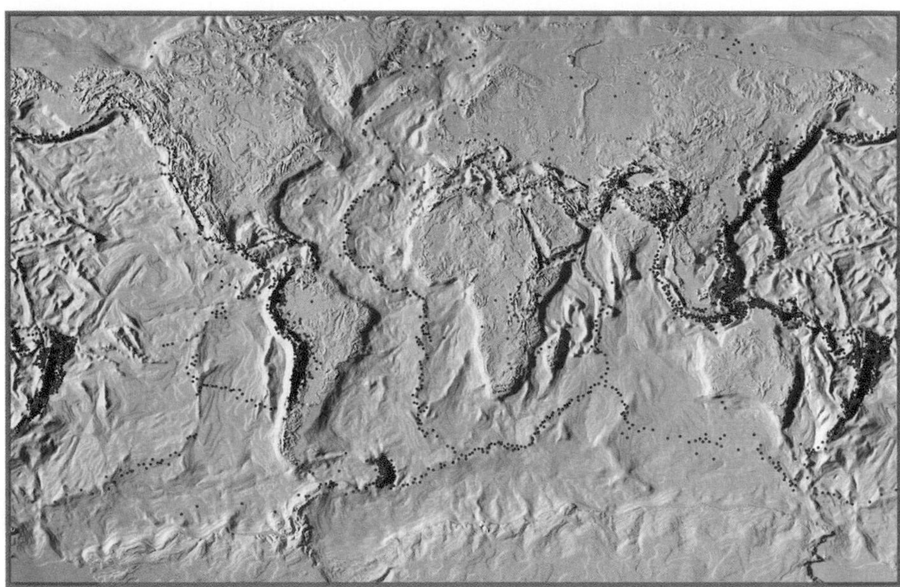

Fig. 11-2 ▶ The global distribution of earthquakes of magnitude 5 or greater on the Richter scale

INTERNET

To learn more about earthquakes in Canada, check the link at www.pearsoned.ca/makingconnections2.

1. On the world map provided by your teacher, colour and label the continents. Lightly shade in the world's oceans.
2. Each dot on the map in Fig. 11-2 represents the location of an earthquake. Which phrase best describes the pattern of earthquake distribution?
   a) evenly spaced
   b) randomly scattered
   c) in lines and arcs
   d) in separate groupings
3. On the world map you used in Question 1, draw lines indicating where you think the boundaries of the plates are located. (Remember that most earthquakes occur at the edges of plates.) Since some plate boundaries are not very active, you may find it difficult to draw them in, but do your best. (Hint: You should end up with a jigsaw pattern—irregularly shaped pieces that fit together.)
4. a) How many plates did you find?
   b) Compare your results with the results of three of your classmates. Did they put their plate boundaries in the same places? Why or why not?
5. Want to know about the direction and speed of plate movement? A link at www.pearsoned.ca/makingconnections2 will provide a plate motion calculator. It looks complicated to use, but is really pretty easy. The only information you need to enter is the latitude and longitude of a place on the plate in which you are interested. A couple of hints follow:

- You do not need to give minutes and seconds of latitude and longitude—for our purposes, whole degrees are accurate enough.
- West longitudes (like those used for Canadian locations) and south latitudes must be entered as negative values.
- The result you get will look like Fig. 11-3.

a) For each of the following places, determine the plate name, direction, and speed of movement.
   i. where you live
   ii. a place in the middle of the African continent
   iii. a place just to the west of where the earthquake was that caused the Indian Ocean tsunami (you can use 0° 90°E for this place)
   iv. a place just to the west of where this earthquake was (you can use 4°N 103°E for this place)
   v. Victoria, BC (48°N 123°W)
   vi. a point in the Pacific Ocean southwest of Victoria (45°N 125°W)

b) The Indian Ocean tsunami was caused by an earthquake that occurred because the Australian plate was **subducting** the Eurasian plate. Describe the relative movement between these plates. (Hints: Consider both the direction and speed of movement. A simple sketch of the position and movement of the plates will also help.)

c) The risk of a major tsunami along the coast of British Columbia and the adjacent area of the United States exists because the Juan de Fuca plate is subducting the North American plate. Compare the risk here with the situation in the Indian Ocean. A diagram will help.

subducting
an adjoining plate carried under

▼ **Fig 11-3** Using a Plate Motion Calculator

Model	Latitude	Longitude	Speed mm/yr	Azimuth (cw from N)	N Vel. mm/yr	E Vel. mm/yr	Plate (reference)	Site Name
GSRM v1.2	60° N 60.000000°	10° E 10.000000°	29.04	84.31°	2.88	28.90	EU(NNR)	Oslo

Check that you have entered the correct latitude and longitude values here.

This is the speed at which the plate is moving.

This is the direction in which the plate is moving. *Azimuth* is a fancy way of saying *compass bearing*. See Chapter 3 for more information about compass bearings.

This is the plate on which this latitude and longitude is located. Check an atlas for plate names or look at the *Reference* field of the first page of this Web site. This place is on the Eurasia plate.

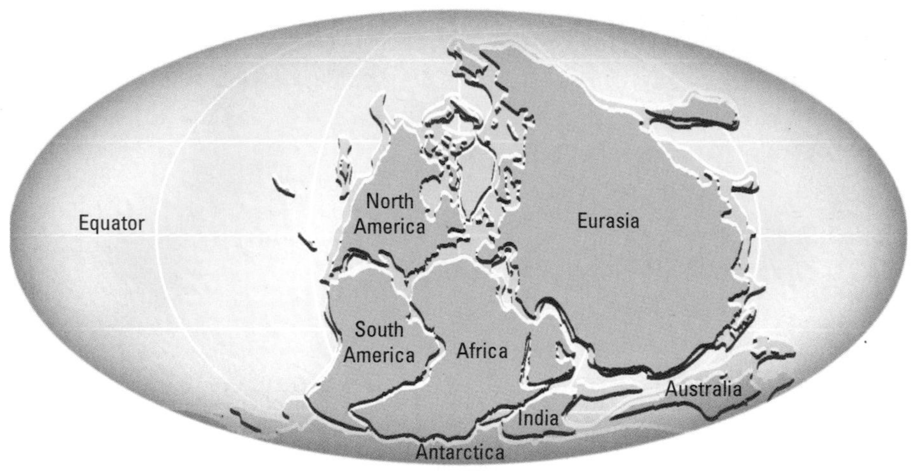

Fig. 11-4 ▶ About 300 million years ago, the moving land masses came together to form the supercontinent of Pangaea.

Plate Tectonics

You may also have noticed that the Arabian peninsula and northeast Africa "fit," as do Labrador and southwestern Greenland.

If you examine a map of the world, you might notice that the shapes of South America and Africa look like they could fit together pretty well. If they were once together, why are they now apart, and what forces could move such large land masses?

In 1915, Alfred Wegener, a German scientist, said that the only possible answer was **continental drift**. He suggested that about 300 million years ago all of Earth's land masses, which were in constant motion, collided to form one supercontinent. He called it **Pangaea**, which means "all land" (Fig. 11-4). About 200 million years ago, the supercontinent of Pangaea started to break up. The pieces drifted in different directions to their present positions.

Wegener's theory of continental drift stated that only continents drifted. Today, we know that plates drift, and that they may also contain both continental and oceanic crust.

Wegener had four proofs for his theory of continental drift (Fig. 11-5). Most scientists at the time did not accept the theory because Wegener could not explain what force was powerful enough to move continents. It was not until the 1960s that the technology existed to develop Wegener's theory further. It was a Canadian, J. Tuzo Wilson, who helped spark new interest in the theory of continental drift. By 1968, a new, more complete **theory** known as **plate tectonics** had been developed.

theory
explanation based on observation and reasoning

Plate tectonics helps explain most geologic processes. The theory states that Earth's outer shell is made up of about 20 plates (Fig. 11-6). Most of these plates are made up of both continental and oceanic crust. They are floating on a layer of hot rock, several hundred kilometres below Earth's surface, which flows like slow-moving plastic. No one fully understands the forces that cause the plates to move. It is likely that the unequal distribution of heat within Earth's core causes **convection currents** to move the plates (Fig. 11-7).

convection
occurs when a heated fluid or gas rises and is replaced by a cool fluid or gas that in turn is heated and rises

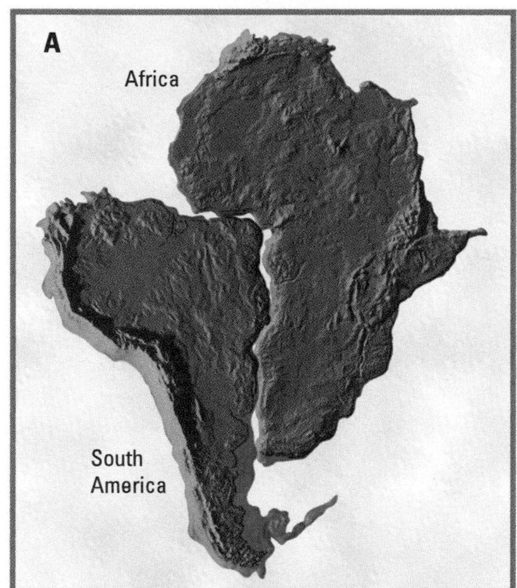

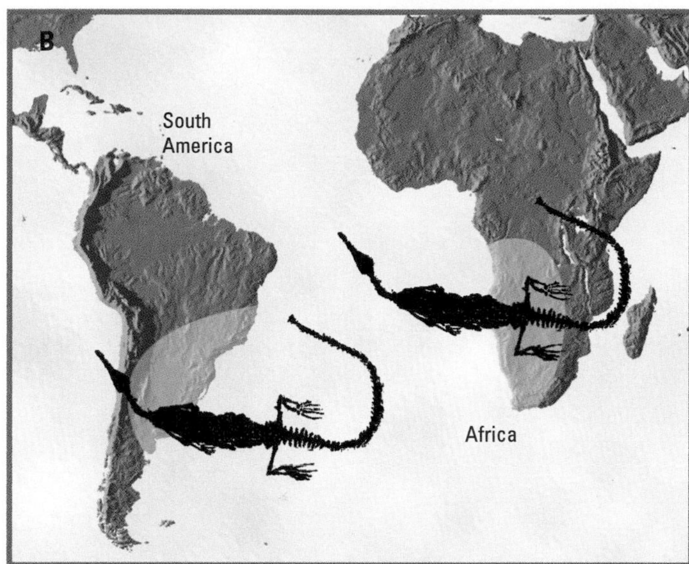

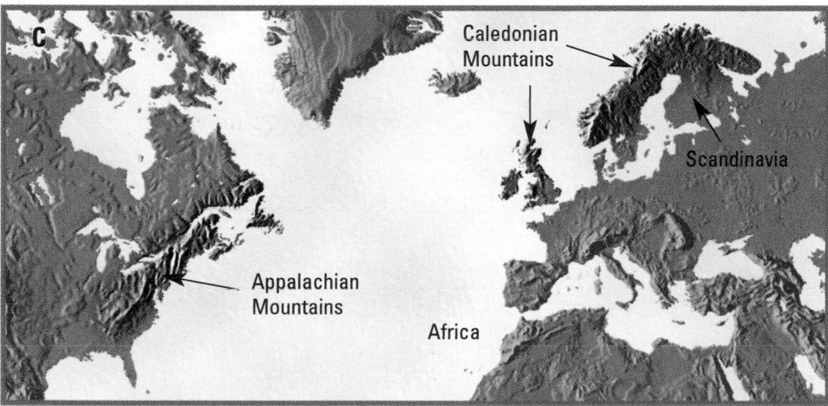

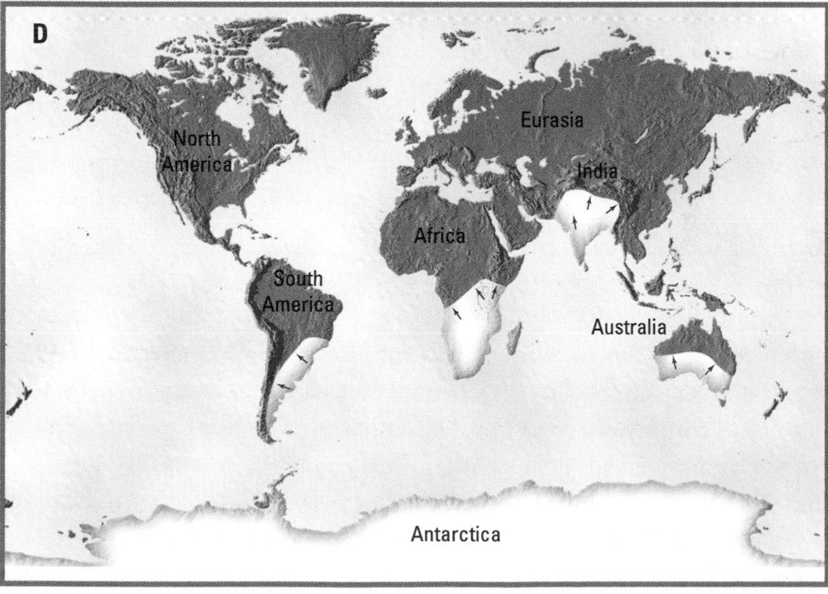

Fig. 11-5
Here is how Wegener tried to prove his theory of continental drift:

A He saw the jigsaw fit between South America and Africa.

B He found fossils of the same plants and animals on both continents. He believed that they could exist in both places only if the continents were once joined together.

C There are mountains similar in age and structure on both sides of the Atlantic Ocean—the Appalachians in the eastern United States and Canada, and the Caledonian Mountains in the northern British Isles and Europe. These mountains formed about 300 million years ago when North America collided with Europe and northern Africa.

D Ice sheets covered parts of southern Africa, India, Australia, and South America about 250 million years ago. How could ice have developed in places that are so warm today? The only explanation seemed to be that at one time the continents were located closer to the South Pole.

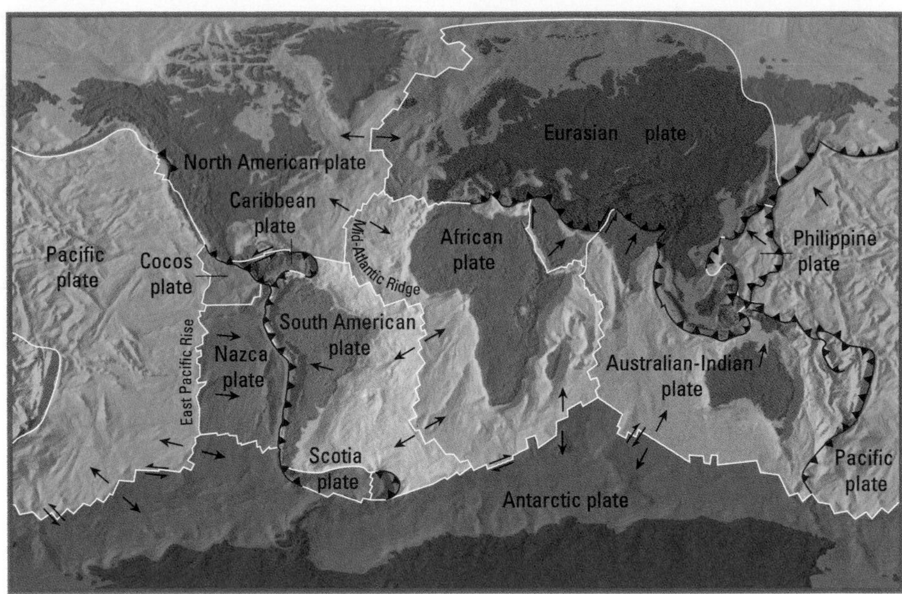

Fig. 11-6 ▶ Earth's crust: a series of plates resembling a jigsaw puzzle

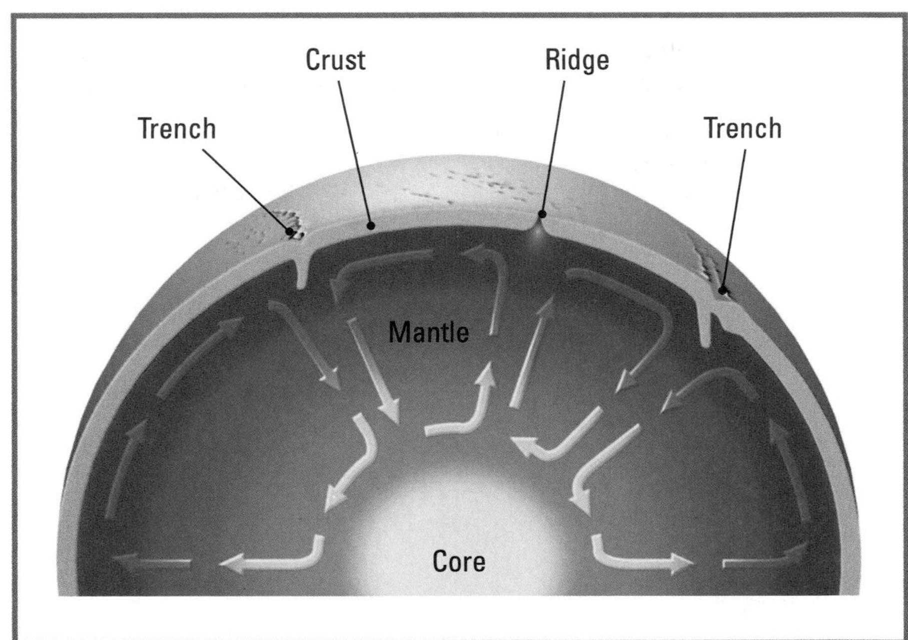

Fig. 11-7 ▶ Convection currents are caused by the uneven temperatures inside Earth. They are the driving force that moves the plates.

As two plates move apart, the sea floor spreads, magma comes up from Earth's core, and a ridge is formed. As two plates collide, one plate descends (subducts) under the other, creating a trench.

INTERNET

To learn more about plate tectonics, check the link at www.pearsoned.ca/makingconnections2.

The movement of Earth's plates has shaped Canada in many ways. For example, the mountain chains on the east and west coasts were formed as a result of plates bumping together. Plate tectonics has also played a role in forming Canada's fossil fuels. Oil, gas, and coal were formed as a result of events that took place when Canada's land mass was located in a warmer, tropical climate. Where will Canada be located in the next few hundred million years? Only time will tell.

Issue

PREPARING FOR A MAJOR EARTHQUAKE AND/OR TSUNAMI ON CANADA'S WEST COAST

◀ **Fig. 11-8** The Government of British Columbia has prepared a guide to help residents prepare for an earthquake.

Background

British Columbia, which is located near the western edge of the North American plate, could be affected by a significant earthquake that occurs on land, or by a tsunami generated by an earthquake occurring under the sea where the North American and Juan de Fuca plates meet.

- With current technology, it is impossible to predict accurately when an earthquake will occur, but geologists agree that the question is not *if* British Columbia will experience a major earthquake and possible tsunami, but *when*.
- Minor and moderate earthquakes are rare in BC compared to California. You might think that this is good, but it isn't. It means that tensions are building up in Earth's crust, and are not being released gradually by smaller quakes over a number of years.
- The scientific proof of the risks along the BC coast is relatively new. Consequently, BC's preparations for earthquakes and tsunamis are not as advanced as they could be. For example, buildings constructed before the mid-1980s were built without earthquake-proof designs and materials.
- The Indian Ocean tsunami was a reminder of the potential risks. To those living on Canada's west coast, however, since earthquake/tsunami preparations are extremely costly, people and governments find them difficult to put into place.

INTERNET

Visit the link at www.pearsoned.ca/makingconnections2 for a discussion of the earthquake hazard on Canada's west coast.

Activities

1. Who in BC is most at risk from a tsunami? From an earthquake? (Hint: Consider both the landforms where people live and the kinds of structures in which they live and work.)
2. How high a priority should earthquake/tsunami preparations be in BC compared to other needs in the province, such as improved healthcare, better schools, and eliminating government deficits and debt?
3. Who should pay for these preparations? On private property, should they be the landowner's responsibility, or should the government pay (or help to pay)? Should preparations be a responsibility of the provincial government alone, or should the federal government also be involved?
4. People from Ontario often move to BC to go to school, work, or retire. Would the threat of an earthquake or tsunami affect your decision if you or your family were thinking of moving there?

QUESTIONS

KNOWLEDGE AND UNDERSTANDING

1. What was probably the first evidence that led people to think that the continents were once connected?
2. a) What did Alfred Wegener mean by "continental drift"?
   b) What proof did he have to support this theory?
   c) Why did most scientists of his day disagree with his theory?
3. Explain the theory of plate tectonics.

THINKING

4. Why are most earthquakes and volcanoes located near plate boundaries?
5. The movement of Earth's plates has shaped Canada in many ways. Explain.
6. a) Examine an atlas map that shows plate boundaries or undersea structure in detail. Identify one ridge and one trench. In which direction are the plates moving at the ridge? At the trench?
   b) The worst earthquakes happen in places where subduction occurs.
      i. What is subduction?
      ii. Is subduction occurring at ridges or trenches?

COMMUNICATION

7. a) Write a newspaper article describing continental drift that could have appeared when Wegener first published his theory.
   b) Write an editorial that either supports or rejects his theory. Fully explain your reasons.

North America's Geologic History

North America's amazing physical diversity is largely the result of its geologic development. The theory of plate tectonics helps to explain part of our geologic history, but other forces come into play. Earth's physical landscape is also partly the result of conflict between forces that build the land higher and those that wear it down. Land that is violently pushed upward by great forces within Earth may form mountains. Mountains and other elevated areas, in turn, are slowly and continuously worn down by wind, rain, running water, and ice. This wearing down is called **erosion**.

We can find out about Earth's early physical history by carefully analyzing landforms, rocks, and fossils.

At different times and in different places, one force has been stronger than the other. When mountain-building forces are more active than erosional forces, the land rises. When erosional forces are more powerful, the land sinks. This conflict has taken place over hundreds of millions of years, and forms the ongoing story of Earth's geologic history.

Geologic Time

How can we imagine how old Earth is, when it is estimated that it formed about 4 600 000 000 years ago? Here is a way to help you understand the passing of **geologic time**. Divide your age into a million years. This will tell you how many of your lifetimes equal one million years. For example, if you are 15, you would have to live your life approximately 66 667 times (1 000 000/15) before you would live a million years. How many times would the length of your life fit into Earth's lifespan of 4 600 000 000 years?

To make geologic time easier to understand, geologists have divided Earth's history into four time periods called **eras**. An overview of these eras is shown in Fig. 11-9. Each era represents a time of major sediment **deposition** and plate movement. While not all researchers agree with one another, the following account of the world's geologic history is widely accepted. Complete the following exercise to help you discover what events occurred during which eras.

INTERNET

To learn more about geologic time, check the link at www.pearsoned.ca/makingconnections2.

deposition
gradual laying down of materials

1. Using the information from Fig.11-9, answer the questions below.
   a) How old is Earth?
   b) What percentage of Earth's age does each era represent?
   c) What is the name of the era in which we live?
2. a) Draw a line 100 mm long on a piece of paper. Divide it into eras based on the percentages calculated in Question 1b).
   b) Using the chart from Fig. 11-9, label the main geological events that occurred in each era along the line.

▼ **Fig. 11-9** Geologic history is broken down into four major time periods called eras. The eras are separated by major periods of mountain building and, in some cases, mass extinctions of animals.

Eras	Time Period (millions of years ago) Began	Ended	Major Geological Events	Major Biological Events
Cenozoic (recent life)	66	—	• ice sheets cover much of North America • continents take on their present shape • formation of the Rocky Mountains completed	• human beings develop • age of mammals • modern forms of life evolve
Mesozoic (middle life)	245	66	• formation of Rocky Mountains begins • Innuitian Mountains formed • shallow seas in the interior of North America at various times	• age of reptiles, such as dinosaurs • first flowering plants • first birds and mammals
Paleozoic (ancient life)	570	245	• periods when large parts of North America are covered by shallow seas • Appalachians formed	• age of amphibians and fish • first insects • large swamps — coal formed from this vegetation • first plants and animals appear on land
Precambrian (earliest life)	4600	570	• Precambrian shields, such as the Canadian Shield, Brazilian Shield, African Shield, and Australian Shield are formed	• first multi-celled organisms • first single-celled organisms

A Checklist for Understanding the Creation of Canada's Landforms

You could spend your entire life studying the creation of Canada's landforms and still have only scratched the surface. Briefly put, if you remember the following eight things, you will gain some appreciation for how Canada's landform regions came to look as they do.

1. The land is built up by tectonic forces such as volcanoes and the collision of plates that creates new mountain ranges. Volcanic activities create new igneous rocks from magma (liquid rock) from under Earth's surface (Fig 11-10a).
2. The land is worn away by the forces of erosion. These forces break down rock and move it to a location that is usually at a lower elevation. Erosion results from the action of moving water, freezing and melting water, wind, glaciers, precipitation, and chemical action such as water on limestone or the effects of acid rain.
3. There is constant conflict between the forces that build the land higher and those that wear it down. When the former are more active, the land will rise. When the erosional forces are more active, the land will wear down (Fig. 11-10b). In general, land building happens quickly over a shorter time, while erosion is a slower, but continuous, process.
4. Eroded **sediments** will eventually become sedimentary rock (Fig. 11-11). The creation of sedimentary rock occurs most often in the ocean, but can occur on land. The tremendous weight of the sediments causes the lower layers of sediment to be compressed into rock.
5. Both igneous and sedimentary rock can be changed into various kinds of metamorphic rock when they are exposed to great heat and pressure under Earth's surface (Fig. 11-11).

Remember that *quickly* and *shorter* are relative terms. Land-building processes occur over tens of millions of years.

▼ **Fig. 11-10** The land is built up by tectonic activities (a) and worn away by the forces of erosion (b).

a)

b)

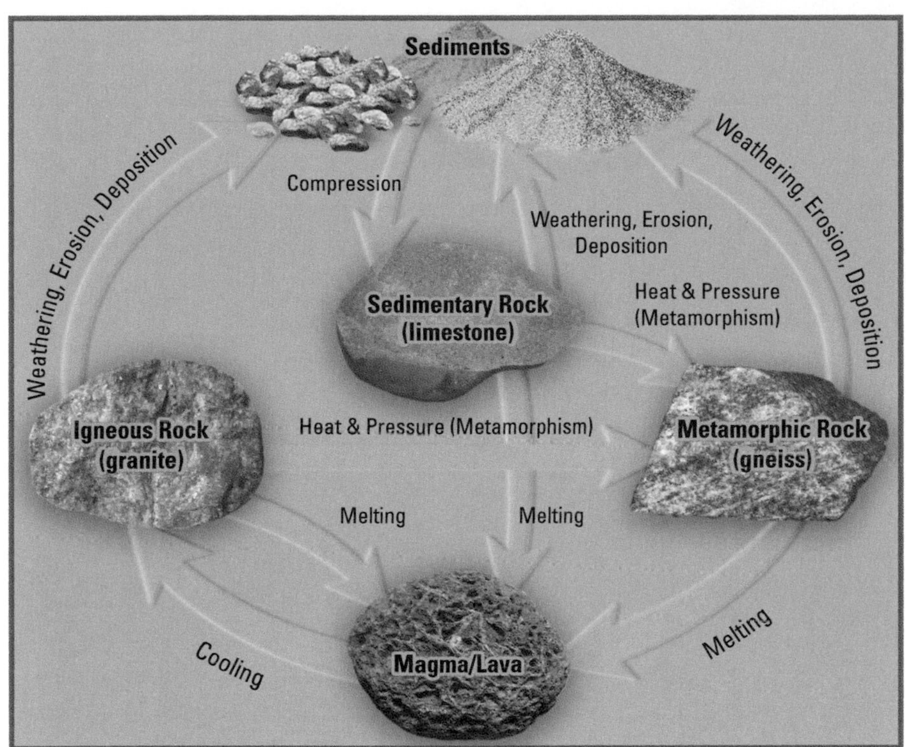

◀ **Fig. 11-11** The rock cycle

6. Economic activity in a particular location is related to the type of rock in that location. For example, oil and gas production takes place in areas underlain by sedimentary rock.
7. There is much clearer evidence of more recent geologic events than of those that happened in the distant Precambrian era. Earth's history is so long that what were once huge mountain ranges have been worn away, leaving no evidence behind that they ever existed (Fig. 11-12).
8. The effects of **glaciation** are central to the appearance and structure of Canada's landforms, not because the power of the **glaciers** was so overwhelming, but because glaciation occurred very recently in geologic time, i.e., within the last million years.

▼ **Fig. 11-12** Mountain ranges in geologic history

Region	When Mountains Formed	Appearance
Canadian Shield	Precambrian (570 to 1500 million years ago)	Ancient mountains that have been levelled by erosion, leaving rock covered by thin soil and many lakes (Fig. 12-8 on page 132)
Appalachian	Paleozoic (245 to 570 million years ago)	Significantly eroded to rounded mountains and hills (Fig. 12-14 on page 140)
Western Cordillera	late Mesozoic and early Cenozoic (30 to 100 million years ago)	Slightly eroded mountains with jagged high peaks (Fig. 12-17 on page 141)

GeoCareers

Geoscience

There is a wide range of careers available within the general area called **geoscience**. People with careers in geoscience carry out a broad range of tasks, including:

- finding new resources such as oil and natural gas, metal and non-metallic minerals, and groundwater
- studying earthquakes and volcanoes and trying to find ways to predict them
- participating in the planning and construction of large structures like major bridges and tall buildings
- working to minimize the impact of environmental problems of many types

INTERNET

Visit the links to various Web sites carrying geoscience job descriptions and career information at www.pearsoned.ca/makingconnections2.

Here are some jobs within the field of geoscience: petroleum geologist, environmental impact consultant, oil spills technician, university professor, structural engineer, paleontologist (fossil expert), and seismologist (earthquake expert). Employment may be found in the oil and mining industries, engineering firms, universities, and the government.

Find Out More

Investigate geoscience-related careers.

1. Begin with a search of a number of post-secondary institutions (universities, community colleges, and technical institutions).
   a) Find ones that offer courses in geoscience-related fields. List three universities and three community colleges that offer such training.
   b) List the specific departments in each institution that offer these courses.
   c) Briefly describe three of the courses that you would take at one of the colleges and one of the universities mentioned in a).
2. What academic requirements are necessary to gain admission to both the college and university you chose in 1c)? Try to determine what high school courses you would need, and how high your marks would have to be.
3. What types of careers do these programs lead to? List at least three possible careers for the programs offered by the university and college you mentiond in 1c).

4. Would you need additional training after college or after the first university degree to get the careers mentioned in Question 3?
5. Find at least one profile or resumé of a person who has pursued a geoscience or geology career, and write a summary of that person's experience.
6. What aspect of geoscience might interest you as a potential career? Explain your answer.

GeoLit Reminder

When writing a summary:

- What is the purpose of your summary?
- Look for the main ideas.
- Look for facts, examples, and reasons that support the main idea.
- Remember to review and edit your written work.

In Closing...

Many geological events occurring over hundreds of millions of years have created Canada's **diverse** landforms. Geological events are still occurring and changing the appearance and location of the country's landforms, but none of us live long enough to see the changes that are slowly taking place. The effects of geologic processes occur over thousands and thousands of lifetimes.

diverse
wide variety

QUESTIONS

KNOWLEDGE AND UNDERSTANDING

1. Without looking at Fig. 11-11, fill in the blanks on the rock cycle diagram that your teacher will give you.
2. a) What part of Canada was created during the Precambrian era?
   b) What types of rocks make up this landform?
   c) How did it differ in appearance from today?
3. Where was the eroded material from the Shield deposited and what did this material become?
4. During the Mesozoic era, the North American plate collided with the Pacific plate. What resulted from this collision?

THINKING

5. Geologists believe that North America was located closer to the equator during the early part of the Paleozoic era. Why has this tropical location been important to Canada? (Hint: Consider the transportation and winter heating needs of Canadians.)
6. What were the main geologic events that occurred in the area of Canada where you live? In which era did they occur? What evidence of these events can you see?

7. Why are the last 570 million years of Earth's history divided into three different eras (Paleozoic, Mesozoic, and Cenozoic), while the preceding four billion years comprise only one era (Precambrian)?

COMMUNICATION

8. "Earth's physical landscape is the result of conflict between forces that build the land higher and those that wear it down." Write 4 to 5 sentences to explain what this means.

APPLICATION

9. Most geologic events happen very slowly. Name two geologic events—one land-building and one erosional—that happen fast enough for people to see.

12 Canada's Landform Connections

Key Ideas

This chapter helps you investigate these questions:

- How do landforms differ in various parts of Canada?
- What forces are responsible for these differences?
- How are the characteristics of the landform regions related to how people use the land?

Key Terms

landform
drainage
meltwater
topography
shield
highlands
lowlands
bedrock
impervious
differential erosion
escarpment
rift valley
lignite
plateaus

The Canadian Landscape

Artists show us the world through their eyes. In a country as vast as Canada, with such a great diversity of landscapes, it is not at all surprising that many Canadian artists have focused on the land in their work. Art historians feel that a distinctly Canadian tradition in art began shortly before World War I with the works of members of the Group of Seven and artists such as Tom Thomson and Emily Carr. Today, their work is highly prized and very valuable.

A.J. Casson and Arthur Lismer, two Canadian artists whose works appear in this chapter, were members of the Group of Seven.

Paintings go beyond what photographs are capable of showing because the artist **interprets** the landscape for the viewer. In this section, we look at four famous Canadian landscape paintings from the perspective of a geographer. In particular, we will consider the two factors most responsible for the appearance of all **landforms** in Canada:

(1) the underlying geology, and

(2) the impact of glaciation.

interprets
paints in a way that conveys personal ideas or feelings about the landscape

The underlying geology is vitally important because it determines a region's landform, e.g., mountains or plains. Glaciation is important because it happened so recently in geologic terms: virtually all of Canada was still covered by ice only 15 000 years ago. If geology provides the structure for a region, glaciation provides the details, for example, the amount of soil, the **drainage** pattern, and whether there are hills or flat land.

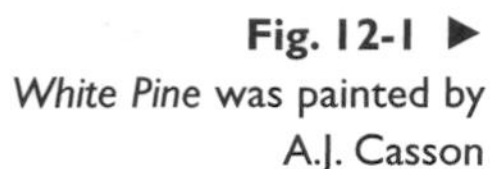

Fig. 12-1 ▶ *White Pine* was painted by A.J. Casson

perception
interpretation; impression

- ***Viewer's Perception of the Scene:*** This is one of the most famous of all Canadian paintings. It shows wind-bent pine trees on the rocky shore of a lake somewhere on the Canadian Shield. How we feel about the image likely depends on whether we have any experience with this part of Canada. If we have no personal knowledge of it, we may find it wild and beautiful, but a little intimidating too. If we have hiked or travelled by canoe in such an area, we may find ourselves very much attracted to the scene.
- ***Geology:*** The painting shows the eroded mix of igneous and metamorphic rock that is common on the Shield. The landscape is particularly rugged.
- ***Glaciation:*** The last period of glaciation in Canada began about 100 000 years ago and ended less than 15 000 years ago. Two effects of this glacial activity can be seen in this painting. The connection of one of these to glaciation is more obvious than the other. Bare rock exists because the glaciers stripped away the existing soils. This has made many parts of the Canadian Shield more attractive for tourists (and painters!) but useless for farming. The lake shown is typical of the vast number of lakes on the Canadian Shield. Many of these lakes were created because the glaciers destroyed most of the drainage system and created depressions within which water could gather. It will be many thousands of years before a fully mature drainage system is re-established.

No one knows exactly how many lakes are on the Canadian Shield, but the number is likely to be in the hundreds of thousands.

◄ **Fig. 12-2** William Goodridge Roberts painted *Hillside, Lake Alphonse.*

- ***Viewer's Perception of the Scene:*** The place shown is in Quebec, but it just as easily could be in southern Ontario, parts of the Maritimes, or the Prairies. Again, different viewers probably have different perceptions of this scene. Urban residents may look at it and dismiss it as a fairly uninteresting place. Farmers, on the other hand, would look at the knobby hills and rocky soil and feel sympathy for anyone trying to make a living off this land.
- ***Geology:*** Because of the surface materials covering the land, the underlying geology is not obvious. Since we know where this painting was done, however, we know the underlying rocks are likely to be horizontal layers of sedimentary rock formed millions of years ago under ancient seas.
- ***Glaciation:*** The landform features and rocks we can see in the soil are all the result of materials deposited by glaciers. Moving ice acts like a bulldozer—scraping, pushing, and mixing materials of all sizes. These materials likely came from places like that shown in Fig. 12-1. They are deposited at the edge of the ice, often in forms such as we see here.

GeoLit Reminder

When reading a painting:

- How is this painting different from a photograph?
- What does the artist want to draw to your attention?
- How does the painting make you feel?
- Describe the landform features illustrated in Fig. 12-2 and in the other paintings in this chapter.

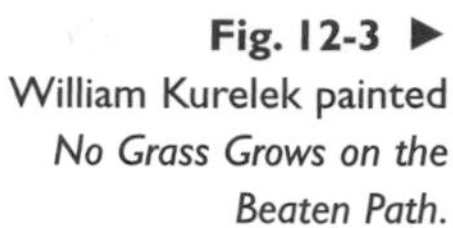

Fig. 12-3 ▶ William Kurelek painted *No Grass Grows on the Beaten Path.*

This technique illustrates the way in which an artist can focus the viewer's eye on a particular feature.

- ***Viewer's Perception of the Scene:*** This painting reflects what many people in eastern Canada think the Prairies look like—entirely flat and featureless. In fact, Kurelek has chosen to paint the horizon farther back than it really is to exaggerate the flatness.
- ***Geology:*** The sedimentary rocks under the land here are horizontal or close to horizontal.
- ***Glaciation:*** Most of the Prairies south of the Canadian Shield are *not* like this. Some parts of the Prairies are more rolling, like Fig. 12-2, because the land was covered by soil materials that were deposited directly by ice. Areas such as the one shown in the painting were created where a rich layer of sorted, finer soil materials were deposited under a glacial lake. These lakes formed near the fringes of melting continental ice sheets where there were vast amounts of **meltwater**. Such lake plains can also be found in southern Ontario, for example, near Windsor and Chatham and along parts of the Lake Ontario shore as well as in southern Manitoba and southern Saskatchewan.

◀ **Fig. 12-4** *The Glacier* was painted by Arthur Lismer.

- ***Viewer's Perception of the Scene:*** Here we actually see a glacier, although it is a mountain (or alpine) glacier rather than the vast continental ice sheet that covered almost all of Canada 20 000 years ago. Most people who look at a scene such as this would like to visit it. Many tourists travel to the mountains of western Canada to see such beautiful scenery. Unfortunately, few people are able to visit the massive glaciers of extreme northern Canada because of their remoteness and the high cost of getting there.
- ***Geology:*** Neither the painting itself nor its title tells us where these mountains are. There are glaciers in the Western Cordillera and in the Innuitian mountains of the northernmost part of Canada. You cannot tell from the painting whether these mountains were created by the folding of sedimentary rocks or from volcanic activity. What you do know is that they were created because of active tectonic activity, likely in the Cenozoic era, because they have not been significantly eroded.
- ***Glaciation:*** Glaciers are obviously an active force in the creation of this landscape. They are carving deep U-shaped valleys (under the ice) and eroding the mountains so that they become more rugged and scenic.

Do you like Lismer's work? You will have to stick to reproductions—some of his paintings have sold for more than a million dollars.

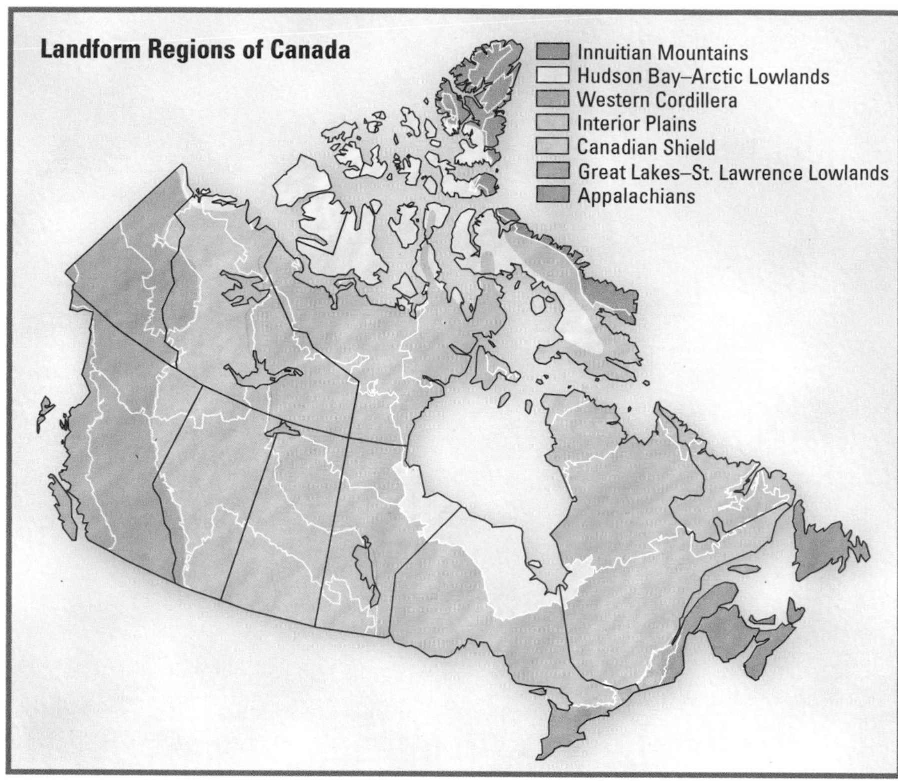

Fig. 12-5 ▶ The white lines indicate ecozone boundaries, which are discussed in Chapter 15.

INTERNET

To learn more about Canada's landforms, check the link at www.pearsoned.ca/makingconnections2.

Canada is a land of great physical diversity. Perhaps this is not surprising since it is the world's second-largest country, and has a very long coastline. We can study Canada's **topography** by focusing on landform regions.

Fig. 12-5 shows Canada's landform regions on a map.

1. What is a landform region? Use your own words.
2. How many landform regions are there in Canada?
3. Which landform region is the largest? Which one is the smallest?
4. a) In which landform region do you live?
   b) Describe the landforms in the region in which you live.

Canada is made up of three distinct types of landforms—**shield**, **highlands**, and **lowlands**. The highlands and lowlands are further subdivided into the regions shown in Fig. 12-6.

The Canadian Shield

The Canadian Shield is the geologic foundation of Canada. The Shield underlies much of Canada and two small parts of the United States. More than half of Canada, about 4 800 000 square kilometres, is covered by the Shield (Fig. 12-5). Some of the world's oldest rocks (3.96 billion years old)

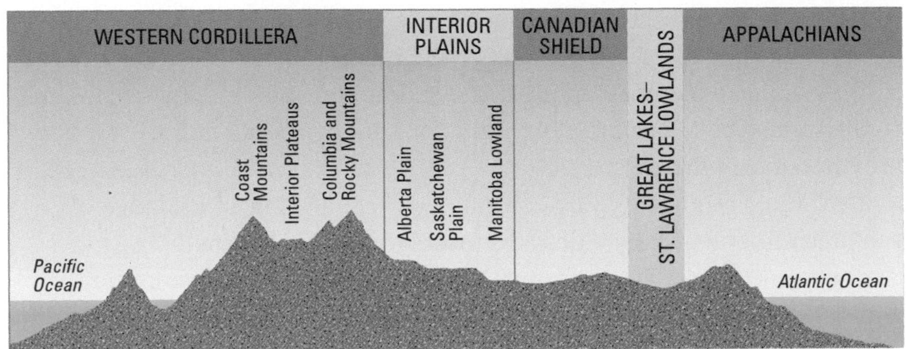

◀ **Fig. 12-6** Profile of southern Canada's landform regions

are located in the Shield near Great Slave Lake. Today, most of the Shield consists of rounded hills of rock that are actually the roots of ancient mountains. The Shield has been eroded for billions of years so it is relatively flat compared with the Appalachian Mountains or the Western Cordillera.

The Canadian Shield is sometimes called the Precambrian Shield because it was formed during the Precambrian era.

Two types of rock, igneous and metamorphic, form most of the Shield. They contain valuable minerals in great quantities. Because of its vast deposits of lead, gold, nickel, copper, zinc, and other important metals, the Canadian Shield is often called the storehouse of Canada's **metallic minerals**. In addition, rich diamond deposits have recently been found where ancient volcanoes once existed. The Precambrian rocks of the Canadian Shield do not contain fossil fuels (coal, oil, and natural gas). The life forms that produced these products did not exist at the time the Shield was created.

See Case Study on diamond mining in Chapter 26.

How were mineral deposits formed in the rock of the Shield? Minerals were present in molten rock, or magma, beneath Earth's crust. As the magma rose toward the surface, it **intruded** into cracks and cavities in the Shield rock. It took thousands or even millions of years for the magma to rise slowly toward the surface. Then, as it cooled, the minerals present in the magma became part of the newly formed igneous rock. Other deposits were formed when very hot water containing dissolved minerals was forced deep into the cracks in the surrounding Shield rock (Fig. 12-7). This process deposited minerals in high enough concentrations to make mining worthwhile.

intruded
forced molten rock into an existing rock formation

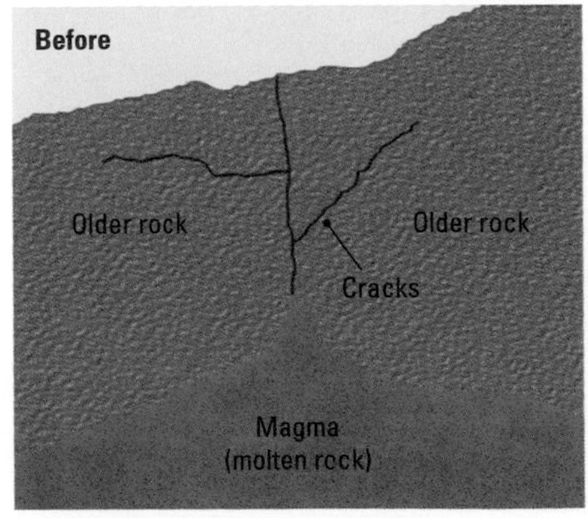

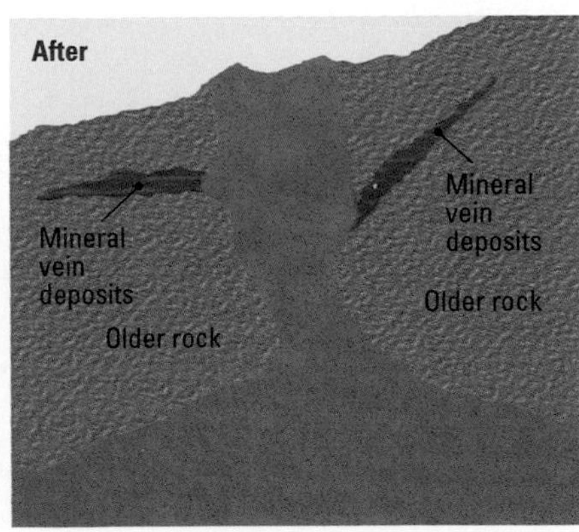

◀ **Fig. 12-7** Mineral deposits formed when magma and very hot water, both containing dissolved minerals, intruded into existing rock. Sometimes the minerals separated into layers within the rock according to their density, and at other times they formed throughout the rock mass.

A simple experiment will show you how liquids can separate into layers.

1. Put 20 mL of vinegar and 60 mL of vegetable oil into a jar with a lid.
2. Shake well and let stand. What happens? Why?
3. Add appropriate spices and salt, shake it again, and pour it on a salad!

smelted
minerals are extracted from ore by melting

In Sudbury, Ontario, large deposits of nickel and copper are mined.

As the minerals in the Shield rock slowly cooled, they separated into layers according to their densities. The lighter ones floated to the top and solidified above the heavier ones. Those that had similar densities floated to the same level. Because nickel and copper have similar densities, they are often found together.

The Shield attracts mining companies because of its abundance of metallic minerals. Many cities and towns on the Shield, including Sudbury in Ontario, Thompson in Manitoba, and Yellowknife in the Northwest Territories, rely on the mining industry for jobs. Some of these jobs are in smelters where the mineral ores are **smelted** to separate the minerals from waste materials. The concentrate minerals are shipped to factories in Canada and other parts of the world where they are used to manufacture products we use every day.

Not much farming takes place on the Shield because most areas have very thin soil. The exceptions are northeastern Ontario and adjacent areas in Quebec where glacial lakes have left thick deposits of clay. However, the Shield is ideal for recreation because of its scenic rivers, waterfalls, lakes, rock outcrops, and vast forests. People visit the Shield to canoe, fish, hunt, and "get back to nature." The tourism industry is very important to the towns and cities in the southern parts of the Shield.

The action of the glaciers affected the drainage of the Shield. The scraping and gouging action of the ice created depressions in the **bedrock**. These depressions filled with water to form the hundreds of thousands of lakes that now dot the Shield (Fig. 12-8). Because the bedrock is **impervious**, water does not pass through it. The glaciers

▼ **Fig. 12-8** The Canadian Shield. Notice the many lakes and the exposed bedrock.

deposited sand, gravel, and clay, which dammed rivers or forced them to flow in different directions. The result is a disorganized drainage pattern of winding rivers, lakes, and swamps. In time, a new, more organized and complete drainage system will develop. There has not been enough time since the retreat of the glaciers for this to happen.

The Shield's plentiful lakes and rivers have made it an excellent source of water-generated energy. The centre of the Shield is much lower than its outer portion. This gives it the appearance of a saucer, with Hudson Bay occupying the low-lying centre. As a result, most of the rivers of the Shield flow toward its centre and into Hudson Bay. This pattern of drainage determines the location of hydroelectric generating stations. These stations have been built where the rivers tumble from the Shield onto the Hudson Bay Lowlands. The energy they produce is transmitted by power lines to cities and towns both on and off the Shield.

Glaciers removed enormous amounts of soil, clay, rock, and gravel from the Shield. Today, most of the Shield is covered by only a thin layer of soil, and the bedrock is visible in many places.

These rivers and swamps are breeding grounds for billions of blackflies and mosquitoes.

QUESTIONS

KNOWLEDGE AND UNDERSTANDING

1. a) What types of rock make up the platform on which most of the rest of Canada is built?
   b) What is the topography of the Shield like?
   c) What geologic processes created this topography?
2. Why is the Canadian Shield also referred to as the Precambrian Shield?
3. a) Why is the Shield called Canada's storehouse of metallic minerals?
   b) Using your own words, describe how mineral deposits form.
   c) Why are nickel and copper often found together?
4. Describe the effects of glaciers on the following:
   a) the land's surface material, such as soil, rocks, and gravel
   b) the drainage of the Shield

THINKING

5. The natural beauty, the minerals, the rivers, and the forests are the economic backbone of the Shield. How have these resources aided in the economic development of this region?

COMMUNICATION

6. a) Review the paintings on pages 126–129. For each painting, write a paragraph in which you provide
      i. a brief description of the geology of the area
      ii. the effects of glaciation
      iii. your reaction to the painting

APPLICATION

7. a) On an outline map of Canada supplied by your teacher, draw the borders of the Canadian Shield.
   b) On your map, locate and label the major cities (population over 100 000) on the Shield. Consult your atlas for this information. Save this map for another activity later in this chapter.
   c) How many major cities are there?
   d) Discuss the following questions in a small group:
      i. Why are vast areas of the Shield sparsely populated?
      ii. Could this change in the future? Explain.

The Lowlands

Three lowland regions surround the Shield: The Interior Plains, the Great Lakes–St. Lawrence Lowlands, and the Hudson Bay–Arctic Lowlands (Fig. 12-5). The bedrock under these lowlands is formed mainly of sediments eroded from the Shield. The sediments were laid down in the seas that existed around the Sheild at various times millions of years ago. As the sediments collected, the weight of the upper layers compressed the lower layers into sedimentary rocks.

INTERIOR PLAINS

The Interior Plains of Canada are part of the Great Plains of North America that stretch from the Arctic Ocean to the Gulf of Mexico (Fig. 12-9). The Interior Plains of Canada extend from the 49th parallel north to the Arctic Ocean, a distance of 2700 kilometres. They are about 1300 kilometres wide in the south but only about 275 kilometres wide in the north.

During their formation, the Interior Plains were often covered by shallow inland seas. Sediments from the Shield and the Rocky Mountains were deposited in these seas over millions of years. Eventually the sediments were compressed by the weight of the layers above into sedimentary rock. The rock layers are several thousands of metres thick and took millions of years to form. Part of the sedimentary rock consisted of coral reefs that formed close to the surface of the seas during the Paleozoic era. Today, the reefs are thousands of metres below the surface of the land. They contain much of the oil and gas found today in Alberta and Saskatchewan.

Remember that Canada was closer to the equator at this time. Over millions of years, plate movements have shifted Canada to its current location.

Fig. 12-9 ▶ The Interior Plains

Other types of mineral deposits lie below some parts of the Interior Plains. At various times during the Mesozoic era, shallow seas covered the region that is now Saskatchewan. When they evaporated, thick layers of mineral deposits were left in the dried-out sea beds. These layers are now deep below Earth's surface, covered by newer rocks and glacial deposits. Potash is mined from these layers and used as fertilizer in Canada and many other countries. The swamps on the edges of these ancient seas produced plants that were eventually changed into coal that is mined today.

Potash is the name given to potassium chloride compounds. It is chemically similar to common table salt. Saskatchewan is the world's leading producer of potash.

Although many people think of the Interior Plains as flat, there are relatively few areas where this is true. The landscape is, for the most part, composed of rolling hills and deep, wide river valleys. Overall, the land slopes gently downward from west to east.

The landscape of the Interior Plains has been shaped by the forces of erosion. Consider the following: some sedimentary rocks are hard and **resistant**; others are quite soft. The softer rock erodes more quickly than the harder rock—a process called **differential erosion**. Different rates of erosion have caused three different levels of elevation on the Prairies—the Alberta Plain, Saskatchewan Plain, and Manitoba Lowland. Each level is separated by a sharp rise called an **escarpment**. Escarpments form when a harder rock layer that overlays a softer layer resists erosion.

resistant
able to withstand the forces of erosion

The Interior Plains, like the rest of Canada, were subjected to glaciation. Glaciation marked the landscape in visible ways and has affected land use. In many areas, the glaciers left deposits that produced a rounded, gently rolling landscape. When the glaciers melted, the meltwater formed a large lake over much of what is now southern Manitoba and Saskatchewan. The floor of this huge lake was covered by sediments that made it very flat. Later, the land rose, causing most of the water to drain into the ocean. Small portions of the ancient lake remain today as Lake Winnipeg, Lake Manitoba, Lake Winnipegosis, and Cedar Lake. The former lake bottom was left as flat land in what is now southern Manitoba and Saskatchewan. The soil that developed on the sediments of the lake bottom is deep and fertile. It is very good for growing grain such as wheat, barley, and oats and oil seeds such as canola, sunflower, and flax.

This ancient lake, called Lake Agassiz, was larger than all of the Great Lakes combined.

Because so much wheat is grown in the southern part of Canada's Interior Plains, the region is known as "Canada's breadbasket." Where the climate is too dry for crops, ranchers raise cattle. Agricultural and beef products from the region are shipped throughout Canada and to other countries.

▲ **Fig. 12-10** In the Great Lakes–St. Lawrence Lowlands, relatively undisturbed sedimentary rocks and a variety of glacial effects have produced a landscape that generally ranges from level to rolling.

GREAT LAKES–ST. LAWRENCE LOWLANDS

There is a famous story about two blind men learning about an elephant solely from touch. One man, holding a leg, states that an elephant is very much like a tree, while the other man, holding the tail, says an elephant is very much like a stout piece of rope. Each man has his own perception of what an elephant is like. Such is the case with the Great Lakes–St. Lawrence Lowlands. A person looking at a map of landform regions of

Canada will see this small but highly populated area as a separate region. On the other hand, a person looking at a North American landform region map will see that it is really only the most northeasterly part of the Great Plains of North America.

Geographers believe that there were water bodies in the Great Lakes region before glaciation. The glaciers deepened and widened the depressions containing these water bodies.

As you might suspect from the name, the region consists of two parts: the Great Lakes Lowlands to the west and the St. Lawrence Lowlands to the east. The parts are separated by a thin wedge of the Canadian Shield that juts across the St. Lawrence River near Kingston, Ontario, and extends into the United States. Like the rest of the Interior Plains, these lowlands have bedrock formed of sedimentary rock from the Paleozoic era. The Paleozoic bedrock can be seen in several escarpments in the Great Lakes Lowlands. The best known is the Niagara Escarpment, which extends from Niagara Falls to Manitoulin Island. The Niagara Escarpment was formed by differential erosion. The most prominent feature of this Escarpment is, of course, Niagara Falls.

In the Great Lakes portion of the Lowlands, glaciation has created a rolling landscape (Fig. 12-10). The glaciers carried huge amounts of material (soil, sand, and gravel) from the Canadian Shield and dumped them throughout the region. The landscape is **characterized** by flat plains with glacial hills and deep river valleys. The Great Lakes are located in basins that were gouged out by glaciers. The lakes were even larger than they are today because of the enormous volume of water from the melting glaciers. They eventually shrank to their present size as much of the glacial meltwater drained into the ocean. The old shorelines of these glacial lakes surround the present-day Great Lakes (Fig. 12-11).

characterized
typical of the way a landscape appears

Much of the water in today's Great Lakes is meltwater from the glaciers.

The St. Lawrence Lowlands were formed in a different way from the Great Lakes Lowlands. A **rift valley** was formed by faulting (Fig. 12-12). This rift valley was flooded toward the end of the last ice age by a part of the Atlantic Ocean called the Champlain Sea.

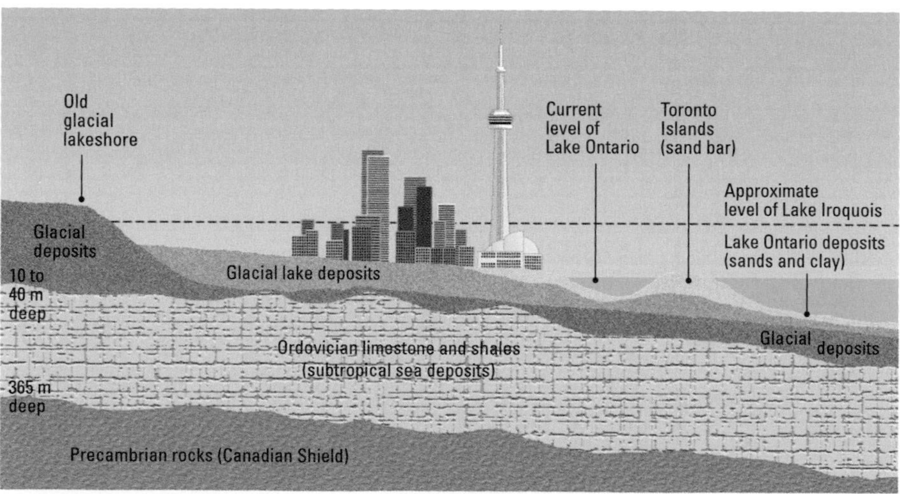

Fig. 12-11 ▶ About 10 000 years ago, the melting glaciers created a glacial lake, Lake Iroquois, that covered the area where Toronto is now situated. The Ordovician was an early part of the Paleozoic era.

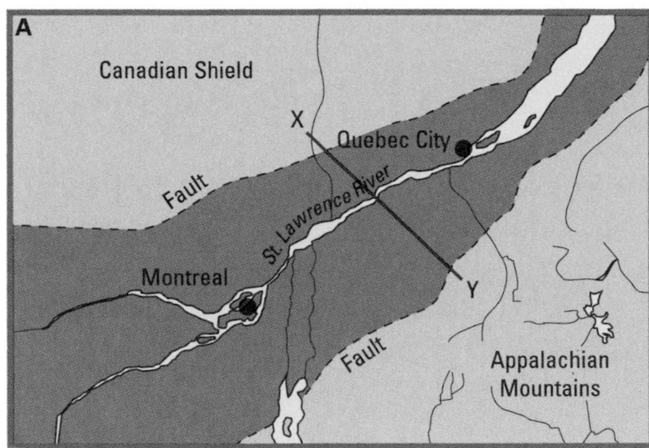

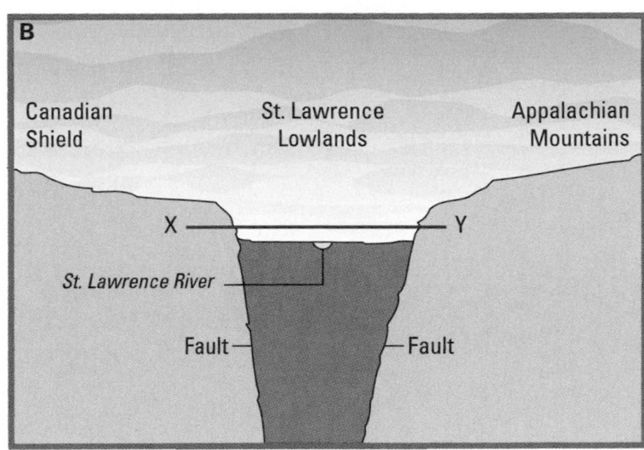

▲ **Fig. 12-12** The cross-section in B shows how the St. Lawrence Lowlands were created as a result of double faulting.

The Great Lakes–St. Lawrence Lowlands region is the most southerly region in Canada. It is well suited to agriculture because of its excellent soils and warm climate. The flat land is also ideal for transportation routes and the development of cities. Because of these factors, it is the most densely populated region in Canada. About 50% of Canada's population lives in the Great Lakes–St. Lawrence Lowlands, which make up only 1.4% of Canada's total area. Canada's two largest cities, Toronto and Montreal, are located here along with 70% of the country's manufacturing industries. Wouldn't you agree that the Great Lakes–St. Lawrence Lowlands could be called Canada's industrial and **urban** heartland?

HUDSON BAY–ARCTIC LOWLANDS

Around the southwestern shore of Hudson Bay and James Bay is a very flat, low area covered by swampy forest (Fig. 12-13). Known as the Hudson

◀ **Fig. 12-13** The Hudson Bay Lowlands

Research is being done to determine whether these lignite, oil, and natural gas deposits are rich enough to make mining worthwhile.

Bay Lowlands, this region has layers of sedimentary rock that rest on top of the ancient rock of the Shield. The waters of Hudson Bay covered much of this lowland at the end of the last ice age and deposited the sand, silt, and clay that became the layers of sedimentary rock.

The Arctic Lowlands, made up of a series of islands located in Canada's far north, have a gently rolling landscape. The harsh climate does not permit farming; the ground remains frozen most of the year. However, the Paleozoic sedimentary rock, from which the Lowlands are formed, contains **lignite** (a poor quality of coal), oil, and natural gas deposits.

QUESTIONS

KNOWLEDGE AND UNDERSTANDING

1. How was the sedimentary rock that underlies the lowlands formed?
2. a) How thick is the sedimentary rock in the Interior Plains and why is it so thick?
   b) Why are the ancient coral reefs of the Interior Plains important today?
3. a) Describe the topography of the Interior Plains as you would see it if you were driving across the region from west to east on the Trans-Canada Highway.
   b) Explain the major processes responsible for what you see.
4. Parts of the southern portion of Canada's Interior Plains are often called "Canada's breadbasket." Why?
5. What separates the Great Lakes Lowlands from the St. Lawrence Lowlands? Where does this occur and what is the appearance of this area?
6. Copy the paragraph below into your notebook. Wherever there is an asterisk (*), insert the correct word from this list:

   sedimentary, escarpment, rift, soft, south, faults, erosion, glaciation, Great Lakes

   To the * of the Canadian Shield is the Great Lakes–St. Lawrence Lowlands. Like the Interior Plains, these lowlands are underlain by * rock. The St. Lawrence Lowlands were created when land between two * collapsed creating a * valley. The landscape of the Great Lakes Lowlands is largely the result of * . The * were carved out by glaciers. The Niagara * is the biggest single feature of the lowlands.
7. a) Describe the characteristics of the Hudson Bay Lowlands and Arctic Lowlands.
   b) What minerals are present in the Arctic Lowlands? How did they get there?

THINKING

8. Examine the photographs of each of the lowland regions (Fig. 12-9, 12-10, and 12-13). Describe the differences you see.
9. Why might people in eastern Canada have an incorrect mental image of the appearance of the Interior Plains, i.e., why might many of them think it is all very flat land?
10. a) Name the four lakes in Manitoba and the five Great Lakes that are remnants of glacial lakes.
    b) Why are these lakes smaller than they were in the glacial period? Why did the lakes not disappear completely?
11. a) Describe any evidence of a glacial lake near your home.
    b) How does this feature affect the lives of those who live in your area?

APPLICATION

12. a) Mark the three different lowlands regions on the outline map of Canada on which you drew the Shield. (See Question 7a) on p. 133.)
    b) Label the lowlands regions on your map.
    c) On your map, label the major cities (populations of 100 000 and over) in each lowlands region. Save your map for another activity later in this chapter.
    d) How many of Canada's major cities are found in the lowlands?
    e) Compare the number of major cities in the lowlands with the number found in the Canadian Shield earlier in this chapter. Which region has more? Why?

The Highlands

Canada's three highland areas lie to the east, north, and west of the Shield and lowlands areas. Each of these three striking mountainous areas—the Appalachians, the Innuitians, and the Western Cordillera—has a different geological history and appearance.

APPALACHIAN MOUNTAINS

The Appalachian Mountains stretch from the state of Georgia in the southern United States through the Maritimes to Newfoundland in the north. They are the oldest highland region in North America, formed about 300 million years ago. Layers of sedimentary rock were uplifted and folded at the end of the Paleozoic era when North America collided with Europe and northern Africa during the formation of Pangaea. Geologists

◀ **Fig. 12-14** Because of their age, the Appalachian Mountains appear rounded and are less striking in appearance than most of the Western Cordillera.

know this because rocks found in the Appalachians of Nova Scotia and Newfoundland are similar to rocks found in Wales and Scotland. The layers of sedimentary rock are rich in deposits of **non-metallic minerals** such as coal. Volcanic activity and faulting created igneous and metamorphic rock in certain areas of the Appalachians. **Plateaus** of this rock contain metallic minerals such as iron and zinc.

Millions of years of erosion have reduced the Appalachians' once-jagged peaks to rolling mountains and hills (Fig. 12-14). In recent geologic times, glaciation played a part in this erosion, grinding down the peaks and separating the hills and mountains with wide glacial valleys. During the last ice age, the weight of the ice pressed the Appalachians down. As the land sank and the ice melted, the small inlets along the east coast were flooded by the sea. The long bays that were created form a "drowned coastline" (Fig. 12-15). These long bays have provided deep harbours for ocean freighters, and some have become the sites of major cities. Other settlement is located mainly in the fertile river valleys and along the seacoast.

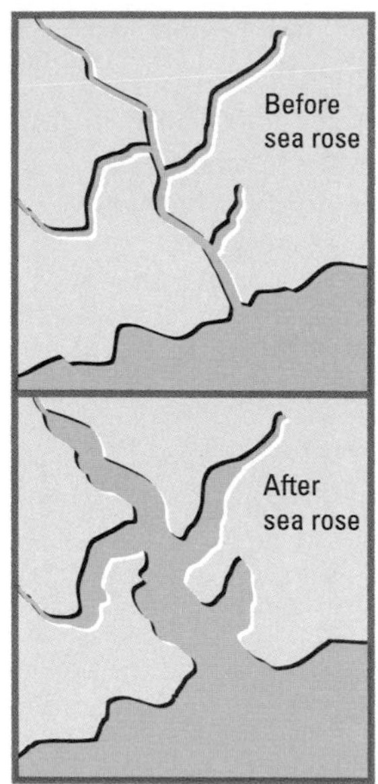

▲ **Fig. 12-15** Formation of a "drowned coastline." Former river valleys that were drowned by rising sea levels form deep, irregular inlets.

INNUITIAN MOUNTAINS

The Innuitian Mountains (Fig. 12-16) stand like icy watchtowers in Canada's far north. In some locations, they measure over 2500 metres in height. They were formed in the middle of the Mesozoic era when the North American plate moved northward. The Innuitians contain some igneous and metamorphic rock, but for the most part are composed of sedimentary rock.

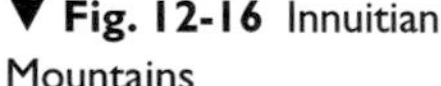

▼ **Fig. 12-16** Innuitian Mountains

Since the Innuitians are younger than the Appalachians, erosion has not had time to wear them down as much. They are **barren** because trees can neither survive the extremely cold winter temperatures nor grow during the short summer. Vast areas are covered by ice and permanent snow. The Innuitian Mountains resemble the Appalachians in composition and, as you might expect, contain similar types of minerals. The mineral resources have not been exploited, however, because the region's **remote** location makes development too costly when cheaper alternatives exist elsewhere in Canada or in other countries.

barren
having no vegetation

remote
far away from the nearest settlement

Western Cordillera

The Western Cordillera stands along the western edge of the continent like a great wall. It consists of range after range of mountains separated by plateaus and valleys (Fig. 12-17). The great height and rugged appearance of these ranges tell us that they are geologically young. The collision of the North American and the Pacific plates is responsible for uplifting this region into several mountain ranges about 700 kilometres wide. The heavier Pacific plate forced its way (subducted) under the lighter North American plate, causing a great deal of folding, faulting, and volcanic activity. The result was the Western Cordillera.

A very narrow strip of flat coastal land exists between the Pacific Ocean and the base of the Western Cordillera. The growth of cities such as Vancouver and Victoria is limited by the presence of the Western Cordillera.

The mountains and valleys of the Western Cordillera run in a north–south direction. This presents an obstacle to transportation

◀ **Fig. 12-17** The Rocky Mountains in the Western Cordillera. The Rockies are the most easterly mountains in the Cordillera.

because main travel routes across the Cordillera must run in an east–west direction. There are only a few passes, or gaps, in the ranges of the Cordillera that are low enough to allow highways and railways to cross over.

Since it is so mountainous, the Cordillera is lightly populated. Most people live in farming and mining towns located in the river valleys. Vancouver and Victoria, the largest Canadian cities in the Western Cordillera, are built on flat land in coastal locations. Mountain towns such as Banff and Jasper have smaller populations, but thrive because of tourists who come to see the beautiful scenery. The scenery is famous partly because the mountains of the Western Cordillera are the site of the only remaining glaciers in Canada apart from those in the Arctic.

During the last ice age, glaciers occupied many coastal river valleys. These glaciers eroded the valleys below today's sea level. When the ice melted, these valleys were flooded by the sea, and became long narrow inlets called **fjords**. The steep sides of these fjords that cut into the towering mountains along the coast create spectacular scenery that today attracts thousands of tourists (Fig. 12-18). These tourists, however, must travel by boat or seaplane because there are few roads along the rugged coast of British Columbia. Roads are not very practical because of the long distances around the fjords.

Sea level during glacial times was much lower because so much of Earth's water was frozen in glaciers.

Many people tend to use the name "Rocky Mountains" and "Western Cordillera" **interchangeably**. This is a mistake. There are three major divisions in the Western Cordillera. See Fig. 12-19.

interchangeably used in place of the other

Fig. 12-18 ▶ A fjord in the Coast Mountains of British Columbia

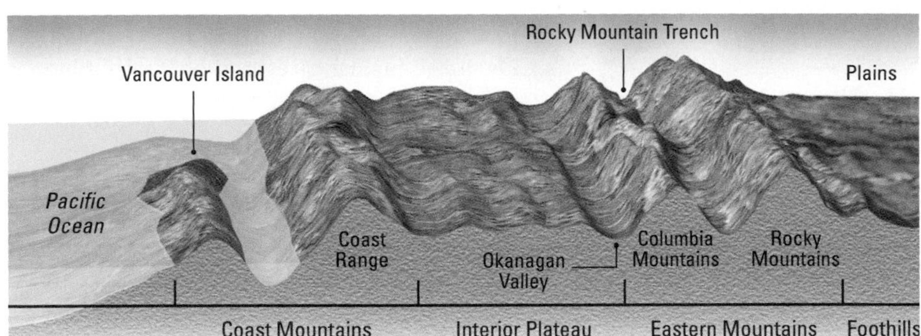

◀ **Fig. 12-19** A profile of the Western Cordillera, from Vancouver Island to near Calgary

In Closing...

The movements of Earth's plates, and the resulting folding, faulting, and volcanic activity, have combined with the forces of erosion and glaciation to create a variety of landscapes that affect the way we live.

Canada could be described as "a core of ancient rock surrounded by lowlands and then highlands on three sides." This may be a simple description, but it summarizes the diversity of Canada's physical landforms.

QUESTIONS

KNOWLEDGE AND UNDERSTANDING

1. Use your own words to describe how the Appalachian Mountains were formed.
2. Why does the Appalachian region have many excellent harbours?
3. a) Describe the composition and appearance of the Innuitian Mountains.
   b) Why has this region not been developed as much as other regions?
4. a) How were the fjords of British Columbia created?
   b) What effect do the fjords have on land transportation along the coast?
5. Explain why the west coast of Canada has so many earthquakes.

THINKING

6. Examine the photo of the Appalachians (Fig. 12-14) and the photo of the Western Cordillera (Fig.12-17). Which mountains are older? How can you tell?
7. a) Construct an organizer in your notebook similar to Fig. 12-20. Complete the information with the help of an atlas.

▼ **Fig. 12-20**

Mountain Range	Name of Highest Mountain	Height of Highest Mountain
Rocky Mountains		
Coast Mountains		
St. Elias Mountains		
Appalachian Mountains (Quebec)		

b) Of these mountains, which one is the highest in Canada?

c) Relate the height of the highest and lowest of these mountains to their age.

GeoLit Reminder

When organizing informational text:

- Re-read any part of the text that you do not understand.
- Use the text glossary or a dictionary for new words and terms.
- Record information in point form using subheadings or an organizer chart.
- Use maps, photographs, and diagrams for additional information.
- Refer back to your organized information when answering text questions.

COMMUNICATION

8. Review the material in this chapter and discuss the following quotation:

   "Canada is an east–west country trying to survive in a north–south continent."

APPLICATION

9. a) Mark the highland regions on the outline map of North America that you used for the Shield and lowlands.

   b) Name each region.

   c) Locate the major cities (population 100 000 and over) in each highland region.

   d) Compare the number of major cities in these highland regions with the number in the lowlands and the Shield. Why does this pattern exist?

10. Use an atlas map or road map of western Canada to identify four transportation routes between the Pacific coast and the Interior Plains of Alberta. Identify the mountain pass(es) used by each, as well as the major cities along each route.

13 Canada's Climate Connections

Key Ideas

This chapter helps you investigate these questions:

- What is the difference between climate and weather?
- What factors affect climate?
- How do maritime and continental climates differ?
- In what ways do the weather and climates of Canada affect us?

Key Terms

weather
climate
air mass
prevailing winds
polar front
jet stream
condensation
relief precipitation
convectional precipitation
continental climate
maritime climate
moderating effect

Weather records have been kept for dozens of places across Canada for many years. When averages are calculated from these records for such things as temperature, precipitation, atmospheric pressure, and winds, the long-term **weather** patterns that make up a location's **climate** become clear.

To help you understand why Canada's climate has so much variety, you should remember four basic facts:

1. Canada is a very large country; it extends for a great distance from north to south and from east to west.
2. Different elevations produce different climate conditions.
3. Coastal regions have different climates from inland regions.
4. Wind and pressure systems move weather conditions from one part of the country to another.

INTERNET

To obtain current weather conditions and forecasts across Canada, check the link at www.pearsoned.ca/makingconnections2.

Some very large lakes, such as the Great Lakes, also have an effect on climate.

Factors That Affect Climate

Six major factors affect climate. They are:

1. ***L***atitude
2. ***O***cean currents
3. ***W***inds and air masses
4. ***E***levation (Altitude)
5. ***R***elief
6. ***Near Water***

The first letter of each factor, along with the last factor, can be combined to make a simple phrase that will help you remember these climate factors.

L O W E R Near Water

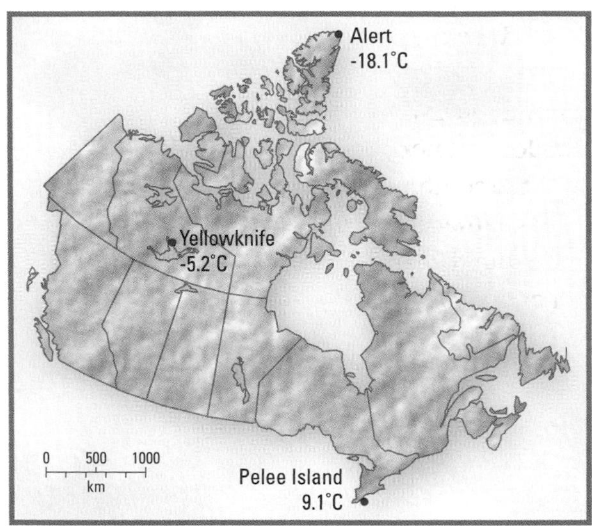

▲ **Fig. 13-1** Canada's great range of average annual temperatures is partly a result of the fact that the country stretches a great distance from north to south.

Latitude

The most southerly inhabited point in Canada is Pelee Island in Lake Erie at 41°N latitude. The most northerly point of the country is Alert, Nunavut, at the northern tip of Ellesmere Island at 83°N latitude. This wide range in latitude has a major impact on Canada's climate. Fig. 13-1 shows the **average annual temperature** at these two locations and at Yellowknife, which is about halfway between them at 62°N. What temperature changes occur as the latitude increases?

Distance from the equator is a key (but not the only) factor in determining whether a region has a hot climate or a cold one. In Fig. 13-2, you can see that the energy from the sun that hits Earth at the equator covers a small area. The same amount of energy that hits Earth at a more northerly location is spread over a larger area because of Earth's curvature. Places closer to the North and South poles experience colder temperatures than those near the equator because the same amount of energy is spread over a larger area.

▼ **Fig. 13-2** Earth's curvature causes the sun's energy to be less concentrated at the poles than near the equator.

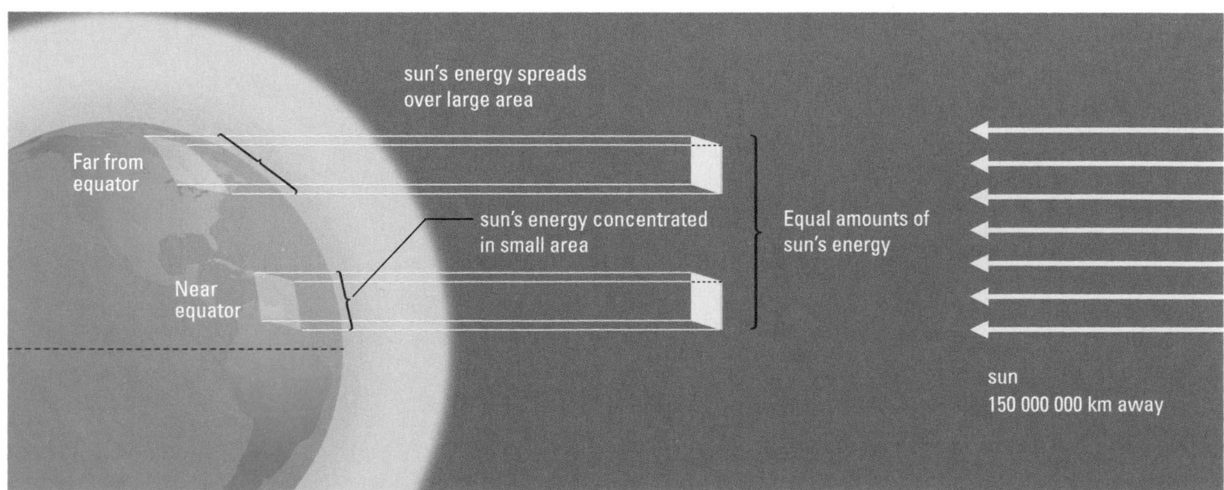

Ocean Currents

Ocean currents affect climate (Fig. 13-3). The temperature of an ocean current affects the temperature of the air that passes over it. The temperature of an ocean current in comparison to the surrounding water determines whether it is a cold or warm current. For example, on the west coast, the warm North Pacific Current heats the cool, moist air that passes over it, giving the coastal regions of British Columbia a milder climate than might be expected at this latitude.

For example, an ocean current of 15°C is a warm current if the surrounding water is 13°C, but it is considered to be a cold current if the surrounding water is 18°C.

On the east coast, the cold Labrador Current, which flows southward from the Arctic, cools the air of coastal locations in Labrador and northern Newfoundland. The Gulf Stream, flowing northward from the southern Atlantic, warms the air of coastal areas in Nova Scotia and southern Newfoundland. Where the air above the two currents meets on the Grand Banks, southeast of Newfoundland, conditions are often damp and foggy. Ships in that area must take special precautions to avoid collisions.

The meeting of warm air and cold air above these ocean currents produces fog more than 100 days per year.

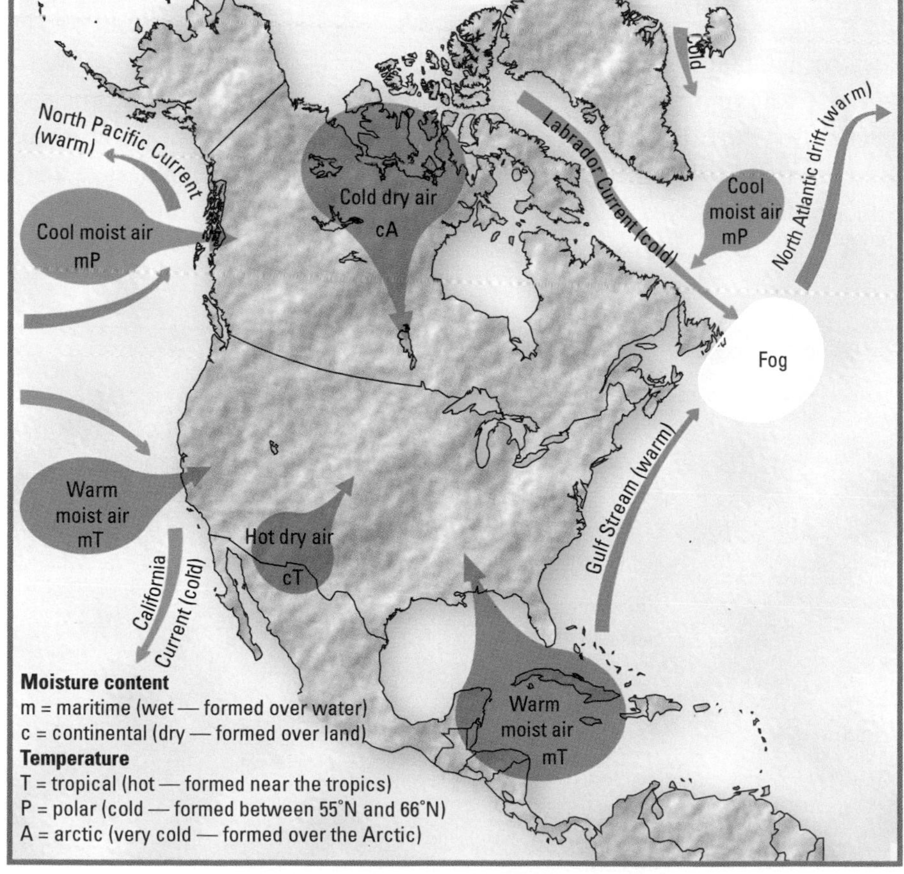

◄ **Fig. 13-3** Canada's weather and climate are affected by air masses and ocean currents.

Winds and Air Masses

An **air mass** is a large volume of air that takes on the climatic conditions of the area where it is formed. An air mass originating over an ocean contains a considerable amount of moisture. As the air passes over land, the moisture may be released in some form of precipitation. As a result, a maritime location is likely to receive more precipitation than an inland, or continental, location. On the other hand, an air mass originating over land, far from the ocean, will be dry because it lacks a ready source of moisture. Air masses also take on the temperature characteristics of the areas in which they form. For example, the *mT* air mass that starts life over the Gulf of Mexico will be warm and moist, while the *mP* air mass that forms over the Pacific Ocean will also be moist, but relatively cold.

As a cold, dry Arctic air mass moves southward, it becomes warmer and picks up moisture. Nevertheless, it remains colder and drier than the air in the region into which it moves.

Air moves along the surface of Earth from high-pressure areas toward low-pressure areas. This moving air causes **wind**. Around Earth, there are high- and low-pressure belts that have created a well-established pattern of **prevailing winds** (Fig. 13-4). Over most of Canada, the prevailing winds blow from west to east. Called the "westerlies," these prevailing winds move air masses that affect our weather. Consider, for example, the *cP* air mass of northern Canada. As it moves southward, its cold, dry conditions are carried across Canada by the prevailing westerly winds. In contrast, the *mT* air mass from the Gulf of Mexico brings warm, moist conditions to eastern Canada.

Several jet streams encircle Earth—two or three in each hemisphere. A pilot needs to consider these high-altitude air currents when calculating the fuel needed for a particular trip.

The boundary between the cold, dry polar air and warm, wet tropical air is called the **polar front**. High in the atmosphere above the polar front is a current of fast-moving air called the polar-front **jet stream** (Fig. 13-5). This jet stream moves from west to east, controlling the location of the polar front: to the north of this jet stream there is colder air; to the south

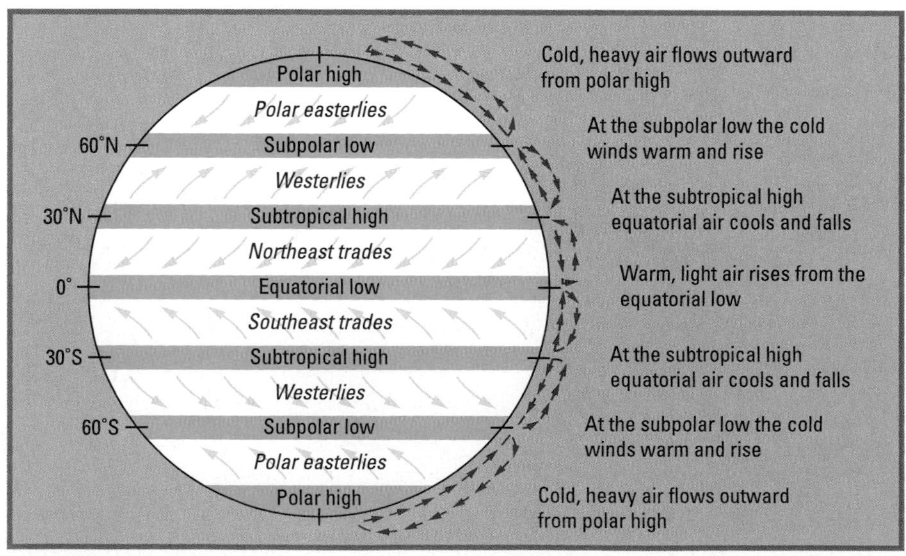

Fig. 13-4 ▶ Global pattern of prevailing winds. The degrees of latitude shown as the location of the pressure and wind belts are yearly averages. The winds shift north or south with the seasons. When you examine the diagram, remember that Canada is between 41°N and 83°N. Notice how the air rises high into the atmosphere at low pressure belts and descends at high pressure belts. The air then flows across Earth's surface from high pressure belts to low pressure belts, creating prevailing winds.

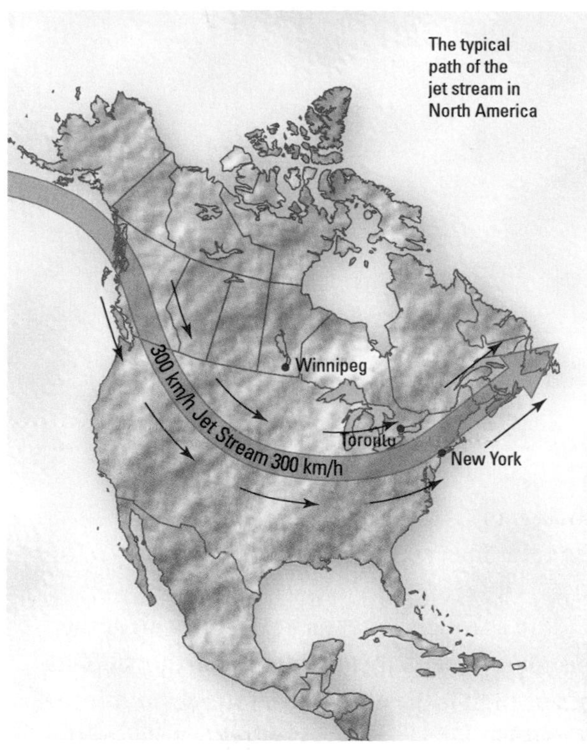

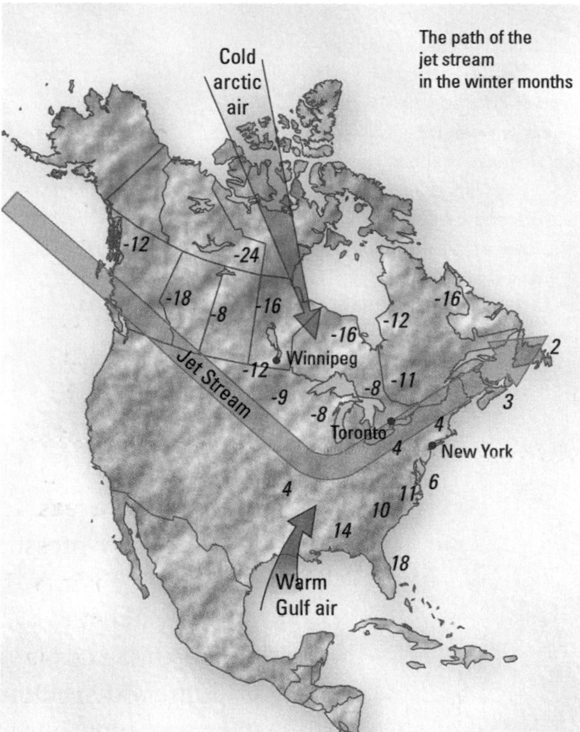

▲ **Fig. 13-5** The polar-front jet stream separates cold, dry air from warm, moist air. The position of the jet stream at any particular time has a major impact on our weather.

there is warmer air. In the summer, it is generally located to the north of where most Canadians live. In the winter, it is located to the south. Occasionally, however, the polar front moves out of its normal location, bringing mild spells in winter—the January thaw that we get most years—and cool spells in summer.

The polar front is also responsible for producing much of the rainfall that occurs in many parts of Canada, including all of Ontario. The production of **frontal rainfall** is a relatively complex process that involves the lighter, warmer air at the polar front being forced to rise over the colder, denser air.

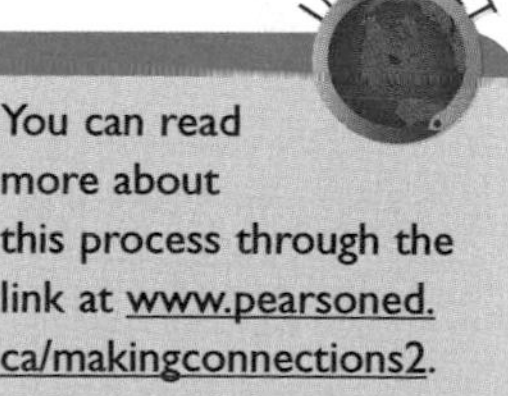

You can read more about this process through the link at www.pearsoned.ca/makingconnections2.

Elevation

If you were to hike from sea level to the top of a high mountain, you would notice that the temperature drops steadily as you climb. As you approach the top, you might even find ice and snow all around you. You probably know that it gets colder as the elevation gets higher. But why does it get colder even though you are getting closer to the sun? Consider what happens as a mass of air moves up a mountain. The example in Fig. 13-6 shows what it could be like in the Vancouver area in the summer. As the air rises, it expands because of the lower **air pressure**. As the air expands, it cools. When air is cooled, it eventually reaches a temperature at which it is saturated with

When discussing an actual temperature, use "degrees Celsius." For example, "the temperature today is 20°C." When discussing a temperature change or a range of temperatures, use "Celsius degrees." For example, "the temperature fell by 10C°."

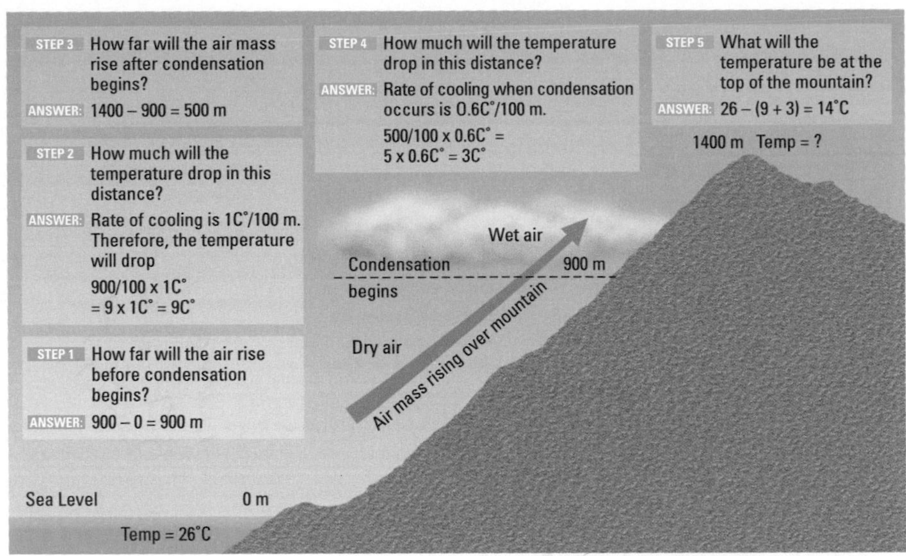

Fig. 13-6 ▶ Calculating changes in temperature of a rising air mass. When condensation occurs, heat is given off. Cooling of the air mass is still occurring, but since heat is being released by condensation, the overall rate of cooling is less than 1C°/100 m. The rate of cooling when there is condensation can vary somewhat: 0.6C°/100 m is an average figure for this cooling.

water vapour, that is, it is holding as much water as it possibly can at that temperature and air pressure. This is called the dewpoint. Further cooling leads to **condensation**. Condensation is the change of water vapour into liquid water. Liquid water becomes clouds and if the droplets grow large they may become rain, snow, or hail depending on the weather conditions. Since the process of condensation releases heat into the air, the air mass cools more slowly as it continues to rise. Fig. 13-6 illustrates how you can calculate the temperature of an air mass as it rises up a mountainside.

Features other than high mountains may also cause relief precipitation. For example, southern Ontario's snowbelt is a result of wind blowing in from Lake Huron and Georgian Bay over hilly areas.

Relief

Mountain barriers create **relief precipitation**. As moist air rises up the **windward** slope of a mountain range, it expands and cools. As air cools, the amount of evaporation decreases while the rate of condensation increases. The result is an increase in the number of water droplets in the air. As more water vapour condenses, the droplets become larger and form raindrops. When they are too heavy to remain suspended in the atmosphere, they fall to the ground as rain. In colder temperatures (below freezing), water vapour **sublimates** into snow.

sublimates
changes directly from a gas to a solid without becoming a liquid

As cool air descends on the more protected **leeward** slope of a mountain range, it contracts and becomes warmer. Since more evaporation than condensation takes place as the air descends (remember that a great deal of moisture was lost as precipitation on the windward slope), cloud formation and precipitation decrease. This results in a drier climate, or **rain shadow**, on the leeward slope of the mountain range than on the windward slope. Rain shadows and wet windward slopes are common in the Western Cordillera, where air masses pass over a series of mountain ranges (Fig. 13-7).

It tends to be warmer on the leeward side of the slope than on the windward side at the same elevation. Can you figure out why?

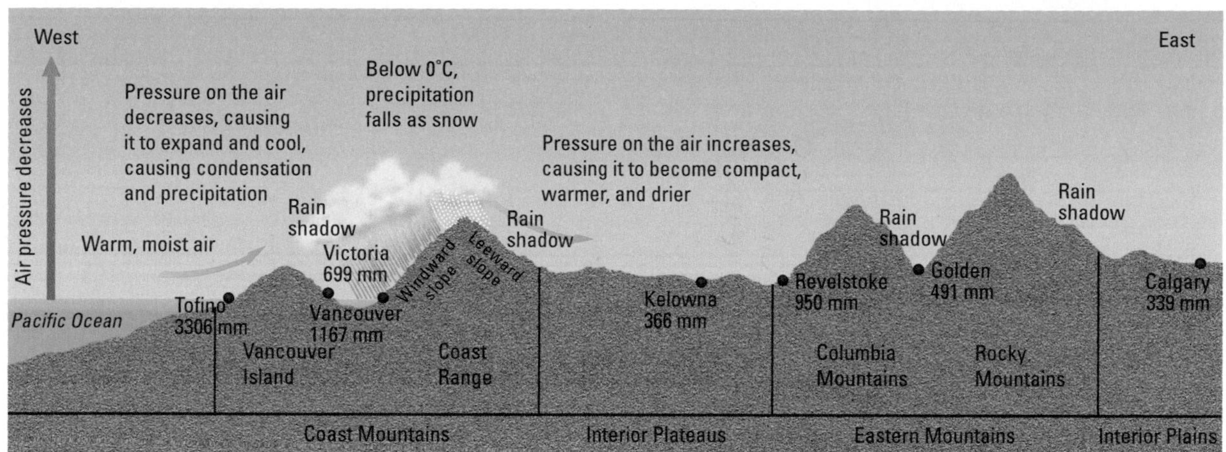

▲ **Fig. 13-7** Relief precipitation in the Western Cordillera

This is the pattern along the coast of British Columbia, which has rainy winters and dry summers.

CONVECTIONAL PRECIPITATION

So far, we have briefly considered two types (or causes) of precipitation: frontal precipitation, which occurs along the polar front and affects most of Canada almost all year, and relief precipitation, which occurs when moist air is forced to rise over an elevated area. Relief precipitation obviously affects only those areas with a noticeable amount of relief. Often, it is only apparent for part of the year since the westerly winds tend to shift with the seasons.

There is a third type of precipitation: **convectional precipitation**. It is the type of rainfall that is responsible for the fact that most parts of Canada get more precipitation in the summer than in the winter. You are undoubtedly familiar with the violent but short-lived rain showers that occur in the afternoons or evenings of hot days: these are an example of convectional precipitation.

Near Water

Areas located in the interior of large land masses, far from oceans, and far from large lakes, have a **continental climate** (Fig. 13-8). The **temperature range** in these areas is great because there is no large water body to moderate the hot temperatures of summer and the cold temperatures of winter. An area with a continental climate tends to have low amounts of precipitation because it is far from sources of moisture.

Coastal locations have a **maritime climate** (Fig. 13-9). In a maritime climate, the range between the highest and lowest average monthly temperature is relatively small because of the **moderating effect** of the large water body. The level of precipitation is relatively high compared to that of a continental climate because of the **proximity** of a large water body (Fig. 13-10).

proximity
closeness

Fig. 13-8 ▶ A typical continental climate

Fig. 13-9 ▶ A typical maritime climate

▼ **Fig. 13-10** Maritime and continental climate comparison

Climate	Typical Seasonal Temperatures	Annual Temperature Range	Annual Precipitation
Continental	warm to hot summers; cold winters	25C° to 50C°	200 mm to 1000 mm (low to moderate)
e.g., Winnipeg, Manitoba	average annual temperature = 2.6°C	37.3C°	514 mm
Maritime	cool to warm summers; cool winters	20C° to 30C°	1000 mm to 2500 mm (moderate to high)
e.g., Halifax, Nova Scotia	average annual temperature = 6.1°C	24.3C°	1474 mm

Areas near the Great Lakes are a special case. While they are far enough from the oceans to be continental, the lakes are large enough to provide a partial maritime influence (i.e., a reduced temperature range and a source of moisture). The climate here is sometimes called *modified continental.*

QUESTIONS

KNOWLEDGE AND UNDERSTANDING

1. Examine Fig. 13-2 and describe the effect of latitude on climate.
2. "Bodies of water have a moderating effect on land temperatures." Explain how this is accomplished.
3. a) How do ocean currents affect climate?
   b) The meeting of the cold Labrador Current and the warm Gulf Stream create special weather conditions. What are these conditions and how do they affect ships?
4. How do prevailing winds affect the movement of air masses?
5. How does the polar-front jet stream affect the movement of air masses?
6. a) Name the three types of precipitation.
   b) In each case, something happens to a mass of moist air. What is it that happens? What are the three different causes?
7. Explain what happens to the temperature and moisture content of air as it passes over a mountain.
8. a) Explain the difference between weather and climate.
   b) Give two examples of how each affects our lives.

THINKING

9. The Labrador Current brings icebergs southward from Arctic regions to the waters near Newfoundland and Labrador. This area of the Atlantic Ocean is called "iceberg alley."
   a) What famous marine disaster occurred in 1912 as a result of these icebergs?
   b) What effect might this current have on the oil exploration and development that is occurring off the east coast of Canada?

APPLICATION

10. Copy Fig. 13-11 into your notebook and complete it using the information in Fig. 13-3.

▼ **Fig. 13-11**

Label	Interpretation	Where Formed	Characteristics
cA	continental Arctic	over land and frozen water in Canada's Arctic	very cold and dry
mT			
mP			
cT			

11. Using the information in Fig. 13-6, calculate the temperature of air as it rises up a mountainside in the following example:

    Mount Garibaldi, north of Vancouver, is 2700 metres high. The temperature at the waterfront in Vancouver is 24°C. What will be the temperature of the air at the mountaintop if condensation starts at 1200 metres?

Canada's Climate Regions

We may not be aware of it, but the weather in various parts of Canada often has a direct impact on us. For example, a drought in the Prairies might cause the cost of a loaf of bread to rise in the region where you live. If you were planning a ski holiday in the Rockies, you would be disappointed if heavy snows caused the closing of railway lines and highways in the mountains. And of course, the climate in your own part of the country determines what clothing you wear each season. Climate and weather patterns also have an effect on many other things: on a region's soil, and the agricultural patterns that develop; on a region's natural vegetation and wildlife, and the economic activities that might result (e.g., forestry); and on population patterns (e.g., harsh climate conditions that might discourage settlement).

INTERNET

To obtain climate information for dozens of places across Canada, check the link at www.pearsoned.ca/makingconnections2.

Areas with similar climates may be grouped together to form a climate region. The climates of Canada may be grouped to create eight climate regions (Fig. 13-12). Complete the following activity to help you understand the characteristics of Canada's climate regions.

Fig. 13-12 ▶

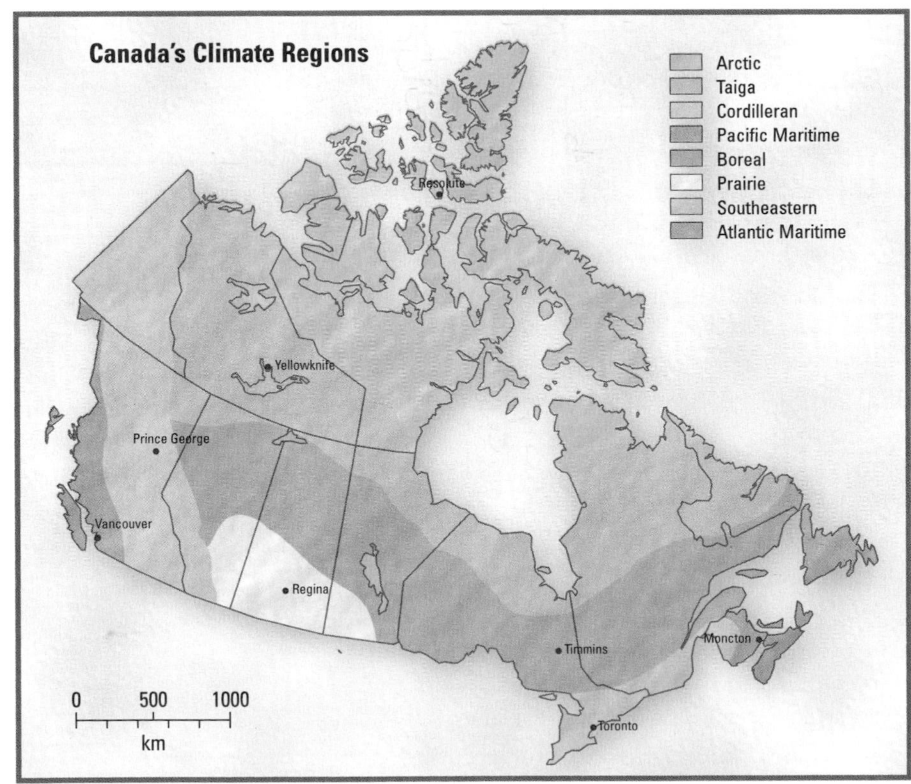

GeoLit Reminder

When reading a map:

- Examine the title, caption, legend, and labels.
- Scan the map for patterns and trends.
- What general information does the map provide?

Construct a chart similar to Fig. 13-13 to compare the climate characteristics of the eight **climate stations** in Fig. 13-15. A climate station is any place where climate information is gathered.

a) Complete columns 1 to 5 using the information on interpreting climate graphs in Fig. 13-14, and the information in the sample climate graphs in Fig. 13-15.

b) In the location column, write the name of the climate station and the climate region beside each letter.

Location	1 Average Temperature	2 Temperature Range	3 Total Precipitation	4 Season of Maximum Precipitation	5 Continental or Maritime
A					
B					
C					
D					
E					
F					
G					
H					

▲ Fig. 13-13

Factor	How Determined	Significance
Average annual temperature	• Add together the 12 average monthly temperatures and divide by 12.	• Indicates whether a location has a warm climate (Toronto), or a cool climate (Yellowknife).
Temperature range	• Maximum temperature (warmest) – minimum temperature (coldest) indicates whether a place has a continental climate (large range) or a maritime climate (small range). large (> 25C°) = CONTINENTAL small (< 25C°) = MARITIME	• Places that do not have a minimum temperature below 0°C will be on the west coast.
Total precipitation	• Add monthly precipitation totals. < 1000 mm = CONTINENTAL > 1000 mm = MARITIME	• Indicates whether a place has a dry or wet climate.
Seasonal distribution of precipitation	• "WINTER" add precipitation totals for Oct., Nov., Dec., Jan., Feb., Mar. Winter max. = MARITIME (large difference between winter and summer = west coast) (slight difference between winter and summer = east coast) • "SUMMER" add precipitation totals for Apr., May, Jun., Jul., Aug., Sep. Summer max. = CONTINENTAL	• Indicates the climate influences at work and therefore different climate types.

▲ **Fig. 13-14** This general guideline will help you to interpret climate graphs of places in Canada.

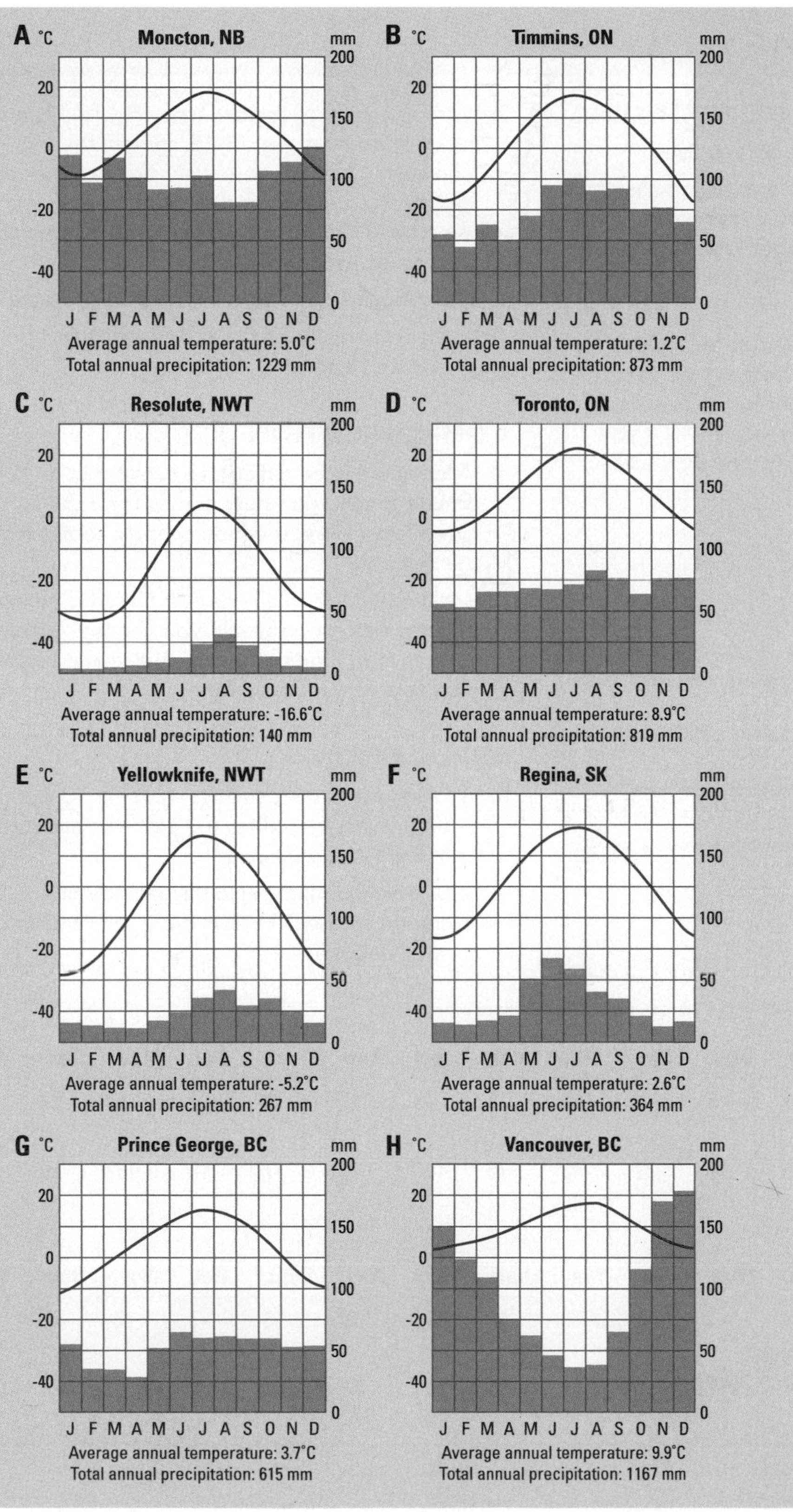

◀ **Fig. 13-15** This figure presents a sample climate graph for a location in each climate region.

QUESTIONS

KNOWLEDGE AND UNDERSTANDING

1. a) In which climate region do you live?
   b) Describe the climate of this region based on your own experience of it. Remember to talk about climate, not weather. Use descriptive words such as "winters are not very cold, but it rains a lot."
   c) Look at the climate statistics for a place in your region. Try to see how your climate experiences are reflected in the numerical data. Why does this only work well if you described your climate, rather than your weather?

GeoLit Reminder

When organizing informational text:

- Re-read any part of the text that you do not understand.
- Use the text glossary or a dictionary for new words and terms.
- Record information in point form using subheadings or an organizer chart.
- Use maps, photographs, and diagrams for additional information.
- Refer back to your organized information when answering text questions.

2. Using the climate regions map (Fig. 13-12) and information from Fig. 13-15, answer the following questions. You might find it easier to identify the similarities and differences if you use a table like Fig. 13-13. What similarities and differences exist between
   a) the Boreal and the Prairie climate regions?
   b) the Atlantic Maritime and Southeastern climate regions?

COMMUNICATION

3. Why would it be difficult to prove that a climate graph you know comes from the Cordilleran climate region actually comes from this region?
4. If you could live in any one of Canada's climate regions, which one would you choose? Explain your choice. Compare your choice and reasons with two other classmates.

APPLICATION

5. a) Using the same headings as in Fig. 13-13, determine the values for each climate station in Fig. 13-16.
   b) In which climate region is each climate station located? Explain how you reached your decision.

▼ **Fig. 13-16** In what region(s) would these climate locations be found?

STATION A	Jan.	Feb.	Mar.	Apr.	May	June	July	Aug.	Sept.	Oct.	Nov.	Dec.	Year
Average monthly temperature (°C)	-14	-11	-5	4	10	14	16	15	10	4	-6	-12	2.1
Average monthly precipitation (mm)	23	15	16	22	43	76	101	70	47	18	16	19	466

STATION B	Jan.	Feb.	Mar.	Apr.	May	June	July	Aug.	Sept.	Oct.	Nov.	Dec.	Year
Average monthly temperature (°C)	-9	-8	-3	3	9	15	19	18	13	7	2	-6	5.0
Average monthly precipitation (mm)	120	96	117	101	91	93	103	81	81	106	114	126	1229

14 Canada's Soil and Natural Vegetation Connections

Key Ideas

This chapter helps you investigate these questions:

- What are the soil and vegetation regions of Canada?
- How are soil and vegetation related?
- Why are soil and natural vegetation of great importance to Canadians?
- Why should we try to preserve fertile soils?
- What products do we obtain from the different types of vegetation in Canada?

Key Terms

soil
humus
soil profile
leaching
calcification
capillary action
tundra
transition zones
permafrost
boreal and taiga forest
coniferous trees
deciduous trees
mixed forest
short-grass prairie
long-grass prairie
parkland

Getting the "Dirt" on Soil

We tend to use the word *soil* very carelessly when it does, in fact, have a precise meaning. A true **soil** consists of four main parts: minerals, bacteria and organic materials; air; and moisture. Technically speaking, if one of these parts is missing, the material should not be considered soil.

1. **Minerals**

The minerals in soil come from a **parent material**. The parent material is usually rock, but it can also be loose materials that have been deposited by a glacier, the wind, or a river. The minerals become part of the soil when the rock is broken down by **weathering** into smaller particles of sand, silt, and clay. Many of these minerals, such as calcium, phosphorous, and potassium, are **nutrients** that plants need for growth.

2. **Bacteria and Organic Materials**

When plants and animals die, they are decomposed by bacteria in the soil. As bacteria break down the organic material, nutrients are released into the soil. As the organic material is broken down by bacteria, it forms **humus**, which provides nutrients and moisture for plants. Humus gives the soil its dark colour.

The process of decay is nature's way of recycling nutrients.

About half the volume of a high-quality soil is composed of water and air.

3. **Air**

Plants need air around their roots. A high humus level helps produce air in the soil because the loose, decaying materials allow for many air pockets. Air pockets are also created by worms, insects, and small animals that tunnel through the soil.

4. **Moisture**

Water dissolves nutrients in the soil and is then taken up by plants through their roots. Water is also necessary in the chemical and physical processes that weather rock and decay organic materials.

Issue

DO WE TREAT OUR SOIL LIKE DIRT?

◀ **Fig. 14-1** Ontario's 67 000 farms produce more than a quarter of Canada's total farm products.

Background

When was the last time you thought about protecting our soil? If you live in an urban area, like most Canadians, chances are you never think about this, but you should. Soil is very important to how we live—in fact, without fertile soils we would have nothing to eat. If you live on a farm, chances are very good that your family talks about the need to protect and improve your farm's soil.

Activities

1. In pairs or small groups, brainstorm possible answers to the following questions. Compile a list of your answers.
   a) What roles does soil play in nature and for people?
   b) What threats does it face?
2. Check your knowledge of why soil matters by reviewing the Web links at www.pearson.ca/makingconnections2. Each group member should select a different Web site to review. In your groups, share any new information you found about the roles soil plays and the threats it faces, and add these to the list you compiled in Question 1.

Soil Formation

A typical **soil profile** is shown in Fig. 14-2. New mineral materials are added at the bottom of the soil by the weathering of the parent material. At the same time, organic materials are added at the top. This top layer of soil containing humus is called **topsoil**. Topsoil formation is a very slow process. Since the end of the last ice age, 6000 to 12 000 years ago, only 15 to 25 centimetres of topsoil have formed under the forests of Canada. In contrast, between 40 and 100 centimetres of topsoil have developed under the grasslands of the prairies.

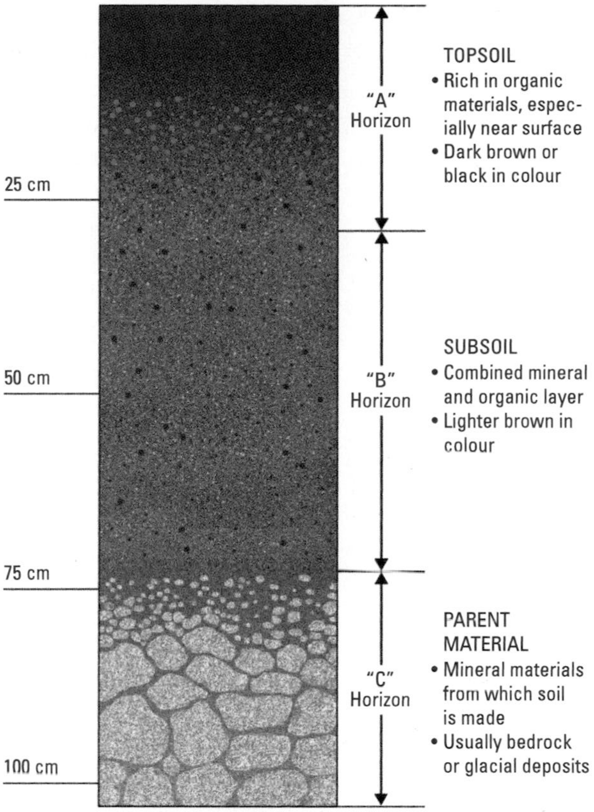

25 cm
50 cm
75 cm
100 cm
"A" Horizon
"B" Horizon
"C" Horizon
TOPSOIL
• Rich in organic materials, especially near surface
• Dark brown or black in colour
SUBSOIL
• Combined mineral and organic layer
• Lighter brown in colour
PARENT MATERIAL
• Mineral materials from which soil is made
• Usually bedrock or glacial deposits

Fig. 14-2 ▶ A typical soil profile

▼ **Fig. 14-3** A typical wet-climate soil profile. In these areas, the downward movement of water means that leaching is the dominant process.

25 cm
Downward movement of water
50 cm
75 cm
100 cm
"A" Horizon
"B" Horizon
"C" Horizon
• Thin "A" horizon
• Soluble organic materials are rapidly washed downward by excess rainfall
• "B" horizon tends to be light brown to greyish in colour
• Most water-soluble minerals are gone
• Only iron and aluminum compounds are left

25 cm
Upward movement of water
50 cm
75 cm
100 cm
"A" Horizon
"B" Horizon
"C" Horizon
• Very thick, dark brown to black "A" horizon
• Dry conditions cause water to move upward through soil profile and evaporate from surface
• Organic materials from decay of plants remain near the surface

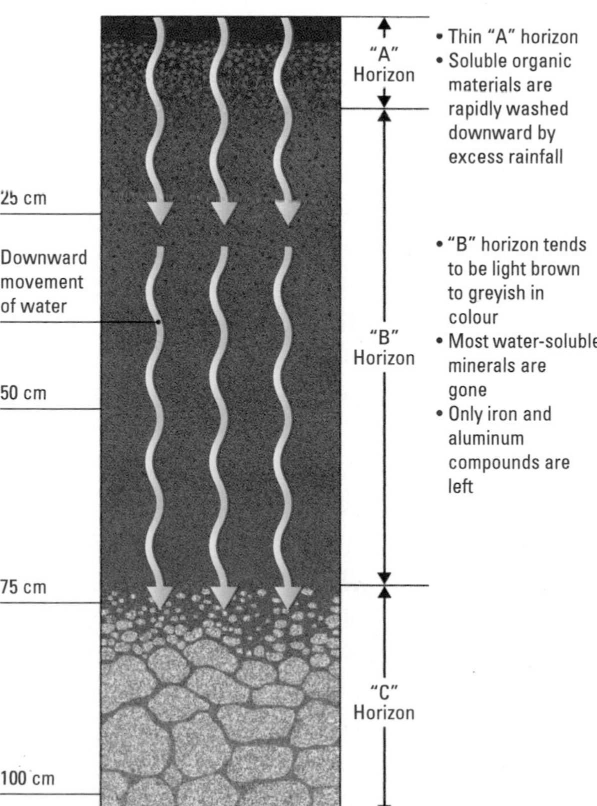

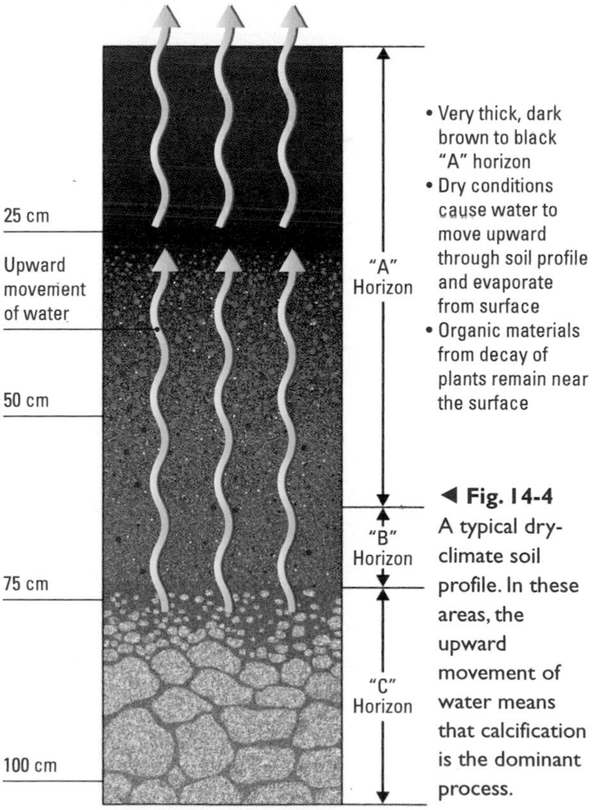

◀ **Fig. 14-4** A typical dry-climate soil profile. In these areas, the upward movement of water means that calcification is the dominant process.

The size of rock particles is an important part of soil structure. The larger particles of sand allow rainwater to drain quickly through the soil, while the smaller particles of more absorbent clay prevent rapid drainage.

A well-balanced mixture of sand, silt, clay, and humus is called **loam.** It is the best soil for growing plants because it encourages root growth and holds moisture, and allows water to pass through it at a rate moderate enough to allow plants to take up nutrients.

Two other processes, which are related to climate, contribute to soil formation. The first is called **leaching**. In areas where there is a great deal of precipitation, there is a continual downward movement of water through the soil (Fig. 14-3). As the water moves down, it dissolves the chemical nutrients in the soil and carries them away. This downward movement of water removes nutrients that plants need. In very wet climates, leaching can take water-soluble minerals so deep that plant roots cannot reach them. You can identify a leached soil by its poor, often thin, topsoil layer. Examine Fig. 14-5 to see how much of Canada is covered with wet-climate soils that are prone to leaching. Leached soils can be much more productive for farming if natural or chemical fertilizers are used to replace leached nutrients.

INTERNET

You can learn more about Canada's soils through the link at www.pearsoned.ca/makingconnections2.

The second process, known as **calcification**, occurs in areas with drier climates (Fig. 14-4). Here, instead of downward movement of water, there is upward movement. As water in the topsoil evaporates, water from below is drawn up to replace it. This process is called **capillary action**. As the water evaporates, it leaves behind the minerals that were dissolved in it. The result is the creation of a thick topsoil layer that is rich in minerals. This process is called calcification because calcium is the main mineral deposited near the surface. In very dry climates, however, the amount of mineral deposition can be so great that it forms a layer poisonous to plants. Dry-climate soils where calcification is common are shown in Fig. 14-5.

This upward capillary action of water can also be observed if you dip the edge of a paper towel into a bowl of water.

Fig. 14-5 shows two other soil regions: complex soils of mountain areas and tundra soils. Because of the Western Cordillera's varied relief and climate patterns, a complex pattern of soils exists, and the characteristics of the soil can change completely over very short distances. In contrast, the harsh climate of the tundra soils region makes soil formation difficult. The short, cool growing season limits plant growth and slows the breakdown of organic materials into humus. Because of the permafrost, the soil drains poorly and is often waterlogged. As a result, air may be missing from the soil's profile.

In the Western Cordillera, you may find highly leached soils and calcified soils—and even bare rock—located within a few kilometres of one another.

Natural Vegetation Regions

Plants must have moisture and heat for their survival. The relative amount of each determines which plants will grow. For example, a warm, moist climate may support a forest of large trees; a warm, dry climate may support only short grasses. Areas with distinct types of natural vegetation are classified as different natural vegetation regions (Fig. 14-6).

Natural vegetation refers to those plants that grow without any human interference. Natural vegetation is usually quite different from plants that

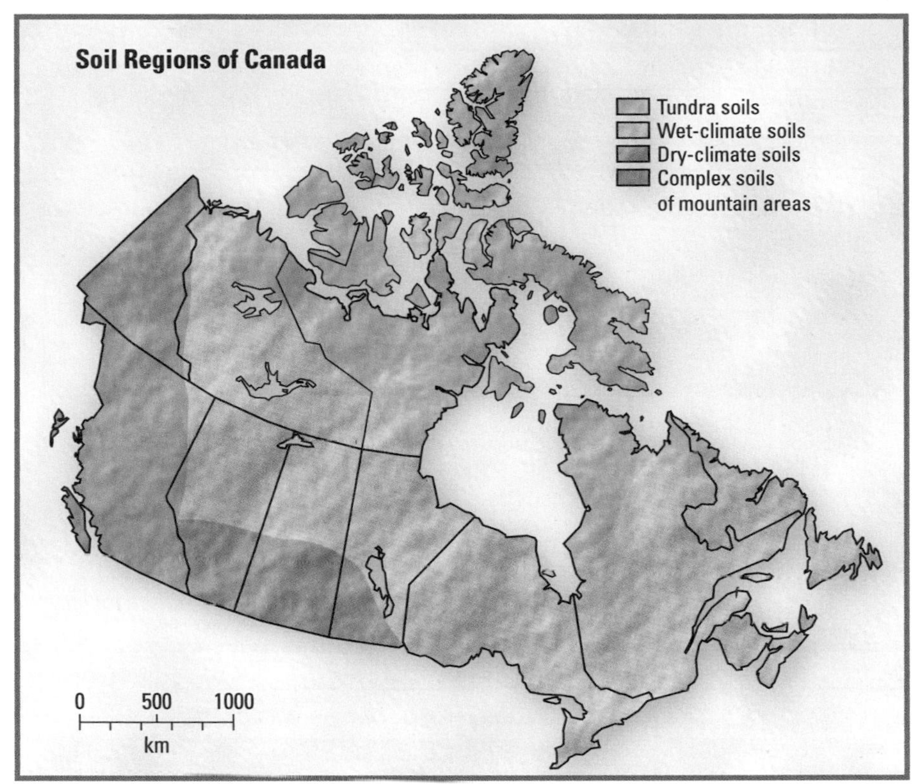

◀ **Fig. 14-5** Soil Regions of Canada

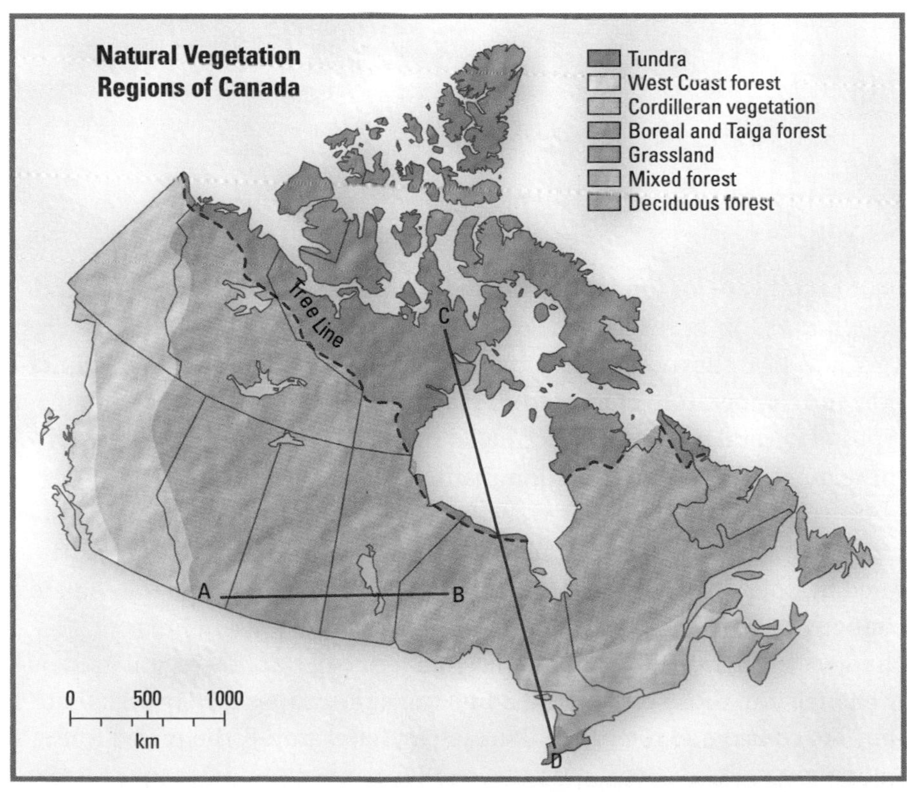

◀ **Fig. 14-6** Natural Vegetation Regions of Canada. The A–B and C–D transects are shown in Fig. 14-7 and Fig. 14-8.

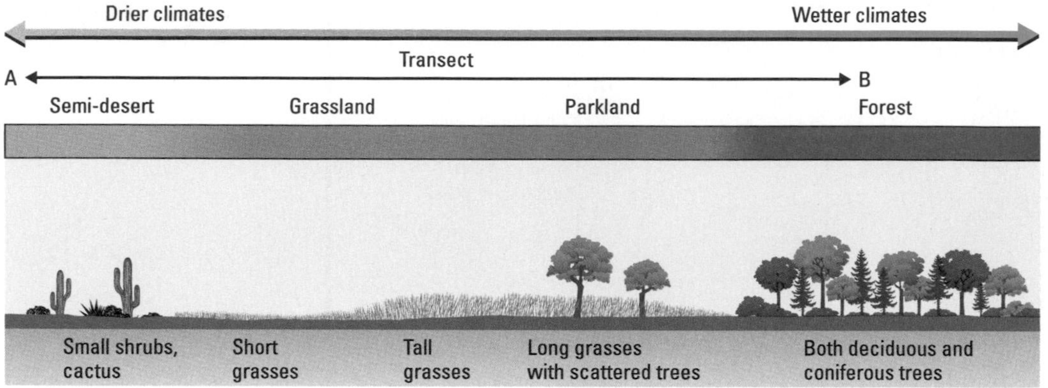

▲ **Fig. 14-7** Vegetation changes as precipitation levels change. The A–B transect refers to Fig. 14-6.

▼ **Fig. 14-8** Vegetation changes as average temperatures change. The C–D transect refers to Fig. 14-6.

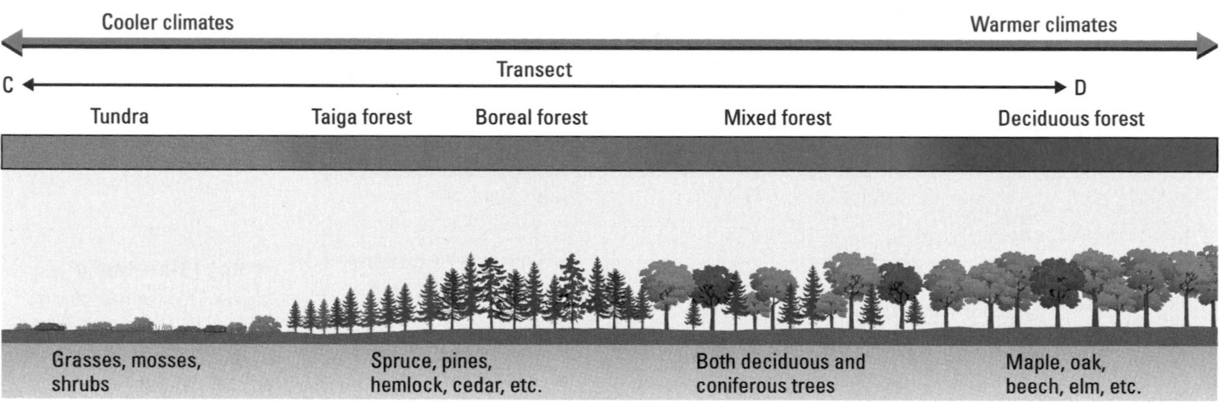

people cultivate for food or for use in industry. Different types of natural vegetation grow in response to different climatic and soil conditions. Figs. 14-7 and 14-8 show the types of natural vegetation that grow as precipitation and temperature change from place to place. There are three main types of natural vegetation in Canada: **tundra**, forest, and grassland. Of these, forest vegetation is predominant.

Geographers have identified seven natural vegetation regions across Canada. Notice that the natural vegetation regions in Fig. 14-6 are separated by lines. It is a mistake to think that these lines show an immediate change from one region to another. Instead, they represent areas of change called **transition zones**. The characteristics of one region gradually change into those of the next. Some transition zones are so large that they are considered regions in themselves, for example, the mixed forest vegetation region.

◀ **Fig. 14-9** Tundra vegetation: plants remain small to obtain warmth from the ground, and protection from cold, harsh winds.

Tundra

The tundra is the most northerly vegetation region of Canada (Fig. 14-9). It is located above the **tree line**, which marks the northern boundary of most tree growth. Only a few **stunted** trees grow in the tundra because the climate is too cold and dry. Most of the tundra has **permafrost**, or permanently frozen ground. Only the top metre or so of permafrost, known as the **active layer**, thaws during the short summer. Since water cannot drain downward, the surface remains waterlogged. This thawing permits a very short growing season. Small shrubs, mosses, and lichens grow close to the ground, where they soak up as much heat as possible from the surface. Lichens are slow-growing plants that cling to rocks. Since tundra plants bloom and mature very quickly, they are able to produce their seeds before the cold weather returns. There is very little humus in the tundra's thin layer of soil because of the small amount of vegetation, the water-logged nature of the soil, and the cold climate. The lack of vegetation limits the variety of wildlife as well as the population of each species.

stunted
smaller than normal size

Some stunted trees are able to grow, however, in sheltered valleys in the southern part of this region.

Forest

BOREAL AND TAIGA FOREST

To the south of the tundra is the **boreal and taiga forest**, the largest vegetation region in Canada (Fig. 14-10). It is separated from the tundra by the tree line. **Coniferous trees** grow south of this tree line because there is a longer growing season and more precipitation than in the tundra. Coniferous trees, or evergreens, lose some needles throughout the year, but are never bare. Since they don't drop many needles, and because leaching occurs, the humus layer beneath them is very shallow. This gives the topsoil a grey colour. Since the needles are acidic, they make the soil acidic. The lack of humus, combined with the high acidity and the

Coniferous trees are also known as needle-leaved trees. The tamarack is an exception. It is a coniferous tree but it is not an evergreen. It drops its needles in the fall.

Fig. 14-10 ▶ Boreal and taiga forest: coniferous trees have the following characteristics that allow them to thrive in harsh, northern conditions.

a) They are able to extract nutrients from the poor soil with their long roots.
b) Their sticky sap acts as an anti-freeze that prevents the needles from freezing.
c) Their waxy needles and thick bark prevent the loss of moisture in times of drought.
d) Their needles and flexible branches easily shed snow to prevent damage.
e) Their needles are able to conduct photosynthesis on warm days beyond the normal growing season.

The cool temperatures and the lack of soil organisms, such as bacteria and earthworms, also slow down the process of humus formation.

leaching effect of water, makes these wet-climate soils infertile and unsuitable for agriculture. The northern part of the region is the taiga forest and the southern part is the boreal forest. The taiga forest tends to be less dense than the boreal forest, and has smaller trees that take much longer to grow. The difference between these two areas reflects the colder and drier climate that exists in the northern part of the region.

Coniferous trees have characteristics that make them well-suited to cold temperatures and short growing seasons (Fig. 14-11a). Trees such as white and black spruce, balsam fir, and pine grow sparsely along the northern edge of the boreal and taiga forest, but more densely farther south. They are harvested by pulp and paper and lumbering companies. Some **deciduous trees,** such as poplar and white birch, are hardy enough to withstand the harsh winter conditions in the southern portion of the boreal forest (Fig. 14-11b).

Deciduous trees are also known as broadleaf trees.

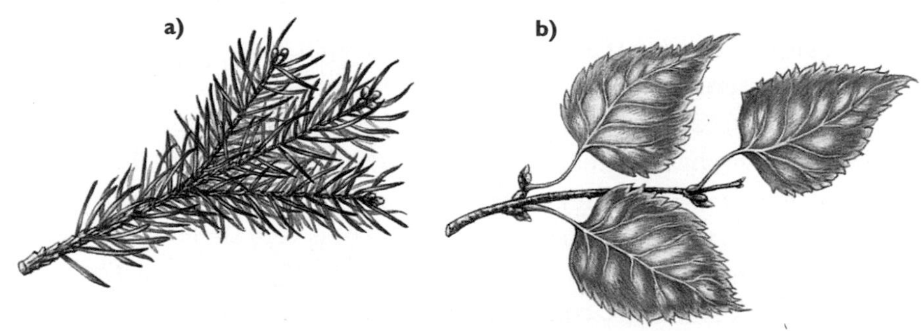

Fig. 14-11 ▶ Typical leaves of coniferous and deciduous trees

MIXED FOREST

South of the boreal and taiga forest in eastern Canada is a **mixed forest** of deciduous and coniferous trees (Fig. 14-12). Maple, beech, ash, oak, and birch are found in the same forest with spruce, fir, pine, cedar, and hemlock. This variety of trees provided an excellent resource for the lumbering industry. Today, little of the forest remains in the southern part of the region because of farming, lumbering, urban development, and transportation routes. Along the exposed coastlines of the Maritime provinces, where the cold winds create a harsher climate, the forest may give way to small shrubs, such as junipers, that grow close to the ground for protection.

The mixed forest is a transition zone between the boreal and taiga forest to the north and the deciduous forest to the south. Both deciduous and coniferous trees can survive in the warm summers and cool winters. The regular, abundant precipitation in this region is suitable for both deciduous and coniferous trees. The humus created from the leaves of such a wide variety of trees creates deep grey-brown topsoil rich in minerals. Because humus holds water, leaching is less of a problem in the mixed forest than in the boreal and taiga forest. Soils in mixed forest regions are well-suited to farming.

▲ **Fig. 14-12** Mixed forest

When settlers first came to the mixed forest region, it was covered in trees. In order to build roads and farms, the forests had to be cleared. This process was so difficult that the forest was often seen as an enemy that had to be defeated.

DECIDUOUS FOREST

The deciduous forest region in Canada is very small. It is found in southwestern Ontario (Fig. 14-13) and is the northernmost portion of the large deciduous-forest regions of the northeastern United States. Only small remnants of Canada's deciduous forest remain, since most of it has been cleared for farming and urban development.

◄ **Fig. 14-13** Deciduous forest: deciduous trees have the following characteristics.

a) They lose their leaves in the autumn. If they kept their leaves over the winter, the weight of the snow on them might break their branches.
b) They are dormant in winter, but with the warmth of spring, sap flows to the buds and causes new leaves to grow.
c) Most deciduous trees need at least five months with average temperatures above 10°C.

hardwood trees broadleaf deciduous trees that have tough, dense wood, often used for making furniture

The summers in southwestern Ontario are long and hot, the winters relatively mild, and the precipitation plentiful. These conditions are ideal for **hardwood trees** such as maple, beech, hickory, ash, and black walnut. These trees need at least five months of warm weather to store up energy in the form of sap in their roots and trunk to survive the winter.

The soils of the deciduous forest are similar to those of the mixed forest but contain more humus and are less acidic because of the greater number of deciduous trees. The humus-rich topsoil is dark brown in colour. Some of the soluble nutrients are leached from the topsoil by the abundant rain. Still, they are the most fertile soils of eastern Canada.

GRASSLANDS

When new immigrants first settled on the grasslands, they often made their homes out of sod since few trees were available to make log cabins.

The grasslands, or the prairies, are located in the southern part of Manitoba, Saskatchewan, and Alberta. The climate here is too dry for most species of trees to survive. Some, such as trembling aspen, willow, and spruce, grow in the most eastern part of the region and in river valleys, where more moisture is available. Native grasses, however, are suited to this dry climate. The deep, intertwined root system of the grass forms a **sod mat**. This sod mat absorbs and stores moisture, and holds the soil in place. The grass dies off on the surface if it doesn't find enough water, but its roots remain alive. When moisture becomes available, the grass sprouts again.

drought-resistant able to live with limited amounts of rainfall

The grasslands consist of three sub-regions. The driest areas of southern Saskatchewan and Alberta make up the **short-grass prairie** (Fig. 14-14). **Drought-resistant** short grasses, sagebrush, and cactus are the only types of vegetation that can survive here. The warm, dry climate limits the growth of vegetation, which in turn limits the amount of humus produced in the soil. The limited rainfall and high evaporation have created calcified brown soils. Without irrigation, such areas are unsuitable for most crops. The land can be used for grazing animals.

▲ **Fig. 14-14** Short-grass prairie vegetation is found in warm, very dry locations.

▲ **Fig. 14-15** Long-grass prairie vegetation is found in warm, dry locations.

▲ **Fig. 14-16** Cordilleran vegetation: from lush forests to barren tundra vegetation

▲ **Fig. 14-17** West Coast forest: a temperate rain forest with the largest trees in Canada

Surrounding the short-grass prairie is a region where increased precipitation encourages the growth of taller grasses (Fig. 14-15). This **long-grass prairie** is ideal for growing grains and **oil seeds**. Year after year as the tall grasses die in the fall, they produce large amounts of humus that result in a rich, black soil. The rainfall is just enough to keep the minerals within easy reach of the grass roots. This is the richest soil in Canada and some of the most productive grain-growing land in the world. Between the warm, dry grasslands and the cooler, wetter boreal forest is the third grassland sub-region, called **parkland**. This is a transition zone of long-grass prairie dotted with clumps of trees.

GeoLit Reminder

When reading visual text:

- Determine the type of visual text.
- Identify elements that stand out,
- How does this image make you feel?
- What is the purpose of this image?
- What additional information do you need to understand this image?

CORDILLERAN VEGETATION

The natural vegetation of the Western Cordillera varies greatly (Fig. 14-16). The variation of vegetation is a result of the wide range of temperatures, rainfall, soils, and elevations throughout the region. Soils of all types are found throughout the Western Cordillera, and account for the variety of natural vegetation in the region, ranging from large coniferous forests in wetter locations to grasses and even cacti in drier areas.

WEST COAST FOREST

Along the west coast of Canada grow lush forests of Douglas fir, Sitka spruce, red cedar, and western hemlock. The heavy rainfall plus the mild climate of the coastal region provide excellent growing conditions for the trees of this **temperate rain forest** (Fig. 14-17). Trees more than a metre in diameter and over 50 metres high are common. These huge trees have played a crucial role in British Columbia's forest industry. Some of the **old-growth forests** have become the focus of environmental groups that wish to protect them. The lush vegetation provides a lot of plant material to make humus, but the high rainfall leaches minerals deep into the soil.

temperate
climate with a range of moderate temperatures, e.g., warm summers and cool winters

rain forest
lush forest in an area with very heavy precipitation

old-growth forest
area of mature forest that has never been cut down

In Closing...

The different vegetation regions in Canada provide us with many products. The coniferous trees of the boreal and taiga forest are the raw materials for pulp, paper, and lumber. Deciduous trees provide wood for eastern Canada's furniture industry. The huge trees of the west coast forest provide lumber for use in Canada and for export. Beef for your next barbecue may come from cattle raised on the short grasses of the western prairies and may be cooked using charcoal from the hardwood trees of eastern Canada.

QUESTIONS

KNOWLEDGE AND UNDERSTANDING

1. Describe the four components that make up a true soil.
2. a) How is topsoil formed?
   b) How long has it taken to form topsoil in Canada?
   c) Why does the topsoil differ in thickness in different parts of Canada?
3. Why is the size of rock particles important to soil structure?
4. Explain the difference between leaching and calcification.
5. In your own words, explain the meaning of the term *natural vegetation*.
6. There are two classes of trees. Which one can survive a harsher climate? Why?
7. Name the Canadian vegetation region that is the
   a) largest
   b) smallest
   c) wettest
   d) coldest
   e) northernmost
   f) southernmost
   g) westernmost
   h) easternmost
8. Explain, in your own words, the term *transition zone*. Give an example of a transition zone so large that it is also considered a vegetation region. Explain why this vegetation region is a transition zone.

THINKING

9. In the Western Cordillera, how is it possible to have leached soils within a few kilometres of calcified soils?
10. Fig. 14-18 shows the relationship between precipitation and soil fertility in temperate latitudes. Copy the graph into your notebook, and mark the following on it:
    a) a brown prairie soil
    b) a lightly leached soil
    c) a black prairie soil
    d) a heavily leached soil
    e) the boundary between wet-climate and dry-climate soils

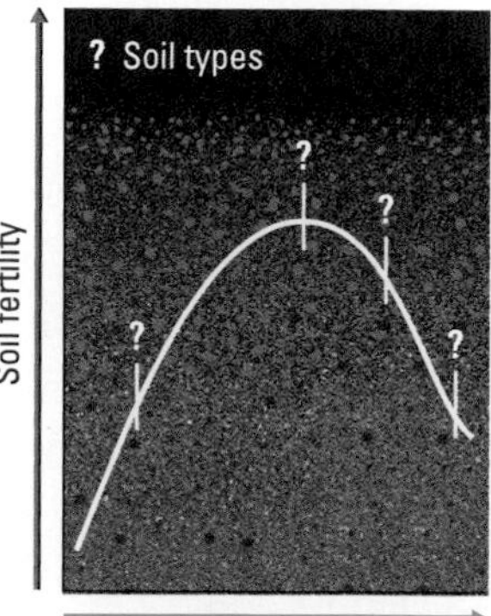

Fig. 14-18 ▶

COMMUNICATION

11. "Natural vegetation is usually quite different from plants that people cultivate for food or for use in industry." Explain the differences.
12. "If you climb up a mountain, you will find a similar sequence of vegetation to that you would find if you travelled from southern Canada to the High Arctic." Explain why this is a valid statement.

APPLICATION

13. Copy Fig. 14-19 into your notebook. Complete the chart using the information in this chapter.
14. a) Using Figs. 14-6 and 13-12, page 154, match each vegetation region to the correspon-ding climate region.
    b) The mixed forest and the deciduous forest regions are found in the same climate region. Explain how two vegetation regions can both occur in the same climate region.

▼ **Fig. 14-19**

Vegetation Region	Types of Natural Vegetation	Temperature Characteristics	Precipitation Characteristics	Soil Characteristics
Tundra	shrubs, mosses, lichens, small flowers	cold, short growing season	very little precipitation, most areas less than 400 mm	thin soils, permafrost
Boreal and Taiga Forest				
Mixed Forest				
Deciduous Forest				
Grassland — short grass — long grass — parkland				
Cordilleran Vegetation				
West Coast Forest				

15 Making the Connections: Canada's Ecozones

Key Ideas

This chapter helps you investigate these questions:

- What is an ecozone, and is the ecozone concept useful?
- In what ways do Canadian ecozones differ from one another, and in what ways are they similar?

Key Terms

ecozone

gross domestic product

Examine Fig. 15-1. Each photograph shows a different part of Canada. The location of each photo is noted on the map. A quick look at these pictures tells you that Canada is made up of different kinds of terrain that offer special opportunities and challenges to the people who live in them. In previous chapters, you learned about Canada's landforms, climate, soil, geological history, water, and natural vegetation regions. In this chapter, you will see how all these things, together with the activities of people and animals, interact to form new kinds of regions called **ecozones** (short for ecological zones).

Ecology is the study of living things and how they relate to each other and the environment.

An area can be defined as a distinct ecological zone based on the way its landform, climate, soil, geological history, water features, vegetation, wildlife, and human activities are linked together. All these factors are connected in such a way that a change in just one factor will result in change and adjustment in the rest of them. For example, a shift in temperature within an ecozone will affect its plant growth, which in turn will affect the food supply of its animals. Here is another example: an increase in the human population within an ecozone leads to the loss of farmland or forest because people need land for urban uses.

INTERNET

You can learn more about ecozones through the link at www.pearsoned.ca/makingconnections2.

Comparing Regions

The photos in Fig. 15-1 represent five of Canada's **terrestrial** ecozones. This exercise will help you understand how Canada's ecozones were determined.

terrestrial
having to do with Earth or the land

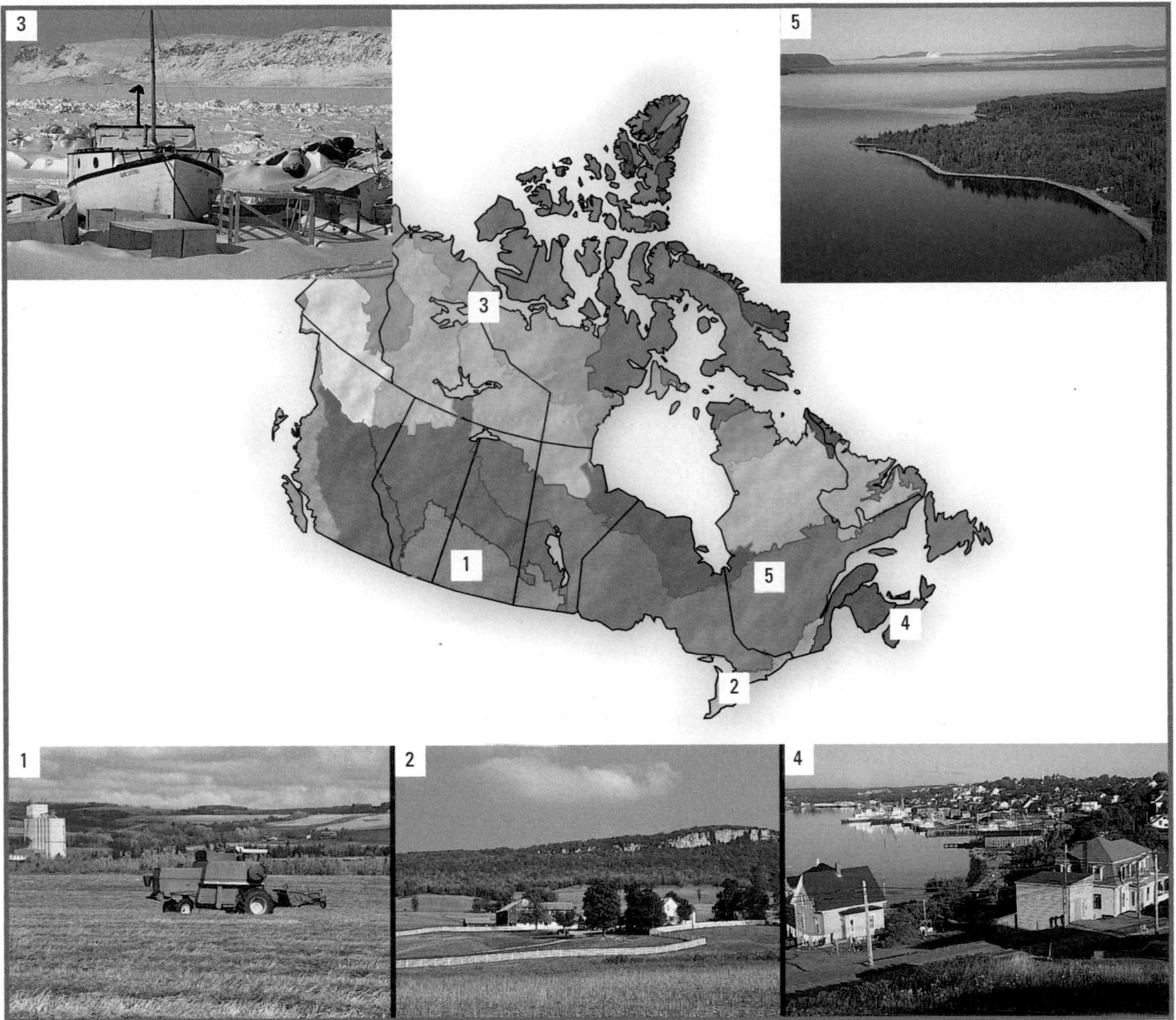

▲ **Fig. 15-1** There are enormous differences among the landscapes of Canada. In this chapter, you will use the idea of ecozones to organize what we know about Canada's land and how people use it.

For each photo, complete the following steps. Begin by copying the graphic organizer from Fig. 15-2 into your notebook, and use it to record your answers.

1. Study the map and photos in Fig. 15-1. Make a mental note of the location of each landscape in relation to major bodies of water and provincial and national borders.
2. Using Fig. 12-5 on page 130, determine the landform region in which each photo was taken.
3. Repeat this process for the climate region (Fig. 13-12 on p. 154), soil region (Fig. 14-5 on p. 163), and natural vegetation region (Fig. 14-6 on p. 163) in which each photo was taken.

GeoLit Reminder

When reading visual texts:

- What types of visual texts are shown?
- Examine the title, legend, and caption.
- What is the general purpose of these visuals?
- How do the visuals compare?
- What do I already know about the topic illustrated by the visual texts?
- What additional information do I need to gather about these visuals?

4. List any human activity you see in each photo.
5. Record any other human activity you think might be common in the region shown in each photo.
6. How do you know that each photo represents a different region?

▼ **Fig. 15-2**

Photo	Landform Region	Climate Region	Vegetation Region	Soil Region	Activities Shown*	Other Activities**
1						
2						
3						
4						
5						

* Human activities shown in the photograph

** Other human activities not shown in the photograph, but that you know occur in this ecozone

The term *bioregion* is often used instead of *ecozone* in other parts of the world, and especially in the United States.

By examining your completed table, you will see that each of these photos represents a region that is distinct as a result of a unique combination of environmental and human factors. Each distinct region is one of Canada's ecozones.

Canada's Ecozones

In addition to Canada's 15 terrestrial (land) ecozones, there are 5 marine ecozones that cover the oceans surrounding the country.

compromise solution that balances opposing sides or demands

Canada has an almost infinite number of different natural environments. Geographers faced the problem of grouping these natural environments together to create a manageable number of ecozones. If too few zones were created, any given zone would have too many different environments within it. If too many ecozones were created, it would be difficult to keep track of them and their characteristics. Fifteen terrestrial ecozones for Canada were selected as a reasonable **compromise** (Fig. 15-3).

Ecozones may differ in some of their characteristics, but they may be similar in others. For example, let's compare the Boreal Shield ecozone and the Mixedwood Plains ecozone (Fig. 15-4). We can see significant differences in landform, climate, and human activities. In regard to their soils, however, there is no difference.

Ecoregions, ecoprovinces, and ecodistricts are even smaller areas that can be used to examine Canada in more detail.

When geographers began to establish Canada's ecozones, they considered many factors in order to determine the boundaries between ecozones. In certain cases, some factors were more important than others in determining these boundaries. For example, in the Northern and Southern Arctic ecozones, climate was an important factor in determining where the boundaries would be drawn. The climate is noticeably colder in

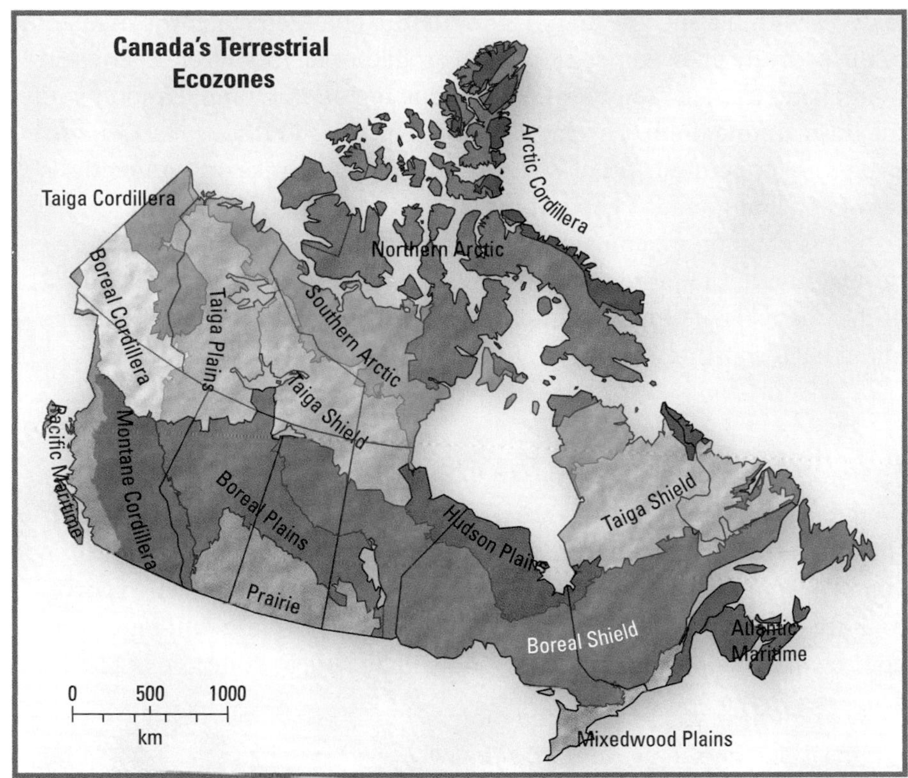

◀ **Fig. 15-3** Canada's terrestrial ecozones

Factor	Boreal Shield	Mixedwood Plains
Landforms	Canadian Shield	Great Lakes Lowlands
Climate	Boreal region	Southeastern region
Vegetation	Evergreen and mixed forest	Deciduous and mixed forest
Soils	Wet climate, leached soils	Wet climate, leached soils
Wildlife (examples only)	Moose, black bear, lynx, boreal owl, woodland caribou	Raccoon, skunk, great blue heron, grey squirrel
Human activities	Forestry, mining, trapping	Agriculture, urbanization

▲ **Fig. 15-4** The Mixedwood Plains and Boreal Shield ecozones are next to each other, yet are very different in many ways.

the area that became the Northern Arctic ecozone and clearly distinguished one ecozone from the other. Human activities, on the other hand, were not an important factor in distinguishing one ecozone from the other because they are similar in both regions.

Why Ecozones Are a Useful Idea

The first map of Canadian ecozones was published in 1986. Before then, people had a tendency to keep environmental and human information about any one particular area separate. They did not usually examine the relationships that existed between the physical, biological, and human features within a specific area. This situation changed when the concept of the ecozone allowed people to bring together all the different environmental and human factors in each unique region in Canada, and to study the links among them. This book is called *Making Connections: Canada's Geography* to remind you of the importance of the links or "connections" between all of Canada's geographic characteristics.

In this chapter, we concentrate primarily on the physical characteristics of Canada's 15 terrestrial ecozones. Later in the book, we will look at human aspects of Canadian life and geography to add to our knowledge about each ecozone.

A Tour of Canada's Terrestrial Ecozones

Canada's terrestrial ecozones are described in the following section. You should start your tour of Canada's ecozones with the one in which you live. Then, gradually move outward from your neighbouring ecozones to more distant ones. The more distant ones may be very different from your own. By using this approach, you will be able to compare other ecozones to the one you know best.

A NOTE ABOUT THE DATA IN THE ECOZONE CHARTS

In the charts that follow, "growing season" is the average number of days per year when the average temperature is more than 5°C. Total population statistics for each ecozone are from 2001 unless otherwise indicated. GDP, which stands for **gross domestic product** and represents the value of all economic production in the ecozone, is given in 1991 figures. Unfortunately, while the ecozone concept has proven useful in understanding Canadian geography, it has not "caught on" with agencies, such as Statistics Canada, that are responsible for collecting and publishing numerical data. However, while GDP for each ecozone has changed since the 1991 data was recorded, the relationship between the ecozones with regard to GDP has not changed very much. In other words, the Atlantic Maritime ecozone still has a GDP greater than the Taiga Cordillera or Boreal Cordillera ecozone, but less than the Boreal Shield or Mixedwood Plains ecozones.

Mixedwood Plains Ecozone:
(Area 107 017 km^2)

Landforms: Plains and rolling hills; Great Lakes are an important feature

Climate: Cool, short winters (-7°C); relatively long, mild summers (20°C); precipitation 700 to 1000 mm; growing season 180 to 260 days

Vegetation: Coniferous (white pine, eastern hemlock, red pine) mixed with deciduous (sugar maple, red oak, basswood); little natural vegetation remains

Soils: Leached, wet-climate soils

Human Activities: Total population 15 631 830; GDP $325.2 billion; urbanization, manufacturing, agriculture, recreation

Major Urban Areas: Toronto (2004: 5 203 600), Montreal, Ottawa, Quebec, Hamilton, Windsor, London

Atlantic Maritime Ecozone:
(Area 192 017 km^2)

Landforms: Hills and coastal plains

Climate: Long, mild winters (-4°C); moderately warm summers (17°C); precipitation 1000 to 1400 mm; growing season 180 to 210 days

Vegetation: Coniferous (white pine, red spruce, red pine) mixed with deciduous (sugar maple, red oak, yellow birch)

Soils: Leached, wet-climate soils

Human Activities: Total population 2 537 685; GDP $39.9 billion; forestry, agriculture, fishing, tourism, urbanization

Major Urban Areas: Halifax (2004: 379 800), Fredericton, Saint John, Charlottetown

Boreal Plains Ecozone:
(Area 668 664 km^2)

Landforms: Level to gently rolling plains

Climate: Long, cold winters (-20°C); short, warm summers (17°C); precipitation 450 mm; growing season 130 to 165 days

Vegetation: Coniferous forests (white spruce, black spruce, balsam fir, Jack pine, and tamarack) mixed with deciduous (aspen, poplar, and white birch); extensive marsh areas

Soils: Rich soils formed under forests; marsh soils in some areas

Human Activities: Total population 771 205; GDP $13.7 billion; forestry, farming, tourism, oil and gas development

Major Urban Areas: Hinton (9405), La Ronge, The Pas, Flin Flon, Peace River, Fort Smith

Boreal Shield Ecozone:
(Area 1 640 949 km^2)

Landforms: Plains and low hills of the Canadian Shield

Climate: Long winters (-15°C); short summers (17°C); precipitation 400 to 1000 mm; growing season 130 to 190 days

Vegetation: Coniferous (black spruce, white spruce, Jack pine, balsam fir) mixed with deciduous (yellow birch, sugar maple, black ash)

Soils: Heavily leached soils; bare rock; swampy areas

Human Activities: Total population 2 821 808; GDP $49 billion; forestry, mining, tourism, recreation, trapping

Major Urban Areas: St. John's (2004: 179 900), Chicoutimi, Sudbury, Sault Ste. Marie, Thunder Bay, Thompson

Prairie Ecozone:
(Area 443 159 km^2)

Landforms: Flat to rolling plains

Climate: Moderately long, cold winters (-15°C); moderately warm summers (18°C); precipitation 250 to 700 mm; growing season 170 to 190 days

Vegetation: Short-grass prairie in drier areas; long-grass prairie in wetter areas; some trees; little natural vegetation remains

Soils: Rich, grassland soils

Human Activities: Total population 4 222 569; GDP $90.8 billion; agriculture, urbanization, oil and gas development

Major Urban Areas: Edmonton (2004: 1 001 600), Calgary, Winnipeg, Regina, Saskatoon

Montane Cordillera Ecozone:
(Area 474 753 km^2)

Landforms: Mountains, plains and plateaus

Climate: Temperatures vary with latitude and elevation; moderate winters (-12°C); moderate summers (15°C); precipitation varies widely with elevation and physical aspects, 500 to 1000 mm; growing season 140 to 240 days

Vegetation: Enormous variations depending on elevation; dominated by coniferous (Engelmann spruce, ponderosa pine, Douglas fir)

Soils: Wide variety of mountain soils

Human Activities: Total population 859 134; GDP $14 billion; forestry, agriculture, tourism

Major Urban Areas: Kamloops (77 281), Prince George, Penticton

Pacific Maritime Ecozone:
(Area 196 200 km^2)

Landforms: Mountains with small areas of coastal plains

Climate: Mild winters (3°C); cool summers (15°C); precipitation 600 to 2000 mm; growing season 200 to 260 days

Vegetation: Varies with elevation; coniferous trees (western red cedar, Douglas fir, western hemlock, Sitka spruce)

Soils: Wide variety of mountain soils

Human Activities: Total population 3 027 206; GDP $58.2 billion; forestry, urbanization, agriculture, fish processing, tourism, recreation

Major Urban Areas: Vancouver (2004: 2 160 000), Victoria, Prince Rupert

Boreal Cordillera Ecozone:
(Area 459 864 km^2)

Landforms: Mountainous, some hills

Climate: Long, cold winters (-20°C); short, cool summers (12°C); very dry, precipitation 300 to 500 mm; growing season 125 to 150 days

Vegetation: Mainly coniferous (white spruce, subalpine fir)

Soils: Variety of mountain soils

Human Activities: Total population 30 690; GDP $0.9 billion; hunting, trapping, forestry, tourism, mining

Major Urban Areas: Whitehorse (19 058), Dawson

Taiga Cordillera Ecozone:
(Area 264 213 km^2)

Landforms: Mountainous

Climate: Long, cold winters (-24°C); short, cool summers (13°C); very dry, precipitation 250 to 400 mm; growing season 90 to 130 days

Vegetation: Tundra of all types; areas of scattered forest

Soils: Variety of poor-quality soils; bare rock

Human Activities: Total population 370; GDP $0.005 billion; hunting, trapping, forestry, tourism

Major Urban Areas: Old Crow (299)

Taiga Plains Ecozone:
(Area 569 363 km^2)

Landforms: Interior plains and some foothills

Climate: Long, cold winters (-23°C); short, cool summers (12°C); dry, precipitation 200 to 400 mm; growing season 80 days to 150 days

Vegetation: Open forest to dense forest (black spruce, white spruce, Jack pine, tamarack, paper birch, trembling aspen)

Soils: Continuous permafrost in north; scattered permafrost further south; wide variety of poor quality soils

Human Activities : Total population 20 726; GDP $0.5 billion; hunting, trapping, tourism, oil and gas development, agricultural

Major Urban Areas: Hay River (3510), Inuvik, Fort Simpson

Taiga Shield Ecozone:
(Area 1 122 504 km^2)

Landforms: Plains and hills of Canadian Shield

Climate: Moderately long, cold winters (-25°C); moderately short, cool summers (12°C); precipitation 300 to 900 mm; growing season 100 to 140 days

Vegetation: Black spruce, Jack pine, paper birch, trembling aspen

Soils: Thin, highly leached soils; bare rock

Human Activities: Total population 38 116; GDP $1.1 billion; tourism, mining, hunting, trapping

Major Urban Areas: Yellowknife (16 541), Uranium City, Happy Valley-Goose Bay

Hudson Plains Ecozone:
(Area 359 546 km^2)

Landforms: Low-lying, swampy plains

Climate: Moderately long, cold winters (-17°C); moderately short, cool summers (14°C); precipitation 400 to 700 mm; growing season 90 to 150 days

Vegetation: Ground-hugging tundra; increasingly dense forest in south (white spruce, black spruce, tamarack, Jack pine)

Soils: Scattered permafrost; poorly developed organic and permafrost soils

Human Activities: Total population 9530; GDP $0.1 billion; hunting, trapping, recreation

Major Urban Areas: Moosonee (936), Churchill, Attawapiskat

Southern Arctic Ecozone:
(Area 702 542 km^2)

Landforms: Plains and hills of Canadian Shield

Climate: Long winters (-25°C), short, cool summers (10°C), dry, precipitation 200 to 300 mm; growing season 80 days

Vegetation: Tundra, including shrubs

Soils: Permafrost everywhere; tundra soils, bare rock

Human Activities: Total population 14 470; GDP $0.15 billion; hunting, trapping, tourism, mineral development

Major Urban Areas: Rankin Inlet (2177), Tuktoyaktuk, Povungnituk

Northern Arctic Ecozone:
(Area 1 371 340 km^2)

Landforms: Plains and upland areas

Climate: Long winters (-30°C), short summers (5°C); precipitation 200 mm; growing season 50 days

Vegetation: Tundra; ground-hugging plants

Soils: Permafrost; tundra soils

Human Activities: Total population 20 451; GDP $0.38 billion; hunting, tourism, some mining

Major Urban Areas: Iqaluit (5236), Cambridge Bay, Resolute

Arctic Cordillera Ecozone:
(Area 234 708 km^2)

Landforms: Innuitian Mountains

Climate: Long winters (-40°C), short summers (0°C); precipitation less than 200 mm; virtually no growing season

Vegetation: Mostly no vegetation; tundra

Soils: Permafrost; tundra soils; bare rock

Human Activities: Total population 1304; GDP $0.012 billion; hunting, tourism

Major Urban Areas: Pond Inlet (1220), Clyde River, Broughton Island

In Closing...

By dividing Canada's land mass into 15 unique ecozones, geographers have made Canada's geography more understandable. Within each ecozone, you can see the cause-and-effect relationships that exist among physical, biological, and human factors. You can also see that ecozones are dynamic in nature: they change as the environment and human activities change within them.

Most of the features that help define an ecozone are natural—the landforms, water, climate, soil, vegetation, and wildlife—but remember that human activities also play a role in setting the boundaries and making each ecozone unique.

QUESTIONS

KNOWLEDGE AND UNDERSTANDING

1. a) What is an ecozone?
   b) Describe the two characteristics of the ecozone concept that make it a useful way to study Canada.
2. Which ecozones list tourism or recreation as a major human activity? How would the kind of tourism/recreation vary in different ecozones?

THINKING

3. a) What is the GDP of an ecozone?
   b) Create a pie graph to show the distribution of Canada's GDP among the ecozones. (Instructions for creating pie graphs are given in Chapter 8.) What does this graph tell you about the location of most of Canada's economic activities?
   c) Rank the ecozones separately from highest to lowest according to
      i. GDP
      ii. area
      iii. population
   d) What relationship do you see between GDP and area?
   e) What relationship do you see between GDP and population?
4. Examine the growing seasons found in each ecozone. In what ecozones would you expect to find most of Canada's agricultural activities?
5. a) Ecozone boundaries exist for various combinations of three major factors: landform boundaries, climate/vegetation/soil boundaries, and human activity locations. Examine Fig. 15-5, where boundaries are identified on the map. The general reason for each ecozone boundary is suggested. For each, give the specific reason for the boundary.
   b) Choose any two other ecozone boundaries and explain why they exist.

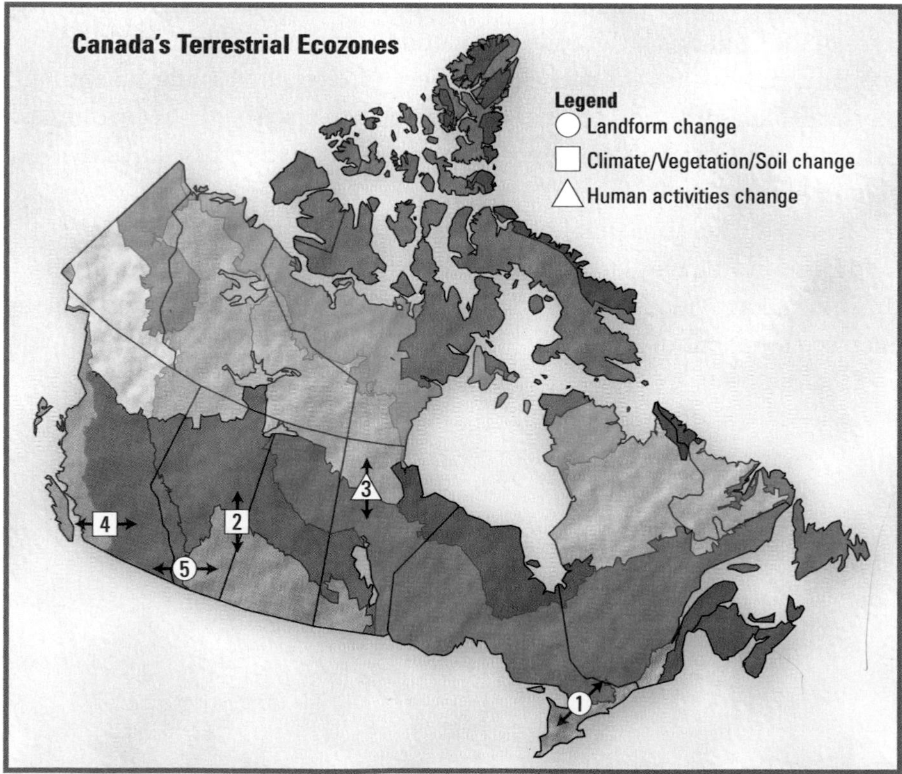

Fig. 15-5 ▶ Canada's terrestrial ecozones

6. In this chapter, you learned about the usefulness of ecozones in helping us to understand and explain Canada's geography. Consider how this would apply in each of these cases:
   a) solving environmental problems
   b) planning how a natural resource should be developed
   c) planning a family holiday trip

COMMUNICATION

7. Complete either Question 7a) or 7b):
   a) If you live in a highly populated ecozone, which lightly populated ecozone would you like to
      i. live in? ii. visit?
      Give reasons for each choice.
   b) If you live in a lightly populated ecozone, which highly populated ecozone would you like to
      i. live in? ii. visit?
      Give reasons for each choice.
8. In most previous studies of Grade 9 Canadian Geography, the four ecozones Taiga Cordillera, Boreal Cordillera, Montane Cordillera, and Pacific Maritime would have been included in one region called the Western Cordillera. Compare the population densities of these four ecozones (see Fig. 15-6). How does this illustrate the difficulty of choosing just the right number of regions?

APPLICATION

9. a) The population density of each ecozone is shown in Fig. 15-6. Divide these values into four categories on the basis of where you think "natural breaks" occur, for example, between the Mixedwood Plains and the Atlantic Maritime. You do not have to have an equal number of ecozones in each group.
   b) On a base map of ecozones that your teacher will supply, shade each category differently. It will be most effective if you use four different shades of one colour rather than four different colours. For example, you may want to use four shades of red. Always use the darkest shade for the highest value.
   c) Be sure to include a legend and suitable title for your map.

▼ **Fig. 15-6**

Ecozone	Population Density, 2001 (people/km^2)
Arctic Cordillera	0.56
Atlantic Maritime	1321.60
Boreal Cordillera	6.67
Boreal Plains	115.34
Boreal Shield	103.31
Hudson Plains	2.65
Mixedwood Plains	14 606.81
Montane Cordillera	180.96
Northern Arctic	1.49
Pacific Maritime	1542.92
Prairies	952.83
Southern Arctic	2.06
Taiga Cordillera	0.14
Taiga Plains	3.64
Taiga Shield	3.40

   d) Comment on the pattern of population density that you see. Remember that Canada's overall population density is about 3 people per square kilometre.

   Question 9 can also be done using ArcView GIS software. Your teacher will give you instructions on how to do this.

10. a) Collect information about your local ecozone through personal observations; interviews with teachers and local experts; and visits to museums, conservation areas, and wildlife organizations. Put this information in an organizer under the headings: Landform, Climate, Vegetation, Wildlife, and Human Activities.
    b) Choose three other ecozones in different parts of the country. Draw an organizer using the same headings as 10a). In what ways are the four ecozones similar? In what ways are they different?
    c) Choose one of the four ecozones. How do climate and landforms affect the types of wildlife, vegetation, and human activity found there?

Destination: Canada!

Fig. CA3-1 ▶

Background

Have you recently travelled within Canada or to another country? If so, the money you spent on accommodations, food, tourist attractions, and even souvenirs contributed to a major global industry. Here are some facts about the tourist industry.

- International tourism spending in 2004 was about $735 billion.
- In Canada, tourists spent roughly $57.5 billion in 2003. Canadians account for about two-thirds of this spending.
- More than 190 000 businesses in every province and territory are involved in the tourist industry. These businesses employ about 1.6 million Canadians directly or indirectly.
- About 39 million international visitors travelled to Canada in 2004. Roughly 80% of these were American. The United Kingdom, France, Germany, Japan, and Australia are the top five sources of tourists after the United States.

Fig. CA3-2 shows the main reasons for the visits by Americans, and by other foreign tourists. Fig. CA3-3 shows the top 10 activities visitors to Canada participated in.

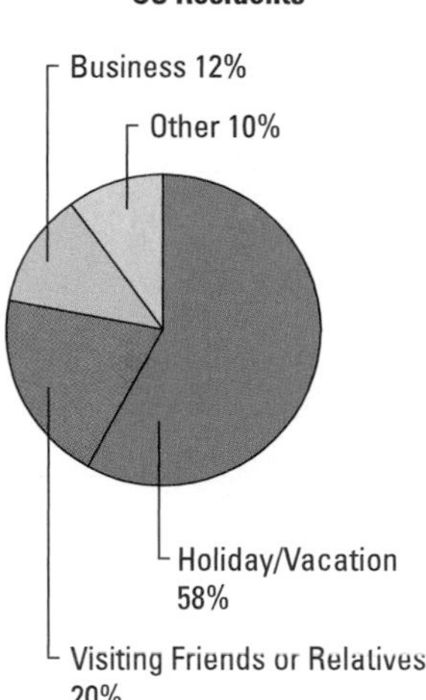

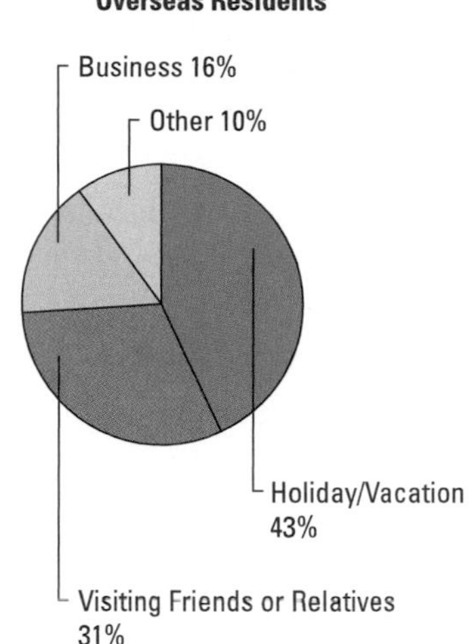

◀ **Fig. CA3-2** Distribution of international tourists to Canada by purpose, 2003

	US Residents %*	Overseas Residents %*
Shopping	62	87
Sightseeing	51	75
Participating in sports/outdoor activities	32	32
Visiting friends or relatives	31	59
Visiting a historical site	28	39
Visiting a national or provincial nature park	23	47
Going to a bar or night club	23	33
Visiting a museum or art gallery	21	37
Attending cultural events	11	14
Visiting a zoo, aquarium, botanical garden	11	27

*More than one activity may be participated in while on a trip.

◀ **Fig. CA3-3** Top activities participated in by international tourists to Canada, 2003

What attracts millions of Canadians and international travellers to visit this country? If you could visit any region of Canada, which region would you choose? If you were a travel operator, how would you promote your choice of Canadian destination? Completing the activity below will help you answer these questions.

Activity

1. Your first task is to decide which ecozones of Canada you would like to visit. Begin by reviewing Fig 15-3, the ecozones map on page 175. Using what you have learned in this unit about Canada's landforms, climate, soil, and vegetation, choose three ecozones that you would like to visit. Review the Tour of Canada's Terrestrial Ecozones information in

Ecozone information is also available at links found at: www.pearsoned.ca/makingconnections2.

Chapter 15 for a summary of your ecozones' features. Then check out Web sites such as www.travelcanada.ca, or resources at your school library or local government tourist office for information about recreational and cultural activities in your selected regions.

2. Once you have gathered all your information, complete Fig. CA3-4 to help you analyze and evaluate the information you gathered. Include at least three items in the "positive," "minus," and "interesting" columns for each of your regions. Remember to note down your reasons for including each item in the column you select.
3. Using the information recorded in Fig. CA3-4, decide on one ecozone for your Canadian tourism destination. Explain why your location will attract visitors from Canada and around the world. What physical features contribute to your region's appeal? How do the physical features of the ecozone you chose affect the recreational and cultural activities available?
4. Now that you have selected a tourism destination in Canada, it is time for promotion! Create a one-page travel summary of your tourism destination that will attract visitors to your destination. Your summary should include:
   - an eye-catching logo and title for your destination
   - a sketch map of the location of your destination
   - point-form descriptions of the natural and human characteristics of your destination
   - an outline of the main activities and attractions for your destination
   - "sensitive tourist" suggestions so that visitors can minimize their impact on the local environment and community
   - additional images, visuals, or drawings to highlight your destination
5. As part of a Web site promotional campaign, write an informational paragraph that concisely describes your tourism destination and encourages people to visit.
6. With your classmates, set up a travel operators' forum, where each of you can display your ad and talk about why you believe your region represents a good tourist destination.

GeoLit Reminder

When writing your travel summary:

- Review the instructions.
- Organize gathered information about your selected travel destination.
- Support main activities and attractions with gathered information and images.
- Conclude your summary with an informational paragraph promoting your travel destination.
- Review and edit your work.

	Positive	**Minus**	**Interesting**
e.g., Northern Arctic	Beautiful and unusual scenery	Hard to get to	For its portion of the ecozone, Nunavut has the slogan "untamed, unspoiled, undiscovered."

▲ **Fig. CA3-4** Positive–Minus–Interesting Organizer

UNIT 4

Cultural Connections

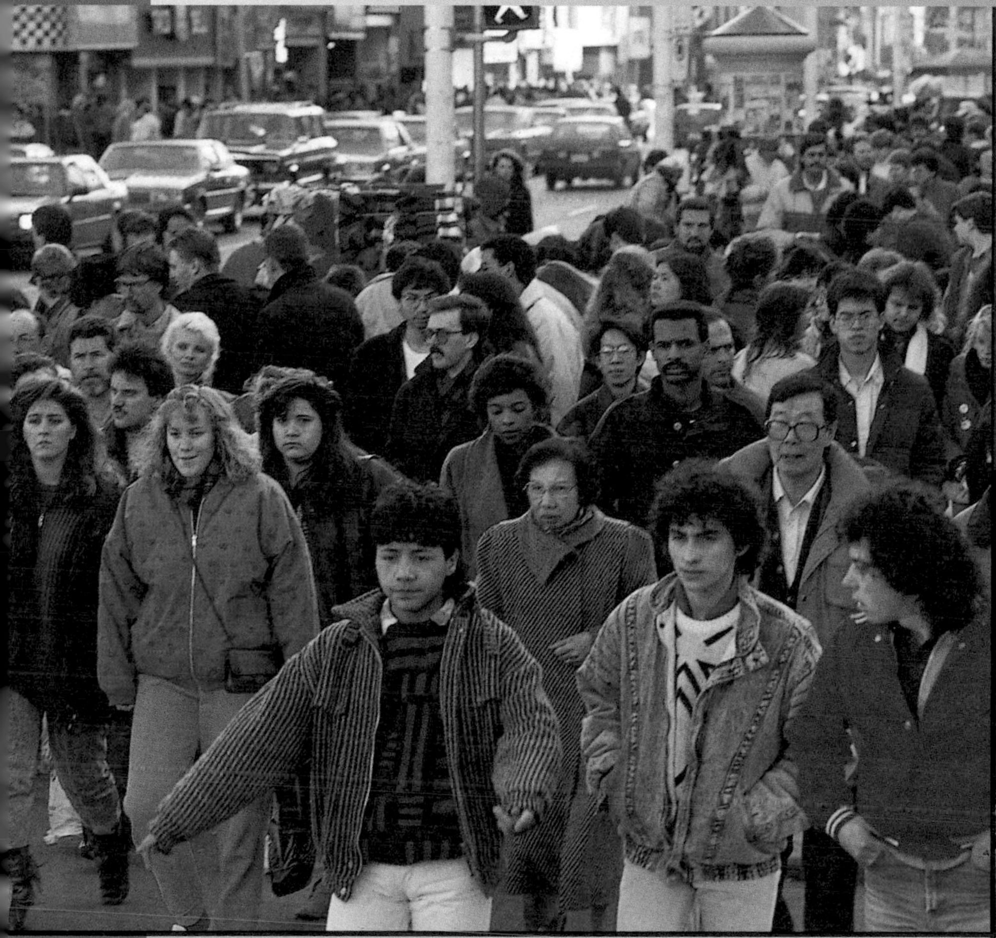

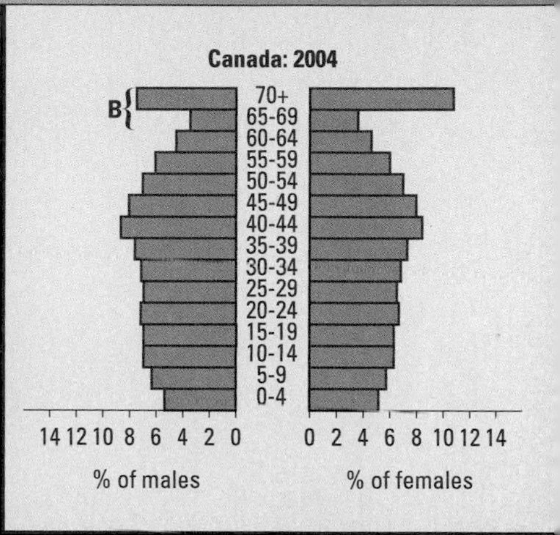
Canada: 2004
B
70+
65-69
60-64
55-59
50-54
45-49
40-44
35-39
30-34
25-29
20-24
15-19
10-14
5-9
0-4
14 12 10 8 6 4 2 0
0 2 4 6 8 10 12 14
% of males
% of females

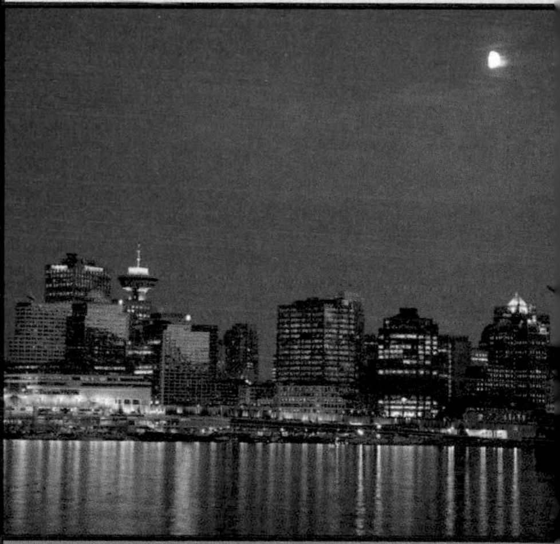

What characteristics define a particular cultural group or community? Is there evidence within your community of diverse celebrations, places of worship, or stores?

Does your community have a large Aboriginal population? What unique issues face Aboriginal members of society?

What settlement pattern was used to settle your part of the country? Does your community currently face issues related to land use, growing urban areas, or declining rural area?

This unit helps you develop the skills necessary to interpret population data, understand Aboriginal issues, and learn how changes in Canada's demographics affect you.

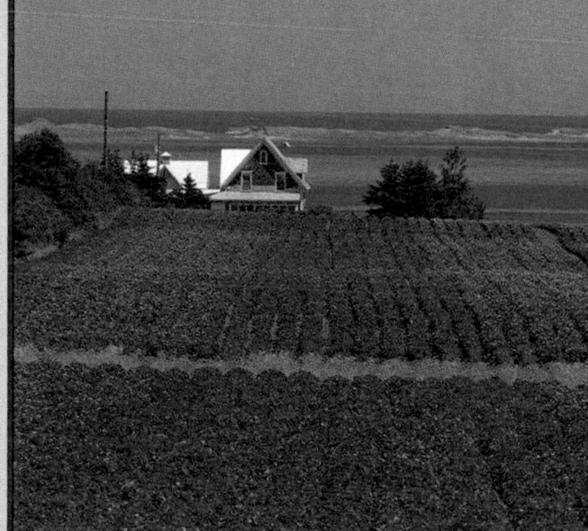

16 An Introduction to the Study of Population

Key Ideas

This chapter helps you investigate these questions:

- How can changes in a country's population growth be identified and calculated?
- What are the characteristics of Canada's population? How is it changing, and why?
- What is meant by the term *dependency load*? How does the dependency load affect a society?
- What do current population trends suggest about the future of Canada's population?

Key Terms

immigrate
emigrate
demography
birth rate
death rate
natural increase rate
immigration rate
emigration rate
net migration rate
population growth rate
doubling time
Rule of 70
dependency load
population pyramid

Changes in Population

906 + 655 – 639 – 107 = 815

Consider the following numbers. On an average day between July 1, 2003 and June 30, 2004, about 906 babies were born in Canada, and 639 people died. Approximately 655 people **immigrated** to Canada, and 107 **emigrated** from Canada to live elsewhere. As a result, at the end of that average day, there were 815 more people living in Canada than there were at the beginning of the day (Fig. 16-1). This simple calculation demonstrates Canada's population growth on an average day. This is your introduction to a fascinating subject called **demography**, which is, in simple terms, the study of human populations. Some knowledge of demography will help you understand the population geography of Canada and other countries. In the section that follows, be sure you understand each idea before moving on to the next.

Use Rates, Not Numbers

You just learned that about 906 children are born in Canada each day. We can compare this number to births in Russia (about 3836 children born each day) and the African country of Togo (about 513 daily births). Or can we? In this case, direct comparisons are somewhat pointless since the

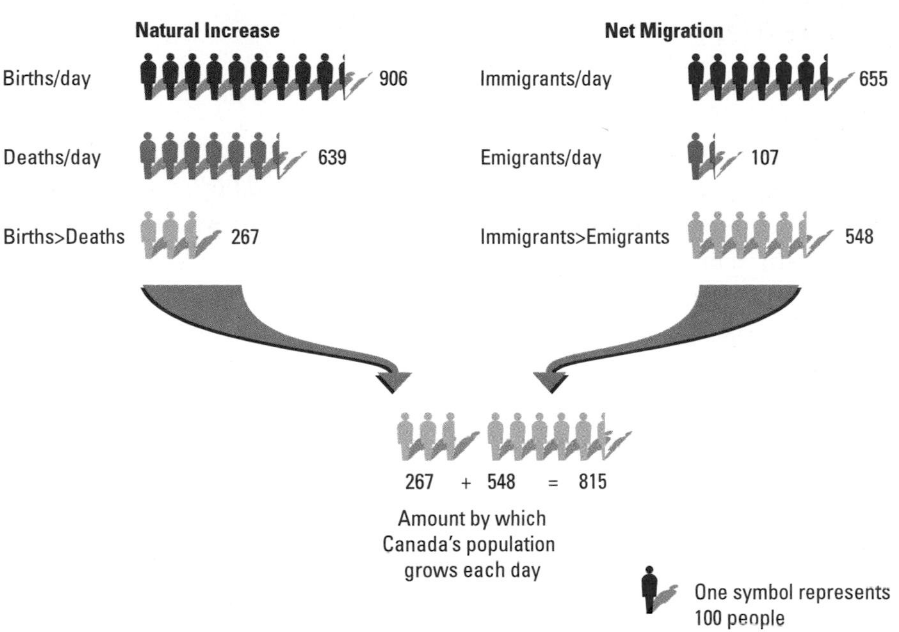

◀ **Fig. 16-1** Canada's population increases for two reasons: natural increase (more births than deaths) and net migration (more people move to Canada than leave Canada).

populations of these countries are so different in size: Canada has about 32 million people, Russia about 143 million, and Togo about 5.5 million. If you think about it, what matters is not the number of births, but the relationship between the number of births and the size of the population. A measurement called the **birth rate** demonstrates this (Fig. 16-2), and gives the number of births per year for every 1000 people. In Canada's case, this is 10 births for every 1000 people. A similar measure, the **death rate**, calculates the number of deaths per year for every 1000 people. In Canada's case, the death rate is about 7 per year for every 1000. If you think about rates rather than numbers, you will find it much easier to compare populations in different countries or at different periods in history.

	Number of Births per Year, 2003	Population, 2003	Birth Rate (Births per 1000 People), 2003
Canada	330 000	32 207 000	10
Russia	1 458 000	144 526 000	10
Togo	191 000	5 429 000	35

◀ **Fig. 16-2** A country's birth rate is calculated by dividing the number of births in one year by the population and then multiplying the result by 1000, e.g., $\frac{330\ 000}{32\ 207\ 000} \times 1000 = 10$ (numbers rounded).

Rates That Determine Changes

We can combine the birth rate and death rate into a very useful measurement called the **natural increase rate.** The natural increase rate can be calculated very simply, as shown in the following example for Canada.

To convert 3/1000 into a percentage,
3/1000 = 0.003
0.003 x 100 = 0.3%

natural increase rate = birth rate - death rate
= 10/1000 - 7/1000
= 3/1000

Canada's natural increase rate is therefore 3/1000. Natural increase rates are often given as percentages, which in this case would be 0.3%. In contrast, Togo has a natural increase rate of 2.4%, while Russia has an increase rate of -0.4%. Natural increase is a very important concept since, in most countries, it is the main reason a country's population increases (or decreases).

What does the negative natural increase in Russia mean?

Another reason why a country's population changes is that people either immigrate to the country or emigrate from it to live elsewhere. You can calculate a country's **immigration rate** in a manner similar to the calculation of birth and death rates. The immigration rate for Canada is 7/1000 (0.7%), and the **emigration rate** is 2/1000 (0.2%). If we combine these two, we get the **net migration rate** for Canada:

Only a few countries have a net migration rate this high.

net migration rate = immigration rate - emigration rate
= 7/1000 - 2/1000
= 5/1000 (or 0.5%)

A final useful measurement is a country's **population growth rate**, which combines both natural increase and net migration. For Canada:

population growth rate = natural increase rate + net migration rate
= 3/1000 + 5/1000
= 8/1000 (or 0.8%)

As you will discover in the next section, the rate at which a country's population grows or declines has an enormous influence on people's lives. If the population is growing very rapidly, there may be serious problems providing enough housing, education, healthcare, and jobs for everyone. On the other hand, if the population is declining, there may be shortages of workers and customers to meet the needs of businesses.

Compounding

Imagine that your parents offer you a reward for your hard work and success in school. To help pay for your future university costs, you may choose to receive either $1000 for each day in the month of June, or 1 cent on June lst, 2 cents on June 2nd, 4 cents on June 3rd, 8 cents on June 4th, and so on. Which one would you choose?

If you choose the first option, you will get $30 000. If you choose the second, you will get a total of $10 737 418.23! Such is the power of compounding, since growth occurs on top of the growth that has already taken place. The impact of compounding in demography is not quite as dramatic, but it is still of enormous importance. Consider the following: a French Canadian couple who married in 1660 could theoretically have 16 million descendants today.

This 16 million figure is based on 30-year generations and the birth of four children to each descendant.

Fig. 16-3 shows the impact of compounding on the populations of Canada, Russia, and Togo for the next 100 years, assuming that their population growth rates remain as they are today. Canada's population will grow slowly to about 67 million, but look at what happens to the populations of Russia and Togo. Russia's population drops to less than 100 million (about two-thirds of today's population), and Togo's population skyrockets to more than 50 million.

It is very likely that these rates will change for reasons that you will discover in the next few pages.

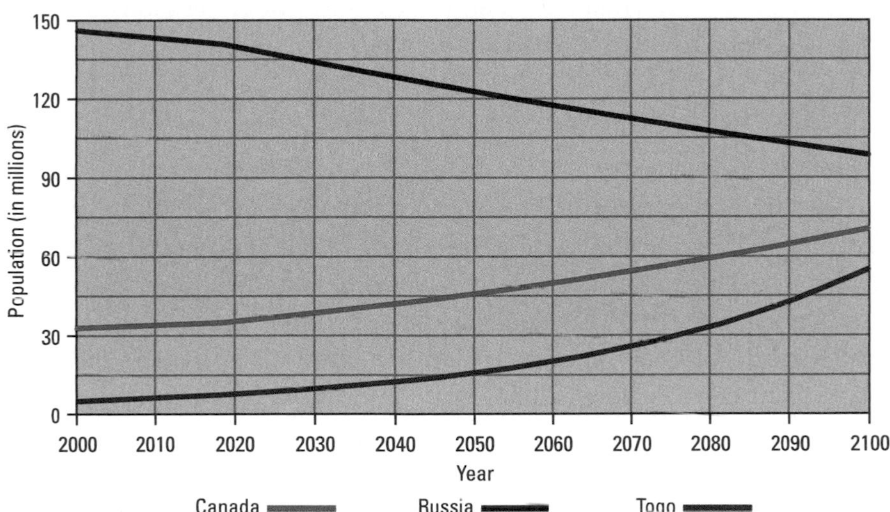

◀ **Fig. 16-3** Differences among population growth rates appear very small, but compounding allows huge increases or decreases in population to occur. Note that these are projected figures for the population.

GeoLit Reminder

When reading a graph:

- What is the type of graph in Figure 16-3?
- Examine the caption and labels.
- What is the purpose of this graph?
- Describe the trends outlined in the graph.
- Do you need additional information to understand this graph?

A simple way to think about the impact of population growth is to consider what is called the **doubling time** for a population. As you might expect by the name, this is simply how long it would take for a country's population to double at the current growth rate. You could calculate it with some fancy mathematics or with a spreadsheet, but it can be estimated very easily using something called the **Rule of 70**. You divide 70 by the population growth rate, and this gives you an estimate of how many years it will take the population to double. For example, with Canada's 0.8% rate, the population will double in about 87 years (70/0.8). With Togo's 2.4% rate, the population will double in less than 30 years (70/2.4). To understand the significance of this, picture how hard it would be for a relatively rich country like Canada to provide all the food, housing, healthcare, education, and other needed items, for twice as many people every 30 years. For a poor country like Togo, the task is almost impossible.

Different Ages—Different Roles

At each stage of our lives, we play different roles. Demographers identify three important stages:

1. Children (under age 15)
2. Working adults (ages 15 to 64)
3. Older adults (65 and over)

1956

Ages	Male	Female
70+	4.7%	5.0%
65-69	2.9%	2.9%
60-64	2.5%	3.5%
55-59	3.0%	4.0%
50-54	4.5%	4.5%
45-49	6.0%	5.5%
40-44	6.5%	6.0%
35-39	7.0%	7.5%
30-34	7.5%	8.0%
25-29	7.5%	8.0%
20-24	7.0%	7.1%
15-19	7.2%	7.3%
10-14	9.0%	8.9%
5-9	11.3%	11.2%
0-4	12.4%	12.3%

2004

Ages	Male	Female
70+	7.8%	10.7%
65-69	3.6%	3.8%
60-64	4.5%	4.6%
55-59	6.0%	6.0%
50-54	7.0%	7.0%
45-49	8.1%	8.0%
40-44	8.7%	8.5%
35-39	7.7%	7.4%
30-34	7.1%	6.8%
25-29	6.9%	6.6%
20-24	7.2%	6.7%
15-19	6.9%	6.4%
10-14	6.9%	6.4%
5-9	6.2%	5.8%
0-4	5.5%	5.1%

▲ **Fig. 16-4** This table shows the percentage of people of each gender and age group in Canada for the years 1956 and 2004.

The assumption is that children and older adults do not work and must be supported by the working population. The part of the population that must be supported is called the **dependency load**. A high dependency load tends to put a great deal of pressure on the society to provide such things as education, housing, healthcare, and seniors' homes. Canada today has a dependency load of 31% (18% children and 13% older people), while Niger in northern Africa has a dependency load of 49% (47% children and only 2% older people). You can imagine Niger's difficulty in trying to support half of its population that is dependent.

Population Pyramids

If someone asked you to compare the percentages for each age group in each set of statistics in Fig. 16-4, you could probably do it. However, it would be easier and faster to understand the information in this figure if the data were graphed. The statistical data we have here is often shown on a special type of graph called a **population pyramid**, which is a series of horizontal bar graphs for the male population placed beside a similar series of bar graphs for the female population. Fig. 16-5 shows population pyramids for the data in Fig. 16-4. Population pyramids make it easy to "see" the percentages of younger and older people within the dependency load.

CHANGES IN POPULATION STRUCTURE

The population pyramids in Fig. 16-5 reveal dramatic changes in Canada's population structure between 1956 and 2004. Let's consider the most dramatic change—the change in the size and nature of the dependency load.

During the 1950s, Canada's population grew rapidly because many immigrants came into the country, and because people were having

▼ **Fig. 16-5** Compare these population pyramids to the tables of data in Fig. 16-4 from which they were made. Which is easier to interpret and to compare? At first glance, population pyramids appear complicated, but they really aren't. Each consists of 34 individual bar graphs.

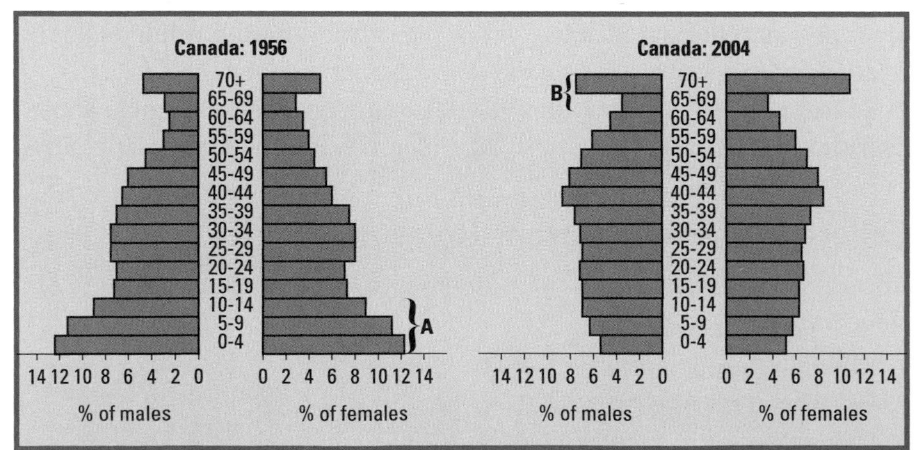

moderately large families. Canada was in the midst of a baby boom—an era in which the birth rate rises sharply. Following World War II, many countries experienced a baby boom, and today, babies born between 1946 and 1961 are referred to as baby boomers. Fig. 16-5 shows the Canadian population pyramids for 1956 and 2004. In 1956, there was a high percentage of 0–14-year-olds in the population (indicated by "A"). In 2004, this same group had become part of the bulge at 40–59 years old. In 2004, however, the percentage of children was considerably lower, while the percentage of older people had increased significantly (see "B" in the 2004 population pyramid).

What significance did this change in the dependency load have on Canadian society at each of these times? In 1956, the emphasis was on providing elementary schools for the growing number of children, since most of these children were between five and ten years of age. Ten years later, the emphasis was on building secondary schools. But by 2004, there was little need for new schools except in a few growing suburban areas, and in some areas, schools were closing down. Why? The reason is that by 2004, Canada's population was growing less than one-third as quickly as in 1956. A combination of smaller family size and lower immigration rates had reduced the number of school-age children. Children who were in Grade 1 in 1956 were now 54 years old, and this large proportion of society was beginning to think about retirement and about such things as expanding the healthcare facilities it would soon need. The difference in the nature and size of the dependency load shifted Canadian society's focus from providing services for children to providing services for a growing, older population. Consider leisure activities, for example. Services for older people might mean an increase in the number of golf courses. This is just one example of how a change in the population structure tends to affect our lives.

INTERNET

Watch how Canada's population changes from 1971 to 2006! A link to dynamic population pyramids is available at www.pearsoned.ca/makingconnections2.

1956 was in the middle of the post-World War II baby boom. Canada's population growth rate in 1956 was slightly over 2%.

Have you ever noticed how many ads there are for RRSPs (Registered Retirement Savings Plans)?

What leisure activities might decline in popularity as the population ages?

▼ **Fig. 16-6** In the 1950s, most Canadian families had at least three children.

▼ **Fig. 16-7** In 2004, Canadian families had an average of 1.6 children.

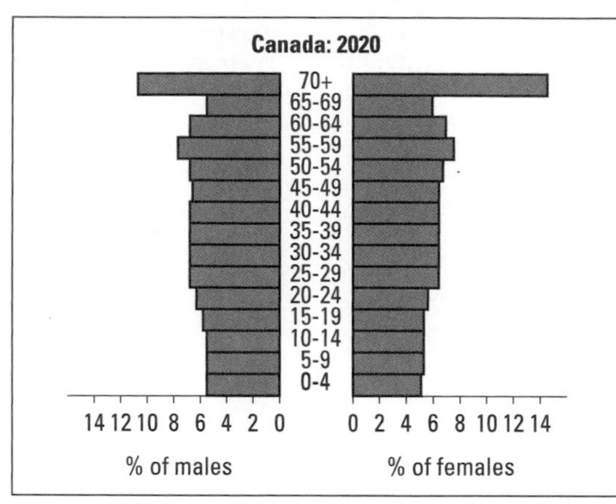

Issue

HOW WILL YOU BE AFFECTED BY CANADA'S DEPENDENCY LOAD IN 2020?

◀ **Fig. 16-8** Canada's population pyramid, 2020 (estimated) illustrates how Canada's population pyramid is projected to look in 2020.

If you compare Fig. 16-8 with the 1956 population pyramid in Fig. 16-5, you can see that there have been significant changes. When major changes occur in society, it can be seen either as a problem or as an opportunity.

Activities

1. In 2020:
   a) How old will you be?
   b) Which age group will be most common?
   c) Which age group will be least common?
   d) What will the dependency load be like?
2. How will the dependency load affect you? With a partner, brainstorm a list of possibilities.

GeoCareers

Growth Careers

How can you use your new knowledge about Canada's changing population when you are choosing a career? With a partner, make a list of jobs that are likely to grow in number to meet the needs of an aging population, and kinds of jobs that will be less in demand because there are fewer young people.

Stages of Population Change

The fact that Canada's population was growing more slowly in 2004 than in 1956 is part of a pattern that is common to other countries of the world. Populations within countries change over time in a predictable manner. Let's look at the stages of population change (Fig. 16-9).

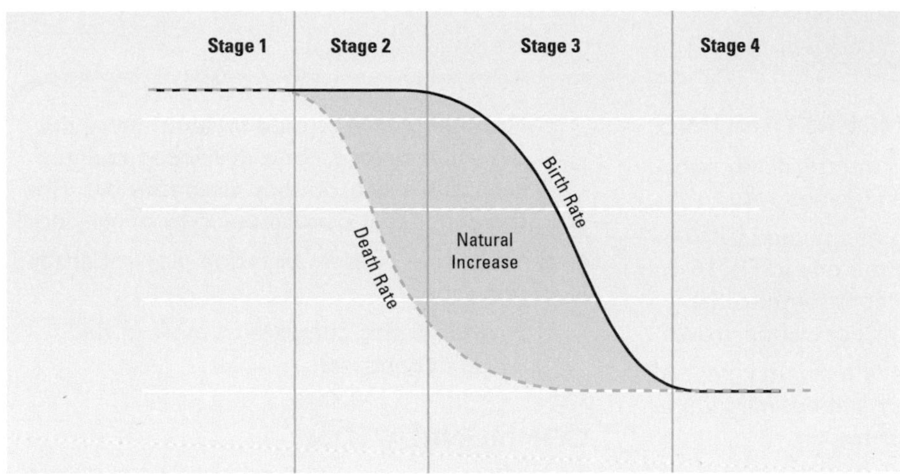

◀ **Fig. 16-9** Stages of population change. A link to demographic data, including population pyramids for every country for a range of years, can be found at www.pearsoned.ca/makingconnections2. The dynamic pyramids are particularly interesting.

Stage 1: The combination of a high birth rate and a high death rate keeps the size of the population stable. This pattern existed in Canada in the 17th and 18th centuries. There is no country in the world today in this stage.

Stage 2: At some point, the death rate drops (especially in infants), usually because of better healthcare and nutrition, while the birth rate remains high. This results in a long period of natural increase in the population. Canada's long period of natural increase began more than 150 years ago and continued through to the early 1960s. The population pyramid for 1956 (Fig. 16-5) shows the country's population distribution during this second stage of population change.

In contrast to developed countries such as Canada, the second stage began to take place in developing countries only in the last 50 years or so. A substantial decline in death rates combined with high birth rates has resulted in rapid population growth in these countries.

Stage 3: A drop in the birth rate occurs. Parents limit the size of their families because they are more certain that all their children will survive to adulthood. Since most families live in cities rather than on farms, they don't need large numbers of children to perform farm chores. Family size decreases as women begin to work outside the home. Canada began to experience this stage in the early 1960s. The third stage has only just begun in many very poor countries.

Stage 4: The birth rate declines to the point where it is close to the death rate. This causes the population to level off. Canada is approaching this point, but has not yet reached it. A few countries, particularly in Eastern Europe, have reached this stage.

This theoretical model suggests that the birth rate and death rate will become equal, but some countries (such as Russia) have found that their death rates are higher than their birth rates. No one knows if this will continue, or if it is just a temporary situation.

QUESTIONS

KNOWLEDGE AND UNDERSTANDING

1. a) Define the following: birth rate, death rate, immigration rate, and emigration rate.
   b) Describe, with the help of a numerical example different from the one in Fig. 16-1, how these four factors contribute to the rate at which a country's population grows.
2. a) The population growth of a country depends on both natural increase and net migration. Define each of these terms.
   b) Compare the importance of both in determining Canada's population growth since 1956. (See Fig. 16-5.) Would this also be the case in other countries? Explain.

THINKING

3. Ignoring the impact of immigration, Canada's population was relatively stable before the year 1800. Since 1800, our population has grown enormously. However, it may stop growing within the next few decades. Some people would say that this pattern is the result of the forces of death control and birth control. Explain what each term means and how each has contributed to Canada's population growth.
4. a) What is the Rule of 70?
   b) Why is the Rule of 70 so useful?
   c) How long would it take for a population to double with each of the following growth rates:
      i. 0.5% ii. 1.0% iii. 1.5%
      iv. 2.0% v. 3.0%
   d) Does the Rule of 70 apply to a negative population growth rate? Explain your answer using Russia's population growth rate of -0.4%.
5. a) What is a population's dependency load?
   b) Describe why this would be a useful concept for
      i. a government planner
      ii. the president of a major bank
   c) Consider the ages used in determining the dependency load. For a developed country such as Canada, do they accurately describe the dependent population? Why or why not?
6. a) What role does immigration play in Canada's population?
   b) How does this compare to most of the world's countries?

COMMUNICATION

7. a) Your parents (and perhaps some of your teachers) may be part of the baby boom. With a partner, brainstorm why this generation has had such an enormous influence on Canada's society since the 1950s.
   b) Is this influence likely to continue?
   c) What effect has the baby boom had on your generation? How will it affect your generation in the future? (Hint: Look at the 2020 population pyramid in Fig. 16-8.)

APPLICATION

8. a) Draw a population pyramid using the data in Fig. 16-10.
   b) These data are for Canada in 1881. How are they different from the 1956 and later pyramids given in the text?
   c) Using the Web link at www.pearsoned.ca/makingconnections2, find a country whose current population pyramid is similar to Canada's 1881 pyramid.
   d) Find countries whose pyramids are similar to Canada's 1956 and 2020 pyramids.
9. In this chapter, we have looked at the "big picture" of population pyramids. Pyramids also show the impact of specific historical events on population. Examine Canada's population pyramids for 1956, 2004 (Fig. 16-5), and 2020 (Fig. 16-8).
   a) Identify and describe two specific historical events.
   b) Can you follow these events from the 1956 pyramid to the later ones? How?

▼ **Fig. 16-10** Canada's population in the year 1881

Age	Male	Female
70+	2.6%	2.4%
65–69	1.7%	1.5%
60–64	2.4%	2.2%
55–59	2.7%	2.5%
50–54	3.3%	3.3%
45–49	4.0%	3.9%
40–44	4.5%	4.5%
35–39	5.3%	5.4%
30–34	6.1%	6.2%
25–29	7.7%	7.9%
20–24	9.8%	10.3%
15–19	11.0%	11.4%
10–14	12.0%	11.8%
5–9	13.0%	13.0%
0–4	13.9%	13.8%

10. In this chapter, we have talked about Canada's population in total, but we have not considered the fact that major differences exist among Canada's provinces and territories. Use the dynamic population pyramids link at www.pearsoned.ca/makingconnections2 to identify a province or territory with each of the following population characteristics.
    a) Growing rapidly in 2001
    b) Relatively stable population for many years
    c) Has a declining population
    d) Growing for many years but likely to decline in the future
    e) Illustrates an unexpected historical population pattern. What was the cause of this?
11. a) Create a multiple-line graph of the data in Fig. 16-11. Your graph should be at least a half page in size. Put years along the x-axis and birth/death rates along the y-axis. Be sure to use a different colour for each line and remember to label each line. Note when you are doing your time scale that Canada went from a ten-year census period in 1956 to a five-year period. Your time scale should not change; you will just have more frequent data points from 1956 onward.
    b) Lightly shade in and label the area of natural increase on your graph. What has happened to the amount of natural increase over the years?
    c) The changes in birth rates and death rates that you see on your graph are caused by two forces. One is the general change of demographic transition that occurs in a country as it becomes more advanced. The other is the impact of particular historical events: e.g., wars and good and bad economic times. Label examples of both of these on your graph.

Census Period	Average Birth Rate During Period (/1000)	Average Death Rate During Period (/1000)
1861–71	42.4	23.5
1871–81	40.1	21.4
1881–91	35.2	20.1
1891–1901	32.0	18.2
1901–11	35.8	16.8
1911–21	32.5	14.8
1921–31	27.5	12.0
1931–41	22.1	10.3
1941–51	27.7	10.6
1951–56	30.8	9.3
1956–61	29.4	8.5
1961–66	24.7	8.0
1966–71	18.5	7.7
1971–76	16.3	7.6
1976–81	15.5	7.2
1981–86	15.1	7.1
1986–91	14.8	7.2
1991–96	13.8	7.3
1996–2001	11.5	7.4

▲ **Fig. 16-11** The trends of a declining birth rate and relatively stable death rate show no sign of changing. In 2003–04, the most recent year of data availability when this book was published, the birth rate was 10.4 and the death rate was 7.0.

17 Canada's Aboriginal Population in the 21st Century

Key Ideas

This chapter helps you investigate these questions:

- In what ways did the treaty-making processes of the past fail to meet the needs of the First Nations?
- What elements are involved in the treaty-making process used today?
- What is the difference between a *comprehensive* and a *specific* land claim?
- How did Nunavut come into being, and what are some of the new territory's key challenges?

Key Terms

Aboriginal peoples
treaty
economic base
First Nations
reserve
Royal Proclamation of 1763
Indian Act, 1876
band
self-government
assimilate
comprehensive claim
comprehensive treaty
specific claim

The population of just under one million people of Aboriginal descent in Canada is similar to the total population of Edmonton.

Aboriginal peoples—descendants of Canada's original inhabitants—have had a complex and often difficult relationship with the non-Aboriginal peoples (mainly Europeans) who have come to Canada over the last 500 years. As it became obvious to the Aboriginal peoples that they were becoming a small minority in their own land, they signed agreements called **treaties** with the Europeans, hoping to accomplish two goals. First, they wanted to maintain an **economic base**, meaning they wanted to retain access to enough land to support themselves by fishing and hunting, and in some areas, farming. Second, they wanted the right to control their own affairs. Most treaties have failed miserably, since neither goal has been achieved. In recent years, however, some First Nations and the government have worked to revive the process of treaty-making in the hope that better ways may be found to help Aboriginal peoples achieve their goals.

INTERNET

Follow the links from www.pearsoned.ca/makingconnections2 for a variety of Internet sites about Aboriginal peoples and Canada's North.

A **First Nation** is an Aboriginal group whose members wish to be treated as a distinct group on the basis of a shared common culture and history. There are many such cultural groups across Canada, as shown in Fig. 17-1. For legal purposes, the federal government divides Aboriginal peoples into three groups: Indian, Inuit, and Métis. In turn, Indians are divided into two groups: *status Indians,* who are entitled to certain rights

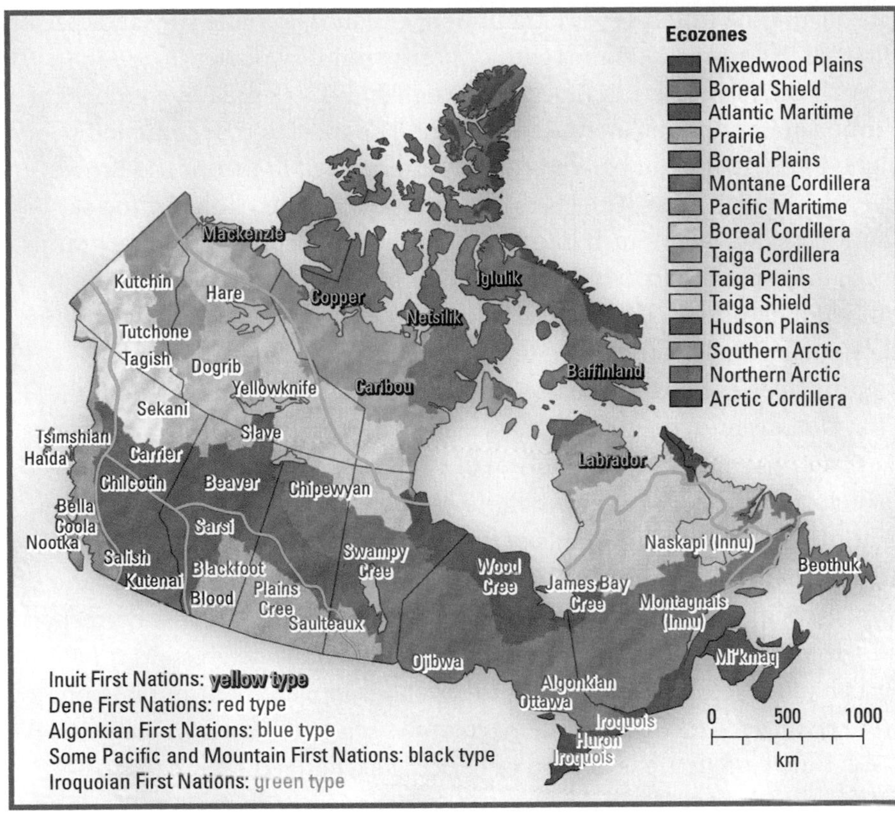

◀ **Fig. 17-1** Canada's First Nations

GeoLit Reminder

When reading a map:

- Examine the caption, scale, legend, and labels.
- What is the purpose of this map?
- Scan the map for patterns and trends.
- What general information does the map provide?
- How are the different pieces of information on the map related?

through treaties made with the Canadian government, and *non-status Indians,* who aren't covered by treaties. The federal government has special responsibilities not only for status Indians but also for the Inuit, who are Aboriginal people living in the Arctic region of Canada. Métis are people of mixed Aboriginal and European descent. It was not until the *Constitution Act, 1982,* however, that the Métis were officially recognized as one of the Aboriginal peoples of Canada.

The Treaty-making Process

Canada's history of treaty-making dates back to 1665, when Quebec was a colony of France. It was the French who first signed treaties with Canada's Aboriginal peoples. In those early years, when there were only small numbers of European explorers, fur traders, and settlers, Aboriginal peoples were in the dominant position. Not only did they outnumber the Europeans, but they knew how to survive in Canada's challenging climate. In fact, they often gave the newcomers the food, shelter, and knowledge they needed to survive. At that time, European governments and Aboriginal peoples made treaties as equals, often to achieve common military goals. For example, the French made treaties with the Huron to help them fight against the English, who had made treaties with the Iroquois. Since the

▼ **Fig. 17-2** You may have driven past First Nations' reserves without knowing it. This road sign points the way to the Tyendinaga Mohawk Territory (M.T.), near Picton, Ontario.

Huron and the Iroquois were traditional enemies, it made sense for each First Nation to make treaties with opposing military powers.

After the fall of New France to the English in 1759, greater numbers of European immigrants arrived in Canada. The treaties that came to be signed were no longer between equals and tended to favour the British over the First Nations. The British government needed land for the settlement of the newcomers. It had to obtain the land from Aboriginal groups by signing treaties. In exchange for large tracts of land, the government offered the Aboriginal groups smaller areas of land called **reserves** where they could fish, hunt, and live undisturbed as they had in the past. Signing treaties for the exchange of land at first made sense to both the First Nations and the Europeans (see Fig.17-2).

The British **Royal Proclamation of 1763** established two important principles to be considered when treaties were negotiated. The first was that the land-ownership rights of the First Nations were to be respected. The second was that First Nations should receive fair payment for land they gave up. Unfortunately, these two principles were not always respected. From 1780 to 1876, many small parcels of land were given to the British (and later Canadians) through treaties in which Aboriginal peoples were given very small one-time payments such as clothing or blankets. By 1850, much larger areas of land were being exchanged for smaller reserves, cash, yearly payments to reserve members, and promises of hunting and fishing rights over what was considered by the Europeans to be vacant, government-owned land.

After Confederation, the federal government began a push to settle the Prairies and expand the west by building a transcontinental railroad. It became clear that the government would have to negotiate with the Aboriginal groups in the West to obtain the rights to the land. Through the ***Indian Act, 1876***, both sides signed treaties that required Aboriginal peoples to give up forever their claims to the lands they occupied. Under the treaties, Aboriginal peoples received the usual cash payments, goods,

▼ **Fig. 17-3**

	First Nations	**Europeans**
Land	• had the land; were prepared to share it	• wanted to settle on it
Wanted	• peace; realized the Europeans had great military power • other things (money, goods, etc.) that the Europeans offered	• peace; realized that the First Nations would always be a threat without a treaty
Experience with Treaties	• had considerable experience using treaties to settle disputes with other First Nations	• had considerable experience using treaties to settle disputes with other countries

and promises of fishing and hunting rights that would allow them to carry on their traditional way of life. They were persuaded to move to reserves, which the Canadian government viewed as temporary—the reserves would disappear when the people living on them were absorbed into mainstream Canadian culture. To show their friendly intentions, the government gave gifts of flags and medals to the Aboriginal groups.

At the end of the 1800s, gold, silver, oil, and other mineral resources were discovered farther north—from the Yukon to Quebec—and the treaty-making process was begun once again. In 1923, the last unsurrendered land in Ontario was signed over by treaty, and with it, the treaty-making process ended for more than 50 years. Although Aboriginal peoples had given up almost half of Canada's land area through treaties, they had never signed treaties in either British Columbia or the Northwest Territories. It wasn't until the 1970s in BC and the NWT that the treaty-making process was revived and revised, and treaties were once again considered as a way in which Canada's Aboriginal peoples could establish their legal claims to the land, or receive proper compensation for land they gave up.

Problems Caused by Treaties

Unfortunately, many treaties proved to be unfair. There were differences between what Aboriginal peoples thought they were signing, and the actual wording of the documents. Furthermore, treaty promises of payments, reserve land, and rights to hunting and fishing were often not respected.

The original treaties failed to meet the needs of Aboriginal peoples in many ways, but two are critical.

1. Aboriginal peoples lost enormous amounts of land, especially in southern and central Canada, where the land is most productive.
2. Aboriginal peoples lost their right to govern themselves.

Loss of Land and Economic Base

By signing treaties, Aboriginal peoples gave up most of the land they had used for thousands of years to the European settlers. Having free access to large areas of land with abundant fish and game was key to the Aboriginal peoples' ability to maintain their traditional way of life. Rarely were the reserves of land they agreed to live on large enough, or rich enough, to support them. They were therefore deprived of a sound economic base.

Today, reserves comprise less than 1% of Canada's area. This is a very small amount of land for the nearly one million people of Aboriginal descent living in Canada. Furthermore, few of the reserves have rich resources of fertile land, minerals, commercial forests, fish, or animals. Consequently, reserve residents face a difficult choice. They may stay on

This number does not include parts of Nunavut ceded to the Inuit.

Snapshots: The *Indian Act, 1876*

Under the *Indian Act, 1876*, the federal government directed many aspects of the lives of Aboriginal peoples and frequently made controversial decisions on their behalf. It decided who "Indians" really were. Those who entered into treaties were status Indians, and only they had the right to live on reserve lands.

- Status Indians were those who were registered with the Department of Indian and Northern Affairs as members of a **band** on a reserve.
- Under the *Indian Act*, the band council was the decision-making organization that represented the reserve. Band council members, however, were not always part of the traditional group of people on the reserve, such as elders, who were making decisions on behalf of the people.
- If status Indians decided to live off-reserve, they surrendered their right to use the land.
- Aboriginal peoples who did not sign treaties were considered non-status Indians, and consequently could not live on reserves.
- The Métis never signed treaties with the federal government.
- The government frequently decided how reserve lands could, or could not, be used.
- Until 1951, Aboriginal peoples were banned from raising money to pursue land claims.
- Until 1960, they were prevented from voting in federal elections.
- Indian women could lose their Aboriginal status by marrying a non-Aboriginal man.

Many aspects of the *Indian Act* are still in place today, but since the 1980s, there has been a move to give bands more control over their affairs through their councils. More than half of the bands now control their own finances, but they still cannot sell or rent land.

Fig. 17-4 ▶
Frank Calder was the first Aboriginal person elected to the British Columbia legislature (1949). In 1973, the Supreme Court of British Columbia agreed with Dr. Calder that Aboriginal title could exist in Canadian law. That decision, known as the Calder Decision, launched the treaty-making process in British Columbia for the first time in more than 100 years. Frank Calder, champion of Aboriginal rights, received the Order of British Columbia in 2004.

the reserve with family and friends, but face a future that frequently includes unemployment and poverty. Or, they may move to the city in the hope of a better economic future, but only by abandoning their community.

Lack of Self-government

Before the arrival of the Europeans, the Aboriginal peoples of North America governed themselves successfully in many different ways. For example, the Six Nations of the Iroquois had one of the oldest democracies in the world. After the Europeans came to dominate Canada, traditions of Aboriginal government were lost when the federal government began to make most decisions about how Aboriginal peoples should live. In effect, the government treaties deprived Aboriginal peoples of the right to govern themselves.

The Six Nations was a confederation of six Iroquois nations in southern Ontario and northern New York state: the Cayuga, Mohawk, Oneida, Onondaga, Seneca, and Tuscarora.

The lack of **self-government** affects Aboriginal peoples in many ways. For instance, they do not have the right to decide for themselves when and where they may carry out their traditional fishing and hunting because of provincial and federal laws protecting wildlife populations. Aboriginal leaders have argued that laws protecting wildlife should not apply to their people because such laws help to destroy their economic base and traditional way of life. There is some indication that their voices are being heard. In 1990, the Supreme Court of Canada ruled, in a case in British Columbia, that the First Nations' use of fish for food, social, and ceremonial purposes has priority over all other uses except conservation.

Courts in Ontario have also established that the Métis have Native hunting and fishing rights.

Aboriginal peoples have sometimes been harmed by developments over which they have had no control. The Bennett Dam in British Columbia, one of Canada's largest hydroelectric projects, is a good example (Fig. 17-5). Although the project provides many benefits for the people and industries of the province, it disrupts river flow hundreds of kilometres downstream in the Peace River delta at Fort Chipewyan, Alberta. The Aboriginal people in this area traditionally earned their living by trapping muskrat in the river and selling the pelts for the production of fur products. The reduced water flow reduced the size and quality of the muskrat habitat. As a result, fewer muskrat were trapped, and those that were caught were of poor quality. Many of the trappers in Fort Chipewyan are now no longer able to earn an adequate living. Their economic base has been damaged by a development over which they had no control, and which is located far away in another province.

Perhaps the decision with the most damaging impact was to send Aboriginal children to residential schools. The purpose of these schools, which were usually located far away from the reserves, was to teach the children the language and culture of mainstream Canadian society in the hope that they would be **assimilated** into it. For many years, Aboriginal

▲ **Fig. 17-5** Although the Bennett Dam provides many benefits in British Columbia, the livelihoods of Aboriginal people who live downstream from the dam have been adversely affected.

duress
doing something against one's will because of threats

parents were persuaded, often under **duress**, to send their children to residential schools. Children were punished if they tried to speak their own language or practise their cultural traditions. Sometimes children were abused while living at these schools. Government and Aboriginal authorities have spent many years trying to repair the emotional damage suffered by Aboriginal people at the hands of those responsible for running residential schools.

Aboriginal peoples today want self-government because they believe that it will give them the ability to strengthen and protect their culture. They believe that self-government will help them develop social programs that will more effectively address problems of isolation, alcoholism, suicide, sub-standard housing, drug abuse, and health. Self-government will help them expand their economic base, which in turn will reduce unemployment, poverty, and financial dependence on government. In short, they want self-government because they wish to control their own destinies.

Treaties Today

The majority of treaties were signed in the 18th and 19th centuries, and by 1923, the treaty-making process as described above had come to an end. In fact, between 1927 and 1951 it was even illegal for a First Nation to hire a lawyer to negotiate with the government on its behalf. The government felt that treaties set the First Nations apart from mainstream Canada. Even if the government did not actually use the term "assimilation," its policy was that assimilation was in the best long-term interests of Canada's Aboriginal population.

Today, different treaty-making processes than those used decades ago are followed. First Nations that never signed treaties in the past may file a **comprehensive claim** with the federal government. Comprehensive claims are based on the acknowledgment that there are continuing Aboriginal rights in areas of Canada that have not been addressed by treaties or other means. These claims are called "comprehensive" because they deal with many issues including land ownership, self-government, ownership and control of resources, hunting/fishing/trapping rights, and financial compensation. The case study on page 206 examines the **comprehensive treaty** that resulted in the creation of the new territory of Nunavut. Although relatively few comprehensive treaties have been signed in recent years, they are important because they usually cover large tracts of land and cause major changes in the lives of the people who live there. Examine Fig. 17-4 to discover where comprehensive land claims have been made, and where comprehensive treaties have been signed.

When First Nations feel that one or more terms of their original comprehensive treaty are unfair, or have not been met over the years, they may make a **specific claim**. For example, if the people of a First Nation did not receive all the land promised in their treaty, they can make a specific claim for that land on the basis of fair treatment. Since specific land

Between 1973 and 2003, 15 comprehensive claims were settled, but more than 40 comprehensive claims remained to be settled.

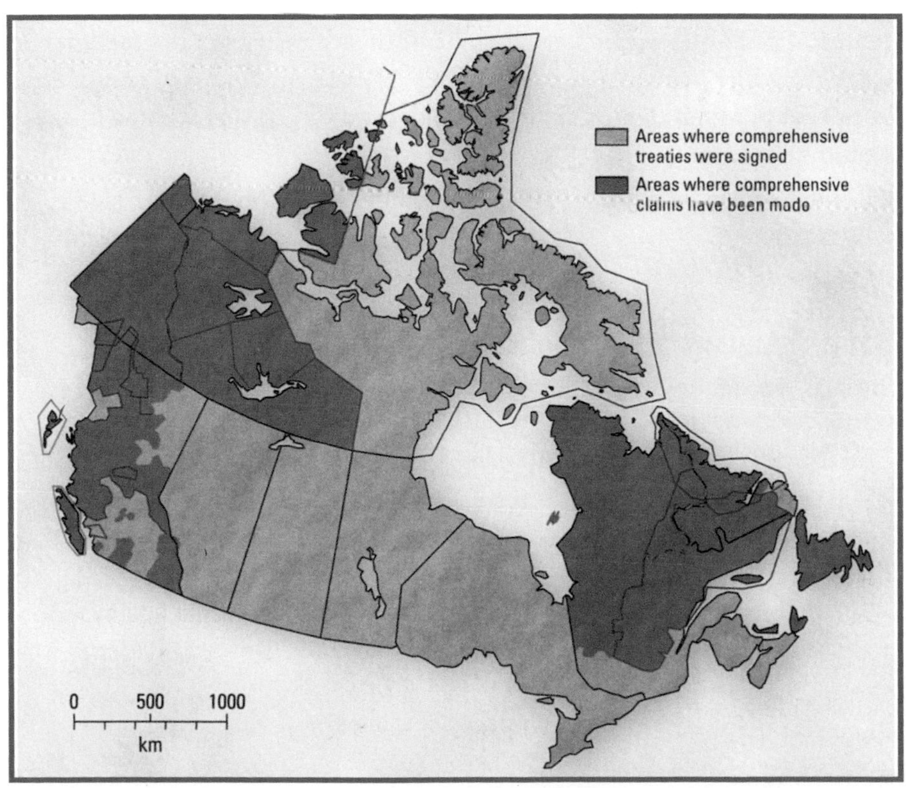

◄ **Fig. 17-6** There are many areas in Canada where comprehensive treaties have not been signed. The most recent comprehensive treaties signed were in Nunavut (1993) and northwestern British Columbia (Nisga'a settlement, 2000).

claims frequently involve land already occupied by many thousands of Canadians, the claim may be for a sum of money instead of for the land itself. Specific claims continue to be made. For example, specific claims have been made for lands in and around Toronto, Montreal, and Vancouver. The amount of money claimed may be very large because the occupied land has become extremely valuable. Since 1973, when the federal government **instituted** the specific claims process, more than 260 specific claims have been settled, and more than 110 are still being negotiated.

instituted
established; put into place

It will take many years to complete all outstanding comprehensive and specific claims because treaty negotiations are extremely complex. The lessons learned during one set of negotiations, however, are always helpful for the next.

In Closing...

In recent years, Canadians and their governments have realized that the Aboriginal people of Canada have been treated unfairly over the centuries. There has been growing acceptance of the idea that treaties and their promises should be reviewed. Beginning in 1973, a number of Supreme Court cases directed governments to investigate problems **inherent** in many treaties, and to ensure that Aboriginal demands for self-government and a sound economic base were respected. The idea that treaties should be reviewed also came about as a result of the *Constitution Act, 1982,* which recognized the right of self-government for Aboriginal groups, although it did not define self-government or specify how it should be achieved.

inherent
existing in something

QUESTIONS

KNOWLEDGE AND UNDERSTANDING

1. a) What two important principles did the Royal Proclamation of 1763 give to British administrators who dealt with First Nations?
   b) Why were these principles a useful beginning to the treaty-making process?
   c) In what ways were the principles of the Royal Proclamation not followed?
2. In what two important ways did treaties fail to meet the needs of Aboriginal peoples?
3. Explain how each of the following affected the traditional lifestyle of the First Nations.
   a) Canada's greatly increased population
   b) the move of First Nations peoples onto reserves
   c) residential schools
   d) fishing and hunting laws
   e) resource and developments projects
4. a) Describe the difference between comprehensive claims and specific claims.
   b) In what parts of Canada would you expect to find First Nations making
      i. comprehensive claims?
      ii. specific claims?
      Why?

THINKING

5. a) What is the purpose of signing a treaty?
   b) What motivation is there for each of the parties to sign a treaty (a particular First Nation or group of First Nations and the federal government)?
6. a) What is assimilation?
   b) Why would some people view assimilation as the best solution to the problems of Aboriginal people? Why would other people consider assimilation harmful?

COMMUNICATION

7. Explain how the lack of self-government and a poor economic base have contributed to the problems faced by many Aboriginal peoples today.
8. a) In Canada today, some Aboriginal people still live off the land by hunting and fishing like their ancestors did. Others have moved to large cities, and have adopted a completely different way of life. Most Aboriginal people lead lives that combine characteristics of both city living and the traditional ways of life. What factors might determine which of these three lifestyles an individual might choose? What are the advantages and disadvantages of each?
   b) Do you think it will be easier or more difficult to live in the traditional way in the future? Give evidence supporting both points of view. In your opinion, which viewpoint is most likely? Why?

APPLICATION

9. The traditional ways of life of the First Nations are related to the characteristics of the ecozones in which they are located. Construct a chart similar to Fig. 17-7. Refer to Fig. 17-1 and identify the ecozones that lie within the six cultural regions: Inuit, Dene, Algonkian, Iroquoian, Pacific, and Mountain. Then state the main ecological characteristics of each cultural region. Consider the landforms, climate, natural vegetation, soils, and wildlife in each.

▼ **Fig. 17-7**

Cultural Region	Ecozones	Ecological Characteristics
Inuit		
Dene		

The Creation of Nunavut

Key Terms

mineral rights

ecotourism

Northern Strategy

▲ **Fig. 17-8** The Nunavut Coat of Arms (left) and flag (right) are rich in symbolism. Visit the link at www.pearsoned.ca/makingconnections2 to find out what each item represents.

In recent years, Canadians have done something that they have not had to do for half a century: buy a new map of Canada because their old one was out of date. The last time we had to buy a new edition of the map of Canada was in 1949, when Newfoundland (now known as the province of Newfoundland and Labrador) became part of Canada. The most recent map of Canada shows a new territory, Nunavut, created out of the eastern and northern parts of the Northwest Territories.

Since the population and economic base of a territory are smaller than those of a province, a territory lacks the governing power of a province and relies more on the federal government.

Changes in the size and political organization of the Northwest Territories have been common in Canada's history. In the past, Manitoba, Saskatchewan, Alberta, Yukon, and even the northern regions of Ontario and Quebec have all been parts of the Northwest Territories. The creation of Nunavut may therefore be regarded as part of the ongoing evolution of Canada's political structure.

The name Nunavut means "our land" in Inuktitut, the language of the Inuit people. The name describes Nunavut very well for three reasons. First, 85% of Nunavut's people are Inuit. Second, with such a majority of the population, the Inuit are better able to control their own lives. When they were a small minority in the Northwest Territories, they felt that they had little political influence. Most decisions concerning them were made in Yellowknife, the capital of the Northwest Territories, which is located very far from where they live in the eastern Arctic. Third, as managers of their own territory, the Inuit feel that they can more easily protect their culture and develop an economic base that meets their needs.

Nunavut was created after a long series of negotiations between the Inuit Tapirisat of Canada (ITC), an organization representing all of Canada's Inuit groups, and the federal government. The initial proposal to create the new territory was made by the ITC in 1976. In 1982, the people of the Northwest Territories voted in favour of dividing their huge region into two parts. The vote was followed by extended negotiations to create the comprehensive treaty that created Nunavut. A wide range of issues was settled under the treaty, and the final agreement that officially created the new territory of Nunavut was signed in 1993 (Fig. 17-9).

◀ **Fig. 17-9** The people of Nunavut live in 27 small communities that range in size from about 5200 in the capital city of Iqaluit to 160 people in the little village of Grise Fiord.

A treaty had never before been signed in this part of Canada.

Features of Nunavut's Comprehensive Treaty

The features of the comprehensive treaty that created the territory of Nunavut, summarized in Fig. 17-10, ranged from the provision of Inuit land ownership to the creation of three new national parks. In keeping with the new generation of comprehensive treaties, it provided many opportunities for economic development. The treaty established conditions for the development of a sound economic base on which both Inuit and non-Inuit people in the new territory could become self-sufficient and build secure futures.

Fig. 17-10 ▶ Features of the Nunavut settlement

- Inuit own approximately 20% of the territory of Nunavut. This *settlement land* covers about 350 000 km^2.
- Inuit own the **mineral rights** to approximately 10% of the settlement land.
- Inuit have equal representation with the federal government on a number of management boards that monitor wildlife, natural resources, and environmental issues.
- Inuit have the right to hunt, trap, and fish on the settlement land.
- Inuit were given a capital fund of $1.1 billion to be paid over a 14-year period. The monies from this fund are for investment in economic activities that will help develop a sound economic base for the people of Nunavut.
- Inuit have preference in the development of the territory's resources.
- The creation of three new national parks in Nunavut will provide administrative and **ecotourism** jobs for citizens, as well as protection for sensitive environmental areas.
- The settlement calls for a form of territorial self-government in which the majority of decisions are made by residents of the Territory.

Self-government in Nunavut

Although the treaty did not directly provide for Inuit self-government, the result has been just that. Since the Inuit make up 85% of the new territory's population, they are in a position to dominate its government. The government consists of a legislative assembly, a cabinet, and a court system. The people in these institutions, based in the territory's capital, Iqaluit (Fig. 17-11), now make many of the decisions that affect the lives of the citizens of Nunavut, instead of leaving those decisions in the hands of government authorities in far-away Yellowknife or Ottawa.

The transition to full control over the territory by the Nunavut government is a long, slow process. It began in 1993 with the signing of the treaty, and should be complete by 2009. This might seem like a long time, but

◀ **Fig. 17-11** Iqaluit is the capital of Nunavut. With a population of just over 5000, it is the largest community in the territory.

creating a new government is a very complex process, especially when the people taking power have had little experience in running their own affairs.

The government of Nunavut has been working hard to overcome the lack of educated and experienced people needed to take senior jobs in the new administration. In the beginning, it hired non-resident as well as non-Inuit people who had the skills to take the senior bureaucratic jobs. Local people were hired as assistants to the outside experts so that they could gain the experience needed to take over the senior jobs at a later date. In addition, the community college in Iqaluit has set up programs to teach the skills that people need to qualify for government jobs.

Government employees include everyone from court workers and teachers to nurses and game wardens.

Challenges Facing Nunavut

As you might expect, the creation of Nunavut has raised great hope for the future of the territory. People have high expectations for economic growth and the protection and enrichment of their culture. Some serious problems, however, must be overcome; for example, the high cost of living. Consider the following statistics. Goods in Nunavut cost more than in southern Canada (Fig. 17-12). Electricity in Iqaluit costs 15.2¢ for the first 700 kWh and 31.6¢ beyond that amount. In Ontario, the cost is significantly less than 10¢ per KWh (and people here still complain about its cost). Imagine what it would cost to heat a home in Iqaluit, where the average January temperature is about -30°C.

Unemployment is also an enormous problem in Nunavut and has brought widespread poverty and a range of social problems. For example, more than one-third of the people of Nunavut live in communities where the unemployment rate is generally more than 40%, while the Canada-wide unemployment rate is less than 8%. This problem may get worse

Communities in the North are not linked by roads and most travel is by air.

Fig. 17-12 ▶ Groceries in Nunavut are much more expensive than in the southern part of Canada because of high transportation costs. Prices in villages outside Iqaluit would be even higher.

Item	Iqaluit	Toronto
Lean ground beef, per kg	$10.29	$7.25
One dozen eggs	$3.09	$1.99
Two litres 2% milk	$5.99	$3.29
One loaf white bread	$2.59	$0.99
White flour, 2.2 kg bag	$8.49	$3.99
Butter, 454 g	$3.99	$3.19
One head iceberg lettuce	$3.99	$1.49
Granny Smith apples, per kg	$5.78	$2.18

since Nunavut has a very young population with a great many school-age children. The two population pyramids in Fig. 17-13 show the dramatic difference in the age structure of the populations of Ontario and Nunavut. Ontario's population pyramid is typical of most of Canada—the largest age group is adults between 35 and 55. In Nunavut, the largest group is children under 15. In many ways, Nunavut is facing the population situation that southern Canada faced in the 1950s and 1960s. Now Nunavut's government must focus on providing educational opportunities for young people. In the years to come, it must try to ensure enough job opportunities as these children become adults.

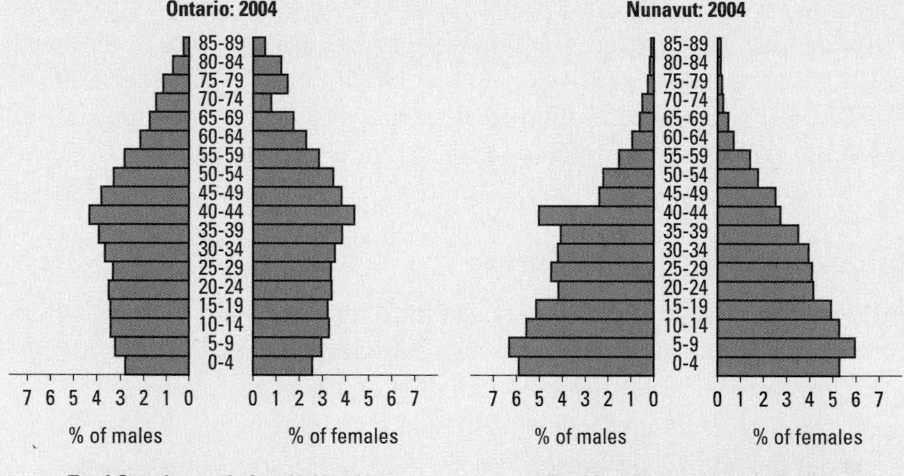

Fig. 17-13 ▶ Population pyramids

Working with a partner, read through Issues 1 and 2, below. Identify the concerns raised, and brainstorm a list of possible solutions. Share your answers with classmates, and compile a class list of solutions.

To learn more about tourism in Nunavut, visit the link at www.pearsoned.ca/makingconnections2.

ISSUE #1:

What is Nunavut's economic potential?

Nunavut's greatest economic growth is likely to come in mining and tourism. The territory's full mining potential is not yet clear. There is good reason to think that Nunavut has rich reserves of copper, gold, silver, lead, zinc, and diamonds.

The question that must be answered is whether these resources can be developed economically and in an environmentally sound manner. Tourism might be a means of developing Nunavut's economy. In recent years, there has been enormous interest in ecotourism. This is environmentally sensitive tourism based on the fascination that people have with the wonders of the natural world—something that Nunavut has in great abundance (Fig. 17-14). Nunavut offers such visitors a unique destination. Before the trickle of tourists to Nunavut increases, transportation connections and tourist facilities will have to improve. Such improvements can be made with monies from the capital fund (see Fig. 17-10).

▲ **Fig. 17-14** Tourism is an industry with great potential for economic growth in Nunavut.

ISSUE #2

Can Nunavut's resources be developed without damaging the sensitive environment?

Resource development must be done with great care since the physical environment of Nunavut is easily damaged and recovers from damage very slowly, due to its cold climate and short summers. The growing season is very short, and this is the time when most environmental recovery must occur. Economic development in the past has often resulted in environmental damage. For example, there are a number of abandoned military radar sites in the North, which now must be treated as hazardous waste sites. On the other hand, there are mines at Nanisivik on Baffin Island and on Little Cornwallis Island that are being operated successfully with strict environmental controls in place.

The Jericho Mine, Nunavut's first diamond mine, is scheduled to go into production in early 2006.

Meeting the Challenge of Life in the Arctic

The challenge of living in the North—including the climate and isolation—are not unique to Canada. They are shared by our Arctic neighbours. Canada is a member of the Arctic Council, an international organization of northern countries that meets to discuss and resolve common concerns. An important part of the Arctic Council is the Inuit Circumpolar Conference (ICC), which includes Inuit peoples from Nunavut, Alaska, Russia, and Greenland.

INTERNET

To learn more about the Arctic Council and ICC, visit the link at www.pearsoned.ca/makingconnections2.

comprehensive
complete, including all or nearly all elements

INTERNET

Find out more about the Northern Strategy through the link at www.pearsoned.ca/makingconnections2.

In 2004, the federal government agreed with the leaders of the northern territories to start working toward the first **comprehensive** development strategy for Canada's North. The purpose of this **Northern Strategy** is to provide an environment within which northern peoples can achieve the best possible political, economic, and social development. The Northern Strategy has many goals, including increasing efforts to sign treaties where they do not exist, encouraging economic development, protecting the environment, and supporting northern cultures. It is the intention of the partners in this venture that the Northern Strategy should be flexible and be able to adapt to meet the changing needs of northerners.

QUESTIONS

KNOWLEDGE AND UNDERSTANDING

1. a) Give three reasons why the name Nunavut ("Our Land" in Inuktitut) suits the new territory.
   b) Describe the steps by which Nunavut became a separate territory.
2. What is self-government?
3. What is the purpose of most of the provisions (listed in Fig. 17-10) of the comprehensive treaty that formed Nunavut?
4. Describe two challenges facing Nunavut.

THINKING

5. Examine a map in your atlas that traces the development of Canada's provinces and territories. Why has the Northwest Territories become smaller over the years?
6. a) Which ecozones are found within Nunavut?
   b) In what ways do the characteristics of these ecozones provide economic opportunities for Nunavut? In what ways might they limit Nunavut's economic future?
7. a) Was the creation of Nunavut well planned? Give reasons supporting your response.
   b) What uncertainties are there about Nunavut's future? Why?
8. What factors do you think the government of Nunavut should consider when planning the following:
   a) transportation
   b) social services
   c) political structures
   d) resource management

COMMUNICATION

9. The Northern Strategy was a new initiative in 2004. Examine the Framework for the Strategy through the link at www.pearsoned.ca/makingconnections2. Look at the *Principles and Goals* and *Objectives* sections of this document. Work with a partner to create a wall chart or PowerPoint presentation that explains the ways this document addresses the specific needs of northern residents of Canada. Identify which aspects of the strategy are likely to be easiest to achieve, and which may prove to be most difficult.

APPLICATION

10. a) What is ecotourism?
    b) Conduct research to determine the main characteristics of typical ecotourists. In your answer, consider such things as where ecotourists might be from, their age, and their level of wealth.
    c) Why might ecotourism prove very popular in Nunavut?

18 Immigration: A Canadian Tradition

Key Ideas

This chapter helps you investigate these questions:

- What patterns can be identified in Canada's immigration history?
- How does Canada's current immigration system work?
- Why do people leave their country (emigrate) to live in another country (immigrate)?
- What patterns of migration exist within Canada, and between Canada and other countries?

Key Terms

multicultural
push factor
pull factor
intervening obstacle
economic immigrant
family immigrant
refugee
interprovincial migration

The vast majority of Canadians—some say as many as 97%— are immigrants or descendants of immigrants. This fact helps to explain why Canada's population can be described as a **multicultural** society. Canada is unique in that it encourages its immigrants to retain their traditions and language while becoming part of the larger Canadian culture.

By completing this activity, you will learn that the number of immigrants varies widely from place to place throughout Canada. You will also learn just how multicultural your own Geography class may be.

Write the answers to the following questions in your notebook.

1. In Fig. 18-1, one set of pie graphs is from a Geography class in the GTA and the other is from a Geography class in a small Ontario town. Which is which? How do you know?
2. a) Conduct a survey to determine the birthplaces of your classmates, their parents, and their grandparents. Your teacher will help by coordinating the survey.
   b) Draw three pie graphs of your survey results, similar to the pie graphs in Fig. 18-1.
3. Compare your pie graphs with those in Fig. 18-1. Did you discover anything unexpected? Discuss your results.

Chapter 8 has instructions for drawing pie graphs.

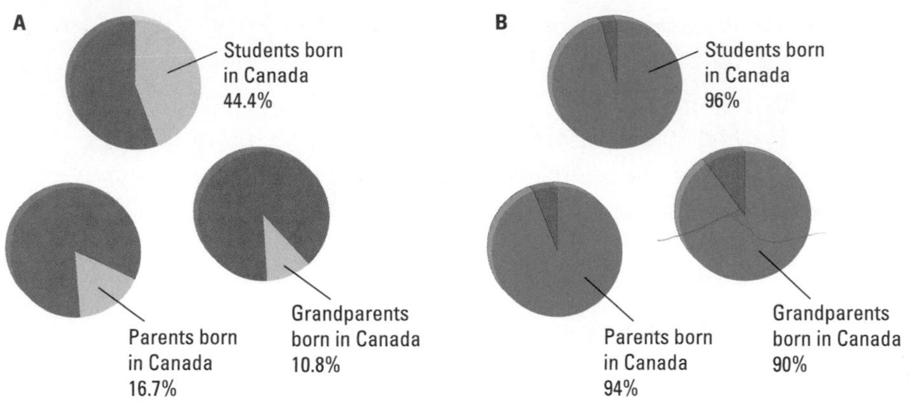

Fig. 18-1 ▶ These two sets of pie graphs represent the cultural makeup of two Geography classes located in different parts of Ontario.

GeoLit Reminder

When reading a graph:

- What is the type of graph?
- Examine the labels and caption.
- What is the purpose of these graphs?
- Describe the trends outlined in the graph.
- Do you need additional information to understand the graph?

Canada's Immigration History

Immigration is one of the dominant themes in Canadian history. There are two reasons for this—the first is related to the growth of Canada's population, and the second to the cultural makeup of the population.

1. The enormous number of immigrants over a period of almost 400 years has been the key factor in Canada's population growth.
2. Immigrants from so many different countries have made Canada the culturally diverse nation that it is today.

In 2005, the government announced that they wanted to increase immigration to 1% of the population, or slightly more than 300 000. Why do you think they did this?

How Many?

Examine Fig. 18-2. This graph shows the number of people who have come to Canada since 1867. As you can see, the number of immigrants has varied enormously from year to year. The number started to increase in about 1905, and reached an annual total of more than 400 000 in 1913. In recent years, more than 200 000 immigrants have arrived in Canada each year.

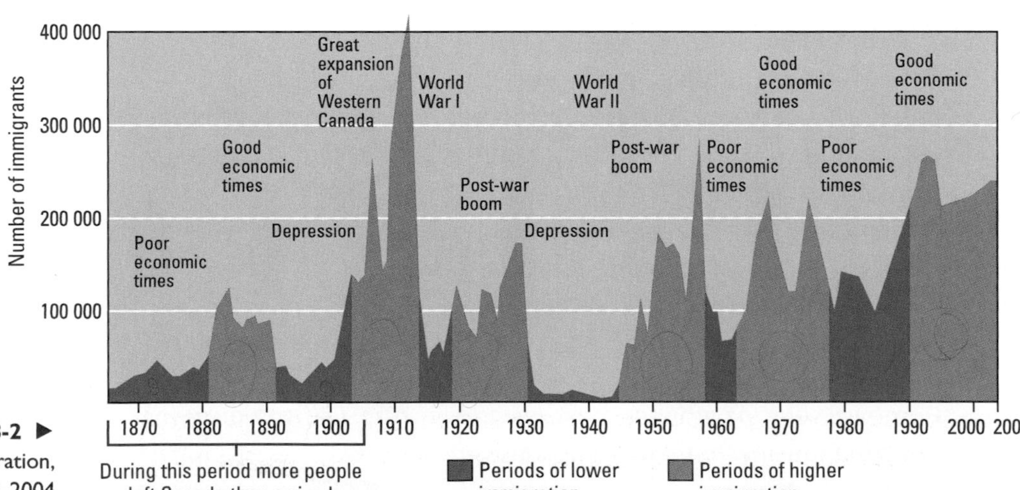

Fig. 18-2 ▶ Canada's immigration, 1867–2004

The reasons for the varying rates of immigration over Canada's history can be traced to a variety of political, economic, and natural factors both in Canada and in other parts of the world. Several of these factors are described in Fig. 18-3. Perhaps you, one of your parents, or another ancestor came to Canada during one of these periods of booming immigration.

When?	What Happened?	Why?
1840s	• Arrival of thousands of Irish settlers	• Irish potato crop fails; facing starvation, many Irish move to Canada and other countries.
1905–1914	• Massive immigration to Canadian west from Eastern Europe	• Canadian government, wanting to settle the Prairies, offers free land and other incentives to immigrants.
1915–1919	• Little immigration	• World War I and worldwide influenza epidemic limit immigration.
1930–1945	• Little immigration	• Worldwide economic depression and World War II limit immigration.
1947–1960	• Many Italians come to Canada	• Italians flee the devastation caused by war and the political and economic uncertainty that followed it.
1956	• Many Hungarians come to Canada	• Hungarian revolt against the Russians fails; refugees come to Canada to avoid punishment.
1980s–1997	• Arrival of thousands of Hong Kong Chinese	• Immigrants seek political stability before China retakes control of Hong Kong in 1997.
1980–2003	• Many people from Afghanistan come to Canada.	• Immigrants seek a safe haven from conflicts that engulfed their country.

◀ **Fig. 18-3** Immigration to Canada has had periods of boom and bust. These were caused by events that occurred in Canada as well as events that occurred in other countries. This table lists some examples of high and low immigration periods and some of the reasons for them.

From Where?

Canada's sources of immigrants have changed over the course of its history. In the 19th and first half of the 20th centuries, people came primarily from the British Isles and Europe, but today people come to Canada from countries all over the world. For the most part, they come because of difficult economic and political conditions in their own countries. Many come because Canada is a **haven** from dangers in their own country. In Canada, they hope to find personal freedom and better economic opportunity.

haven
place of safety

Where will immigrants to Canada come from in the 21st century? Only time will tell as political and economic conditions change all over the world. Most immigrants are likely to come from Asia, but there will also be significant numbers of immigrants from dozens of the world's other countries.

Issue

WHERE DO IMMIGRANTS SETTLE IN CANADA? WHAT IMPACTS RESULT?

◄ **Fig. 18-4** Storefronts, street signs, and newspapers serving different cultures are very familiar in large cities like Toronto, Vancouver, and Montreal, but are almost unknown in many smaller cities and rural areas.

Background

As you learned by completing the exercise related to Fig. 18-1, some classes in Canada are composed primarily of students born outside Canada, while other classes, in different parts of Canada, contain only a very few students born outside Canada. Such an uneven distribution of immigrants within Canada is not new. For example, in 1911, about 57% of the population of both Alberta and British Columbia were born in other countries, while less than 10% of Quebec's population was born outside Canada. Consider the following.

- The uneven distribution of immigrants continues across the country today. In 2001, 18.4% of Canadian residents were born in other countries, but 95% of these immigrants were living in just four provinces: Ontario, British Columbia, Quebec, and Alberta.
- When we examine the number of immigrants living in each province as a percentage of the province's total population (Fig. 18-5), we see that only two provinces, Ontario (26.8%) and British Columbia (26.1%), have a higher proportion of foreign-born residents than the country as a whole (18.4%).

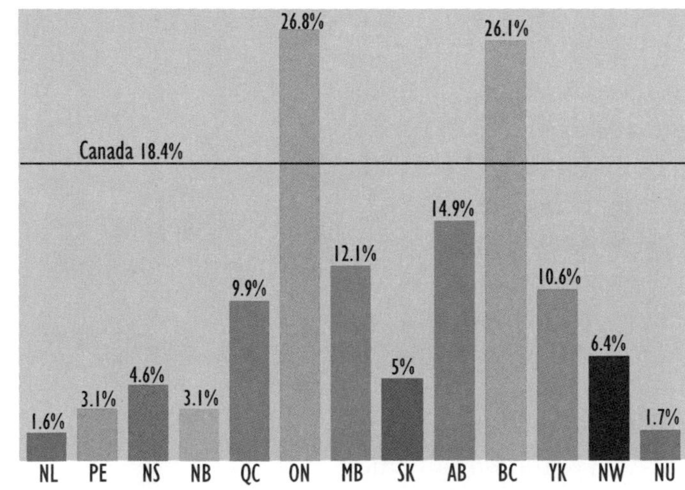

◄ **Fig. 18-5** This bar graph shows the percentage of Canada's and each province's and territory's population that is made up of immigrants.

GeoLit Reminder

When reading graphs:

- What type of graph is shown in Figs. 18-5 and 18-6?
- Examine the captions and labels. What is the purpose of these graphs?
- What general trends are illustrated?
- What additional information might help you further understand these graphs?

Now let's examine immigration to individual cities. Most immigrants choose to settle in cities—and in particular, in Canada's largest ones. Fig. 18-6 shows what proportion of the population of each Census Metropolitan Area (CMA) is foreign-born. It is easy to see the role played by Toronto and Vancouver in explaining the large number of foreign-born residents in Ontario and British Columbia.

Today's immigrants continue to settle in the largest cities. In 2004, almost 100 000 immigrants chose to settle in Toronto. This was more than 42% of all immigrants to Canada. In the same year, 16% chose Montreal and 13% chose Vancouver. Together, these three cities accounted for almost 72% of all immigrants.

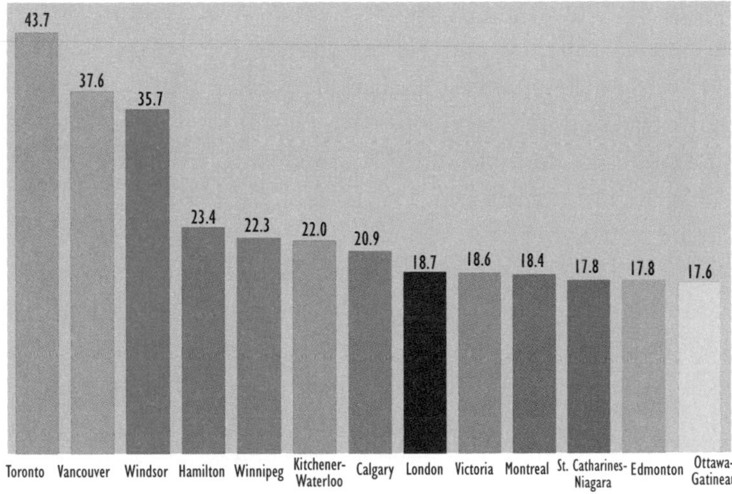

◀ **Fig. 18-6** Percentage of foreign-born population for CMAs with at least 50 000 foreign-born residents

CMAs include the central city as well as the surrounding built-up areas. For example, the Toronto CMA goes as far west as Oakville, as far east as Ajax, and as far north as Newmarket.

Activities

1. Why do most immigrants choose to go to only a few destinations? Consider the advantages that these large cities provide to new residents from other countries.
2. What benefits do new immigrants bring to cities such as Toronto, Montreal, and Vancouver?
3. What burdens do the new arrivals put on these cities?
4. In November 2005, the governments of Canada and Ontario entered into the first-ever Canada–Ontario Immigration Agreement. Visit the link at www.pearsoned.ca/makingconnections2 to read the news release about the agreement and then answer these questions:
   a) What is the purpose of the agreement?
   b) What is the term of the agreement?
   c) How many immigrants does Ontario accept each year?
   d) How will the agreement help immigrants to Ontario?

▼ **Fig. 18-7** Immigration by top source countries, 2004

China	36 410
India	25 568
Philippines	13 299
Pakistan	12 796
US	7 493
Iran	6 063
UK	6 056
Romania	5 655
S. Korea	5 337
France	5 027

Why People Become Immigrants

Why do people leave the country in which they were born and move to another country? Fig. 18-3 on page 215 lists just some of the events of the last 150 years that convinced people to leave their homelands to come to Canada. War, absence of human rights, poor economic and educational opportunities, religious persecution, terrorism, and natural disasters are other factors that may force people to emigrate from the land of their birth. Reasons such as these that cause people to leave their country are called **push factors.**

Sometimes people leave their homelands not because of push factors, but because they are attracted by what they view as favourable conditions in another country. For example, they may wish to join relatives or close friends living in the other country. Or the climate there may be more to their liking. Perhaps job opportunities are better and taxes are lower. Factors such as these that draw people to a country are called **pull factors.** Generally, a combination of both push and pull factors causes people to become immigrants.

Sometimes **intervening obstacles** discourage (or even stop) people from following through on their decision to immigrate. Consider the following examples of intervening obstacles. People might not be able to meet the requirements of the Canadian government that would qualify them as legal immigrants. The huge distance between someone's homeland and Canada might discourage a person from immigrating. Canada might be just too far away from everything a person knows and loves. The costs of immigrating in general, including fees charged by the Canadian government, airplane fare, and accommodation and food upon landing, may be too high.

How Someone Becomes an Immigrant to Canada

Many people want to move to Canada, but the Canadian government has strict rules to decide who will be admitted to the country and who will not (Fig. 18-8). Most people who want to come here do not qualify. Without these restrictions, far more people would come to Canada than the country could accommodate. The government frequently fine-tunes these restrictions as it attempts to balance the number of potential immigrants with the number who would contribute to Canada's economy and society.

Canada accepts three types of immigrants: **economic immigrants**, **family immigrants**, and **refugees**. The number of immigrants in each category who came to Canada in 2004 is shown in Fig. 18-9.

INTERNET

To see what the Canadian government says about immigrating to Canada, go to the link at www.pearsoned.ca/makingconnection2.

◀ **Fig. 18-18** Fifty-three new Canadians are sworn in during a citizenship ceremony at the Museum of Civilization in Gatineau, Quebec.

Economic Immigrants

Economic immigrants include skilled workers and business immigrants. In both cases, if one person qualifies, all the members of the immediate family qualify.

To be accepted as a skilled worker, a person must receive 67 points in a complicated system that is designed to identify which people are most likely to become successful residents of Canada. Fig. 18-10 summarizes the point system used by the federal government to determine which people should be allowed into Canada. The point system is adjusted by the government from time to time to ensure that the immigrants who best meet Canada's economic needs are chosen.

Business class immigrants must show immigration officials both a willingness and an ability to make a significant financial contribution to Canada's economy. They can do this by establishing a business, buying a business, or making an investment that creates at least one job outside their own family. The amount of investment will vary depending upon where the business immigrant wants to settle. For example, a larger investment is needed in Ontario than in Newfoundland and Labrador. Immigrants applying in the business class category need to score only 35 points under the point system to gain entrance to Canada.

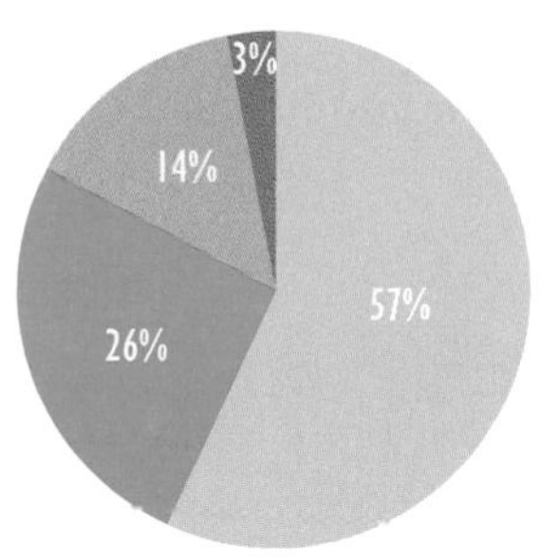

economic class 133 743
family class 62 745
refugees and other protected persons 32 683
other 6 435

▲ **Fig. 18-9** Permanent residents by category, 2004

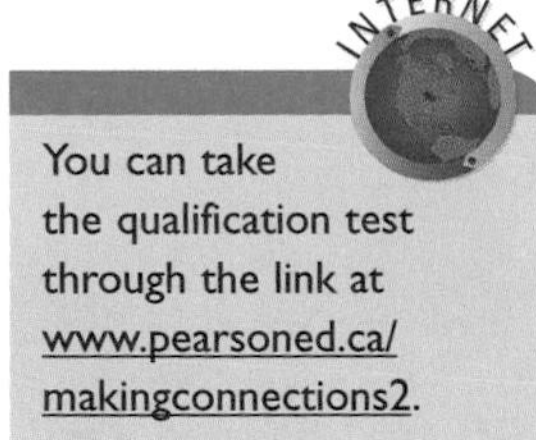

You can take the qualification test through the link at www.pearsoned.ca/makingconnections2.

Family Immigrants

The purpose of this category of immigration is to allow Canadian residents (both citizens and landed immigrants) to reunite their families by bringing their close relatives to Canada. Eligible relations include spouses, dependent children, parents, grandparents, and, in some cases, brothers and sisters, nephews and nieces, and grandchildren.

The length of the period of support depends on the immigrant's age and the relationship to the sponsor.

Every family immigrant must be sponsored by a relative in Canada. The sponsor agrees to provide the immigrant's housing and other needs for three to 10 years if the immigrant runs into financial difficulty. In an extreme case, a sponsor might have to sell his or her home or borrow money to meet this obligation. The risks associated with sponsorship, along with stricter government rules, have made it harder to sponsor family members than in the past. These factors have gradually reduced the number of family immigrants.

Refugees

A special category of refugee includes victims of natural and human disasters, such as famines and wars.

A refugee is someone who fears cruel or inhumane treatment (or even death) in his or her home country. This persecution may occur for reasons of race, religion, nationality, political opinion, or membership in a particular social group. People can apply to become refugees while in Canada as visitors, or while living in their home country. In a typical year, the number of refugees coming to Canada ranges from 24 000 to 33 000.

▼ **Fig. 18-10** The point system is used to decide which people will be allowed to become economic class immigrants. In 2005, a skilled worker needed 67 points and a business immigrant needed 35 points to qualify. Family class immigrants and refugees are not assessed using the point system.

Factor	Maximum Points	To Get the Maximum Points You Need:
Education	25	A graduate degree and at least 17 years of full-time or full-time equivalent study
Language ability	24	High proficiency in both English and French
Work experience	21	Four or more years of experience
Age	10	To be 21 to 49 years of age
Arranged employment	10	A confirmed offer of permanent employment recognized by Human Resources Development Canada (HRDC)
Adaptability	10	A spouse who is well-educated; the applicant or spouse to have studied and worked in Canada; to have an arranged job; family living in Canada
Total Score	100	

Interprovincial Migration

Migration occurs between the provinces of Canada as well as between countries. **Interprovincial migration** is an important force in Canada's geography. Year after year, some provinces gain migrants from other provinces; this is referred to as in-migration. Other provinces lose population to other provinces; this is referred to as out-migration.

Complete the following activity to help you understand the relationship between international migration and interprovincial migration.

1. Fig. 18-11 shows the number of international immigrants and emigrants for each province and territory. Calculate the net number of international migrants for each province and territory.

Net Interprovincial Migrants		Number of International Immigrants	Number of International Emigrants	Net International Migrants
—	Canada	244 579	35 866	208 713
-1875	NL	547	78	469
-222	PE	312	30	?
-473	NS	1705	793	?
-1650	NB	870	300	?
-2332	QC	43 459	5601	?
-8375	ON	129 998	15 991	?
-3832	MN	7676	1327	?
-4583	SK	2089	599	?
16 615	AB	17 353	4043	?
7456	BC	40 423	7063	?
-6	YT	58	12	?
-427	NW	80	17	?
-296	NU	9	12	?

◀ **Fig. 18-11** This table shows the number of immigrants and emigrants for each province and territory and the number of interprovincial migrants for period July 1, 2004 to June 30, 2005.

2. Using the results of your calculations in Question 1, and the information about net interprovincial migration given in Fig. 18-11, construct a model for each province like the one shown in Fig. 18-12. One bar will show net international migration, and the other bar will show net interprovincial migration. Use one colour for international migration and a different colour for interprovincial migration.
3. Compare the impact of interprovincial and international migration on the population of each province.
4. Which provinces gained the most migrants from other parts of Canada? Which provinces lost the most migrants to other parts of Canada?
5. Using the idea of push and pull factors, explain the results shown in Question 4.

▼ **Fig. 18-12** Graph showing the interprovincial and international migration of Newfoundland and Labrador

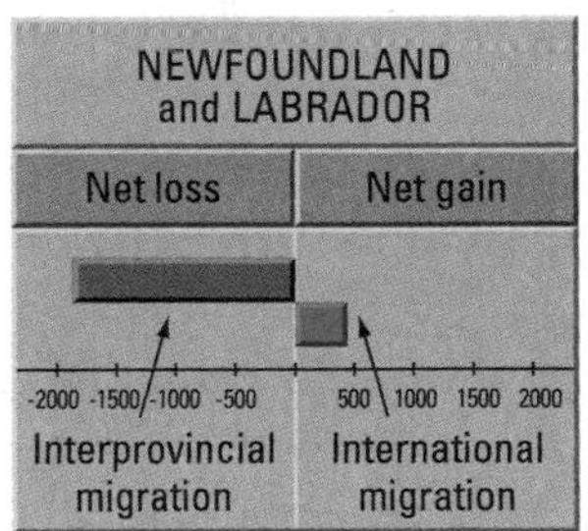

In Closing...

Canada has a long history of immigration and will continue to accept immigrants well into the future. Why? Canada has a low birthrate, and the country needs immigration to boost an aging population that will not grow by natural increase alone. It also needs immigrant workers to replace the large numbers of baby boomers who began to leave the work force at the turn of the 21st century. Immigration is good not only for the country, however, but also for immigrants themselves who, because of their hard work and determination, are able to work toward a secure and prosperous life in our multicultural society.

QUESTIONS

KNOWLEDGE AND UNDERSTANDING

1. a) Name two countries that have only recently become major sources of immigrants to Canada.
   b) Why do the sources of immigrants change over the years?
2. a) Examine Fig. 18-2. Name two time periods when immigration was high and two periods when immigration was low.
   b) What factors caused these periods of high and low immigration?

THINKING

3. a) Which four provinces have traditionally attracted the most immigrants?
   b) Give three reasons why these provinces are the most attractive destinations for immigrants.
   c) Could this pattern change in the years to come?
   d) Now examine Fig. 18-5. Which four provinces attract the most immigrants in relation to their total population?
   e) Is there a difference between the four provinces in your answers to part a) and part d)? If so, explain why.
4. a) Define *push* factors and *pull* factors.
   b) List two push factors that were mentioned in the text, then add two more that were not mentioned in the text.
   c) List two pull factors that were provided in the text, then add two more that were not mentioned.
   d) Define *intervening obstacles*.
   e) List two intervening obstacles that were given in the text, then add two more that were not mentioned.
5. a) Determine the push and pull factors involved in the decision of your family, or that of a classmate, to move to Canada.
   b) Did any intervening obstacles have to be overcome at that time?
6. a) Examine Fig. 18-10. What factors does the immigration system favour in potential immigrants? Why does the government think that each of these factors is important?
   b) Does the current immigration system benefit Canada? Explain.
   c) Does it benefit the countries from which immigrants come? Explain.
   d) What changes, if any, would you make to the immigration system? Explain your recommendations.
7. The point system is very demanding for potential immigrants. Review Fig. 18-10 and information from the link at www.pearsoned.ca/makingconnections2. Would your family get the required 67 points to gain admission to Canada? Why or why not?

8. If you are an immigrant to Canada, what did you find surprising when you arrived in Canada? If you are not an immigrant, ask someone who is an immigrant to describe what he or she found surprising about Canada.
9. Over the past 10 years, an average of about 50 000 people per year have emigrated from Canada.
   a) Where do you think most of these people go?
   b) Identify at least two push factors and two pull factors that might contribute to such a decision.
   c) This emigration number is lower than it has been in previous decades. Why might this be?
10. a) The United States has been called a "melting pot" of immigrants. What does this mean?
   b) How is the term "melting pot" different from the Canadian idea of "cultural mosaic"?
   c) Describe the advantages and disadvantages of each approach.
   d) Which approach do you think makes more sense for a country that receives many immigrants?
11. How would Canada be affected
   a) if we had no limits on immigration?
   b) if we allowed no immigrants to come to Canada?

COMMUNICATION

12. Discuss the following questions with a number of your classmates. Be sure to take notes on your discussion.
   a) What is a refugee?
   b) Why are refugees allowed to come to Canada?
   c) Is it fair to people who are waiting to be accepted as independent immigrants to have refugees admitted quickly?
   d) In a court, juries convict someone only if they think that person is guilty "beyond a reasonable doubt." How strong should the evidence be to prove that a person is a legitimate refugee?
13. The economic immigrant system has been criticized for how skills are evaluated. Two complaints in particular have been made:
   i. Doctors, engineers, teachers, etc., are recognized as professionals when seeking admission to the country. On their arrival, however, they discover that their qualifications are not accepted for work in their profession.
   ii. Canada has a growing need for skilled trades (electricians, plumbers, machinists, etc.). The point system, however, does not allocate enough points for people with these skills. Hence they do not qualify for entry.

   Research one of these issues and write a formal letter to your Member of Parliament suggesting what you think should be done about the issue you select. Before mailing (no stamp needed!) or e-mailing your letter, show it to your teacher for comments.

APPLICATION

14. a) Some people say that business immigrants get into Canada much more easily than others (they only need 35 points instead of 67) because they are rich. Do you think this is a fair statement? Why or why not? Should the business classification for immigrants be eliminated or changed?
   b) Research the contributions of business immigrants to Canada.
   c) Did the opinions you expressed in part a) change as a result of your research in part b)? Explain.

19 Rural Settlement Patterns

Key Ideas

This chapter helps you investigate these questions:

- What factors affect rural settlement patterns?
- What role do survey systems play in determining rural settlement patterns?
- Why did scattered settlements develop?
- In what ways is rural settlement changing and what are the potential impacts of those changes?

Key Terms

settlement pattern
rural
population distribution
population density
rural settlement
survey system
long lot
tributary
concession system
section system

Canada's population is not evenly distributed throughout the country. This uneven distribution pattern can be illustrated by comparing the populations of two of Canada's ecozones. Go back to Fig. 15-3 and locate the Taiga Cordillera and the Mixedwood Plains. More than 15 million people live in the Mixedwood Plains, while only about 300 live in the Taiga Cordillera, and 80% of those people live in one village. Differences in population between other regions may be less dramatic, but it is fair to say that **settlement patterns** in Canada vary enormously from place to place. Large cities, **rural** areas, ocean coasts, and remote regions have been settled for very different reasons, and have unique settlement patterns as a result. In this chapter, we will focus on rural settlement. Urban settlement will be the subject of the next chapter.

An Introduction to Population Distribution

In general, people tend to live in one of two settlement patterns: spread out from one another, or close together. The term **population distribution** refers to these two characteristics of settlement patterns. Dispersed patterns are typical of areas with an agricultural base because people tend to live on farms that are spread out over the region (Fig. 19-1). Concentrated patterns occur where other natural resources are present. The economic opportunities that result from the development of the resource draw people to settle close together near the resource. For example, a gold mine attracts miners and their families to live close to the mine. Other

Towns and cities that provide services to farmers also tend to be dispersed.

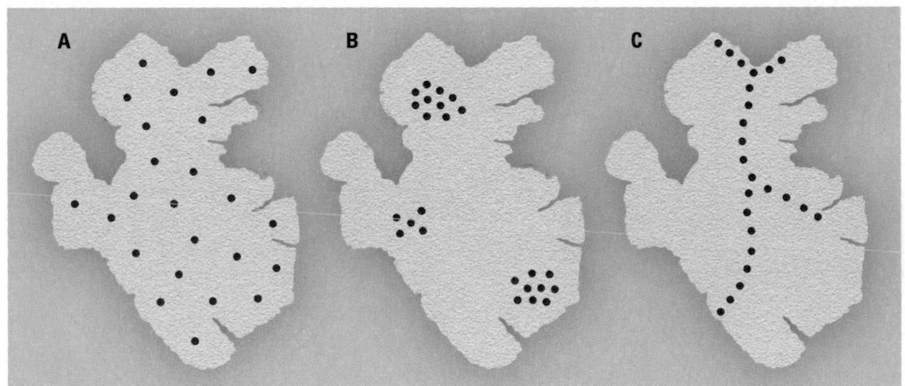

◀ **Fig. 19-1** Population in an area can be either dispersed (A) or concentrated (B). A linear pattern (C) is a specialized example of a concentrated pattern. The island shown in each of these patterns is one square kilometre in size.

people settle close to the mine to offer goods and services to mine workers and their families. This results in a concentrated pattern of population distribution around the mine, creating a town.

Sometimes settlement occurs in a line that stretches out for some distance over the landscape. This is a special kind of concentrated settlement pattern known as a linear pattern. Linear patterns exist where the economic activities that support people have developed in a line. For example, linear patterns of settlement occur along major highways in isolated areas. People have settled along highways because they can make a living offering services to travellers. Linear patterns also exist along ocean coasts where fishing is an important industry.

In Canada, population distribution patterns vary: the population is concentrated in some places and dispersed in others (Fig. 19-2). For example, more than 90% of Canadians live within 600 kilometres of the border with the United States. This area represents less than 10% of Canada's land area. Almost all of Canada's major cities and productive farmland are located here. The remaining 10% of Canadians are scattered throughout the rest of the country.

Be careful not to confuse **population density** with population distribution. Population density refers to the number of people living in a square kilometre; it is expressed by a mathematical calculation. The areas shown in Fig. 19-1 have the same population density (24 people/km^2), but each has a very different population distribution.

Rural Settlement Patterns

Settlement in Canada can be divided into two major categories: rural and urban. **Rural settlement** occurs outside cities and towns. Rural settlement is characterized by low population density and a dispersed population distribution pattern.

Three key factors affect the pattern of rural settlement in any area.

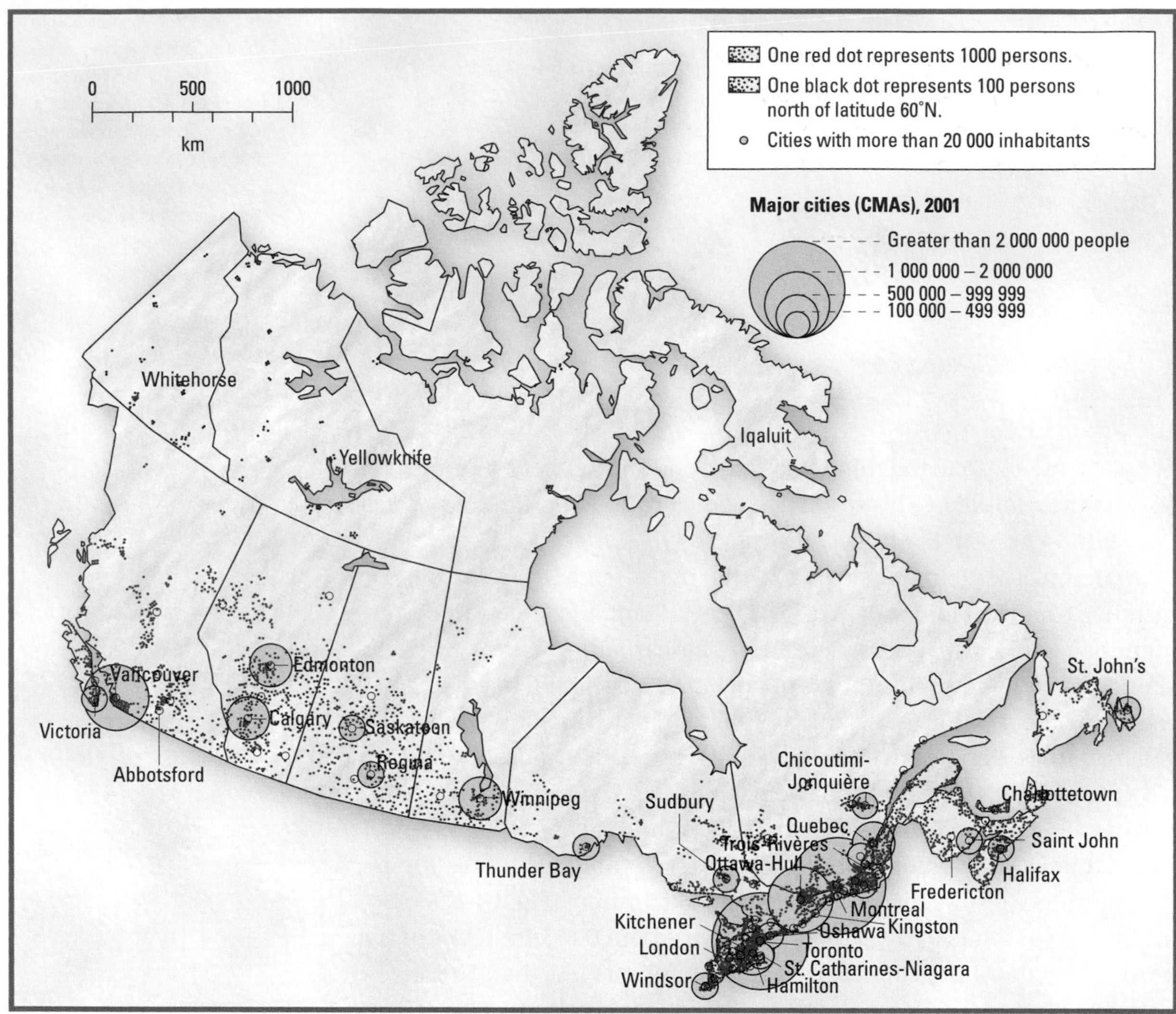

▲ **Fig. 19-2** Canada's population distribution is anything but even.

1. ***The kind of resources found in the area:***
   Perhaps the most important factor that determines the rural settlement pattern is the kind of resource that attracts people to the area in the first place. For example, southwestern Ontario, an area with rich agricultural resources, developed a settlement pattern very different from that of the Canadian Shield, where forestry, mining, recreation, and transportation provide the economic base.
2. ***The transportation methods available at the time of settlement:***
   Before 1800, settlement occurred in areas where the most efficient transportation was by water, since rivers and lakes were the transportation routes used by settlers. After 1800, settlement generally occurred along roads and where railroads were built. As time passed and technology advanced, people could settle almost anywhere they wished because they were able to build the transportation routes to get there.

3. ***The role played by government policy:***
   In some areas, settlement occurred with little, if any, government input. In other areas, the government carefully planned how, where, and when settlement would occur. A set of rules that controls how land will be settled and specifies the pattern of land division is called a **survey system**. Survey systems were used to determine the size and shape of farms, the pattern of roads, and the location of towns so that each area would have the services it required. Different survey systems were used in different parts of Canada.

The combination of these factors results in three **distinct** rural settlement patterns that are clearly visible on topographic maps and in aerial photographs and satellite images.

distinct
clearly different

You would be able to see one of these rural settlement patterns from an airplane window if you were flying over any one of three particular areas of Canada:

- the long lots of southern Quebec
- the concession system of southern Ontario
- the section system of the Prairies

Let's now look at each area and investigate how its settlement pattern was affected by the three factors discussed above.

Note that all three areas are in either the Mixedwood Plains ecozone or the Prairie ecozone. Most of Canada's rural residents live in these two ecozones.

Long Lots of Southern Quebec

- The rich agricultural resources of southern Quebec attracted people to settle on farms along the shores of the St. Lawrence River.
- Southern Quebec was settled long before the development of roads and railways, and before a survey system was in place.
- The **long lot** pattern of settlement was a result of the fact that transportation was by boat (by sled in winter) along the rivers of southern Quebec—the St. Lawrence River and its tributaries being the most significant.
- Since people had to have access to water for transportation, each farm was built with a relatively small frontage along the St. Lawrence River (or a **tributary**). The settlement pattern took the shape of many narrow farm lots that stretched back long distances from the river.
- The settlement pattern in southern Quebec took the form of long lots. When all the river lots had been settled, a second row (and sometimes a third and fourth row) of long lots was settled along a road parallel to the river. The long lot rural settlement pattern is shown in Fig. 19-3.

Fig. 19-3 ▶ The long lots of southern Quebec give the region a very distinctive appearance. In early Quebec, it was desirable to have a narrow lot because taxes were based on the amount of river frontage.

Concession System of Southern Ontario

- Rich agricultural resources similar to those in southern Quebec attracted people who settled on farms in southern Ontario.
- Roads (and later railways) rather than waterways were the major transportation routes for settlers. Rural settlement patterns were influenced by the presence of roads rather than water.
- Major settlement of southern Ontario occurred after the concession survey system had been put in place.
- In the **concession system**, the land was surveyed into blocks (Fig. 19-4). Concession roads and sideroads ran perpendicular to each other, and were approximately two kilometres apart. Farms were usually 40 to 80 hectares in size. Settlement occurred on farms spread out along the concession roads and sideroads. A variety of concession systems was used by surveyors.
- A group of concession blocks is called a township; a group of townships is called a county. Townships and counties in southern Ontario are of irregular size and shape.

Concession roads and sideroads remain as the major roads today in both rural areas and in cities.

Section System of the Southern Prairies

- The Prairies were surveyed before major settlement occurred. Surveyors used the **section system** (Fig.19-5), a very simple survey system that had been used in many areas of the United States.
- The Canada–United States border at 49°N latitude was used as the base line. The land was divided into blocks, each with an area of 94 square kilometres (9.6 km by 9.6 km).

The section system was in use before the metric system was introduced in Canada. Each block was 6 miles (about 9.6 kilometres) by 6 miles in size.

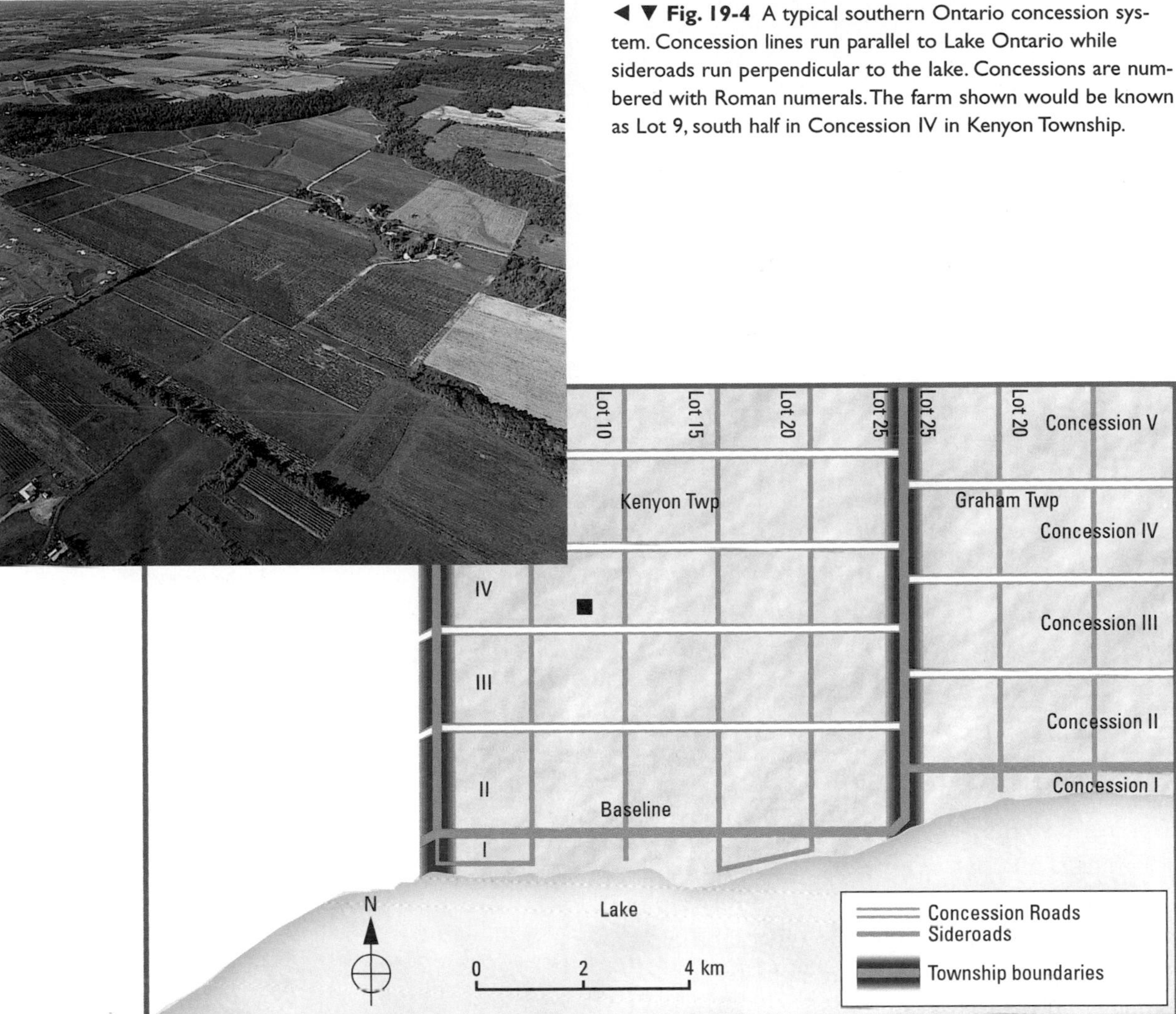

◄ ▼ **Fig. 19-4** A typical southern Ontario concession system. Concession lines run parallel to Lake Ontario while sideroads run perpendicular to the lake. Concessions are numbered with Roman numerals. The farm shown would be known as Lot 9, south half in Concession IV in Kenyon Township.

Each block was divided into 36 sections; each section was then divided into four quarter-sections. Quarter-sections were about 64 hectares in size.

- The section system was originally developed for the American Midwest, where rainfall was substantially greater than in many areas of the Canadian Prairies. It soon became obvious that some farms needed to be bigger than the Canadian government had planned because lower rainfall resulted in less production per farm than in the US. Some farmers began to buy neighbouring quarter-sections because they needed to enlarge their production base, or because their neighbours' farms were failing. This started a process that came to be known as farm **consolidation.**
- The rural settlement pattern of the southern Prairies was determined by the section system. Pioneer families settled on farms that were spread out along roads bordering sections and quarter-sections.

consolidate
combine separate items (e.g., small farms) into a single unit (e.g., one large farm)

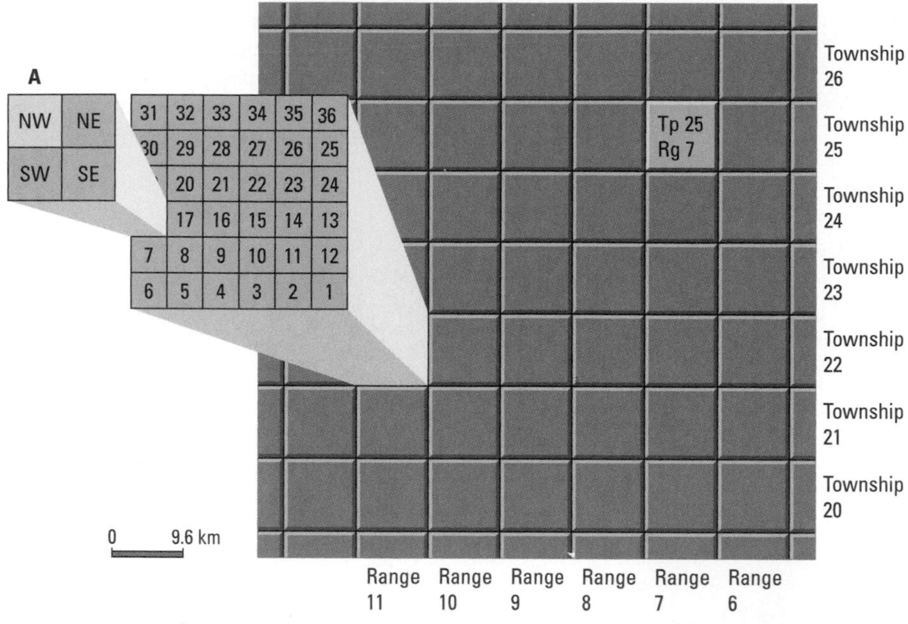

◀ **Fig. 19-5** The Prairie section system is based on the creation of townships, which are identified by the intersection of township rows (numbered from south to north) and range columns (numbered from east to west). Within each township there are many blocks, each with 36 sections, which are numbered as shown. Each farm family received one quarter-section. The farm labelled A on the diagram would be described as Subdivision NW, Section 18, Township 22, Range 11. Can you see the outline of the sections and quarter-sections in the photo? ▼

Comparing Southern Quebec, Southern Ontario, and Prairie Rural Settlement Patterns

Each rural settlement pattern has particular advantages and disadvantages. In southern Quebec, farmhouses on long lots are very close to their neighbours. People can rely on others nearby for companionship and help in emergencies. On the other hand, long narrow lots are not very efficient to work. Since the back of the lot is a long way from the farmhouse, the farmer has to travel a long distance to work the fields at the back of the farm.

Large consolidated farms on the Prairies are efficient to work because they are very well-suited to the use of modern farm machinery. However, families on these large farms frequently suffered from feelings of isolation because they lived so far away from their neighbours. Farm consolidation only made this problem worse because consolidation resulted in fewer farms located farther apart. Today, the problem of isolation is somewhat reduced because most people have vehicles. Nonetheless, they still have to drive long distances to work, school, and social activities. The farms on concessions in southern Ontario fall midway between those of southern Quebec and the Prairies with regard to efficiency and problems of isolation and long travel distances.

Scattered Settlements

Canadians have settled in other rural areas besides southern Ontario, southern Quebec, and the Prairies. In general, settlement that is scattered about in the more isolated parts of Canada has occurred for two main reasons: the presence of resources and the need for services.

RESOURCE-BASED SETTLEMENT

Only a few resource-based settlements are scattered throughout the ecozones of northern Canada. In southern Canada, there are a number of ecozones in which the presence of resources has been the cause of isolated rural settlement: the Atlantic Maritime, the Boreal Shield, the Boreal Plains, the Montane Cordillera, and the Pacific Maritime ecozones. Fig. 19-6 summarizes the importance of the resources that led to settlement in each of these areas. Isolated resource-based settlements are not present in the Mixedwood Plains or Prairie ecozones of Southern Canada.

Ecozone	Agriculture	Commercial Fishing	Forestry	Mining/Energy Production	Recreation
Atlantic Maritime	* * *	* * *	* *	*	* *
Boreal Shield	*	* *	* * *	* * *	* * *
Boreal Plains	* * *		*	* * *	*
Montane Cordillera	* *		* * *	* * *	* * *
Pacific Maritime	*	* * *	* * *	*	* *
* * * important		* * somewhat important		* limited importance	

◀ **Fig. 19-6** This figure shows the resources that have led to isolated rural settlement in five ecozones in southern Canada. The importance of each resource was determined by examining the economic base of each ecozone.

SERVICE-BASED SETTLEMENT

Some people settle in isolated rural areas because they can earn a living by providing services to residents and to travellers passing through. Service-based settlements in isolated areas are scattered along major roads that are usually lightly populated (Fig. 19-7). People who work in service-based settlements of this kind usually own gas stations, souvenir shops, motels, and small restaurants that cater to travellers on busy highways.

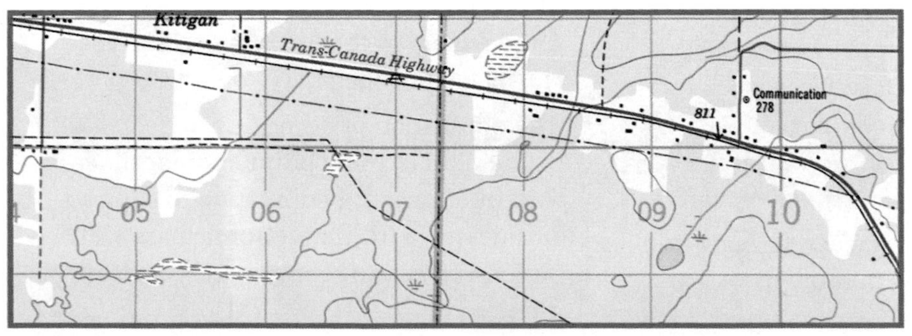

◀ **Fig. 19-7** Many of the people who live along the Trans-Canada Highway in this part of northern Ontario earn their living by providing services to people travelling along the highway. On topographic maps, houses and other buildings are represented by tiny black squares and rectangles.

Issue

RURAL POPULATION; RURAL DEPOPULATION

◀ **Fig. 19-8** More than 5 million people live within a 200-kilometre radius of Huntsville, a town at the heart of Muskoka cottage country. Between 1996 and 2001, the permanent resident population of the town grew by 8.9%.

Rural Population Growth

Some rural areas and small towns in Canada are increasing in population. These places are usually located near large urban centres. *Urban sprawl*, the term that describes the **phenomenon** of rapid and widespread urbanization, is especially prevalent where large cities grow outward from their core, engulfing farmland and small communities. Urban sprawl is also occurring in cottage country north of Toronto and Montreal. Rural population growth is also occurring in small towns where people wish to retire and in some northern communities because of high Aboriginal birth rates and the development of resource-based industries.

phenomenon
an occurrence that can be observed

Rural Depopulation

In some parts of Canada, however, **rural depopulation** is occurring. This is particularly true in Saskatchewan and Newfoundland and Labrador where the rural population has been decreasing for decades.

The decline in population in rural areas and small communities can be attributed to several factors.

- Changes are occurring in the scale of agriculture. The need for large farming populations has decreased because modern agricultural technology now allows fewer farmers to accomplish the tasks that were once performed by many.
- As farming expenses increase, farmers find their profits declining. In order to maintain or expand their profit margin, they must farm larger tracts of land. They often buy or rent more land from other farmers. As their farms become larger, the total farming population decreases.
- Young people leave rural areas to pursue post-secondary education in large urban areas. Many do not return because there are no businesses in which they can find employment in the field they studied at university or college.
- The population of a small town decreases as the rural farming population declines. Without a farming population to support businesses, a town's economic base will suffer. This, in turn, affects the provision of

other services such as postal delivery and healthcare.

In 2003, a report commissioned by the Ontario government concluded that much of rural Canada is economically unsustainable and that it is futile to try to artificially sustain rural industries, such as farming and resource-based activities. The report suggested that young people should be encouraged to leave, that subsidies designed to develop the rural economy should be eliminated, and that the government's traditional role of providing public services in rural areas should be eliminated.

Activities

1. Define the term *rural depopulation*.
2. Describe the reasons for rural depopulation.
3. Do you agree or disagree with the 2003 government-commissioned report regarding the fate of rural Canada? Explain your answer.
4. Would you like to live in a rural area or small town? Explain.

QUESTIONS

KNOWLEDGE AND UNDERSTANDING

1. a) Explain the difference between population distribution and population density.
   b) Draw labelled sketches in your notebook of the two main kinds of population distribution.
2. What is a survey system? Why were survey systems used?
3. Why did the original farms on the Prairies turn out to be too small? What happened as a result of this?

THINKING

4. a) What are the three general factors that affect rural settlement patterns?
   b) Explain the impact that each of these had on the long lot, concession, and section settlement systems.
5. When sons of French-Canadian families reached adulthood in the 1600s and 1700s, they were given a share of the family farm with frontage on the river. What problems would this cause after a few generations? How might these problems have been solved?
6. A growing number of people are choosing to live in rural agricultural areas but not to farm.
   a) Why might they make this choice?
   b) How might these people earn their living?

COMMUNICATION

7. a) Identify two advantages and two disadvantages of living in a resource-based community in a remote area.
   b) What effect are new communication technologies having on life in remote communities?
   c) Would you want to live in such a remote community? Why or why not? Explain.

APPLICATION

8. Each of the maps in Fig. 19-9 represents rural settlement in a different part of Canada. Indicate which part of Canada each comes from and explain what evidence you have of this.
9. Use an atlas to identify four areas of Canada that have scattered populations.

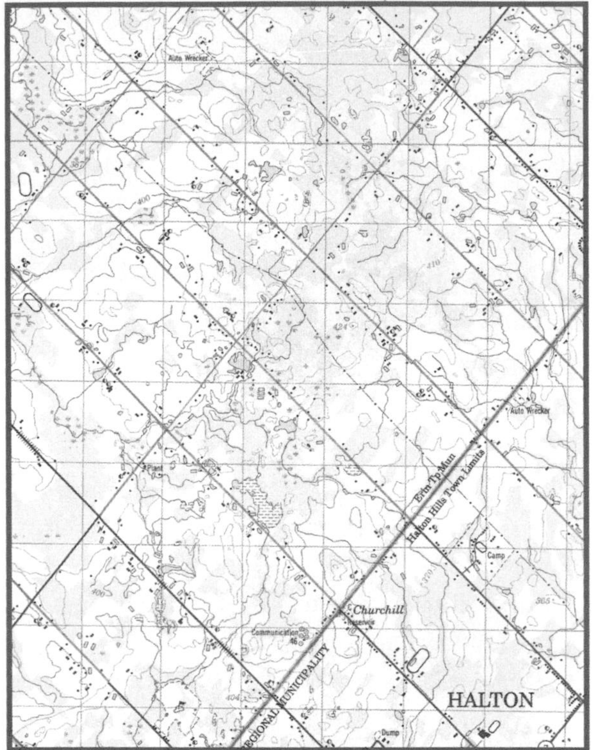

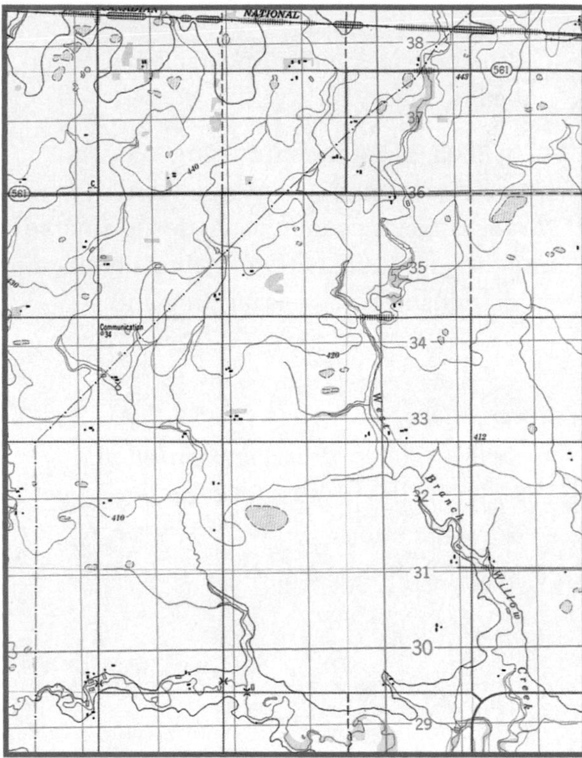

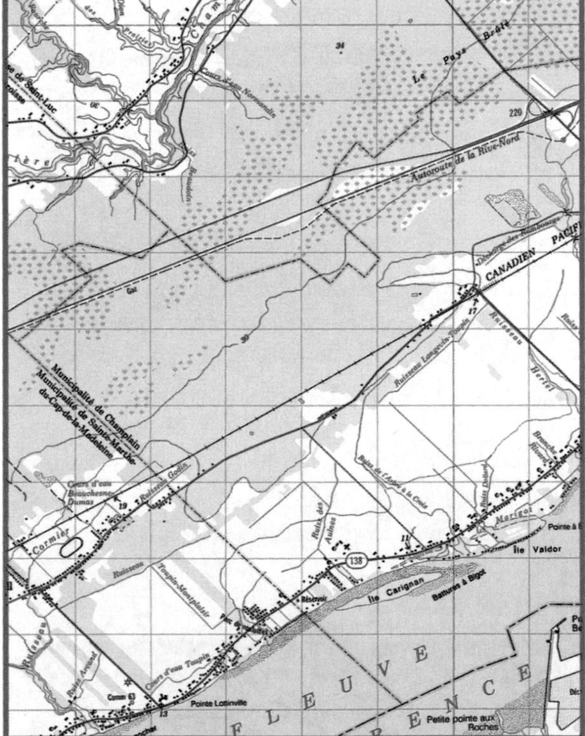

◀ **Fig. 19-9** Rural settlement in different parts of Canada

GeoLit Reminder

When reading visual texts:

- What types of visual texts are included in this activity?
- Examine the caption and labels.
- What is the general purpose of these visuals?
- How do the visuals compare?
- What do you already know about the topic shown in the visual texts?
- What additional information do you need to gather about these visuals?

20 Urban Settlement Patterns

Key Ideas

This chapter helps you investigate these questions:

- What factors influence the location and growth of urban centres?
- What is the relationship between urban centres and hinterlands?
- In what ways do urban places differ one from another?
- What characteristics define "metropolitan dominance?" Which Canadian cities possess those characteristics? What is the impact of metropolitan dominance on the country as a whole?

Key Terms

urban
hinterland
basic industry
economic base
non-basic industry
multiplier effect
central place
threshold population
high-order good or service
low-order good or service
middle-order good or service
diversified urban centre
site
situation
resource-based community
urban growth
urbanization

The Beginnings of Urbanization—The Provision of Goods and Services

Before the **Agricultural Revolution**, the effort of virtually every individual was needed to find enough food for survival. The Agricultural Revolution, however, spared some people from agricultural work because even the most primitive forms of farming produced food surpluses. Freed from the need to produce their own food, people became specialists in other fields, such as weaving, making metal objects, and milling grain. Since these specialists were offering goods and services to others, it made sense for them to live close together; buyers could find all they needed in one place. This is how the first villages came into existence.

Agricultural Revolution the cultivation of plants and domestication of animals that likely started in the Middle East about 10 000 years ago

As agricultural productivity improved over time, and as manufacturing jobs became available, more people moved into **urban** places. Villages grew into towns, and towns into cities. The goods and services produced in towns and cities were exchanged for food products produced in the country. The countryside that trades products for goods and services offered by towns and cities is called a **hinterland**. The **mutual** reliance of

mutual shared

hinterlands and urban places exists today, although it is much less important than in past centuries. For example, rural residents can shop in nearby towns or cities, but they can also shop on the Internet. City residents may buy food products produced on nearby farms, but they may also buy foods from remote places, for example, kiwi fruit from New Zealand and apples from South Africa.

Basic and Non-basic Industries

functions
activities or roles

While the provision of goods and services is the original and still very important reason why a town or city exists, it is certainly not the only one. An urban place exists because there is one or more economic activities that bring money into the community. The **functions** that bring money into the community, and on which the city depends for its existence, are known as **basic industries**. Basic industries provide jobs for residents. For example, if you and your family visit the ski resort of Collingwood, Ontario, part of the money you spend at the ski hill and hotel goes to pay the salaries of resort employees (Fig. 20-1). Workers use this money to buy goods and services. If this money were not flowing into the Collingwood area, people would lose their jobs and move away to look for work.

A community's basic industries make up its **economic base**. An economic base is critical to the existence of both urban and rural places, and its presence or absence helps explain why some places are growing while others are in decline.

Not all business activities contribute to a city's economic base. Some do not bring money into the community. Such activities are known as **non-basic industries**. Consider the example of a small grocery store in a

◀ **Fig. 20-1** In the last few decades, Collingwood's most important basic industry has changed from manufacturing to tourism and recreation.

tourist town. If a local family spends money shopping at the store, the money is actually being "recycled" because it is already present in the town. The store is then acting as a non-basic industry because it is not bringing in money from outside the local community. In fact, most of the money the store takes in will actually leave the town to pay companies and farmers for the groceries that it sells. If new "outside" money is not coming into the community, its economic base will be weak, and the community will not be able to sustain itself. In other words, an urban place cannot survive on non-basic industries alone.

If tourists from out of town shop at the store, however, they spend money that comes from outside the local economy. The store then acts as a basic industry.

Most jobs in urban places are non-basic. Non-basic jobs depend, however, on the existence of basic jobs. Generally speaking, about three non-basic jobs (e.g., in stores, schools, government, etc.) owe their existence to one basic job. When a news story announces the opening of a new factory that has hired 100 workers, it really means that a total of about 400 jobs has resulted—100 basic plus 300 non-basic. The economy of the town will actually grow more than you might expect. This concept is known as the **multiplier effect.** Now consider the multiplier effect in reverse. Suppose a paper mill closes in a small town, and 150 workers are laid off. In the long run, 600 jobs will be lost: 150 basic plus 3 × 150 non-basic.

Christaller's Central Place Theory

A German geographer named Walter Christaller created a theoretical model in 1933 to explain why large cities or towns are located far apart, while small towns or villages are located relatively close together (Fig. 20-2). Christaller's theory is based on the idea that any good or service offered by a **central place** needs a minimum number of customers in the hinterland to stay in business. This minimum number of customers is known as a **threshold population**.

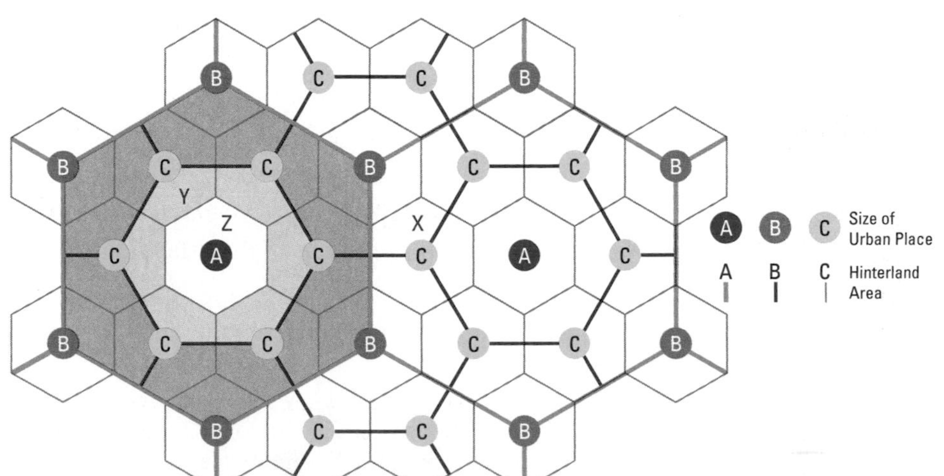

◀ **Fig. 20-2** Christaller's Central Place Theory: **High-order goods and services** are provided only in cities (A) to a relatively large hinterland (shown in green). **Middle-order goods and services** are provided only in cities (A) and towns (B) to medium-sized areas (shown in red). **Low-order goods and services** are provided in cities (A), towns (B), and villages (C) to much smaller areas (shown in grey).

▲ **Fig. 20-3** The Hospital for Sick Children in Toronto provides high-order medical services to children from across Canada and, in some cases, around the world.

An urban place that provides **high-order goods and services** requires a large threshold population. High-order goods and services require a large population to draw from because they are expensive or are purchased infrequently. It follows that a large threshold population is spread throughout a large hinterland. Because their hinterlands are large, urban places offering high-order goods and services grow up far apart from one another. These urban places are large towns and cities. A hospital that provides specialized services, such as cancer treatment, is a high-order service that requires a very large threshold population to survive. You won't find such hospitals in villages or small towns located close to one another, but rather in cities that serve very large areas.

The reverse applies to an urban place that provides **low-order goods and services**. Low-order goods and services require only a small threshold population to remain in business. The people who make up the small threshold population live not too far away in a relatively small hinterland. Because their hinterlands are small, urban places offering low-order goods and services grow up close to one another. Urban places located close together take the form of villages and small towns. A post office is a low-order service that you can find in almost every small town. It survives because it offers a service that is used by a small number of customers, but on a very frequent basis.

Other stores sell **middle-order goods or services**, such as compact discs, clothing, shoes, and office supplies. Middle-order services include family doctors' offices and hair salons. Because we need these goods and services only from time to time, there are relatively fewer customers shopping for them at any given time. As a result, a larger threshold population is needed than for a convenience store. For example, a clothing or sporting goods store might have a threshold population of several thousand families.

Examine Fig. 20-2.

1. Your teacher will provide you with a line master showing Fig. 20-2. Use arrows to show where a person on a farm at X, Y, and Z on Christaller's model would go to purchase high-order goods, middle-order goods, and low-order goods.
2. What factor(s) determine which central place a person will visit to purchase a good or service?
3. Suggest a reason why Christaller chose to use hexagons to represent the hinterlands around central places.

4. Like all theoretical models, this one provides a simple, easily understood explanation of a complex real-life pattern. To do this, Christaller made a number of assumptions. These include the following: the land is flat, and transportation in any direction is equally easy; the population is evenly distributed across the land; and all consumers are equally wealthy. How would the model have to change if these assumptions were not true?
5. How well does Christaller's model work in real life? Your teacher will give you a map of southwestern Ontario that has urban places of varying sizes marked on it. Draw the boundaries between central places of similar size to see if the pattern you get is anything like Christaller's.
   Here are some hints:
   i) Start out by classifying the cities and towns on your map into three levels of urban places, according to population.
   ii) Do not try to get perfect hexagons. The landscape you are working with does not follow all the assumptions of the model.
6. Describe how successful you were in applying Christaller's model to a real place. Indicate why you had this level of success.
7. Give at least two other regions of Canada where this model would work well. Give two regions where it would not work well. Explain your answers. (Hint: Consider the relationship between different kinds of economic bases and different population distributions.)

Different Kinds of Urban Places

Some cities, especially large ones such as Toronto, Montreal, and Vancouver, exist and grow because they fulfill several functions. They act as manufacturing centres, transportation hubs, service centres, cultural centres, and industrial centres. Because they have many functions, as opposed to one dominant one, they are called **diversified urban centres**.

In some cases, however, cities depend to a large extent on one urban function for their economic base. Let's look at five Canadian urban centres, each of which specializes in one particular urban function.

Manufacturing Cities

Some towns and cities came into existence as people began to live near factories where they could find jobs producing and distributing manufactured goods. Urban places where goods are mass produced in factories are known as manufacturing cities.

Fig. 20-4 ▶ An oil refinery takes crude oil as it comes from the ground and breaks it down to its parts. These include various kinds of fuels (e.g., gasoline, diesel fuel, and home heating oil), lubricants (e.g., engine oil and grease), and industrial materials (e.g., asphalt, solvents, and raw materials for making plastics).

North America's first oil well was in Oil Springs, Ontario, which is less than 40 kilometres from Sarnia.

Sarnia, Ontario, is a prime example of a city that owes its existence primarily to the presence of manufacturing. Central to Sarnia's growth has been its role as an oil-based manufacturing centre. This industry began in the late 1800s with the processing of oil from nearby small oil fields in southwestern Ontario. A number of oil refineries were built in Sarnia, especially after 1900, when the growth in the use of cars and trucks fueled a great demand for gasoline (Fig. 20-4).

petrochemical industry industry dealing with chemicals made from petroleum

The next crucial factor in the growth of Sarnia was the beginning of the **petrochemical industry** during World War II. Two huge factories were built: one to make artificial rubber and the other to make plastic. Rubber and plastic were desperately needed for the war effort. The factories were built in Sarnia because the raw materials they needed were by-products of oil refining. After the War, rapid economic growth resulted in a growing demand for rubber and plastic.

In the early 1950s, the Interprovincial Pipeline was built to carry crude oil from Alberta through the United States to southern Ontario and Quebec. Because it was the leading refining and petrochemical centre in southern Ontario, Sarnia was selected as the place where the pipeline would cross over from the United States into Canada. Other major pipelines have been built to bring the city's refineries and chemical plants raw materials of crude oil, natural gas, natural gas liquids, and petroleum by-products. The access to abundant, reliable supplies of raw materials and to nearby markets secured Sarnia's importance as a manufacturing centre.

INTERNET

To learn more about Sarnia, visit the link at www.pearsoned.ca/makingconnections2.

Transportation Hubs

Some urban places become established and grow because they provide important transportation functions. For example, Winnipeg's early growth resulted from the fact that it was a major hub for railways that were built across the country. The port cities of Vancouver and Halifax have developed as important transportation hubs because ship, train, and truck routes connect within each city. This means that cargoes can be transferred efficiently from one means of transportation to another.

Thunder Bay, located in the Canadian Shield on a flat area bordering the western shores of Lake Superior (Fig. 20-5), is one of Canada's most important transportation hubs. As early as 1800, the area was recognized as an excellent **site** for trade.

In 1885, the Canadian Pacific Railway was built through the area; the Canadian Northern Railway (now part of CN Rail) followed in 1902. These rail links permitted the shipment of grain and other raw materials from western Canada to Thunder Bay.

In Thunder Bay, the raw materials were loaded onto ships for transport through the Great Lakes. The transference of raw materials from train to ship makes sense because ships can carry bulk cargoes like grain more cheaply than trains can. With the opening of the St. Lawrence Seaway in 1959, ocean-going ships were able to load grain or other raw materials in Thunder Bay, and then travel directly to ports around the world.

Thunder Bay has one of the largest grain-handling facilities in the world. In addition to grain, the port handles coal and potash from the Prairies, and forest products from the Canadian Shield. Thunder Bay's **situation** has given it enormous transportation advantages for two centuries. As a result, it has become the major city of its region.

The city of Thunder Bay was created in 1970 when the cities of Fort William and Port Arthur were joined.

The Trans-Canada Highway was built along the route of the railways—also through Thunder Bay.

INTERNET

To learn more about Thunder Bay, visit the link at www.pearsoned.ca/makingconnections2.

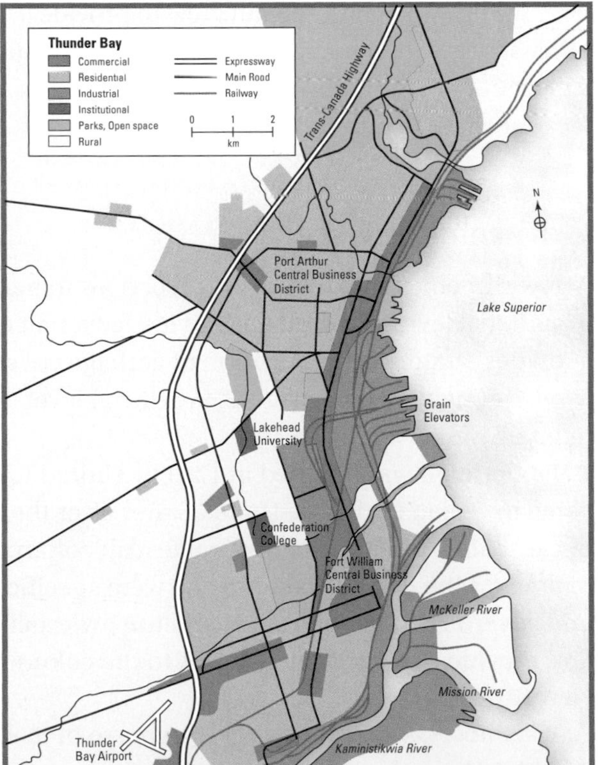

◀ **Fig. 20-5** Notice how the city of Thunder Bay is dominated by transportation facilities.

GeoLit Reminder

When reading a map:

- Examine the caption, scale, legend, and labels.
- What is the purpose of this map?
- Scan the map for patterns and trends.
- What general information does the map provide?
- How are the different pieces of information on the map related?

▲ **Fig. 20-6** More than 3.1 million tourists from across Canada and around the world visit Banff annually.

Tourist Cities

Tourist towns or cities are urban places that develop as a result of a physical or human feature that people are attracted to see or experience. For the most part, a tourist city's jobs are basic jobs because the money that supports the local economy comes in from outside the community. Visitors who pay for goods and services such as accommodation, food, postcards, gas, and entry tickets to the tourist attractions—not to mention tips—bring "new" money into tourist towns.

The town of Banff is a famous tourist town located on the Bow River in the Rocky Mountains of Alberta. In 1884, surveyors for the Canadian Pacific Railway (CPR) were searching for a southern route through the Rocky Mountains and the other ranges in the Western Cordillera. Three railway workers came across a cave on Sulphur Mountain where mineral hot springs bubbled out of the ground.

As people arrived in the park to enjoy the hot springs, scenery, and abundant wildlife, the town of Banff grew to provide accommodation, food, and other services to tourists. Today, Banff is a top tourist destination (Fig. 20-6). Its location on the Trans-Canada Highway makes it accessible by car, and its location close to Calgary's airport makes it easy to reach by air.

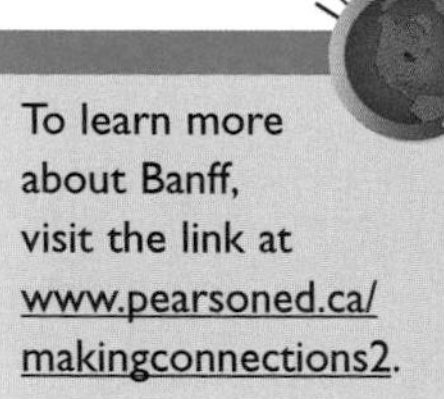

To learn more about Banff, visit the link at www.pearsoned.ca/makingconnections2.

Government Centres

A government centre may provide services to people at a local, regional, or national level. Government services cover an enormous number of activities ranging from provision of garbage collection at the municipal level, through healthcare at the provincial level, to old-age pensions at the federal level.

Fredericton was founded in 1783 by United Empire Loyalists, who came to Canada from the United States after the American Revolution because they preferred to live in a British colony. At the time, large tracts of land on the designated town site were specifically set aside for military and government buildings. Fredericton eventually became a capital city and provided government services to the colony (later the province) of New Brunswick.

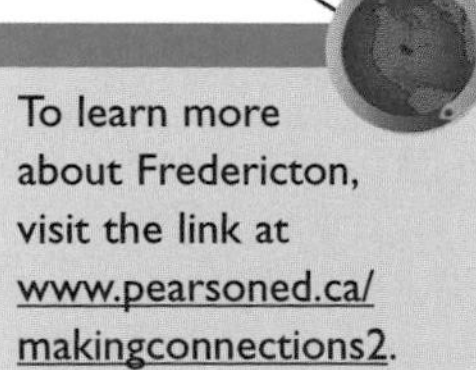

To learn more about Fredericton, visit the link at www.pearsoned.ca/makingconnections2.

Like most capital cities, over the course of its history, Fredericton became a provider of other types of services besides government. As the city expanded, it became a service centre that also offered religious, cultural, medical, and educational services to the region. For example, it became the home of the University of New Brunswick (Fig. 20-7). The presence of students from all over the country caused the further growth of services such as housing, retail stores, and transportation. Fredericton now owes its existence and growth not only to its role as a provider of government services, but also to its ability to supply other services to local citizens and to the rest of the province.

▲ **Fig. 20-7** The University of New Brunswick is just one of the services provided in the city of Fredericton.

Resource-based Communities

Many communities in Canada owe their existence to the presence of a rich natural resource. Villages, towns, or cities that are established to develop a resource are known as **resource-based communities**. Throughout Canada's history, resource-based communities have grown up where natural resources such as forests, fur, iron ore, oil, copper, nickel, water, fertile land, and fish are located. The development of these resources sometimes brings millions of dollars into the community.

Flin Flon, Manitoba, located 800 kilometres northwest of Winnipeg on the Canadian Shield, is a typical resource-based community. Its natural resource is one of the richest copper-zinc deposits in Canada (Fig. 20-8).

◀ **Fig. 20-8** The smoke-stack of the Hudson Bay Mining and Smelting Company towers above the town of Flin Flon.

To learn more about Flin Flon, visit the link at www.pearsoned.ca/makingconnections2.

Although its basic industry is mining, the town has grown to become a service centre for its hinterland and for tourists. It would never have existed in the first place, however, if it weren't for mineral deposits that have been mined since the 1920s.

Urbanization in Canada

When Canada became a country in 1867, 18% of Canadians lived in towns and cities. Today, almost 80% of the population lives in cities and towns (Fig. 20-9). Urbanization is characterized by an increase in population density and by a highly concentrated population distribution pattern. The growth of services and manufacturing further contribute to urbanization.

The terms **urban growth** and **urbanization**, although they sound similar, actually describe two different ideas. *Urban growth* refers to the actual number of people by which a city's population grows. For example, between 1996 and 2001, the urban growth in the city of London, Ontario, was +10 870 people. We arrive at this figure by subtracting the city's population in 1996 from its population in 2001 (336 539 – 325 669 = 10 870). *Urbanization*, on the other hand, refers to the percentage of a country's total population living in urban places.

Urbanization is one of the most important forces in Canadian geography over the past 150 years. In general, urbanization has occurred as a result of new technology and the changes that took place in the economies of both rural and urban places. In rural areas, the use of newly invented agricultural machinery that could do the work of many people eliminated farm jobs. Forestry and mining jobs also disappeared as the use of more efficient tools and machinery became prevalent. Unemployed people began to move to towns and cities in search of jobs. At the same time, manufacturing in urban

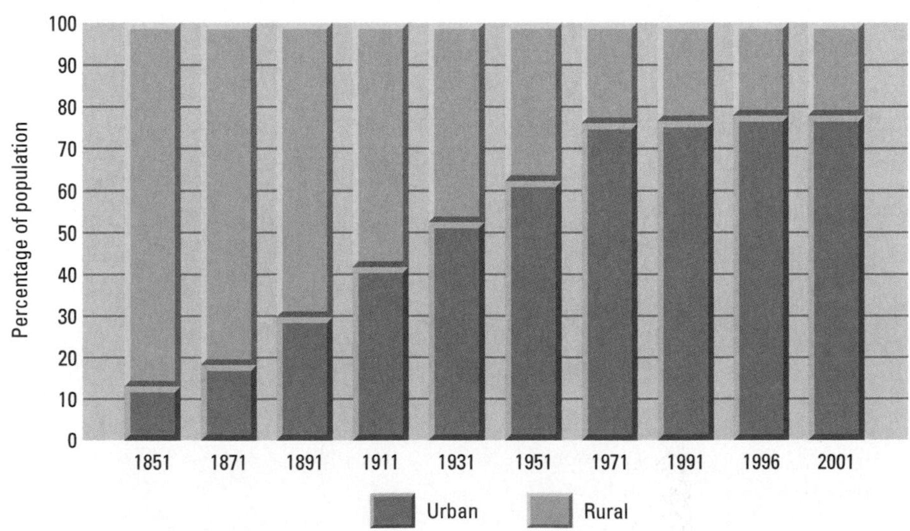

Fig. 20-9 ▶ Canada's urban population has increased dramatically over the years. Why has this happened?

areas began to develop. The rise of manufacturing created new jobs that drew people from rural to urban areas. In growing urban areas, service industries developed to support rising populations. Jobs in the service industries drew more people to live and work in cities. Urban areas continued to grow when immigrants, who in earlier years had settled on farms, settled in cities where they were most likely to find jobs.

How important are cities and large towns in determining Canada's settlement patterns? Consider the rather odd-looking map of Canada in Fig. 20-10. We are used to seeing maps drawn in proportion to the land area they represent. This map is drawn in proportion to the population in each region. It gives dramatic evidence that Canadians live concentrated in cities, not in rural areas.

▼ **Fig. 20-10** On this isodemographic map, the areas of provinces and cities are drawn in proportion to their populations. Describe the pattern you see.

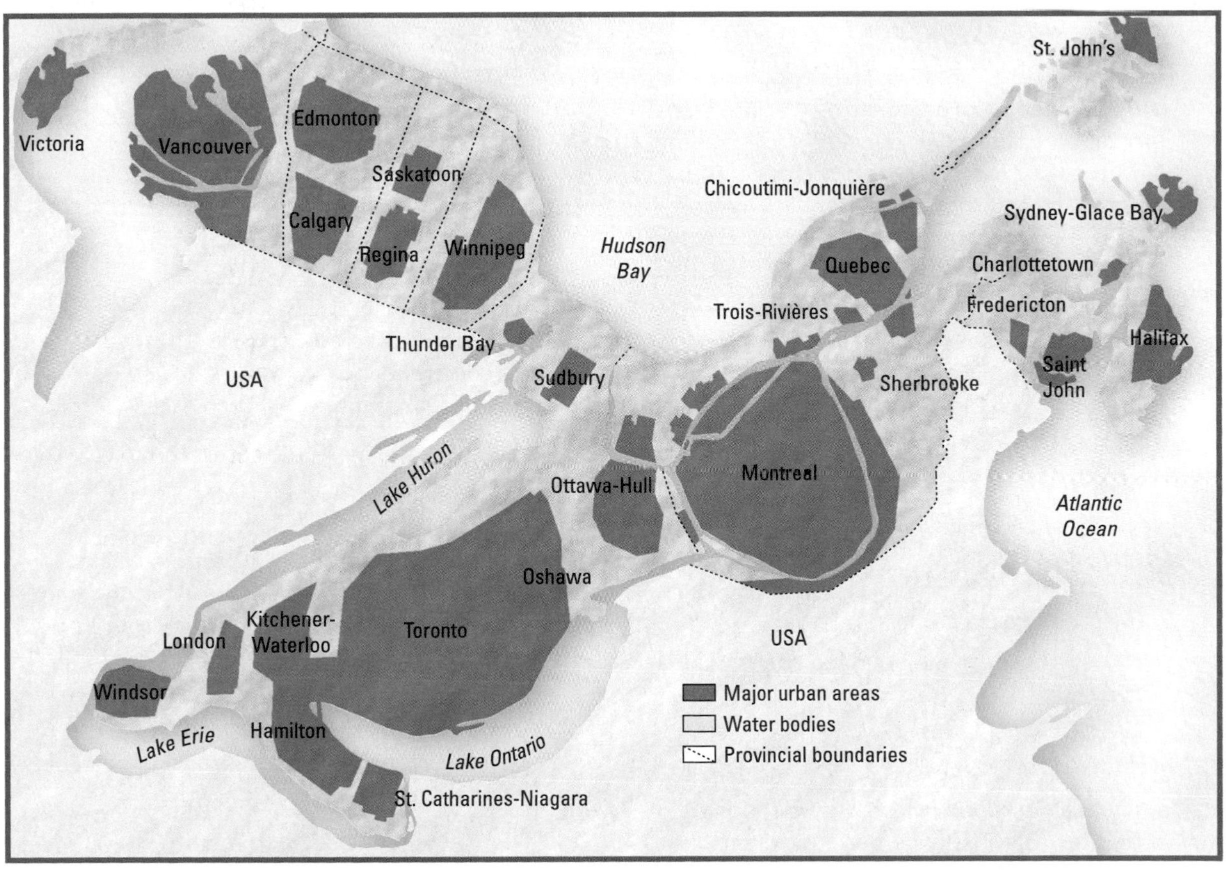

QUESTIONS

KNOWLEDGE AND UNDERSTANDING

1. Define these terms:
   a) economic base
   b) basic industries
   c) non-basic industries
2. Differentiate between the terms *urban growth* and *urbanization*.

THINKING

3. a) What is the multiplier effect?
   b) Give an example of how it works when a new factory is built.
   c) How does the multiplier effect work when a factory closes down?
4. a) With the aid of an atlas, identify at least three Canadian urban centres that are transportation hubs. (Hint: they are small cities, and they are located where a change in the method of transportation occurs. Thinking about the characteristics of Thunder Bay will help you identify them.)
   b) Why is a transportation-based urban centre likely to be relatively small in size?
5. a) Suggest why mining towns and forestry towns rarely become very large.
   b) Under what circumstances might one of these towns grow larger?
6. a) Identify one Canadian town that developed because of the following resources: mining (other than Flin Flon), forestry, hydroelectric power, and recreation.
   b) Why do these towns not tend to grow into large cities?

COMMUNICATION

7. Identify push and pull factors not mentioned in this chapter that influence the movement of people from rural areas to cities.
8. a) While many universities and colleges are located in very large cities, in some parts of Canada there are many smaller college towns. Name at least three of these.
   b) What advantage(s) and disadvantage(s) would there be for a university located in a smaller community?
   c) Would you prefer to go to university in a smaller town or in a big city? Why?
9. Think about the town or city in which you live (or the town or city nearest to you, if you live in a rural area). Describe its major urban functions. Provide evidence to support your answer.

APPLICATION

10. Copy Fig. 20-11 into your notebook, and complete it by indicating where you would find the services listed.

Service	Small Town	Small City	Large City
brain surgery			
daycare for a child			
major league baseball			
daily newspaper			
dental checkup			
Internet connection			
symphony concert			
elementary school			
recreational soccer			

▲ **Fig. 20-11**

11. a) On a map of Canada, locate and label the communities discussed in the "Different Kinds of Urban Places" section. Use a colour code to identify the type of community (diversified, manufacturing, tourist, etc.).
    b) Add two more urban places to your map for each category. Only one of each pair may come from this textbook. Use the same colour code you used in part a).
       i. Manufacturing-based community
       ii. Resource-based community
       iii. Transportation-based community
       iv. Tourism-based community
       v. Government-based community
       vi. Diversified community

21 Urban Land Use

Key Ideas	Key Terms	
This chapter helps you investigate these questions: • What are the principal types of urban land use? • What factors affect land-use patterns? • In what ways does urban expansion affect the surrounding countryside?	land use residential density anchor big-box store zoning winter-city concept	rural–urban fringe urban sprawl new urbanism Smart Growth greenbelt

This chapter will familiarize you with the principal types of urban **land use**. In addition, you will see how these land uses combine to produce our towns and cities. Fig. 21-1 illustrates the amount of land used for each major land-use category in a typical Canadian city.

Fig. 21-2 is an aerial photograph that shows the major urban land uses.

a) On a piece of clear acetate or tracing paper placed over the photograph, trace an outline of the part of the city you can see.
b) Draw and identify the land used for transportation in turquoise.
c) Repeat the process for each other land use that you can identify. Colour each land use according to the colour scheme shown in Fig. 21-1. Note that it is unlikely that you will be able to see all of these land uses in the photo.

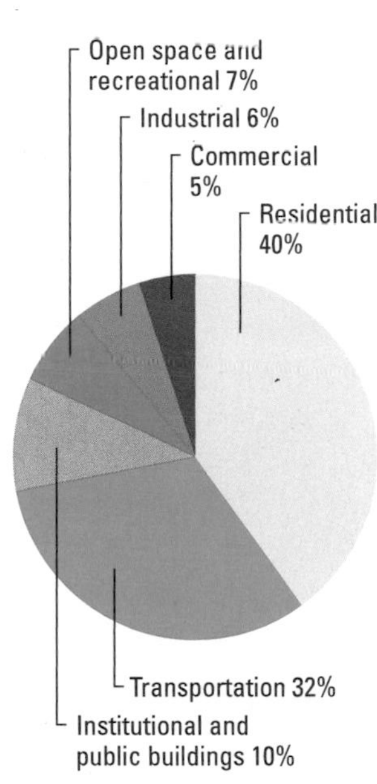

▲ **Fig. 21-1** The percentage of a city's area occupied by major land uses. The colours of each wedge of the pie graph show the most common colours used for each category on Canadian land-use maps.

Land-use Patterns

Almost 80% of Canadians live, work, travel, shop, and spend leisure time in cities. To meet the needs of its citizens, a city must have, among other things, factories, offices, houses, apartments, roads, rail lines, stores, parks, cemeteries, and schools. All these features fall into one of six major land-use groups: residential, transportation, institutional and public buildings, open space and recreational, industrial, and commercial. Each land use serves the needs of individuals, businesses, governments, and the community at large.

Fig. 21-2 ► Urban areas have a variety of land uses in close proximity to one another.

Residential Land Use

Residential land use includes all the places where people live—everything from single-family houses to huge apartment buildings (Fig. 21-3). It is the largest land use in most cities, often taking up 40% or more of the developed land.

Residential density may also be calculated as the number of housing units per square kilometre.

The most important characteristic of residential land use is its density. **Residential density** refers to the number of housing units per hectare (Fig. 21-4). Two factors influence residential density. The first is the cost of land. Where land values are low, usually on the outskirts of cities, single-family homes on large lots are common. In such areas, the residential density is low. Where land is more costly, such as downtown or along major transportation routes, higher density buildings are built because they generate enough income to pay for the expensive land. In those areas, the residential density is higher.

The second factor that influences density is the age of the neighbourhood. Residential areas built before World War II (1940s) tend to have higher densities than those that were developed after World War II. Before

▼ **Fig. 21-3** Different types of residential housing

RESIDENTIAL HOUSING

Types	single-family	semi-detached	duplexes	townhouses	apartments
Characteristics	separate houses with their own yards	two houses joined by one common wall	buildings containing two dwellings, one on top of the other	houses attached together in a row	buildings containing multiple dwelling units, low-rise or high-rise

▼ **Fig. 21-4** Different residential densities. Remember that 1 ha = 100 m x 100 m.

Density	Types of Dwelling	Residential Density (number of units per hectare)	Approximate Number of People per Hectare
Low	Single-family houses, semi-detached houses, duplexes	Less than 30	Up to 75
Medium	Townhouses, low-rise apartments	30 to 100	75 to 250
High	High-rise apartments	More than 100	More than 250

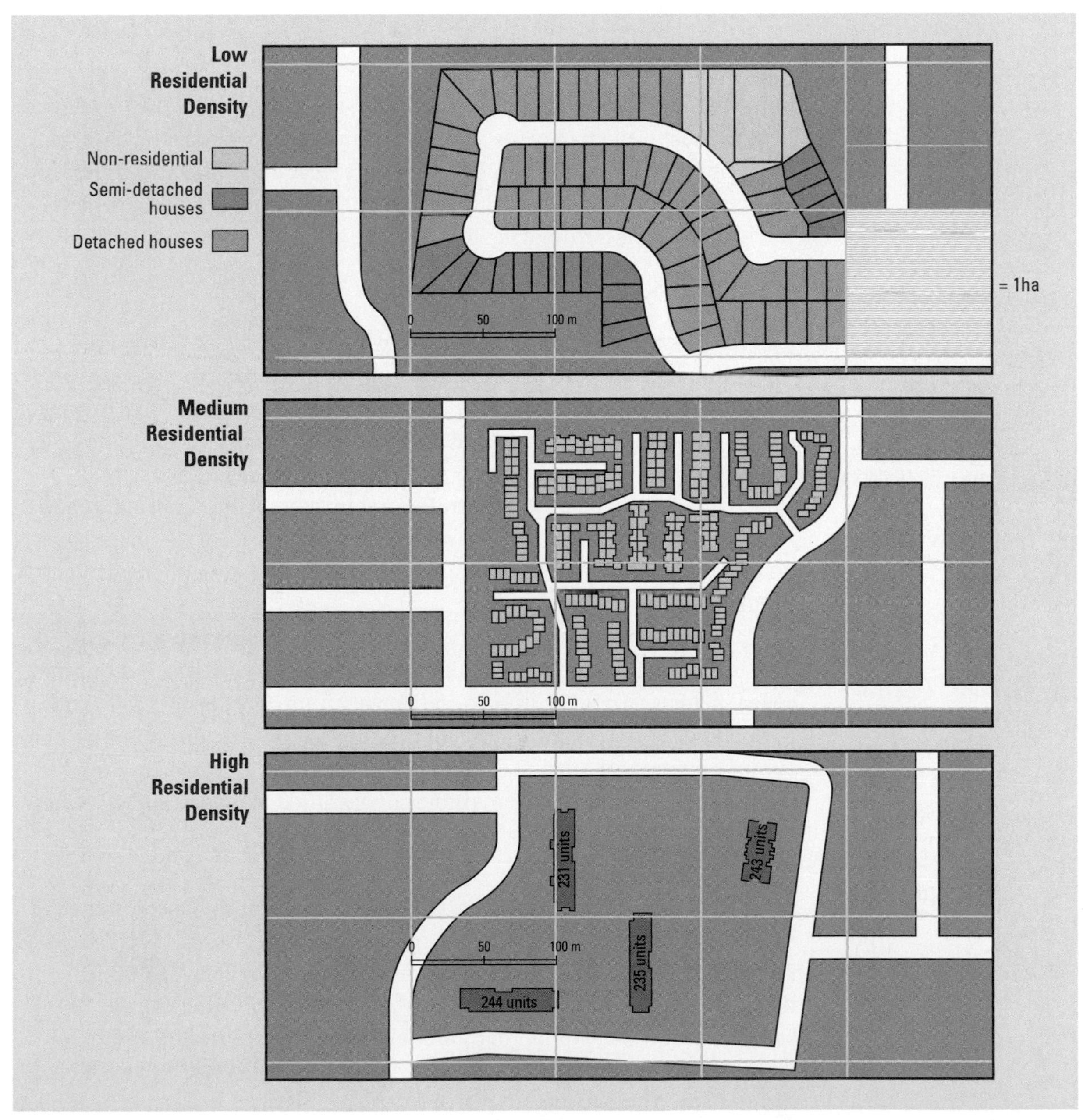

Some older neighbourhoods have lanes and garages at the rear of the backyards.

the 1940s, most people did not own a family car and used public transportation or walked to work, school, or shops. Neighbourhoods were built without garages, large driveways or wide streets for cars. Since most people had to walk (at least to the bus or streetcar stop), it made sense to have narrow house lots. This made the neighbourhood very compact and gave it a higher density. New residential areas in the suburbs are designed with wider lots, wider streets, driveways, and large garages to accommodate one or more vehicles. These new subdivisions generally have lower densities than older areas.

Transportation Land Use

Many people are surprised to learn that about one-third of the developed land in most Canadian cities is used for roads and highways. This large amount of land is needed for the transportation of people and goods. A city's transportation system is made up of three different parts: vehicles, travel paths, and terminal facilities.

The term *automobile* is used to describe a car, van, sport-utility vehicle, or small truck.

A car carries an average of only 1.5 passengers per trip in the city.

VEHICLES

Travelling by private transportation may involve the use of bicycles, motorbikes, or automobiles. The automobile, in particular, provides fast and convenient travel by a route that we select. The automobile, however, can be a relatively inefficient way to travel within a city's boundaries when large numbers of people want to go to the same place at the same time. Large amounts of vehicle traffic create congestion on urban roads. A mass-transit system such as a subway, light-rail line, or dedicated bus lane is a more efficient way to transport people. These methods can carry up to 30 000 people per hour.

Mass-transit systems are very expensive to construct, but are worth the cost in areas with a high population density. They do not make economic sense in areas where the population density is low because there are not enough people to cover the costs of running the system. Residents in a suburban area without a mass-transport system are forced to use their automobiles, and this leads to traffic congestion downtown and elsewhere.

TRAVEL PATHS

Urban roads and highways are classified into four types based on their size and purpose (Fig. 21-5). The largest-capacity roads are *expressways.* They are designed to carry huge amounts of traffic quickly over long distances. *Arterial roads* carry moderate amounts of traffic over shorter distances. Arterial roads are the major transportation routes within cities. Commercial and industrial development takes place along these roads. There are two types of arterial roads: major arterials that have

◀ **Fig. 21-5** Identify the expressway, arterial, and local roads shown in this photograph

four lanes of traffic in peak periods, and minor arterials with two lanes of traffic in peak periods. The third type of road is called a *collector* road: collectors move (collect) traffic from local roads to arterial roads. The last type of roads are *local* roads that are smaller and narrower than arterial roads. They take people from their homes to the arterial roads. Travel paths also include subway, streetcar, and railroad rights-of-way.

Collector roads are most commonly seen in suburban areas.

TERMINAL FACILITIES

Terminal facilities are necessary at the end of all travel paths. Terminal facilities include train, subway, and bus stations, rail freight yards, air ports, docks, and parking lots and parking garages. They can use up considerable amounts of land in a city—with parking lots in particular occupying large areas. In downtown areas, parking lots are frequently temporary fixtures, on land awaiting future development.

Commercial Land Use

About 5% of a city's land is used for commercial activities. These activities include the buying and selling of goods and services in retail businesses, wholesale buying and selling, financial establishments, and a wide variety of services that are broadly classified as "business." Even though these commercial activities use only a small amount of land, they are extremely important to a community's economy. They provide jobs and bring money into the community.

There are six main types of commercial land use (Fig. 21-6).

Type	Range of Goods or Services	Typical Stores	Number of Stores
1. Local service centres	Low-order	Drug store, milk store, variety store	1–5
2. Neighbourhood plazas and ribbons	Low-order	All of the above, plus supermarket, bakery, hair salon, hardware store, bank	5–30
3. Community shopping centres (malls)	Low-, middle-order	All of the above plus small department store, travel agent, jewellery, clothing, and shoe stores	20–100
4. Power centres (big-box stores)	Middle-, high-order	Very large stores of national and international chains, e.g., Wal-Mart, Canadian Tire, Home Depot, Rona, Costco	3–20
5. Regional shopping centres (malls)	Low-, middle-, high-order	All of the above plus major department stores, bookstores, cinemas, and specialized stores	75–300
6. Central Business District (CBD)	Low-, middle-, high-order	All of the above plus very specialized stores	Depends on the population of the city and its region

▲ **Fig. 21-6** Types of commercial land use

1. *Local Service Centres*

- Street-corner shops provide mainly low-order goods and services for people in the surrounding area.

2. *Neighbourhood Plazas and Ribbons*

- In newer parts of the city, small shopping centres contain a number of small to medium-sized stores along with parking areas.
- Businesses also locate in long strips or "ribbons" along major arterial roads in older and newer parts of city. Parking is along the street or in small parking lots in front of the stores.
- They attract local residents as well as customers just driving by.

3. *Community Shopping Centres (Malls)*

- Malls are usually found at major street intersections in large cities, or on the outskirts of towns.
- Most shopping needs can be satisfied in centres of this type.
- They are usually designed around department stores and supermarkets that act as **anchors** for the mall. These stores are located at opposite ends of the mall and attract great numbers of customers to other stores in-between. For example, a shopper may come to the mall to purchase a coat at the department store, have something to eat in the food court, buy a magazine in a bookstore, and then pick up a watch battery at a kiosk before leaving.

- The same types of stores may also be found in ribbons along arterial roads in older parts of the city.

4. *Power Centres*

- The development of **big-box stores** is relatively new in Canada. Companies that need a large amount of floor space for their stores, such as those selling appliances and furniture, home and garden products, large volumes, or a very wide range of merchandise and electronics, have moved away from locations in community and regional shopping malls to separate "big-box" buildings.
- Power centres with three or more big-box stores are located along major roads and highways with abundant parking available.
- Car dealerships are often found grouped together, in many cases near big-box stores along high-traffic roads. Having several car dealerships in one area attracts comparison shoppers for this very high-order good.

> A recent study counted approximately 60 power centres in the Greater Toronto Area (GTA). Across Canada, there are more than 300 power centres.

5. *Regional Shopping Centres (Malls)*

- Large regional shopping malls contain not only the types of stores and activities found in smaller community shopping centres, but also specialized stores that require high threshold populations.
- They are located along major highways in the suburbs of large cities.
- They have large parking lots to accommodate their customers who drive from the city and the surrounding region.
- Their focus is on high- and middle-order goods and services.

6. *The Central Business District*

- The central business district (CBD) is what most people call "downtown."
- It is easily identified by the greatest concentration of the tallest buildings.
- The high demand for office space elevates the land values in the CBD. In order to maximize the use of this expensive land, development companies build tall buildings.
- The CBDs of Canada's largest cities may have financial, retail, entertainment, and hotel land uses (Fig. 21-7). Some land uses are large enough to be found in distinctive districts. The financial district, for example, usually has the tallest buildings and provides offices for banks, lawyers, and stockbrokers. The CBD may also have a retail district. By locating together, retail stores attract more shoppers than they would if they were scattered. Stores in the retail district attract customers from all over the city because the CBD is well served by roads and mass-transit systems. The retail district is usually located next to the financial district because of the large numbers of workers in the office towers.

> The CBD is often not situated at the geographic centre of the city. Over time, the location of the CBD will shift as the city grows and changes.

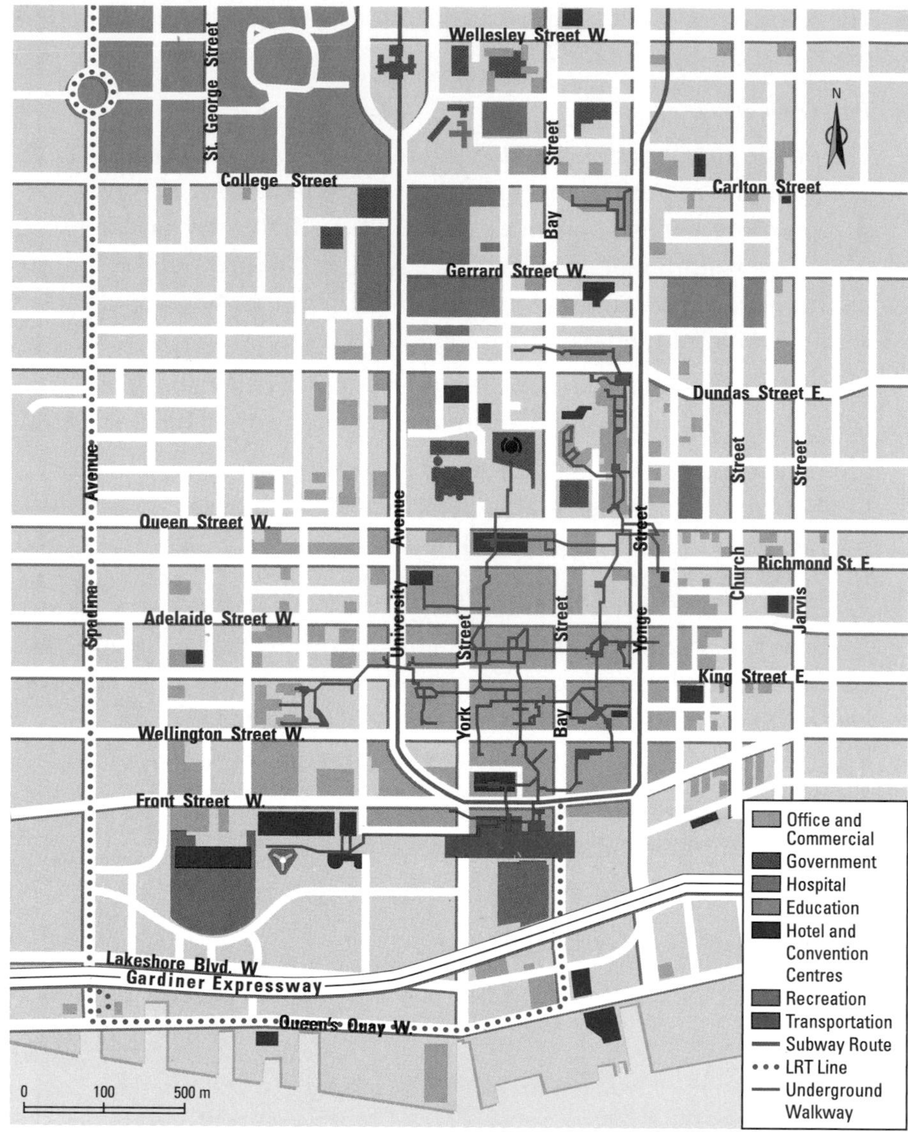

Fig. 21-7 ▶ Toronto's CBD has a number of major land uses.

- Regional shopping malls and big-box stores have grown along with the suburbs and often have a negative impact on downtown businesses. Their large, free parking lots, climate-controlled environment, and one-stop shopping often attract customers who might otherwise shop in the CBD. To compete against suburban malls, city governments and downtown businesses frequently work together to revitalize downtown areas (Fig. 21-9). Or they may build new indoor malls downtown in direct competition with suburban shopping malls. For example, Toronto, Ottawa, Montreal and other cities have built large downtown indoor malls. These indoor malls have been a mixed success. They have attracted shoppers to the CBD, but they have also tended to isolate shoppers in the mall from the surrounding streets. In 2005, a major

◀ **Fig. 21-8** Kingston has been more successful than many Ontario communities in keeping its downtown core healthy.

redevelopment of Toronto's Eaton Centre was completed. One of the purposes of this project was to connect the Centre more effectively to the neighbouring street.

▼ **Fig. 21-9** Some ways to revitalize a declining downtown area (CBD)

Problem	Solutions
Old buildings in downtown	• Tear down and replace • Modernize and expand existing structures • Renovate but maintain "historic" character • Do not try to compete directly with suburban stores; instead, make downtown shopping more specialized—often tourist-focused (see Fig. 21-8)
Congested roads make it hard to get downtown	• Widen roads • Change two-way streets to one-way streets • Expand public transit • Encourage carpooling • Restrict private car access to CBD • Eliminate on-street parking
Limited parking	• Build parking garages • Expand on-street parking
Crowded, unattractive pedestrian areas	• Widen sidewalks • Ban cars on some shopping streets to create a pedestrian mall • "Landscape" sidewalks • Build mini-parks downtown

Industrial Land Use

Industrial land use is an important feature of most towns and cities. On average, about 6% of the developed land in most communities is committed to industrial land use such as factories (processing and manufacturing), warehousing (storage), and shipping products. Modern cities are characterized by four main types of industrial land use—CBD industries, ribbon industries, suburban industrial parks, and suburban business parks (Fig. 21-10).

Before the 1940s, most factories were built on land near waterfronts and railway lines. After the 1940s, better highways and long distance trucking gave manufacturers an alternative to rail transportation. Since the 1950s, many downtown industries have relocated to suburban sites. Their new factories and warehouses are built in industrial parks away from residential areas. Companies custom-built modern, spacious buildings with specially designed water, sewage, power, and fire and police protection facilities. Many have attractive landscaping to hide their factories from view. They are located on the urban fringe, where property taxes are lower, and close to highways to take advantage of modern truck transportation.

▼ **Fig. 21-10** Do you know where each of these industrial land uses is found in your community?

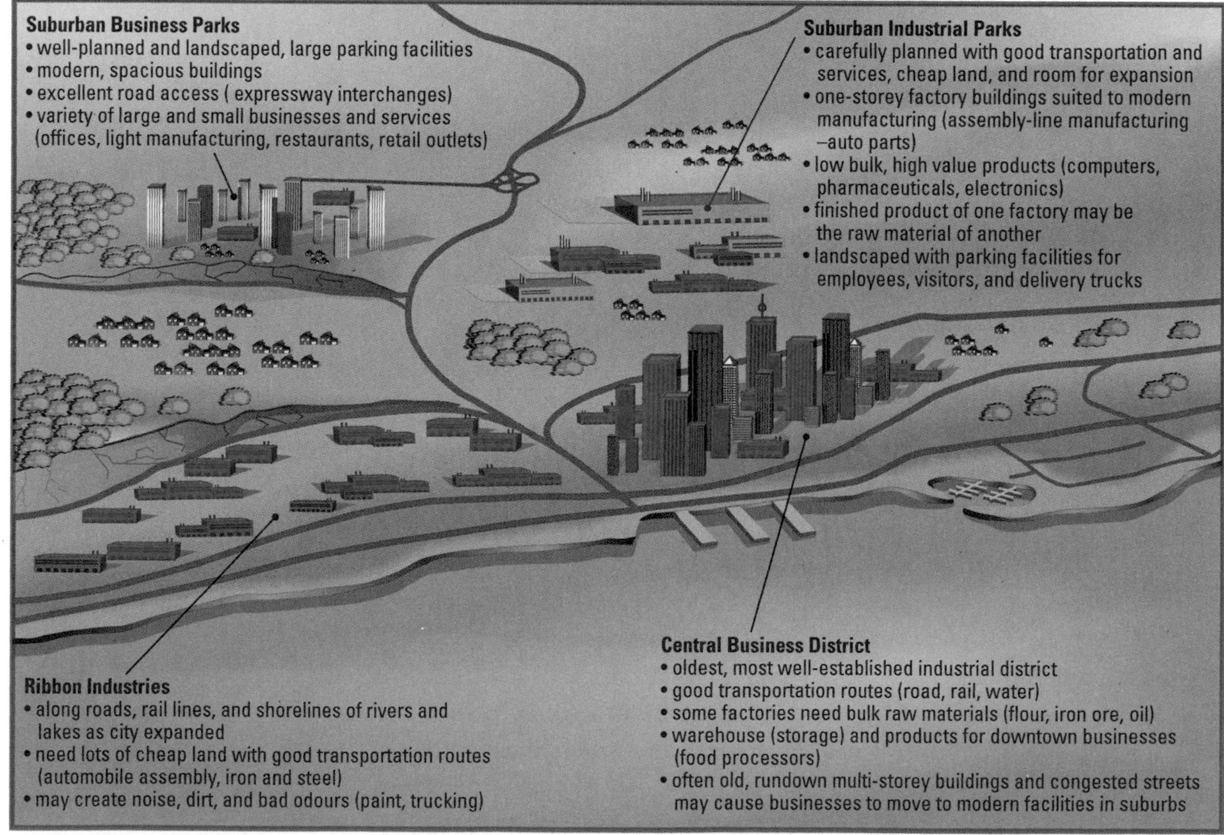

Many older factories and warehouses in or near central business districts are now obsolete. Furthermore, the land they sit on is now too valuable to support inefficient industrial activities. Some may be torn down, and the sites used as parking lots until new buildings are constructed. Other old buildings may be renovated and converted to loft apartments, artists' studios, galleries, nightclubs, offices, and restaurants. Old waterfront factories are often torn down and replaced by residential, commercial, or recreational facilities. In this manner, the downtown area undergoes renewal, and usually becomes more interesting and attractive.

Other Land Uses

Land is used in other ways in towns and cities.

- *Institutional and Public Buildings* About 10% of urban land is occupied by schools, hospitals, government offices, and places of worship.
- *Open Space and Recreational Land* Open space and recreational land occupy about 7% of urban land. Open space may be previously developed land that is now vacant or land that has been left largely in a natural state—for example, a wood lot or a cemetery. Recreational land consists of parks, playgrounds, playing fields, golf courses, fairgrounds, community centres, and arenas. The use of land for recreational purposes in towns and cities is important because recreation enhances the quality of urban life. In February, 2005, the Ontario government passed a law creating a 7200-square-kilometre greenbelt in southern Ontario. It is designed to limit urban sprawl and protect environmentally sensitive land from development.

Factors Affecting Land-use Patterns

Why is an office building built in one particular location in a city, a sewage treatment plant in another, and a golf course somewhere else? Many factors determine land use, but the four most important are land value, zoning, technology, and climate.

There used to be a driving range and small golf course in downtown Toronto, but the land is now being used for high-rise residential buildings.

Land Value

Why are there no one-storey, single-family homes on large lots in the middle of the CBD of large cities such as Toronto and Montreal? It would seem like a perfect location for someone who worked downtown. You could walk to work or to shop, and hop on the subway to go to other places. The obvious reason is that a home like this would cost too much in this area. The land alone might cost millions of dollars. As a result, those who might want to live in the middle of the downtown area have to live in high-rise buildings that may have 40 or more floors. Such high-density development makes economic sense in areas where land is so expensive.

most accessible
most easily reached from all parts of the city

In general, land values are highest in areas of the city that are **most accessible**. The CBD has the highest land values because it is the most easily accessible location in the city. High land values are also found along major transportation routes, especially where such routes intersect (Fig. 21-11). This is why the CBD has the tallest buildings and activities that generate a large amount of income, such as prestige offices and condominiums.

▼ **Fig. 21-11** High land values exist in parts of the city where accessibility to transportation is good.

Land value affects land use not only in the CBD, but also in other parts of the city. Lots for new houses are smaller than they were 20 to 50 years ago because of the increasing cost of land. Businesses that require a large area of land but produce relatively low income, such as a golf driving range, must find inexpensive land on which to locate. This land is usually found on the edge of the city. In most cases, these businesses will stay until the land is needed for permanent uses that produce more income.

Zoning

Zoning bylaws are laws, usually passed by city governments, that control the kind and amount of development in an area. Can you imagine what it would be like to live next to a dirty, smelly factory? Zoning laws are meant to avoid such conflicts between land uses. Governments pass laws that state which land uses are allowed in an area. Fig. 21-12 is a typical zoning map. Conflicts, however, often exist in older areas because these were built before zoning bylaws were enacted.

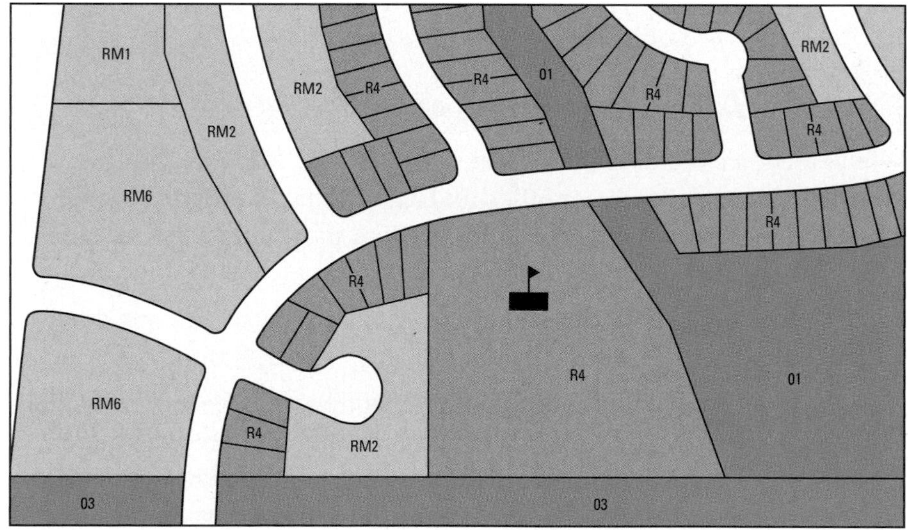

Fig. 21-12 ▶ Zoning maps use a standard code to identify land uses. In residential areas, higher numbers mean higher densities are allowed. For example, an RM6 zoning would allow high-rise apartments, while an RM1 zoning would allow townhouses.

R is single-family residential (schools may also be built in these zones)

RM is multiple-family residential

O1 is open space—park

O3 is open space—utilities

Technology

oblique
aerial photo in which the view is seen from the side, rather than from above as in a vertical aerial photo

Land-use patterns reflect the technology that existed when the land was developed. Compare the two **oblique** aerial photographs in Fig. 21-13. One shows a district built 80 years ago; the other shows a district built in

▼ **Fig. 21-13** These two aerial photographs show two parts of the same city. Which area is older? How do you know?

	Road Pattern	Road Width	Housing Density
Older Area	Grid	Narrower	Higher; smaller lots
Newer Area	Garden	Wider	Lower; larger lots

the past 20 years. The differences in the two photographs can be explained as a result of the widespread use of automobiles after World War II. Urban areas built since then feature wider arterial roads to speed travel and local roads designed to slow traffic in residential areas. Large parking lots and parking garages near schools, shopping, and office buildings are much more evident in the newer areas.

Climate

Canada is one of the coldest nations in the world. The **winter-city concept** advocates the building of cities with inside and outside environments that are livable during long, harsh winters.

Many Canadian cities have built underground walkways in their downtown areas. Toronto and Montreal each have an "underground city" that stretches for many blocks. Workers can get off the subway and shop as they walk to their offices without ever having to venture outside into the snow. Some people live in condominiums that are connected to the underground city. They can work, shop, and pursue recreational activities—all inside.

Fig. 21-14 ▶ The World Water Park at the West Edmonton Mall

Indoor shopping malls have been built, usually in the suburbs, in response to our harsh climate. The West Edmonton Mall is a famous example (Fig. 21-14). It has hundreds of stores as well as extensive indoor recreation facilities, which include an amusement park and a water park. Living plants and trees, running water, and natural light that filters through glass ceilings create an indoor environment that shuts out winter.

Planners with the winter-city concept in mind give just as much thought to the outdoor environments of cities. Bus shelters, sidewalk barriers, and covered walkways protect pedestrians from wind, snow, and flying slush. The location of buildings, the design of public spaces, and the use of natural vegetation are carefully considered in order to protect citizens from harsh weather and at the same time allow ample amounts of sunlight. Skating rinks, toboggan runs, and ski hills encourage outdoor activity.

The winter-city concept is changing people's attitude toward winter. Properly designed winter cities allow people to move around comfortably and to participate in city life—both indoors and outdoors—all year-round.

Urban Expansion

A city expands as its population grows. It expands to make room for new housing, industries, stores, and services for its increasing population. Sometimes a city will expand within its boundaries by constructing high-density buildings on vacant land. Or it may tear down low-density buildings and replace them with high-density ones.

When a city expands outwards beyond its suburbs, it grows into the **rural–urban fringe**. This is an area adjacent to the city where rural land uses are gradually being replaced by urban activities. It is an area of mixed land use and contains such things as farms, gas stations, mobile-home parks, garden nurseries, golf courses, parks, landfill sites, and housing subdivisions. Since residential density is lower in the rural–urban fringe, and land-use activities are farther apart, the public transportation system is not usually well developed. The automobile is therefore a necessity. Automobile use increases the ecological footprint of the residents of the rural–urban fringe.

See Chapter 39 for a discussion of ecological footprint.

Often, development in the rural–urban fringe is not continuous and seems **haphazard**. Ribbons of mixed activities such as motels, auto wreckers, and car dealerships develop beside farmland, vacant land, and low-density residential subdivisions along major highways. This type of development is known as **urban sprawl.**

haphazard
random, without a plan

Some new developments in suburban locations are now being designed more like downtown neighbourhoods, with narrower lots and higher-densities. This type of design, called the "**new urbanism**," reduces urban sprawl on the outskirts of the city.

Urban expansion into the rural–urban fringe contributes significantly to the loss of productive farmland, because most cities are built on land that is well suited for farming. Developers purchase farmland to build new residential communities and to create serviced land for industries.

Protecting the Oak Ridges Moraine

Beginning about 1990, urban expansion in the Toronto area led to increasing concern about the impact on the Oak Ridges Moraine (Fig. 21-15). The Oak Ridges Moraine was formed by glaciers about 12 000 years ago. Located north of Lake Ontario, it consists of a series of rolling sandy hills and river valleys that stretch for 160 kilometres from the Niagara Escarpment in the west to the Trent River in the east. The sand and gravel of the moraine act like a giant sponge, soaking up rainwater and snowmelt. This underground water forms the headwaters of 65 river systems that flow south into Lake Ontario and north into Georgian Bay, Lake Simcoe, and the Trent River system. The unique **hydrological,** geological, and environmental features of the moraine have created an ecosystem vital to southern Ontario. People, agriculture, certain industries, commercial activities, and recreational uses rely on the moraine for drinking water, growing and grazing land, wooded areas, and aggregates (sand and gravel).

65% of the area of the Oak Ridges Moraine lies within the Greater Toronto Area.

hydrological
to do with the science of the properties of Earth's water, especially of its movement in relation to land

In 2001, the Ontario government passed the *Oak Ridges Moraine Conservation Act* and in 2002 passed the Oak Ridges Moraine Conservation Plan. These two pieces of legislation are part of the Ontario government's **Smart Growth** policy. This policy is intended to promote and manage growth of communities, sustain a strong economy in the region, and promote a healthy natural environment.

The conservation plan specifies four types of areas in the moraine, and then sets out the land uses permitted in each area so that the moraine as a whole may be protected.

1. *Natural Core Areas:* These are lands with the greatest concentration of natural features that are crucial to the healthy ecology of the moraine. In these areas, only agriculture, low-intensity recreation, home businesses, transportation and utility uses, and already existing uses are allowed.
2. *Natural Linkage Areas:* These are critical natural and open-space linkages between the natural core areas and rivers and streams. The only uses allowed are those listed for the natural core areas plus some aggregate resource operations.
3. *Countryside Areas:* These provide an agricultural and rural transition buffer between the natural core areas and natural linkage areas and the urbanized settlement areas. Most of the uses typically allowed in agricultural and other rural areas are allowed here, e.g., farms, small hamlets, recreational activities, and aggregate development.
4. *Settlement Areas:* These are areas with a range of urban uses that are set out in the municipal plans of existing communities on the moraine.

The Oak Ridges Moraine Conservation Plan is a long-term plan that will be formally reviewed once every 10 years. The 10-year review cannot remove land from the natural core areas or the natural linkage areas, but can consider such things as changing the boundaries of the countryside areas and settlement areas. The formal review may also consider new science or practices that might improve the plan's effectiveness. Further, it may examine the plan's policies on aggregate extraction in natural core areas, and any other matter that the Ontario government **deems** appropriate.

deems
judges

Fig. 21-15 ▶
The rolling hills, streams, and lakes of the Oak Ridges Moraine provide habitats for wildlife and recreation areas for the residents of southern Ontario. The Moraine acts like a sponge, soaking up rainwater and snowmelt and recharging the groundwater that feeds more than two dozen river systems.

The Greater Golden Horseshoe Greenbelt

Over the next 30 years, an estimated four million people are expected to move to Ontario—most of them to the Greater Golden Horseshoe area. In an effort to curb urban sprawl and protect environmentally sensitive land, provincial legislation to protect 7200 square kilometres in southern Ontario became law in February, 2005. The Greater Golden Horseshoe **Greenbelt** includes and adds to the land within the Niagara Escarpment Plan and the Oak Ridges Moraine Conservation Plan. It covers an area extending 325 kilometres from the eastern end of the Oak Ridges Moraine near Rice Lake in the east, to the Niagara River in the west (Fig. 21-16).

The greenbelt permanently protects thousands of hectares of prime agricultural land in southern Ontario from urban uses such as residential subdivisions, industrial parks, and shopping malls. It protects forests, rivers, and watersheds from recreational uses such as golf courses and ski hills that dramatically alter the landscape. Trail systems, parklands, tourist activities, and sports and recreational facilities that do not significantly alter the landscape will be permitted.

The government has also begun the process of developing a Greater Golden Horseshoe Growth Plan. It will restrict where and how growth occurs in the areas beyond the Greater Toronto Area over the next 30 years.

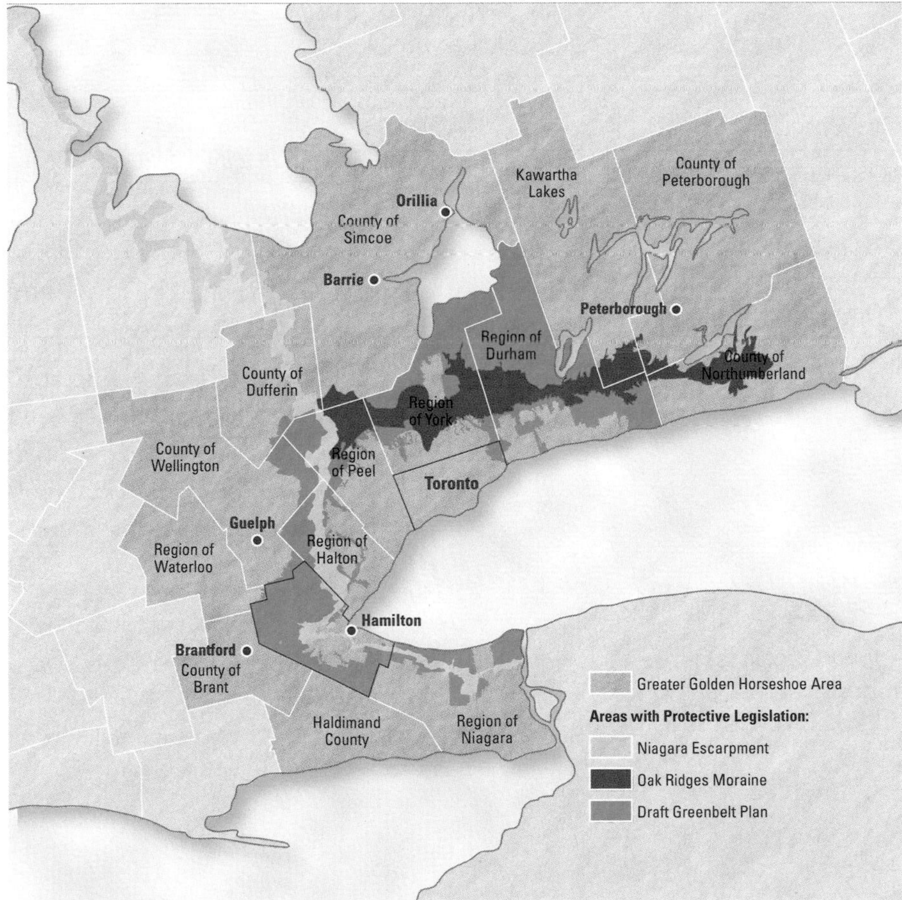

◀ **Fig. 21-16** The Greater Golden Horseshoe (GGH) includes the cities of Toronto, Hamilton, and Kawartha Lakes; the regional municipalities of Halton, Peel, York, Durham, Waterloo, and Niagara; and the counties of Haldimand, Brant, Wellington, Dufferin, Simcoe, Northumberland, and Peterborough. In addition, the cities of Guelph, Peterborough, Barrie, Orillia, and Brantford are within this region.

In Closing...

Land-use patterns in towns and cities do not develop by chance. They result from decisions made by people about such matters as where to work, what type of home to live in, what kind of local government to have, and how to spend money. Your decisions will affect the way your community looks in the future.

QUESTIONS

KNOWLEDGE AND UNDERSTANDING

1. a) Explain the differences between low-, medium-, and high-density residential land use.
   b) Explain the two factors that influence residential density.
2. Describe the differences between the four major types of roads.
3. What are the differences between low-order, middle-order, and high-order goods and services?
4. In your own words, describe the following commercial centres:
   a) local service centres
   b) neighbourhood plazas and ribbons
   c) community shopping centres
   d) regional shopping centres (malls)
   e) CBD
5. a) Describe the characteristics of the four types of industrial land uses.
   b) Compare the location of industries before the 1940s and after the 1940s.
   c) Why has the location changed?
6. How do land values affect land use?
7. Explain why the Oak Ridges Moraine is such an important area to southern Ontario.
8. The Oak Ridges Conservation Plan divides the moraine into four land-use designations. Describe each.

THINKING

9. Examine the three diagrams in Fig. 21-4 on page 249.
   a) Calculate the residential density for each of the three types of housing in the following manner.
      Total the number of housing units in the six grid squares (each one is one hectare in size). Divide this number by 6 to obtain the average residential density.
   b) What do you think are the advantages and disadvantages of each type of housing?
   c) What types of housing are found in the neighbourhood where you live? Estimate the housing density in your neighbourhood.

GeoLit Reminder

When reading visual texts:

- What types of visual texts are included in Question 9?
- Examine the titles, legend, and caption.
- What general information are these visuals communicating?
- What do you already know about the topic shown in the visual texts?
- What additional information do you need to gather about these visuals?

10. Examine Fig. 21-6 on page 252.
    a) Where would you go to buy a roll of film?
    b) Where would you go to buy an expensive piece of clothing?
    c) Are specialized stores more or less likely to be close to where you live? Explain.

11. a) Define *big-box* store.
    b) Give an example of a company in each of these categories that tends to use big-boxes.
       i. appliances and furniture
       ii. home and garden products
       iii. general merchandise
       iv. electronics
    c) Name two additional big-box stores in retail categories not mentioned in b).
    d) What advantages and disadvantages do these big-box stores have for your community?
12. Explain why activities located in the CBD are dependent on one another.
13. a) How do cities plan for Canada's climate by using the winter-city concept?
    b) What other methods of urban planning can you suggest for dealing with Canada's climate conditions?
14. a) What is the purpose of requiring a review of the Oak Ridges Moraine's Conservation Plan every 10 years?
    b) Do you see any problems with the 10-year review process?
15. What is the purpose of the Golden Horseshoe Greenbelt?
16. Name two transportation and two utility uses that you think are most likely allowed in natural core areas of the Oak Ridges Moraine.

COMMUNICATION

17. a) In your opinion, is urban expansion a more positive or more negative aspect of urban development? Give at least three reasons to support your answer.
    b) What can be done to limit the negative impacts of urban sprawl?
18. Would you rather shop at stores in the CBD or in a large shopping mall? Fully explain your choice.
19. Using examples from your own town or city, or the nearest town or city, research how each of the following factors has influenced land use: physical features, period of development, land values, and government land-use policies. Your teacher will tell you how to present your findings.
20. Are older districts of cities or newer suburbs the more interesting places in which to live? Construct a chart to compare the advantages and disadvantages of each. Where would you prefer to live? Why?

APPLICATION

21. Examine the closest regional shopping mall to your neighbourhood. Identify one example of each of the following:
    a) an anchor store
    b) a chain store
    c) a local merchant
22. a) What is meant by the term *smart growth*?
    b) Conduct an Internet search to determine the pros and cons of the smart growth concept.

GeoLit Reminder

Developing written ideas:

- Review Questions 12–16.
- Re-read sections of the text relating to these questions.
- Use related visual and written text to support your answers.
- Check that your written ideas answer the questions.

Canadian Communities of Today and Tomorrow

Statistics Canada reports the following trends:

- By 2026, Canada's population will reach about 36 190 600.
- About half of Canada's "rural" residents currently live in **metro-adjacent** communities, and this number will increase.
- The Greater Golden Horseshoe area has the fastest-growing population in Canada. By 2035, it will have grown by an estimated 3.7 million people—from 7.7 million (2005) to more than 11 million.

metro-adjacent communities situated next to, or near, existing metropolitan areas

Activity

As you learned in this unit, growth brings with it challenges; numerous issues that we need to address. Your task is to investigate one of the issues listed below, or another issue of your choice (approved by your teacher). Gather information related your issue from newspapers, municipal or provincial Web sites, and other resources at your school or local library. Make sure you have the information you need to answer these questions:

- **What** is the issue about?
- **Where** is the issue taking place?
- **Why** is this issue a concern to the community?
- **Who** is involved with the issue (e.g., local residents, politicians, businesses), and **why**? **What** are their respective positions on the issue?
- **How** do you think this issue can be resolved?

Present your findings as directed by your teacher. Your choices might include one or more of the following:

- research paper
- magazine or newspaper article
- oral presentation
- wall poster
- video report or infomercial
- debate

Issue #1 Dealing with aging communities—How can communities **renew** older areas with rundown buildings or make better use of the land for alternate purposes? Should developers tear them down and replace them, or renovate them and use them again?

Issue #2 Controlling urban (or suburban) sprawl—Many communities surrounding urban centres expand rapidly, often onto excellent agricultural lands or environmentally sensitive areas. How can we minimize the negative impacts of urban sprawl while addressing the need for residential, commercial, industrial and other community services as urban and suburban populations grow?

Issue #3 Protecting environmentally sensitive areas—How can our growing and changing communities preserve and protect environmentally sensitive areas? What regulations exist and how do these regulations affect the members of our community?

Issue #4 Loss of the community's economic base—Sometimes a community loses its main industry or source of employment for its residents. What factors can cause this change in a community's economic base? How can this affect the residents and businesses of the community? What new industries and services could a community introduce in order to diversify?

Issue #5 Designing sustainable communities—Existing suburban communities often attract criticism for being unsustainable because of their low housing densities and their residents' reliance on the car to shop, work, and play. As our urban and suburban populations increase, how can we design communities so that they are more "livable" for their residents today and tomorrow? How can planners successfully incorporate the principles of **new urbanism** into future communities?

Issue #6 Promoting efficient transportation within communities—The efficient movement of goods and people is an important feature of any community. What different modes of transportation does the community use? How can communities improve the efficiency and environmental sustainability of their transportation systems?

◀ **Fig. CA4-1** In January 1999, Toronto's transportation services were severely affected by a winter storm.

▲ **Fig. CA4-2** Toronto's Green Bin Program allows city residents to separate organic waste, such as food scraps, from garbage and recyclables.

Issue #7 Dealing with "social ills" of communities—Crime, poverty, and homelessness are important issues that face all communities, large or small. Did you know that in a wealthy country like Canada over 1 million children—or almost one child in six—live in poverty? What types of crime are prevalent in our communities? What approaches and programs exist to help reduce crime, poverty, and homelessness in our communities?

Issue #8 Meeting the needs of residents in our communities—What services and programs do teenagers, the elderly, and people with special needs in our communities require? What changes, modifications, or improvements should we make to these services and programs?

Issue #9 Waste management in Canadian communities—What happens to household trash, industrial garbage, and hazardous waste in your community? How does this affect the members of the community environmentally and economically? What types of recycling initiatives or other approaches does your community use?

Issue #10 Future energy and water needs of communities—How can we efficiently meet the energy and fresh water needs of our growing and changing communities? How can communities avoid power "blackouts" as experienced in Toronto in August 2004, or the critical situation faced by Walkerton, Ontario, with *E. coli* in their water supply? What conservation strategies or alternative energy sources can we use in our communities?

Issue #11 Emergency planning for Canadian communities—Some communities face natural disasters such as Hurricane Juan that hit Halifax in 2003, the flooding of Calgary in 2005, and even the potential risk of a powerful earthquake in Vancouver. Communities may also be affected by human-driven events such as the 2004 SARS outbreak in Toronto or an act of terrorism. How can communities prepare and protect their residents from such natural or human-made catastrophes?

Fig. CA4-3 ▶ In June 2005, floods in Calgary forced the evacuation of thousands. The Bow and Elbow Rivers, along with Fish Creek, overflowed their banks.

UNIT 5

Economic Connections

What types of industries make up Canada's economy? Where are they located? What is the difference between a "basic" and a "non-basic" industry? In what ways do transportation and communication systems support the production and distribution of Canada's goods and services? How do employment opportunities differ from industry to industry? What factors influence where industries locate? If you wanted to start a business in your community or somewhere else in Canada, what business would you choose? Where would you locate your business? Why? This unit helps you explore these questions.

22 Sectors of Canada's Economy

Key Ideas

This chapter helps you investigate these questions:

- What are the sectors of Canada's economy, and how important is each?
- How do basic and non-basic activities contribute to the economy?

Key Terms

primary industries
secondary industries
tertiary industries
quaternary industries
raw materials
manufacturing
value added
services

▲ **Fig. 22-1** Kapuskasing is a typical forest town in Ontario.

pulp
partially processed material from logs; a preliminary step in paper-making

It just didn't make sense. Kapuskasing, Ontario (Fig. 22-1), was supposed to be a major forest products centre, but when Marina tried to prove it, the numbers did not support her case. Marina believed that she had a great idea for her Geography project—she would create a summary of all the jobs in her hometown to show how important the forestry industry was to Kapuskasing. At first, she expected to find that most of the workers in the town were employed in the **pulp** and paper industry. Fig. 22-2 is a summary of what she actually found. Remarkably, she found that only one-third of Kapuskasing's workforce worked in forestry. How could this be? You will find the answers in this chapter.

Marina got this information from Statistics Canada. You can access a wide range of Statistics Canada databases through an Internet-based service called E-STAT. This is not a free service, but your school library or public library will have a subscription to E-STAT.

EMPLOYMENT IN KAPUSKASING

	No. of Workers	% of Workforce
Primary Industries (forestry workers and other primary workers)	155	3%
Secondary Industries (forest products manufacturing and other secondary workers)	1460	31.4%
Tertiary Industries	3040	65.3%
Total Workers	4655	100%

▲ **Fig. 22-2** Marina found these employment statistics for Kapuskasing; they were not what she expected. She thought that most of the people in the town worked in the forestry industry.

Types of Industry

The jobs that people do can be divided into three categories: **primary**, **secondary**, and **tertiary industries**. The relationship between these categories can be seen by looking at the case of a pair of ice skates (Fig. 22-3). The progress of this pair of skates from manufacture through purchase shows how Canada's economy works.

Tertiary means third and quaternary means fourth.

Many geographers think that there is, in fact, a fourth group of industries and jobs. These are termed **quaternary industries**. In simplest terms, quaternary industries involve the processing of ideas rather than products. There are many jobs that fall into this category, such as computer programmers, accountants, and university professors. This segment of the economy has grown explosively in recent years. Such growth has given agencies such as Statistics Canada a problem when it comes to classifying economic activity and reporting job statistics, because most quaternary jobs are closely linked to economic activities in the other three categories of industry. For example, a university professor conducting research in the morning is working in the quaternary sector because she is processing ideas. When lecturing to students in the afternoon, she is working in the tertiary sector because as a teacher, she is providing an educational service.

The quaternary sector of the economy will be examined more in Chapter 29.

The solution chosen by Statistics Canada and most other statistical agencies is not to report quaternary industries separately, but to include them in the totals of one of the other industry categories. Remember, though, when you do the activities in this chapter, that there is a large and growing number of quaternary workers in Canada. The overwhelming majority of these are included in the tertiary category, although there are a few in the primary and secondary sectors.

Primary Industries

Industries that take **raw materials** from the natural environment are called primary or extractive industries. They are called *primary* because the **extraction** of natural resources must happen first before anything else can occur. Mining and agriculture, the primary industries related to the production of the skates, are listed in Stage 1 of Fig. 22-3. These primary industries (and jobs) are located in parts of Canada where the appropriate resources are found.

extraction
removal of a natural resource from the ground or water

Only Russia, the United States, Australia, and Brazil compare to Canada as sources of natural resources.

Primary industries (agriculture, mining, forestry, and fishing) make a critical contribution to Canada's wealth. Without them, and the money they bring into the country through sales to other nations, Canada's economy would not exist in its current form. In fact, few countries in the world can rival Canada as a source of so many natural products. It is therefore quite surprising that such a small percentage of Canada's labour force

A greater percentage of Canada's labour force worked in primary industries before machinery replaced human labour for many tasks.

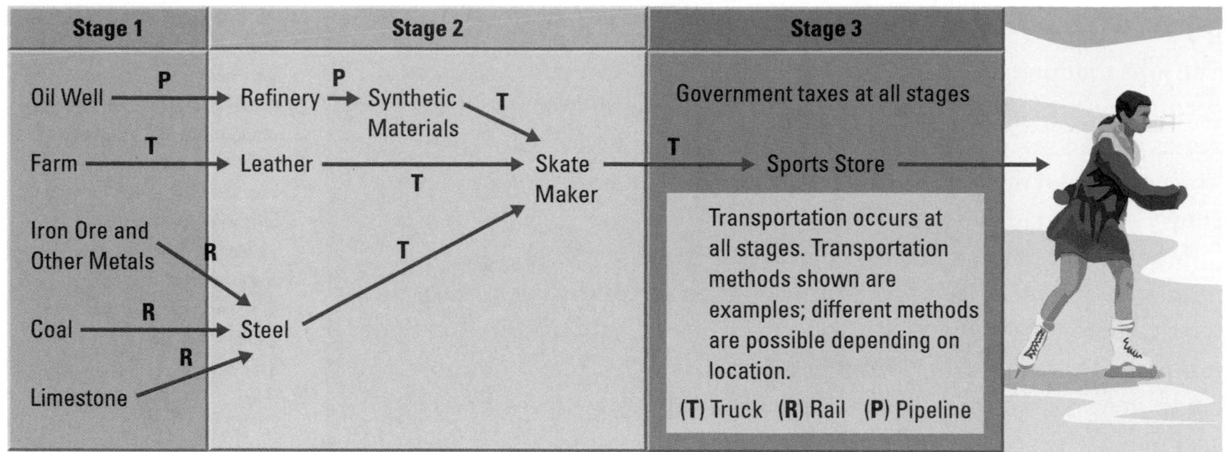

▲ **Fig. 22-3** A simple product like a pair of skates involves all sectors of the economy.

identified
associated with by most people

works in primary industries (Fig. 22-4). The employment statistics that Marina found for Kapuskasing are a reflection of the fact that relatively few people work in extractive industries—even in parts of Canada that are strongly **identified** with a primary industry.

Secondary Industries

Secondary industries involve the processing of primary-industry products into finished goods. This relates to Stage 2 of the skate story in Fig. 22-3. The most important secondary industry is **manufacturing**, which is responsible for making the enormous range of products needed by consumers and by businesses. Manufacturers make everything from computers and diamond rings to cans of fruit and bulldozers. As you can see in Fig. 22-4, secondary industries employ far more Canadians than do primary industries. Construction alone has more workers than all the primary industries combined, while manufacturing employs three times as many.

Manufacturing a product often involves several steps. Consider the production of the steel blades for that pair of skates. Primary manufacturing takes place when iron ore, coal, limestone, and other metals are manufactured into the kind of steel needed for a skate blade—resistant to rust and able to hold a sharp edge. Secondary manufacturing occurs when that steel is further processed into skate blades, which are then added to the skate boot to make the final product. Cars, clothing, and even a seemingly simple product like chewing gum are the products of both primary and secondary manufacturing processes.

The various raw materials that went into the skates obviously have value, but in total the raw materials used in one pair of skates is worth about one dollar. After all, there are only a few kilograms of crude oil, iron ore, coal, and other raw materials in each pair of skates. When these

	No. of Workers	% of Workforce
Primary Industries		
Agriculture	349 000	2.2%
Fishing, forestry, mining, oil, and gas	308 000	1.9%
Total	**657 000**	**4.1%**
Secondary Industries		
Manufacturing	2 183 000	13.5%
Construction	1 042 000	6.4%
Utilities	128 000	0.8%
Total	**3 353 000**	**20.7%**
Tertiary Industries		
Wholesale and retail trade	2 570 000	15.9%
Transportation and warehousing	813 000	5.0%
Finance, insurance, and real estate	971 000	6.0%
Education	1 118 000	6.9%
Health and social services	1 739 000	10.7%
Business and personal services	4 138 000	25.5%
Government	839 000	5.2%
Total	**12 188 000**	**75.2%**
Total in All Industries	**16 198 000**	**100%**

◀ **Fig. 22-4** Employment in Canada, 2005

materials are processed, though, their value increases. For example, the steel that eventually will be made into the skate blades is worth much more than the raw materials that were used to make the steel. Similarly, when the steel is further processed to make the skate blades, it gains more value. When the skate blades become part of the finished skates, there is even more **value added**. One dollar's worth of raw materials might now sell for $200 or more. Many critics of Canada's economy have pointed out that we lose many value-added opportunities—and jobs—by exporting too many goods in an unprocessed form. They say that we should do more processing of timber, minerals, and agricultural products in Canada and then sell the finished products. Unfortunately, in a global market it is impossible to force companies to do this. They choose to do their processing where it most benefits their company's profits. In recent years this has meant that many Canadian manufacturing plants have closed as new factories have sprung up in China and other countries where labour costs are lower than in Canada.

Manufacturing companies try to build their factories in densely populated areas because they want to be near their customers. This means that the cost of shipping their products will be as low as possible. If you know where most Canadians live, you will have a pretty good idea where most manufacturing occurs.

See Fig. 19-2 on page 226 for a population distribution map of Canada.

The importance to the economy of the construction sector is often overlooked. It can be seen at all levels of the economy. Locally, it may be a small crew building a deck behind a neighbour's house. Provincially, it may be a large company expanding a highway from two lanes to four. Nationally, it may be a multi-billion dollar "megaproject," like the construction of an arctic gas pipeline that involves a dozen companies.

Tertiary Industries

Tertiary industries provide a wide range of **services** that support primary and secondary industries and society in general. Without them, society could not function. With regard to those skates: the sports store that sells them (Stage 3, Fig. 22-3) is providing a service to the person who buys them, and is therefore considered a tertiary industry. In addition, at each stage of the manufacture, sale, and even use of the skates, taxes are paid to governments. These taxes pay for such other services as health-care, education, and road maintenance.

What Marina did not take into account when she started her project was that a substantial majority of Canadians do not make *goods* in their jobs. Rather, they provide *services* for others. In fact, almost three times as many Canadians work in tertiary (and quaternary) industries as in primary and secondary industries combined. These services are so varied, and so much a part of everyday life, that often we do not give them much thought.

Consider your day. In the morning, you may *read a magazine* while you *ride the bus* to school. At noon, you may go to the *local burger place* for lunch. After school, you may have a *dental appointment*. At night, you may go to the mall to *shop* and see *the latest movie*. Of course, during the day you are *in school*.

Service industries, in one form or another, are spread across the country. The majority of service industries are found in towns and cities because most services are provided for the people and companies that are concentrated in urban areas. In some cities and towns, one service industry dominates. Think for a moment of Ottawa. One service industry should come to mind: the government. Can you think of other cities or towns that are closely identified with a particular service?

Basic and Non-basic Industries

Compare the jobs of two people who live in Kapuskasing. Joan works in the shipping department of the pulp and paper mill, while Henry cooks in a restaurant on the main street of town. Beyond the obvious differences in the two jobs, there is one important distinction that must be made. The money to pay Joan's salary comes primarily from outside the economy of the local town. It is provided (indirectly) by the customers who buy paper products from the mill. As you learned in Chapter 20, jobs like hers are in basic industries (and are called basic jobs) because they provide the money needed to support the local economy. Without them, there would be no money entering the town, and it could not exist.

On the other hand, the money earned by Henry in the restaurant comes almost entirely from customers who live in the local area. Jobs like his are in non-basic industries, since they do not bring new money into the local economy. Instead, they *recycle* the money that is already there. While non-basic jobs are important, the survival and growth of an economy depends on having enough basic jobs.

How can you tell if a job is basic or non-basic? Sometimes it is not clear because some jobs can be a combination of both. Consider the examples in Fig. 22-5. How does the job of an actor at the Stratford Festival compare to that of an actor at a theatre in Toronto? In Stratford, the vast majority of people who attend the theatre would be from out of town, so an actor would be a basic job. In Toronto, though, many of the people going to the theatre are local residents, so an actor could be both basic and non-basic.

There is money continually leaving the town to pay for all the goods and services that are brought in from outside. The town must earn money to pay for these goods and services.

Stratford's permanent population is less than 30 000.

Job Description	Category
Coal miner in northeastern British Columbia	Basic
Hairdresser at a shopping mall	Non-basic
Art teacher	Non-basic
Actor at the Stratford Shakespearean Festival	Basic
Teller at the local bank	Non-basic
Vice-president of Scotiabank	Basic
Professor at Queen's University	Basic
Receptionist at a dentist's office	Non-basic
Air Canada pilot	Basic
School-bus driver	Non-basic

◄ **Fig. 22-5** Can you suggest why each of these jobs is in the category shown?

In Closing...

Now that you are familiar with the ideas of primary, secondary, tertiary, and quaternary industries, and with basic and non-basic industries, you should be able to answer Marina's question as to why only about a third of the people in her town work in the forestry industry.

QUESTIONS

KNOWLEDGE AND UNDERSTANDING

1. Define, in your own words, and give three examples of each of the following: primary industry, secondary industry, tertiary industry, and quaternary industry.
2. In your notebook, match the industry in Column A with the items in Column B.

Column A	Column B
1. Primary industry	a) raw materials
	b) laboratory
	c) manufacturing
	d) factory
2. Secondary industry	e) mining
	f) civil service
	g) research and development
	h) natural resources
	i) ski resort
3. Tertiary industry	j) services
	k) novelist
	l) construction
4. Quaternary industry	m) farming
	n) transportation

THINKING

3. a) What is the difference between a basic industry and a non-basic industry?
   b) Which of the following are basic and which are non-basic jobs? Explain each answer.
      i an assembly line worker in the Ford factory in Oakville, Ontario
      ii. a firefighter in your community
      iii. a wheat farmer in Saskatchewan
      iv. the artist who illustrated this book
   c) Describe a situation in which each of the following jobs can be basic in nature and a situation in which it can be non-basic:
      i. a doctor
      ii. a bus driver
      iii. a golf professional
   d) Are most quaternary jobs basic or non-basic in nature? Why is it important to know this? (Hint: consider how the government tries to help economic growth.)
4. How would you expect the pattern of primary, secondary, and tertiary industries for 1911 to differ from the pattern revealed by the statistics in Fig. 22-4 for 2005? Why?
5. a) Why is it so difficult to provide statistical data about the number of quaternary jobs?
   b) Is this situation likely to change in the future? Why or why not?

COMMUNICATION

6. A geographer once said that tertiary industries are, at the same time, the most important and the least important segment of Canada's economy. What do you think this statement means?

APPLICATION

7. Draw bar graphs to show the percentage of the labour force employed in each sub-category shown in Fig. 22-4 (e.g., agriculture, manufacturing, wholesale and retail trade, etc.). Use a different colour for each category (primary, secondary, and tertiary).

GeoLit Reminder

When constructing a bar graph:

- Determine the best size for your graph.
- Choose the vertical scale. (Hint: Which item will have the longest bar?) Label the vertical axis.
- Draw a bar for each item of data, spaced evenly along the horizontal axis.
- Label the horizontal axis and each bar on it.
- Add a legend, if appropriate.
- Give your graph a title.
- Check that all information is correctly drawn and labelled and that you have used colour appropriately.

8. a) Fig. 22-6 shows the distribution of workers of each industry in the major regions of Canada. Create a set of bar graphs for each region. Fig. 22-7 shows a sample bar graph for Atlantic Canada.

   b) Compare the percentage of Canada's population in each region to the percentage of workers in each type of industry. If the figures are similar, then the region has its fair share of jobs in that category. If not, then an imbalance exists. What significant differences do you see? Why might they exist?

Region	Percentage of Canada's Primary Workers	Percentage of Canada's Secondary Workers	Percentage of Canada's Tertiary Workers	Percentage of Canada's Population
Atlantic Canada (NL, PEI, NS, and NB)	9.8%	5.6%	7.0%	7.6%
Central Canada (QC, ON)	37.1%	74.1%	61.9%	62.1%
Western Canada (BC, AB, MB, SK, Territories)	53.1%	20.3%	31.1%	30.2%

▲ **Fig. 22-6** Regional distribution of employees in Canada for 2003

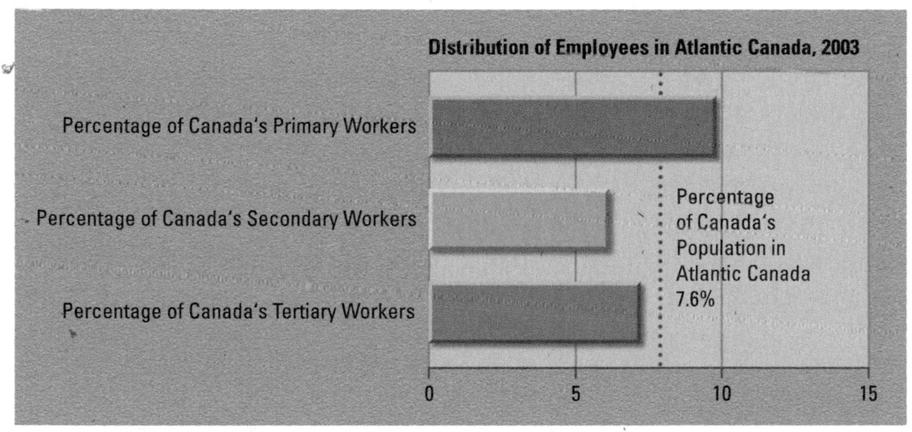

◀ **Fig. 22-7** Employment by category in Atlantic Canada compared to regional population, 2003.

9. a) Work with a partner to conduct a survey of the occupations of at least 50 people in your community. Divide the jobs into primary, secondary, and tertiary industries and into basic and non-basic. In each case, convert the results into percentages.

   b) Did the results surprise you? Why or why not?

   c) For the types of industries, are the results that you obtained what you would expect based on what you know about the national distribution of jobs (Fig. 22-4) and the distribution of jobs in your region (Question 8)?

   d) How many of the jobs that you found could be classified as completely quaternary? How many could be classified as partly quaternary? Was this a surprise? Explain.

23 Fishing: An Industry in Crisis

Key Ideas

This chapter helps you investigate these questions:

- Why is Canada a major producer and exporter of fish?
- How is Canada's fishing industry structured?
- In what ways is Canada's fishing industry threatened, and how can the impact of these threats be minimized?

Key Terms

renewable resource
groundfish
pelagic fish
shellfish
balance of trade
continental shelf
banks
inshore fishery
offshore fishery
sustained yield management
aquaculture

To learn more about fishing, check the link at www.pearsoned.ca/makingconnections2.

For centuries, those who fished for a living looked forward to years of regular employment because the fish in the oceans, lakes, and rivers of Canada were a **renewable resource**. The collapse of the fisheries during the 1990s changed all this (Fig. 23-1). Fish stocks on the east coast declined to the extent that, in 1992, the cod fishery was shut down. A few years later, the salmon fishery collapsed on the west coast. This chapter examines the history and importance of the fishing industry, the reasons for its recent decline, and its prospects for the future.

Introduction

Ocean fishing is Canada's oldest industry. Beginning in the early 1500s, ships from Great Britain, France, Spain, and Portugal came to Canada every summer to harvest the rich fishing grounds off Newfoundland. At first, the Europeans set up summer fishing stations. Eventually, they established permanent fishing villages. Here the fish were dried or salted and then sent to Europe, the United States, and the West Indies. Fishing provided the economic base for European settlement in parts of the east coast, Quebec, and British Columbia.

Although commercial fishing today makes up only about 0.1% of the total value of Canada's economy, it is the foundation of the economy in some inland areas and parts of the Atlantic and Pacific coasts. Commercial fishing is the basis for a traditional way of life that has a special place in Canada's cultural **heritage**.

heritage
inherited traditions

◀ **Fig. 23-1** The 1990s marked the beginning of the most serious crisis in the history of the Canadian fishing industry.

Commercial fishing occurs on the east coast, the west coast, and in large freshwater lakes. In the mid-1990s, about 100 000 Canadians had commercial-fishing licences, and another 10 000 were employed in fish processing. Production from the east coast is higher than that from the west coast, and freshwater production is smaller than either (Fig. 23-2). The different kinds of ocean fish caught by Canadian fishers are categorized as **groundfish** (bottom feeders), **pelagic fish** (open-water feeders), and **shellfish** (Fig. 23-3).

Canada is not one of the top 10 fishing nations in the world. It is, however, one of the world's leading exporters of fish, largely because Canadians do not eat much fish that is caught here. As a result, more than 80% of the Canadian catch is exported. Canada's fish exports are much greater than our seafood imports, which helps our **balance of trade**. For example, in 2004, exports of fish were valued at $4.4 billion, while imports

Fishery	Number of Commercial Fishers	Tonnes of Fish Caught	Percentage of Total Catch	Value of Catch ($ millions)	Total Exports ($ millions)
East Coast	42 897	893 051	75.1	1 853 572	3 322
West Coast	15 000	258 213	21.7	358 800	985
Freshwater	3 257	37 383[1]	3.2	83 722[1]	139[1]
Canada (Total)		1 188 647	100	2 296 094	4 446

[1] 2003

◀ **Fig. 23-2** Canada's three commercial fisheries (2004 except where noted).

CATEGORY	DESCRIPTION	EXAMPLES
Groundfish	Fish that feed and are caught near the ocean floor	cod, pollock, haddock, halibut, redfish
Pelagic fish	Fish that feed and are caught near the surface	salmon, herring, mackerel, tuna, caplin
Shellfish	Animals without backbones but with hard, protective shells	shrimp, lobster, oysters, scallops, mussels

▲ **Fig. 23-3** There are three categories of catch for Canada's fishing industry.

of fish were valued at about $2.0 billion. The most important markets for our fish are the United States, Western Europe, and the countries of the Pacific Rim, particularly Japan.

QUESTIONS

KNOWLEDGE AND UNDERSTANDING

1. Why are fish a renewable resource?
2. Explain the economic and social importance of the fishing industry to Canada.
3. a) Name the three types of seafood that are caught.
   b) Give two examples of each type. Which ones have you eaten?

THINKING

4. a) Why are fish exports important to Canada's balance of payments?
   b) To which countries are most of our fish exports shipped? Why?
5. Examine the value of the catch and the total exports in Fig. 23–2. Why are the two amounts so different?

APPLICATION

6. a) How many times a month do you eat seafood (consider both at home and in restaurants)?
   b) Where does seafood rank on your list of favourite foods? Why do you think this is so?
   c) If the average person eats 0.2 kg of seafood per serving, estimate the amount you eat per year. You can do this by determining how many times you have seafood each month and then multiplying by 12 and by 0.2 kg. How does this compare to the national average of 10 kg?
   d) Describe two health benefits that come from eating seafood.

The East Coast Fishery

Until recently, the ocean waters off the east coast of Canada were one of the world's great fishing grounds. A number of favourable conditions combined to produce waters extremely suitable for fish. Atlantic Canada has a particularly wide **continental shelf** that is less than 200 metres in depth. On this shelf are even shallower areas called **banks** that are less than 150 metres deep (Fig. 23-4). Here, sunlight penetrates to the bottom,

▲ **Fig. 23-4** Sunlight can penetrate to the bottom of the fishing banks because they are so shallow. This creates ideal conditions for the growth of plankton that, in turn, attracts fish.

causing a lush growth of **plankton** that attracts large numbers of fish. The largest and best-known fishing region on the east coast is the Grand Banks, with an area of 282 500 square kilometres. By comparison, the island of Newfoundland is 111 400 square kilometres.

plankton
the name given to microscopic plants and animals eaten by small fish and shellfish. The small fish and shellfish are, in turn, eaten by larger fish.

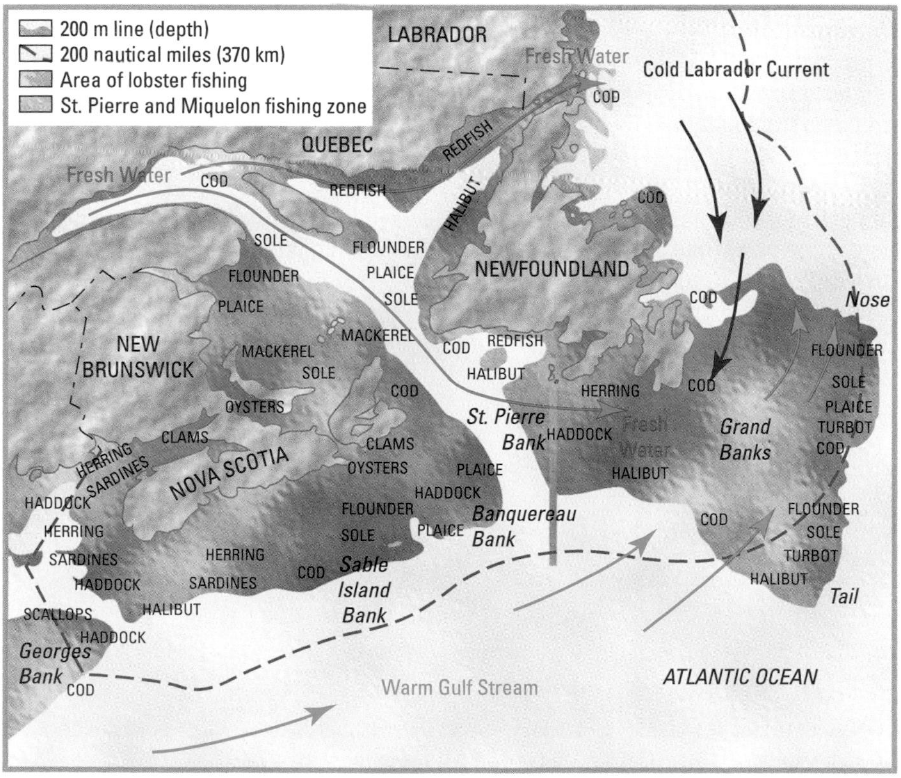

◀ **Fig. 23-5** About 10% of the Grand Banks—known as the "Nose" and the "Tail"—are outside the 200-km limit of Canada's east coast fishery.

GeoLit Reminder

When reading a map:

- Examine the title (or caption), legend, and labels.
- What is the purpose of this map?
- Scan the map for patterns and trends.
- What general information does this map provide?

Feature	Inshore Fishery	Offshore Fishery
Location	Within 16 to 25 km of shore	To edges of continental shelf, up to 370 km from shore
Percentage of the fishing industry labour force	85%	15%
Percentage of total catch	10%	90%
Type of boat and equipment (see photos below)	Smaller boats (up to 20 m in length), usually with fixed gear (fish weirs, lobster traps, etc.)	Larger boats (up to 50 m in length), usually with mobile fish nets; foreign factory-trawlers can be larger still
Ownership of boats and equipment	Individuals and families	Large companies
Type of employment	Self-employment	Unionized employees of fishing companies
Crew size	1 to 6	12 to 16
Fishing season	Mainly warmer months	All year long in all types of weather
Fishing procedures	Fishing boats travel to coastal fishing areas each morning.	Trawlers travel to the fishing grounds for up to two weeks at a time.
Processing	Fish are processed onshore, usually in small- to medium-sized plants.	Fish may be partially processed on board before being taken to large processing plants.
Lifestyle	People often live in small coastal communities; incomes earned are often low and unstable; widespread dependence on government support	People live in larger coastal communities; incomes are higher and more stable.

▲ **Fig. 23-6** A comparison of the inshore and offshore east coast fisheries before the 1992 ban on catching cod

The meeting of the cold Labrador Current and the warm Gulf Stream on the Grand Banks also contributes to the rich natural environment. The mixing currents churn up nutrients from the bottom that are necessary for the growth of plankton (Fig. 23-5).

The waters off the east coast have been among the world's greatest fishing grounds for centuries. They are home to two distinct types of fisheries: the **inshore fishery** and the **offshore fishery** (Fig. 23-6).

INTERNET

You can learn more about the collapse of the cod fishery through the link at www.pearsoned.ca/makingconnections2.

Crisis in the East Coast Fishery

In the 1980s, people in the east coast fishery noticed they were catching fewer and smaller fish. In particular, the northern cod off Newfoundland and southern Labrador seemed to be disappearing. The statistics for the northern cod catch in the Atlantic fishery illustrate what happened (Fig. 23-7). While the catch of cod and other groundfish had declined before (consider 1978–79), the collapse that occurred in 1991 was unexpected. The Canadian government responded in 1992 by halting all fishing for northern cod and by making major cuts in the catches allowed for other groundfish species.

When the groundfish ban was imposed, scientists, governments, and the fishing industry expected that fish populations would recover in five to seven years. This has not happened: cod stocks have remained at or below 1992 levels, and many people now fear that they may never recover. The fishing industry has responded by **diversifying** its catch. Fishers now catch much larger quantities of other fish, in particular, shellfish such as crab and shrimp. Fishery critics, including many of those who work in the industry, suspect that we may not have learned our lesson and that we may be overfishing these fish stocks too.

A very limited cod fishery is allowed in some inshore areas only.

One fishing village reported catching only three cod in 1992.

diversifying
increasing the variety

▼ **Fig. 23-7** The decline of the east coast cod fishery

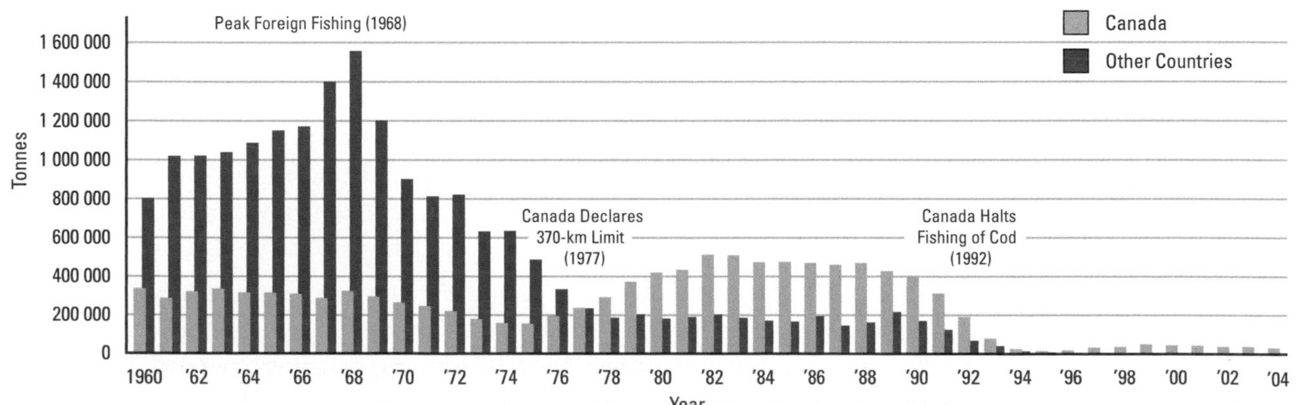

The number of adult fish that are capable of breeding is called the breeding stock. These fish must be protected if the total population of fish is to be maintained.

Politicians may not have wanted to act on the warnings of scientists because people in the fishing industry might have lost their jobs. They might have blamed the politicians and not re-elected them.

At the same time, the fishing industry may have under-reported the number of fish caught.

Why the East Coast Fishery Collapsed

Many theories have been suggested to explain the serious decline in the numbers of groundfish, but no single cause is responsible. Keep in mind that fish are a renewable resource, and that renewable resources must be managed properly. Fish can be harvested forever *if* the number caught each year does not exceed the number reaching maturity in that year. This is a conservation technique called **sustained yield management**. The attempts to manage the fishery to maintain a sufficient number of breeding fish in eastern Canada have obviously failed. Scientists, governments, and especially those who work in the industry are trying to discover what went wrong so that the fishery can be managed better in the future.

People have suggested five major factors responsible for the collapse of the fishery.

- **Overfishing** The catch allowed by the federal government each year appears to have been too high. Government scientists may have overestimated the number of fish that reached adulthood each year. If this was the case, then more fish were caught than reached maturity. Sustained yield management did not occur.
- **Improved Fishing Technology** After World War II, larger, more powerful, engine-driven trawlers were developed. Technological developments, such as sonar and satellite navigation systems, helped fishers locate schools of fish faster and more accurately. Over the years, fewer fish escaped the fishing nets. It is ironic that the "advances" in technology made overfishing easier.
- **Uncontrolled Foreign Fishing** By the late 1960s, the fishing fleets of countries such as Russia and Japan caught far more fish than sustained yield methods would have allowed (Fig. 23-7). Countries with ocean coastlines began to urge the United Nations to allow an extension of their national fishing limits over their continental shelves. Countries like Canada could then protect their fish stocks. In 1977, the UN allowed Canada to extend its control of the seas to 370 kilometres (200 **nautical miles**). Foreign fishing fleets working inside this limit had to follow Canadian fishing restrictions.
- **Destructive Fishing Practices** When trawlers were trying to catch one kind of fish, for example, cod, many other types of fish may have become caught in the nets. These unwanted fish, called the "by-catch," were usually just thrown away. Only the remaining fish were reported to the authorities as having been caught.
- **Changes in Natural Conditions** Changes in environmental conditions have been blamed for the decline in the fish stock. Two specific changes have been identified. First, water temperatures have dropped and ocean **salinity** levels have changed since the mid-1980s. The fish

nautical mile
measurement of distance used by sailors and pilots. It is equal to one minute of latitude (1/60th of a degree), or about 1850 metres.

salinity
saltiness of water

may have altered their migratory routes to avoid areas where these changes have occurred. Second, some people have suggested that the decline of the sealing industry in the late 1970s caused an increase in the seal population. They contend that the greater number of seals ate larger quantities of caplin, a small fish that is a major food source of groundfish. A reduction in the number of caplin reduced the stock of groundfish. The greater number of seals may also have eaten greater quantities of young cod, thus contributing to a decline in cod stocks.

QUESTIONS

KNOWLEDGE AND UNDERSTANDING

1. Describe, in detail, the conditions that have produced outstanding fishing grounds on the east coast.
2. Your teacher will provide you with a map of Atlantic Canada. On this map, draw the major fishing banks and currents.
3. Fully explain five major factors that may have led to the collapse of the east coast fishery.

THINKING

4. Two ocean currents meet in the area of the Grand Banks.
   a) Where does each come from and how does this affect their temperatures?
   b) What climate conditions are common on the Grand Banks as a result of the meeting of these currents? (Fig. 13-3 on p. 147.)
5. a) Describe the major differences between the inshore and the offshore fishery (Fig. 23-6).
   b) If you were a fisher, would you prefer to work in the inshore fishery or the offshore fishery? Explain.
   c) Inshore fishing has been called a way of life, and offshore fishing a business. With specific reference to Fig. 23-6, explain what this means.
6. a) Why was the foreign cod catch so high during the 1960s and early 1970s?
   b) What effect did the introduction of the 370-km (200-mile) limit in 1977 have on the size of the foreign catch in Canadian waters?
7. a) Explain the conservation technique of sustained yield management as it applies to fishing.
   b) Select another industry that harvests natural resources and explain how sustained yield management can be applied to it.
8. a) When the Canadian government extended our territorial limits to 370 km, it expected certain effects. What effects do you think it expected for the following:
      i. the east coast fish stocks
      ii. the number of people employed in the fishery (as fishers and processors)
      iii. the number of foreign vessels fishing in our waters
      iv. the amount of fish eaten by Canadians
   b) Did it create the expected results? Explain.
9. The *Bluenose*, the ship on the back of the dime, is the type of fishing schooner that was used to catch cod on the Grand Banks in the 19th and early 20th century. Do research to determine how fishing, as it was done using schooners, contributed to sustained yield management (even though the concept was not used at that time). How has technology changed the situation today?

COMMUNICATION

10. Some people think that when the Atlantic fishery recovers, most of the resource should be allocated to the inshore fishery because it supports a way of life. Other people believe the offshore fishery should get most of the fish because it catches fish more efficiently and

provides higher paying jobs. Write a paragraph indicating with which view you agree and why.

APPLICATION

11. a) What does the expression "tragedy of the commons" mean? You may have to do some Internet or other research to determine this.

    b) How does this concept apply to the management of fish stocks?

12. In 1995, Canada broke international laws by seizing a Spanish trawler and cutting the nets of Spanish and Portuguese fishing vessels outside Canadian territorial waters. These events became known as "The Turbot War." Research these events and determine
    - what events occurred
    - the actions of Canada, Spain, and the European Union
    - how the conflict was resolved
    - if Canada was justified in this action. Explain your answer.

Spring salmon are also called chinook salmon.

Atlantic salmon have a similar life cycle, except that after spawning, the salmon do not die but return to the sea. They may return to the spawning grounds three or four times during their lifetime.

spawning
production of offspring

The West Coast Fishery

The most important catch on the west coast is salmon. There are five kinds of salmon: coho, chum, pink, spring, and the most valuable of all, sockeye. The Pacific harvest also includes herring, halibut, cod, crab, tuna, shrimp, and oysters (Fig. 23-8).

Although salmon are found on both coasts, the west coast catch has traditionally been over 400 times larger than the east coast catch. Pacific salmon hatch in freshwater streams and then swim to the Pacific Ocean, where they spend their adult lives. Mature Pacific salmon leave the open sea and enter coastal waters during the summer and fall. It is here that British Columbia's large modern fishing fleet has traditionally awaited them. The salmon that escape the nets head for the same freshwater streams where they were hatched. They lay their eggs in the gravel beds of these streams, which tumble out of the mountains along the coast. After **spawning** takes place, both males and females die.

More than 140 spawning runs along the coast of British Columbia no longer occur, and over 800 more are in trouble.

The Collapse of the West Coast Fishery

The failure of the fish management system in the Atlantic fishery caused scientists and politicians to re-evaluate the handling of the west coast fishery. Their concern was brought sharply into focus in 1994 when one million fewer salmon than estimated arrived at spawning grounds on the upper Fraser River in British Columbia. There are several possible reasons for the partial collapse of the west coast salmon fishery.

- **Overfishing** During the 1990s, Canadian and American salmon-fishing boats were catching over 800 000 tonnes of fish per year between California and Alaska. The salmon stocks were severely affected by this massive yearly catch, and too few adult fish reached the spawning

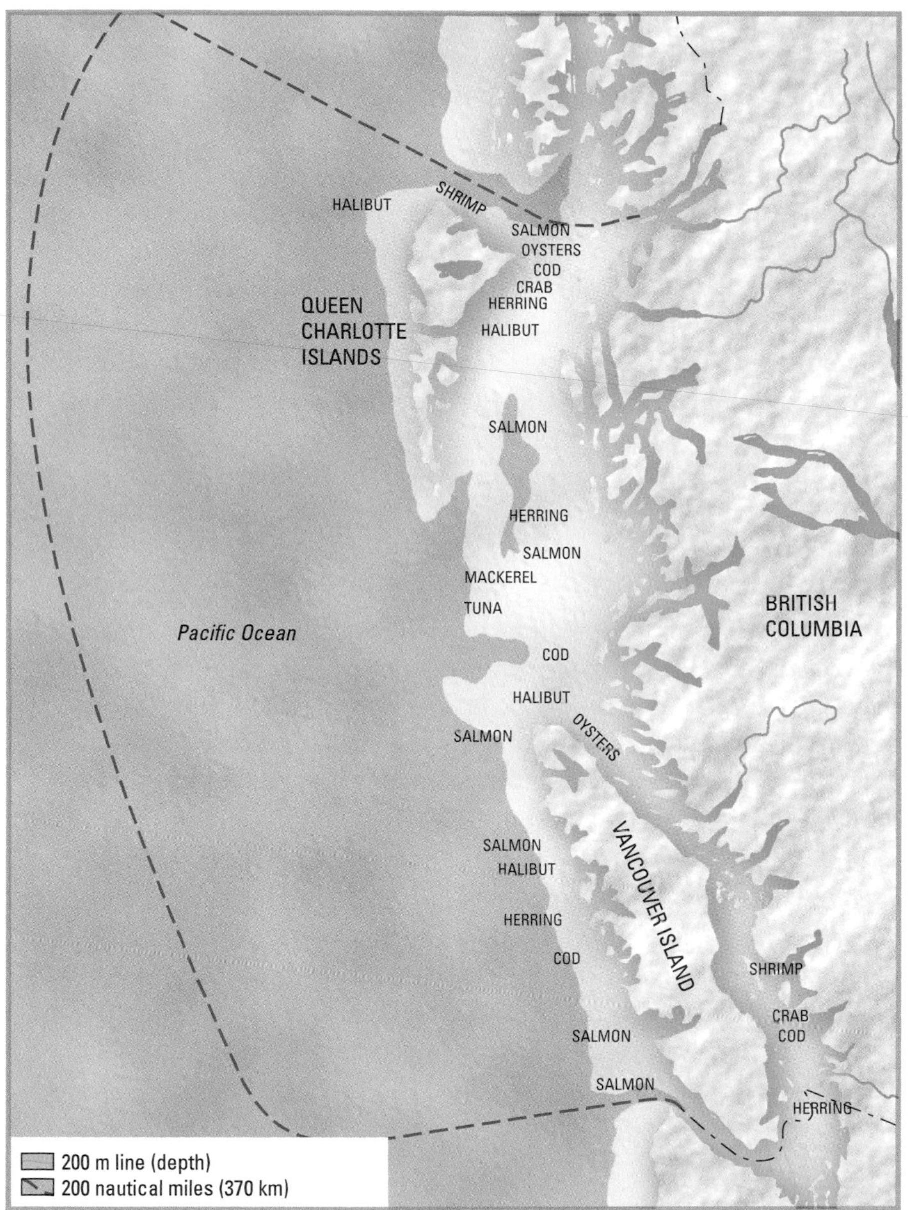

◀ **Fig. 23-8** Canada's west coast fishery

rivers. Where there were once over 100 major fish-processing plants in British Columbia, there are now fewer than 10.

- **Changes in the Environment** The causes of environmental change in the ocean are still a mystery, but global warming appears to be increasing the temperature of the Pacific Ocean. This could threaten the salmon's habitat. Salmon prefer water that is below 7°C. This temperature establishes the southern limit of the salmon's range. Northern California has already lost most of its salmon runs because of warmer water.

If the Pacific Ocean continues to warm, the salmon's range will shift northward toward the Bering Sea, where the water is cooler. They will spawn in Alaska rather than in British Columbia. As a result, Canada will lose its west coast salmon fishery.

- **Lack of a Salmon Fishing Treaty** A long-standing dispute continues between Canada and the United States concerning where salmon may be caught and how much may be taken by each country. Canadian officials claim that fewer salmon, particularly coho, should be caught in order to preserve the stock. American officials in Alaska, on the other hand, claim that there is enough salmon and that restrictions are not needed. As long as the two countries cannot come to an agreement on a Pacific salmon treaty in which fishing and conservation are properly balanced, this precious resource may disappear (Fig. 23-9).

Challenges to the West Coast Fishery

As the supply of salmon decreases, there is the difficulty of balancing a limited supply of fish with a growing demand. There are three competing demands for salmon in British Columbia: commercial fishing, sport fishing, and fishing by the First Nations. In the 1980s and early 1990s, the commercial fleet caught 94% of the salmon, while each of the other groups accounted for about 3%.

The topic of First Nations land claims is examined in more detail in Chapter 17.

1. **First Nations** The demand for salmon by Aboriginal people is growing for two reasons. First, a Supreme Court decision in 1990 guaranteed the right of the First Nations to fish for their own food as well as for social and ceremonial purposes. The Court established that this use takes precedence over all other considerations except conservation. Second, the right to fish commercially is a focus of many First Nations land claims in British Columbia.

Fig. 23-9 ▶ In 1997, Canadian salmon fishers were not allowed to fish, while Alaskan fishers could catch as much as they wanted. In protest, some Canadian fishers surrounded an Alaskan passenger ferry and prevented it from continuing its journey.

2. **Sport Fishing** The sport-fishing industry also wants a bigger share of the available salmon. The argument here is economic: a salmon caught by a recreational angler yields a much greater economic benefit than a salmon caught by a commercial fishing boat.
3. **Commercial Fishing** If the First Nations and the sport-fishing industry are to gain greater shares of the fish, and the government is to ensure an adequate breeding stock, commercial fishers will have to reduce their catch. The federal government is assisting with this cutback by gradually purchasing commercial fishing licences and fishing boats so that the number of commercial fishers is reduced.

Issue

AQUACULTURE—BLESSING OR CURSE?

◄ **Fig.23-10** Atlantic salmon farm in Burdwood Islands, British Columbia. Note the pens in which the fish are raised.

Background

An additional challenge facing the west coast fishery is **aquaculture**. There are a number of reasons why aquaculture is a threat to the fishery in British Columbia:

- Farm-raised salmon can be sold more cheaply than wild salmon.
- Fish farms, which raise salmon in pens, are now producing more salmon than are caught in the wild.
- Atlantic salmon, rather than the local Pacific salmon, are raised on fish farms because the former has proven to grow faster in the pens that are used for fish farming. Many scientists worry about what might happen to the wild salmon population on those occasions when the more aggressive Atlantic salmon escape into the sea from their pens.
- Aquaculture pens are increasingly being criticized for causing the spread of a pest called salmon lice to wild salmon. When tiny baby salmon, called smolts, swim to the ocean from the streams where they are hatched, they pass near aquaculture pens. Here the density of salmon and salmon lice is very high. Scientists have found that 30 000 times as many salmon lice live in these locations compared to areas away from fish farms. The smolts, fish that are about the size of your finger, are often unable to survive a lice infestation. The

result has been a decline in the number of smolts that will eventually reproduce or be caught.

You can read an online aquaculture magazine at www.pearsoned.ca/makingconnections2.

Activities

1. Make a personal field trip to your local supermarket or fish market. By observation and by asking questions of the staff and your parents, try to identify three fish species that come from aquaculture operations rather than from being caught in the wild. Why might some people prefer to buy aquaculture products rather than wild products? Why might some prefer to buy wild products?
2. Some observers have suggested that the change from *catching* salmon (and other species of fish and shellfish) to *raising* them is an exact parallel to what happened thousands of years ago when the farming of plants and animals replaced hunting and gathering. Is this a good comparison? Why or why not?
3. Considering both the advantages and problems of aquaculture, do you consider the great growth of fish farming to be a desirable change or not? Explain.

The Freshwater Fishery

Canada's freshwater (inland) fisheries are located in the Great Lakes, Lake Winnipeg, Great Slave Lake, and 600 or so smaller lakes. The Great Lakes have the most important freshwater fishery, with Lake Erie as the largest producer. The major species sent to market from these lakes are whitefish, perch, pickerel, and trout.

The freshwater fisheries are much less important to the Canadian economy than those of the east or west coast. In 2003, 4% of the total value of the Canadian fishery came from inland waters. Only about 7000 people have jobs in the freshwater fishery. In spite of these small numbers, the freshwater fishery is very important to the areas where it takes place. This is especially true in northern Canada, where up to 90% of those involved in commercial fishing are Aboriginal people. Fish not only provide cash income where jobs are scarce; they also make up a major (and very nutritious) part of people's diet.

Sport fishing in freshwater lakes and rivers is much more important economically than commercial fishing in these waters. Each year, billions of dollars are spent on everything from fishing equipment and bait to new boats and fishing magazines.

In Closing...

Canada's fishing industry is in crisis. In Atlantic Canada, a renewable resource has been exploited beyond its capacity. In British Columbia, the same thing may be happening as different interests compete for a limited supply of fish. Changes must be made to rescue both fisheries, not only because they provide employment in regions where jobs are scarce, but also because they support a lifestyle that is part of our Canadian heritage.

QUESTIONS

KNOWLEDGE AND UNDERSTANDING

1. Describe, in detail, the factors that may have led to the collapse of the west coast fishery.
2. What challenges are facing the west coast fishery?
3. a) Describe Canada's freshwater fishery.
   b) Describe the challenges that are facing this fishery.

THINKING

4. How do the concepts of a renewable resource and sustained yield management relate to the following:
   a) the collapse of the groundfish fishery in Atlantic Canada
   b) the problem of trying to meet the demand for salmon in British Columbia

COMMUNICATION

5. Write a brief, two-paragraph report comparing the collapse of the east coast fishery with the collapse of the west coast fishery.

APPLICATION

6. In 1993, the General Motors van plant in Toronto shut down, and 4200 people were out of work. These people have not received the long-term financial support that the fishery workers on the east coast have received over the years.
   a) Why do you think financial support varies for different groups?
   b) Should fishery workers be treated differently than other workers in Canada? Explain.

24 The Business of Farming

Key Ideas

This chapter helps you investigate these questions:

- How does the interaction between climate, soil, biology, and topography determine the success of agriculture?
- What is sustainable agriculture, and how is it achieved?
- What domestic and international issues affect Canadian farmers today?

Key Terms

growing degree-days (GDDs)
fertilizer
pesticide
herbicide
land capability
mechanization
intensive farming
extensive farming
agribusiness
sustainable agriculture
organic farming
genetically modified organisms (GMOs)

The Nature of Agriculture

Canadians are fortunate to have a relatively inexpensive, reliable supply of food. You probably don't think much about food and where it comes from because it is usually available when you are hungry and because few of us have direct experience producing it. Let's start our study of farming by examining how agriculture depends on the interaction of four natural systems: climate, soil, biology, and topography (Fig. 24-1).

Climate

Two variables in climate contribute to the success of farming. The first is solar energy, or heat; the second is moisture. If you want an orange for breakfast, you can't buy Canadian. Canada can't grow citrus crops because there is no place in the country that receives enough heat. However, we can grow plenty of other crops. If farmers know how much heat there is in their area, they can determine what they can grow and how long it will take. The amount of heat may be measured by **growing degree-days (GDDs),** often referred to as "degree-days."

Growing degree-days are calculated by determining the number of degrees the average temperature exceeds 6°C on a given day. For example, if the temperature averaged 14°C at a specific location on May 3, that day

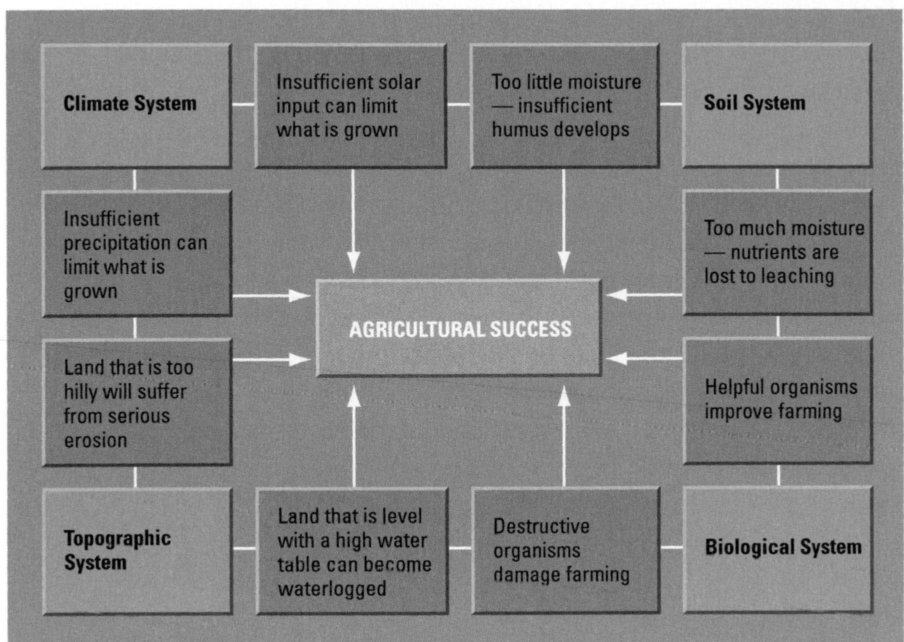

◀ **Fig. 24-1** Many factors affect the success of agriculture.

would contribute 8 growing degree-days. (14 – 6 = 8). Daily GDDs over the period of a year are added together to determine the amount of heat available in one location (Fig. 24-2). If farmers know how many degree-days they have in their location, they know whether or not they have enough heat to grow a particular crop. Farmers know that specific plants need a specific amount of heat to develop from one point in their life

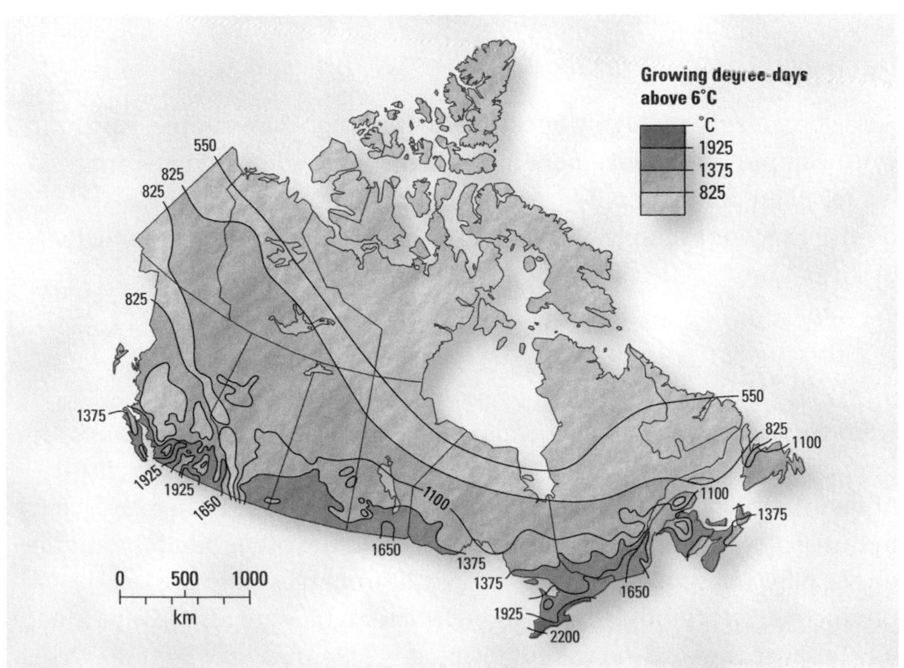

◀ **Fig. 24-2** A map showing growing degree-days (GDDs) across Canada can be drawn when the daily GDDs for a year are totalled. If you know the total number of GDDs that a crop needs to reach maturity, you can determine where in Canada it can be successfully grown.

cycle to another. By calculating degree days, farmers also know when the crop has reached the best stage for applying **fertilizer**, **herbicides**, or **pesticides**.

Farmers use other heat measures to grow crops. They consider the **growing season**—the number of days during which crops can ripen. They also consider the **frost-free period** (the number of days between the last frost in spring and the first frost in autumn). Farmers will not plant if there is a possibility that newly sprouted seedlings may freeze.

The second variable in climate that contributes to the success of farming is moisture. Farmers need to know not only how much precipitation they get, but also how much **evapotranspiration** takes places in their location. Farmers know that warm areas experience more evapotranspiration than cool areas, and will therefore require higher levels of precipitation (or irrigation) for good plant growth.

Soil

organic
relating to living things

Soil is a complex substance composed of minerals, water, air, bacteria, and humus, which is decaying **organic** material such as leaves, twigs, grass, and pine cones. Humus is the most important factor determining a soil's fertility. The amount of humus is determined by the amount of moisture and plant growth. In dry areas, the shortage of moisture limits plant growth. Limited plant growth reduces the amount of humus in the soil. In excessively wet areas, **leaching** may reduce plant growth and the consequent formation of humus.

See Chapter 14 for more information about soils.

Biology

Some organisms are highly beneficial to farming. For example, earthworms improve the movement of air through the soil, and bees are essential for plant pollination (Fig. 24-3). Other organisms are highly destructive. For example, weeds and insect pests reduce the productivity of agriculture.

▲ **Fig. 24-3** Bees are among the insects that are helpful to farming.

Topography

Land features have an effect on agricultural productivity. Level, well-drained land is generally best for farming. Fertile valleys, such as the Annapolis Valley in Nova Scotia, and deltas, such as the Fraser River delta in British Columbia, are highly productive. On the other hand, mountainous or hilly areas that tend to lose topsoil through erosion are less productive. Flat, sandy areas with high water tables are also less productive because they are too wet for farming.

Correcting Deficiencies

Few farming areas in Canada have a perfect combination of rich soil, level land, good biological conditions, sufficient moisture, and a long growing season. To overcome deficiencies in their land, farmers have developed corrective measures (Fig. 24-4 and 24-5).

▼ **Fig. 24-4** There are numerous ways of dealing with agricultural deficiencies.

Agricultural Deficiency	Human Adjustment
Growing season too short or too cool	Grow a crop with a shorter growing season. Develop varieties that mature more quickly. Start seedlings in a greenhouse.
Insufficient moisture	Provide irrigation. Use growing methods that preserve moisture. Develop crops that require less water.
Infertile soils	Add natural fertilizers, e.g., manure, compost. Add chemical fertilizers. Use appropriate plant rotations.
Hilly terrain	Build terraces. Use cropping practices that minimize erosion.
Low-lying, wet terrain	Choose crops that tolerate or need abundant water, e.g., paddy rice. Drain soils.
Shortage of beneficial insects	Introduce them, e.g., ladybugs and bees can be bought on the Internet.
Excess of harmful insects	Use chemical insecticides. Introduce predator insects. Use cropping methods that limit insects. Grow genetically modified, insect-resistant crop varieties.
Excess of weeds	Use chemical herbicides. Manually remove weeds. Grow genetically modified plant varieties that work with herbicides. Use cropping methods that minimize weeds.

◀ **Fig. 24-5** Large farms can use centre-pivot irrigation systems to provide moisture. A pipe with many sprinkler heads rotates around a central point, which is connected to a pressurized water supply. The pipe can be up to 400 metres long. To better imagine the size of this irrigation rig, remember that a Canadian football field is about 100 metres long.

Of all the agricultural regions of Canada, only the prairie provinces export a greater value of agricultural products than they import.

Canadians spend a smaller percentage of their income on food than people in most countries.

The Importance of Agriculture to Canada

Crop and animal production contribute about 1.4% to Canada's GDP. When all the people involved in the growing, processing, transportation, and selling of food are counted, however, about 20% of jobs are related to the agricultural sector of the economy. Agricultural products play an important role in our trade with other countries. Furthermore, Canada has a large surplus in agricultural trade. Most of this surplus is the result of the export of grains and vegetable oil products from the Prairies.

Canadians rely on farmers to produce food that is relatively inexpensive after the costs of production, transportation, processing, and profit are added. In the 1950s, Canadians spent about 25% of their income on food; today, they spend only about 11%, including meals eaten outside the home. There are many problems facing Canadian agriculture that could cause people to spend a greater percentage of their income on food. Some of these will be examined later in the chapter.

Land: The Basic Resource

The American writer Mark Twain once wrote: "Buy land. They've stopped making it." His humorous advice has a serious side. Most Canadians, especially farmers, value ownership of land. Land is a **renewable resource** in the sense that, if properly used, it can support new crops year after year. On the other hand, land can be classified as a **non-renewable resource** because, as Mark Twain reminds us, there is a limited amount of it available, especially land that is suitable for farming. If land is seriously damaged as a result of bad farming practices, or if it is paved over to build a town or highway, it can no longer be used for agriculture. In this sense, it is a non-renewable resource.

During the 1960s and 1970s, the federal and provincial governments surveyed parts of Canada (2.5 million square kilometres) to determine the land's suitability, or **land capability**, for agriculture. As part of the Canada Land Inventory (CLI), the **survey** divided Canada's land into seven classes (Fig. 24-6) to form a classification system that is helpful in land-use planning. According to the CLI, only 13% of Canada's vast land mass (Classes 1 to 6) is suitable for agriculture (Fig. 24-7). Although the country is the second largest in the world, the amount of its agricultural land is relatively small, and much of that land is threatened by urban growth. The proportional circle graphs in Fig. 24-8 illustrate the distribution of agricultural land capability across Canada.

survey
a measuring of quantity or quality

The amount of good farmland (Classes 1 to 3) in Canada is about equal to the amount of good farmland in the state of California!

Class 1: Land has deep soils and is *excellent* for farming. It has no climatic or land limitations. **0.5% of Canada's land area.**

Class 2: Land is *very good* farmland. It has no serious climatic or land limitations. **1.8% of Canada's land area.**

Class 3: Land is *good* farmland, but has some climatic or land limitations that make some farming activities impossible. **2.7% of Canada's land area.**

Class 4: Land is at the "break-even" point for commercial agriculture because of a short growing season, poor soil conditions, or other significant limitations. **2.7% of Canada's land area.**

Class 5: Land has serious limitations for agriculture, such as a very short growing season, hilly landscape, thin soil, or poor drainage. Class 5 land may be used for grazing or producing hay. **3.7% of Canada's land area.**

Class 6: Land is similar to Class 5 except that the limitations are more severe. Crops cannot be grown successfully. These lands can be used only for rough grazing. **1.8% of Canada's land area.**

Class 7: Land has no capability for farming or was not classified (this includes the land in the northern part of Canada). **86.8% of Canada's land area.**

◀ **Fig. 24-6** The Canadian Land Inventory created seven classes of agricultural land.

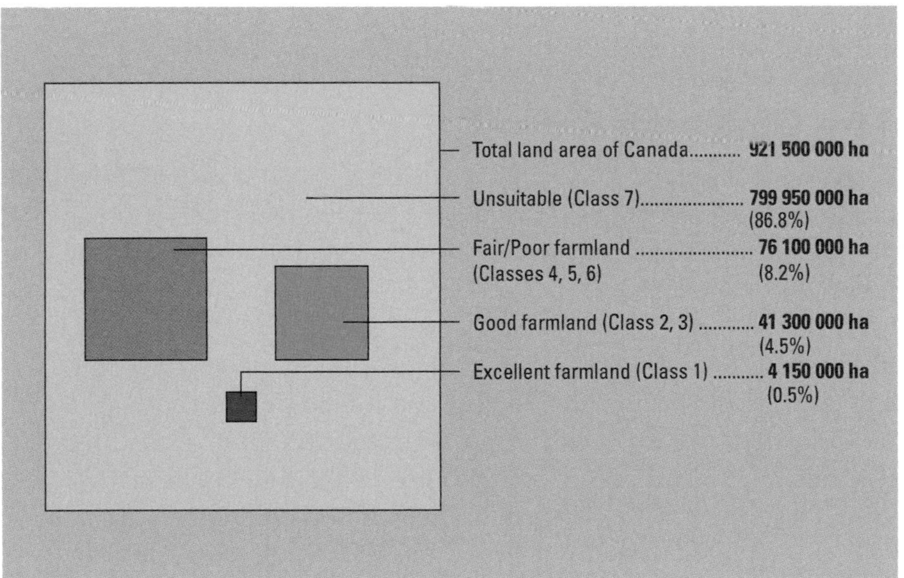

◀ **Fig. 24-7** The total amount of farmland in Canada is very small—less than 15% of Canada's land area!

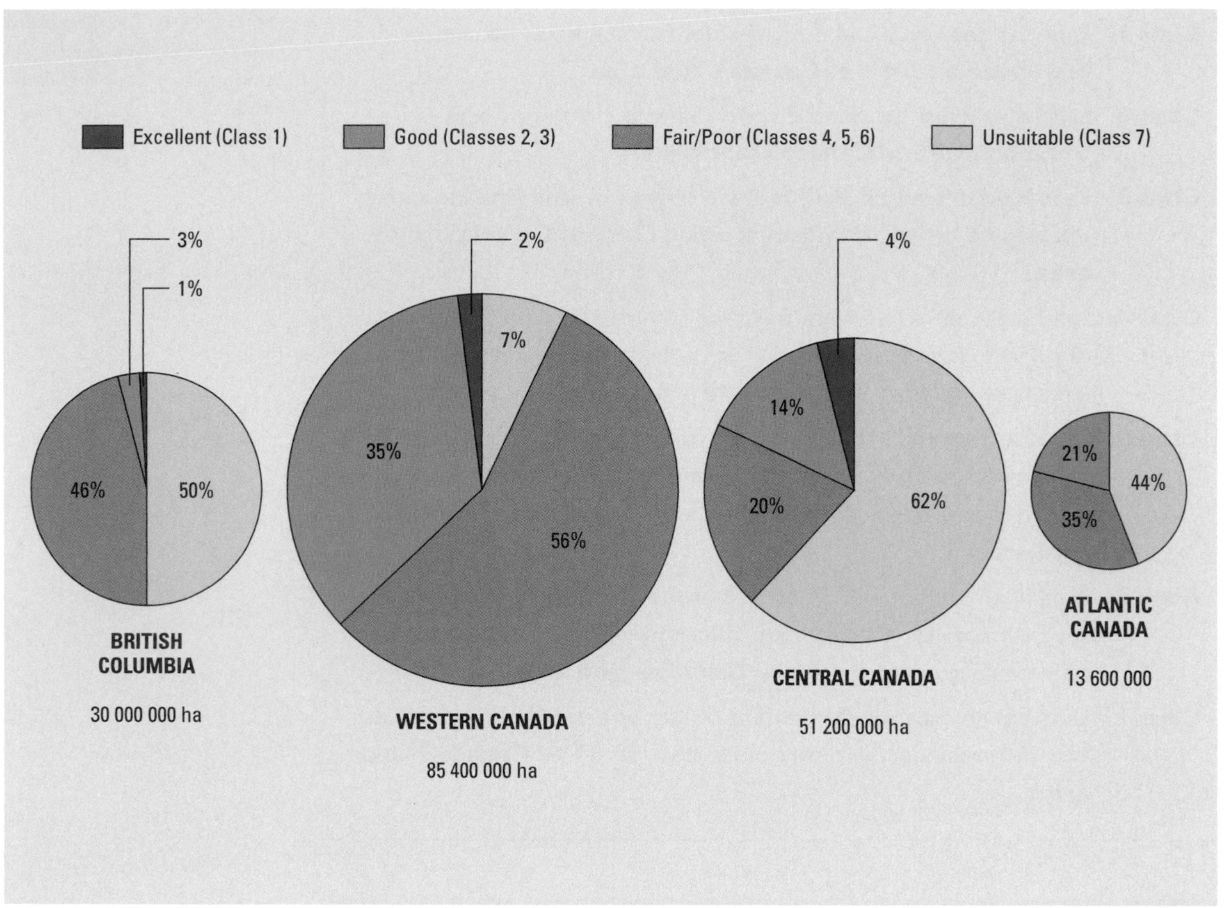

▲ **Fig. 24-8** The distribution of farmland of different capabilities across Canada

The Changing Farm

In 1867, about 82% of Canadians lived in rural areas. More people worked in agriculture than in any other industry. Today, almost 80% of Canadians live in urban areas, and farmers account for about 3% of Canada's labour force. What has caused this staggering change?

In the 1880s, farmers were able to manage only small farms of about 50 hectares in size. Farm work was accomplished by horses pulling plows and wagons, and by human muscle power for most other chores. Today, one or two people can operate a farm over 200 hectares in size with the help of modern equipment. Increased **mechanization** has brought about an increase in the size of farms and a decline in their numbers.

Between 1901 and 2001, changes occurred in the amount of farmland, the number of farms, and the amount of equipment used on farms. Complete the following activity and you will be able to determine these changes.

Use a spreadsheet or a calculator to perform the following calculations using the information in Fig. 24-9.

Year	A Number of Farms	B Average Farm Size (ha)	C Number of Workers
1901	511 000	50	718 000
1911	683 000	65	928 000
1921	711 000	80	1 025 000
1931	729 000	91	1 118 000
1941	733 000	96	1 074 000
1951	623 000	113	826 000
1961	481 000	145	649 000
1971	366 000	188	510 000
1981	318 000	207	508 000
1991	280 000	242	533 000
2001	247 000	273	346 000

◀ **Fig. 24-9** Changes in Canadian agriculture, 1901–2001

1. a) i. Calculate the total amount of farmland for each year by multiplying the data in column A by the data in column B.
   ii. Plot these results on a line graph.
   b) Construct a similar graph for the number of farms for each year.
   c) i. Compare the amount of farmland and number of farms in 1931 to the amount of farmland and number of farms in 2001.
   ii. What factors might explain these changes?
2. a) Calculate the number of workers per farm for each year by dividing C by A.
   b) Plot these results on a line graph.
   c) What pattern do you see? Why do you think this pattern exists?
3. a) Calculate the average number of hectares per worker for each year by dividing B by the number of workers per farm that you calculated in Question 2a).
   b) Plot these results on a line graph.
   c) What do you think has caused the change since 1971?
4. The amount of mechanized farm equipment changed considerably during the 1900s. The number of tractors and combines was 114 000 in 1931, 705 000 in 1961, and 849 000 in 2001.
   a) Create a line graph to show the amount of mechanized farm equipment used over this time period.
   b) i. Calculate the number of pieces of farm equipment per farm for each of the three years. (Hint: Divide the amount of farm equipment by the number of farms.)
   ii. Add the results to your graph.
   c) What has been the trend? Do you think this will continue in the future? Explain.

Remember to put the years on the x-axis since they represent the independent variable.

Types of Farming

Farms differ widely across Canada in their size and in their products (Fig. 24-10). The type of farming is determined by important natural factors such as soil fertility, precipitation levels, and the length of the growing season. It is also determined by certain economic factors that include:

- *Cost or value of land:* If the farmland is expensive to buy, the farmer will produce products that earn a high profit. The farmer will use the profit to pay the mortgage, or to pay higher taxes usually associated with land of higher value.
- *Proximity to market:* If farms are close to their markets, farmers will most likely produce perishable products such as vegetables, milk, and eggs. If they are far from markets, they will produce less perishable products such as grain and oilseeds.
- *Competition:* If there is an oversupply of a particular product, its price will drop, and farm incomes will diminish. The farmer will then choose to grow another product for which there is a greater demand and higher returns.

Farmers must take both natural and economic factors into account when deciding whether to practise intensive or extensive farming. **Intensive farming** is common in densely populated areas such as southern Ontario, southern Quebec, and in the Fraser River Valley near Vancouver. Farms tend to be small but they require large investments in labour and machinery to produce high profits per hectare. Intensive farming commonly produces fruits, vegetables, dairy products, poultry, and hogs. Many of these items are perishable and must be quickly processed and transported to market.

See Figure 14-1 for an illustration of intensive farming.

Extensive farming occurs where the population density is low and land is plentiful and inexpensive. Since farms tend to be large, low yields per hectare will still allow a profit. Compared to intensive farming, extensive farming is usually highly mechanized and requires few workers. Extensive farming is common in the prairie provinces, the interior of southern British Columbia, and parts of Ontario and Quebec that are located away from major cities. It includes cattle farming and ranching, grain and oilseed growing, and mixed farming. Since extensive farming operations are located away from major markets, their products are usually less perishable than products produced in intensive farming operations.

See Fig. 13-8 for an illustration of extensive farming.

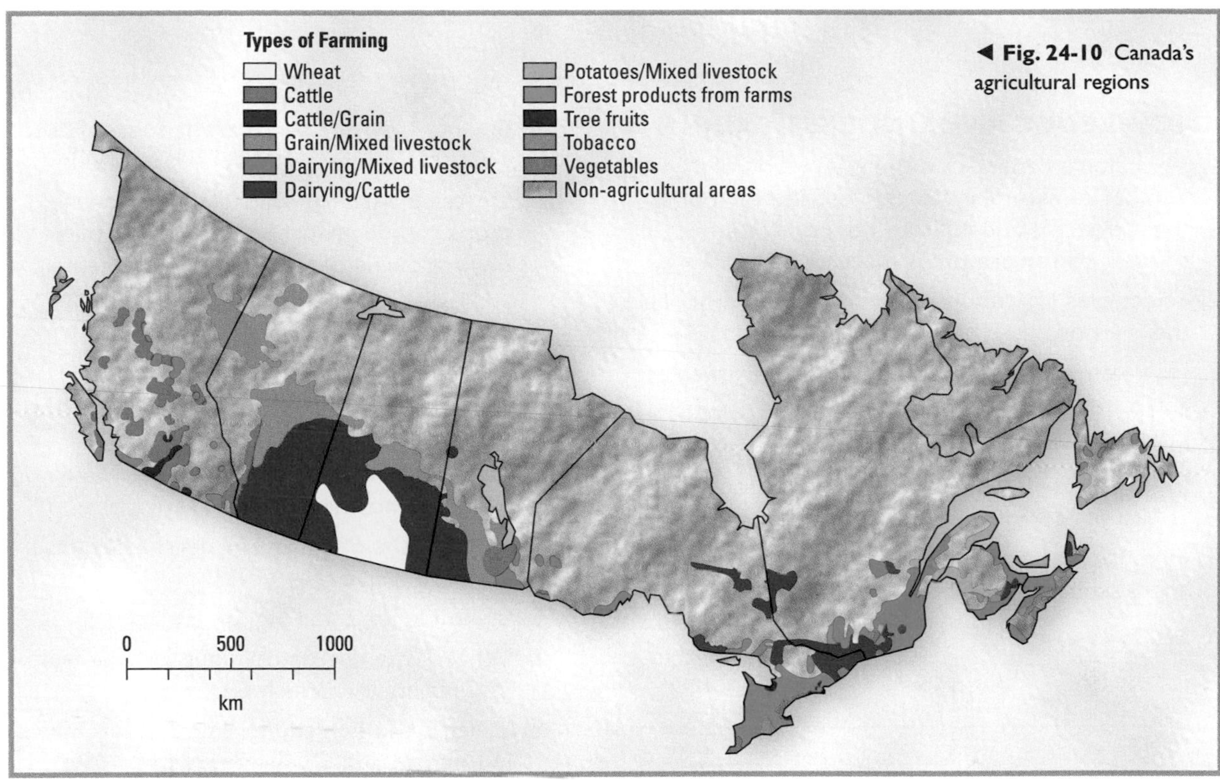

◀ **Fig. 24-10** Canada's agricultural regions

Wheat

- The wheat and grain farms of Saskatchewan, Alberta, and Manitoba are large, highly specialized, and mechanized.
- The Ontario farms are also specialized and mechanized but much smaller.
- The cool, wet springs and dry, hot summers on the Prairies produce high-quality hard wheat for bread and durum wheat for pasta.
- The yield per hectare in the Prairies is low compared to the more humid southern Ontario, but the large prairie farms produce 90% of Canada's wheat.

Beef Cattle and Grain

- In the dry grassland areas of Alberta, Saskatchewan, Manitoba, and British Columbia, large ranches raise most of Canada's beef cattle.
- Large ranches are needed because the cattle are raised in areas too dry or too hilly for wheat or grain crops.
- In the more moist areas of the Prairies, grain crops and other livestock are raised.
- The cattle are either sold before winter, or are fed grains during the winter before sale in the spring.
- Oil seed crops such as canola and sunflowers are becoming more popular in the Prairies since they are seen as healthier than animal fat or coconut oil when used in salad oils, shortening, and margarine.
- Ontario and Quebec farmers raise cattle on smaller farms for local markets.

Dairy and Livestock (beef cattle, sheep, hogs, poultry)

- Dairy products are very perishable and must be shipped quickly to urban markets, or processed into cheese and butter.
- The majority of dairy farms are located in Quebec and Ontario not far from major population centres.
- Dairy farming is an intensive activity involving daily feeding and milking of cattle and large investments in barns, feed, and milking and refrigeration equipment.
- Livestock is often raised farther from populated centres.
- The livestock feed on grass in pastures during the summer but in winter they must be fed.
- Many farmers grow their own hay and grains for winter feed.

Fruits and Vegetables

- Intensive farming techniques are commonly used for the production of fruits and vegetables.
- Market gardening involves growing perishable vegetables for nearby urban markets.
- The fertile soils near Montreal, the well-drained soils of the Fraser delta near Vancouver, and the peat soils of Holland Marsh north of Toronto produce lettuce, onions, celery, and carrots.
- Since land near urban areas is expensive, high yields per hectare are required.
- Tender fruits (peaches, sweet cherries, apricots, and grapes) are grown in the Annapolis Valley of Nova Scotia, the Niagara fruit belt of Ontario, and the Okanagan Valley of British Columbia. Tender fruits are more likely to be damaged by low temperatures than apples, plums, pears, and sour cherries.
- These areas are unique in Canada because they have fertile, well-drained sandy soils, mild winters, and nearby water bodies that reduce the likelihood of late spring and early fall frosts that could damage the buds or fruit.
- The highly perishable fruit must be processed or marketed quickly.

QUESTIONS

KNOWLEDGE AND UNDERSTANDING

1. Agriculture depends on the interaction of a number of natural systems. Describe each of these systems and indicate how each contributes to (or prevents) successful agriculture.
2. Select four agricultural deficiencies and describe the methods used to overcome them.
3. How can land be considered both a renewable and a non-renewable resource?
4. a) What is the Canada Land Inventory?
   b) In your own words, outline the characteristics of each of the seven land classes.
5. In your notebook, construct and complete a chart similar to Fig. 24-11.

▼ **Fig. 24-11**

	Intensive Agriculture	Extensive Agriculture
Size of Farms		
Use of Labour/Machinery		
Types of Farming		

THINKING

6. Construct a chart similar to Fig. 24-12. Use the map in Fig. 24-10 and information in Fig. 24-13 to complete this chart.
7. Why is agriculture in the Prairies mainly extensive wheat and cattle farming, while in southern Ontario and Quebec much of the farming is intensive vegetable, fruit, and dairy farming?
8. What would life be like for a family whose farm consisted only of Class 6 and 7 land? What options would they have?
9. Use Fig. 24-2 to answer the following questions.
   a) Explain, in your own words, what a growing degree-day is.
   b) In what part of Canada are farmers able to grow the greatest variety of crops? Why?
   c) Describe where in Canada the following crops can be grown based on their minimum growing degree-days requirements.
      i. Flax requires a minimum of 1600 GDDs.
      ii. Grain corn requires a minimum of 2200 GDDs.
      iii. Sunflowers require a minimum of 1800 GDDs.
   d) Generally speaking, how many degree-days mark the northern limit of agriculture?
   e) Why do the 555 and 277 degree-day lines have the shape they do?
10. Examine Fig. 24-2 and Fig. 24-10.
    a) What is the degree-day limit for tree fruits in Ontario and British Columbia?
    b) What is the degree-day limit for vegetables in Ontario and Quebec?
    c) Why doesn't Newfoundland have commercial vegetable and fruit-tree farming?
11. Examine Fig. 24-8.
    a) Rank the regions in terms of the amount of excellent and good farmland found in each.
    b) Rank the regions in terms of the amount of land that is fair or poor.
    c) What do these rankings suggest about the agricultural potential of each region?

COMMUNICATION

12. The agricultural land capability survey was carried out in the 1960s. What do you think has happened to the amount of agricultural land since that time? What effect might this have on Canada's future food supply?

▼ **Fig. 24-12**

Province	Value of Farm Production	Location(s) of Farming Area(s)	Major Types of Farming

APPLICATION

13. Fig. 24-13 shows the value of farm production by province for 2003.
    a) Calculate the percentage of the total value of agricultural products from each province.
    b) Construct a pie graph to show the percentages produced by each province.
    c) Which province produces the highest value and which one produces the lowest value? Explain the reason for the highest and lowest values.
    d) How does the value of production relate to the availability of good farmland? (Refer back to Fig. 24-8.)

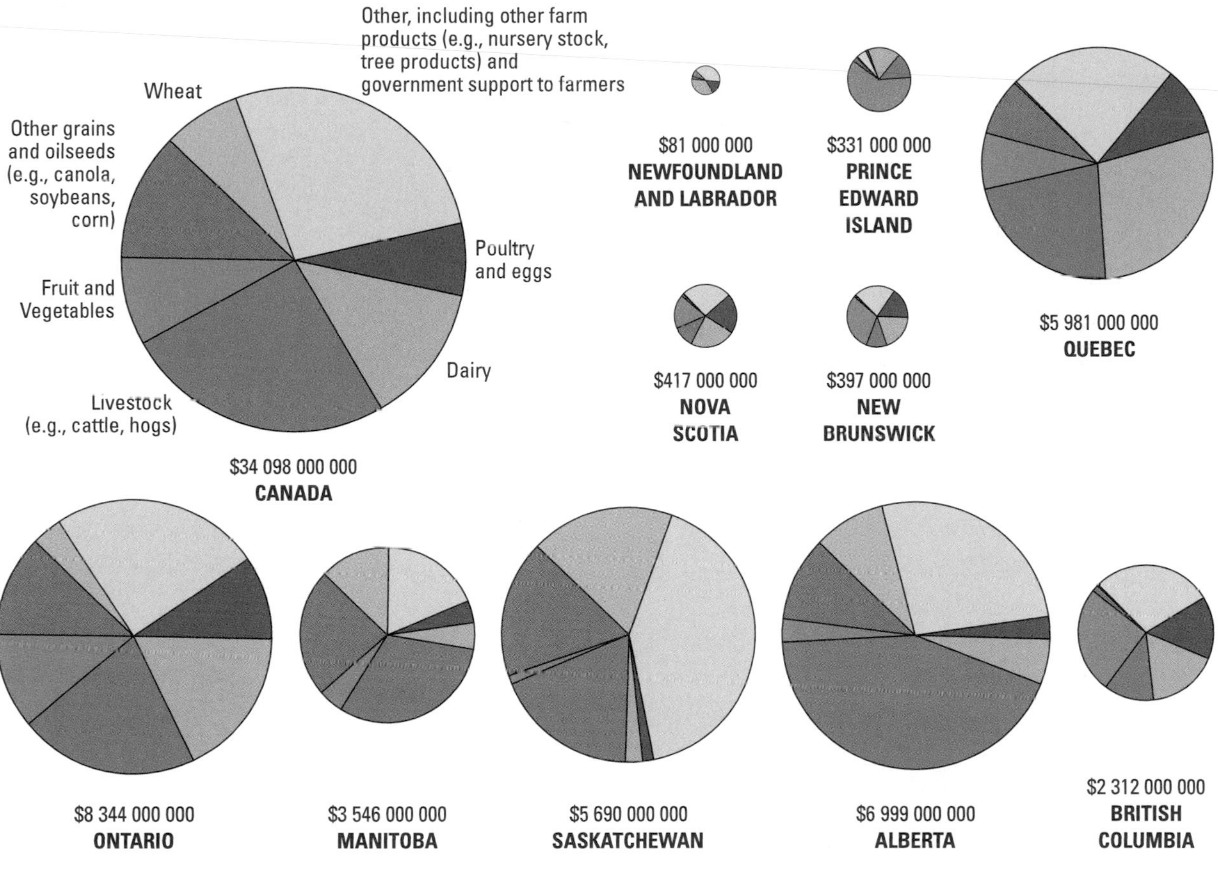

▲ **Fig. 24-13** Provincial farm receipts

Other Issues Facing Canadian Farmers Today

The agricultural sector of Canada's economy is very complex. Farmers face many problems beyond such things as finding buyers for their farms when they retire, or dealing with the effects of international subsidies. The issues box below guides you in exploring these problems using a *jigsaw* approach. Your teacher will explain the details of the jigsaw to you, but in general you will work in an "expert group" that researches one issue in detail.

Issue

ISSUES FACING CANADIAN FARMERS TODAY

◀ **Fig. 24-14** Small family farms have increasingly given way to "factory farms" owned by large corporations.

Loss of Farmland

Most of Canada's best farmland is located adjacent to our largest cities—all of which are growing outward onto this land. What attempts are being made to protect farmland in southern Ontario? Should we protect this land from urban growth? Is it possible to do so?

Decline of the Family Farm and the Growth of Agribusiness

Traditionally, farming in Canada took place on relatively small family farms passed down from one generation to the next. Increasingly though, farming is being carried out by **agribusiness** on much larger farms. Why is this happening? What are the advantages and disadvantages of this trend? Can we/should we do anything about this change?

Sustainable Agriculture

Farming that can be carried on indefinitely without harming the soil or the environment is known as **sustainable agriculture**. Many agricultural practices can cause damage to the soil and other parts of the natural environment. The result, over a period of many years, is a decline in agricultural productivity. What are some practices that cause damage to the soil? What can farmers do to encourage sustainable agriculture?

Organic Farming

Organic farming focuses on the production of crops and animals without the use of chemical fertilizers and pesticides, radiation, or GMOs (see below). Sales of organic crops are increasing at a rapid rate, reaching more than $3 billion in Canada in 2005. What exactly is an organic crop and why are organic products becoming so desirable? What are the disadvantages of organic products?

BSE (Mad Cow Disease)

In 2003, the discovery of a single case of mad cow disease in Alberta halted the trade of Canadian beef to the United States and 33 other countries.

What exactly is the risk of **BSE** and how has this risk been addressed? How is growing world trade in farm products making the risk greater? Are there other agricultural-related diseases that we should be worrying about?

Fig. 24-15 ▶
A butcher in Germany stands on a pile of cows slaughtered to prevent an outbreak of BSE from imported cattle. The brains of the cows were later examined for signs of the disease.

Genetically Modified Organisms (GMOs)

GMOs are created when scientists transfer a gene from one organism to another in order to introduce some desirable characteristic to the target plant or animal. For example, a plant can be genetically modified to resist the effects of a herbicide or a killing frost.

What features do GMOs have? Why do many people have concerns about GMOs? How do attitudes to GMOs vary from country to country?

A powerful herbicide could be used to kill everything but the crop.

Activity

With three or four of your classmates, form your "home group" and select one issue to research. Your group will teach other home groups about the issue you have selected, and you will learn from those groups about the issues they researched.

When you do your research, try to answer the following questions. Remember that you must learn this material well enough to teach it to other students.

- What is the background of the issue?
- What are the "sides" in the issue? Note that there may be more than two sides.
- What efforts have been made to find solutions to the problems that are part of the issue?
- How successful have these efforts been?

GeoLit Reminder

Presentation skills:

- Work with your home group to review issues and gather information.
- Choose your presentation style.
- Organize your presentation using an introduction, supported main points, and a conclusion.
- Rehearse your presentation.
- When presenting your information, clearly explain each point before moving on to the next.
- Respond to questions as specifically as possible.
- Reflect on the completed presentation. What went well? What will you do differently next time?

Start your research through the link provided for each issue at www.pearsoned.ca/makingconnections2.

CASE STUDY

Agricultural Subsidies

▲ **Fig. 24-16** Canadian farmers receive considerably lower subsidies for many agricultural products, including wheat, grain, and oilseed crops, than do farmers in the United States or the European Union.

Background

Government grants, or **subsidies**, began during the Great Depression of the 1930s to help farmers whose crops had been destroyed by drought and whose products were fetching low prices in the marketplace. Since then, their use in North America, Europe, and Japan has expanded enormously. Why has their use expanded, and what effects do they have?

Subsidies are given when droughts and other natural events occur and threaten the farmers' livelihood. They are also given to help farmers compete with subsidized farmers in other countries (or regions). They are frequently given to farmers threatened by political events such as the ban on imports of Canadian beef into the United States that occurred in the 1990s and early 2000s.

If you think about it, you'll see that subsidies, or the lack thereof, are an artificial means of restricting or encouraging trade. In a world that professes to believe in free trade, agriculture remains the one sector in which little progress toward free trade has occurred.

- Small countries such as Japan, South Korea, and Switzerland have the highest subsidies. These countries are followed by the European Union, then the United States, and then Canada and Australia. Because farm subsidies in Canada are not as large as those of the United States and the European Union, Canadian farmers are at a disadvantage and face

Consider that the annual per capita GDP of 79 countries in the world is less than the amount of subsidy paid for each cow in Japan every year.

unfair competition in world markets. The size of some subsidies is startling. For example, in Europe, almost 40% of all farm income comes from subsidies. In Switzerland alone, this number rises to more than 70%. In Japan, each dairy cow is subsidized by about $9 a day!

- Farmers in developing countries are hurt by the subsidies given to farmers in developed countries. When grain and other products that are produced in Europe and the US are sold to developing countries in Africa, Asia, and South America, the producers can afford to sell them at prices well below the cost of production in the developing countries. Why? Because the subsidies they receive from their governments make up the difference. Since farmers in developing countries cannot compete against the low cost of subsidized imported products, they lose their local markets. Furthermore, they cannot compete for markets in richer countries because they receive no subsidies from their own governments. Subsidies awarded to farmers in developed countries frequently hinder the economic growth of developing countries.
- It has proven very difficult to eliminate or reduce subsidies in developed countries. In Canada, but more so in the United States, Europe, and Japan, farmers have an influence on their governments far beyond what their numbers would suggest. Observers, farmers' organizations, and governments have frequently discussed the reduction of subsidies, but nothing has been done to eliminate them.

QUESTIONS

KNOWLEDGE AND UNDERSTANDING

1. a) What was the original purpose of subsidies?
   b) In general, are they now meeting this purpose?

THINKING

2. a) Why is it proving difficult to reduce, to any great degree, the level of agricultural subsidies?
   b) What organizations are pushing to reduce subsidies?
   c) Should Canada continue to cut subsidies if other nations do not?

APPLICATION

3. a) Summarize the impact of high subsidy levels on the following:
   i. farmers in developed countries
   ii. farmers in developing countries
   iii. food shoppers in developed countries
   iv. taxpayers in developed countries
   b) What would the impact be on each group mentioned in 3a) if subsidies, other than for short-term emergencies, were eliminated?

25 Forest Resources and Their Uses

Key Ideas

This chapter helps you investigate these questions:

- How important are Canada's various forest regions to the economy?
- How are trees harvested and used?
- What are the key issues in forest management today?

Key Terms

sustained yield forest management
softwood
hardwood
commercial forest
non-commercial forest
clear-cutting
shelterwood logging
selective cutting
acid precipitation
stewardship

There are different viewpoints on how our forests should be managed and used (Fig. 25-1). Which one is correct? How can we harvest the forests for products that we need, and at the same time protect the forest environment? The answer to this question is complex. We can gain some understanding, however, if we examine the nature, importance, and use of the forests, and learn how to achieve **sustained yield forest management**—the controlled use of forest resources at a rate that allows forests to renew themselves.

INTERNET

To compare viewpoints about BC forests, look at an industry view and an environmental view through the links at www.pearsoned.ca/makingconnections2.

New Pulp and Paper Mill Will Earn Company Millions of Dollars and Bring 500 New Jobs to Community

Protesters Block Logging Road to Stop the Cutting of Old-Growth Forest

◀ **Fig. 25-1** Forest companies and environmental groups focus on different goals.

Forest Facts

Imagine driving at 100 kilometres per hour for 12 hours a day. It would take you more than four days to cross the continuous band of forest that stretches from British Columbia to Newfoundland. Forests cover close to half (4 187 820 square kilometres, or 42%) of Canada's total area. This is an area greater than the total area of 15 Western European nations combined! Only Russia (with 8 196 000 square kilometres) and Brazil (with 5 022 080 square kilometres) have more forests than Canada.

Coniferous trees are cone-bearing trees with needle leaves. Deciduous trees lose their leaves every year.

Softwood forests make up 66% of Canada's forest cover. They consist mainly of coniferous trees such as fir, pine, and spruce.

Hardwood forests account for 12% of the forest cover. They are made up mainly of deciduous trees such as poplar, maple, and birch. The remaining 22% are mixed forests that contain both coniferous and deciduous trees.

Characteristics of Forests

Commercial forests consist of trees that can be harvested profitably (Fig. 25-2). They exist in the warmer, wetter areas of Canada where trees grow relatively quickly. Because these forests are near roads, railways, and waterways, their timber can easily be shipped to markets in Canada and

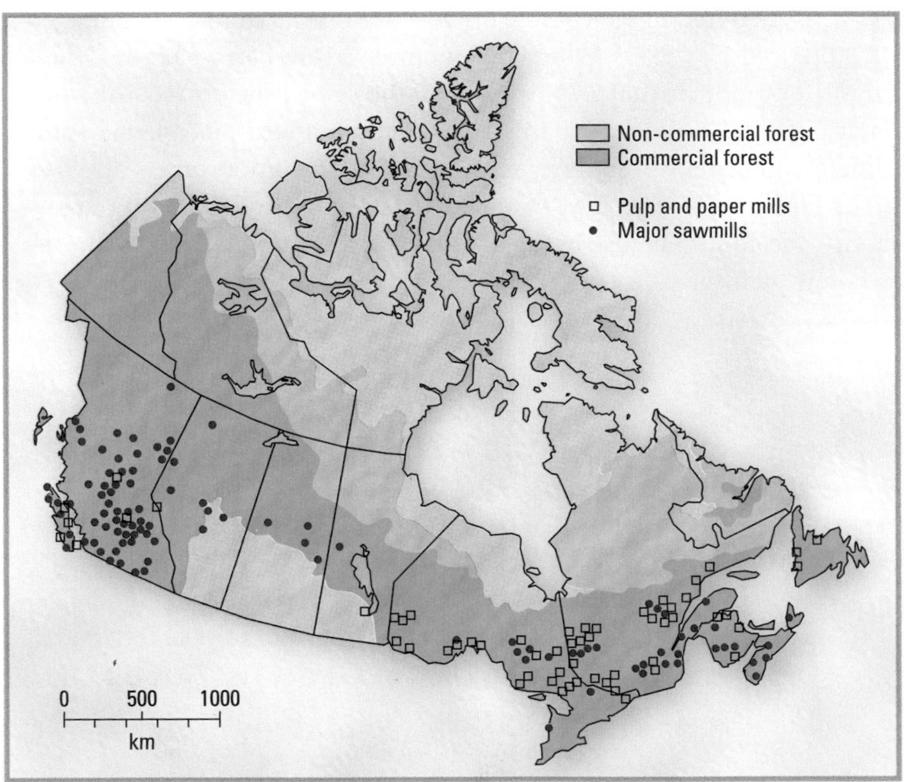

Fig. 25-2 ▶ Canada's commercial and non-commercial forests and the location of sawmills and pulp and paper mills

abroad. Today, only half of Canada's potentially commercial forests are accessible by road.

In contrast, **non-commercial forests** are those that are unlikely to be harvested. They exist to the north of the commercial forests, where temperatures and precipitation levels are too low for trees to grow quickly or large enough for harvesting. These forests are too far from transportation routes that would make their shipment economical.

In Canada, a tree may take 80 years to reach the size at which it can be harvested profitably. In tropical countries, a tree may need only 20 years to reach a similar size.

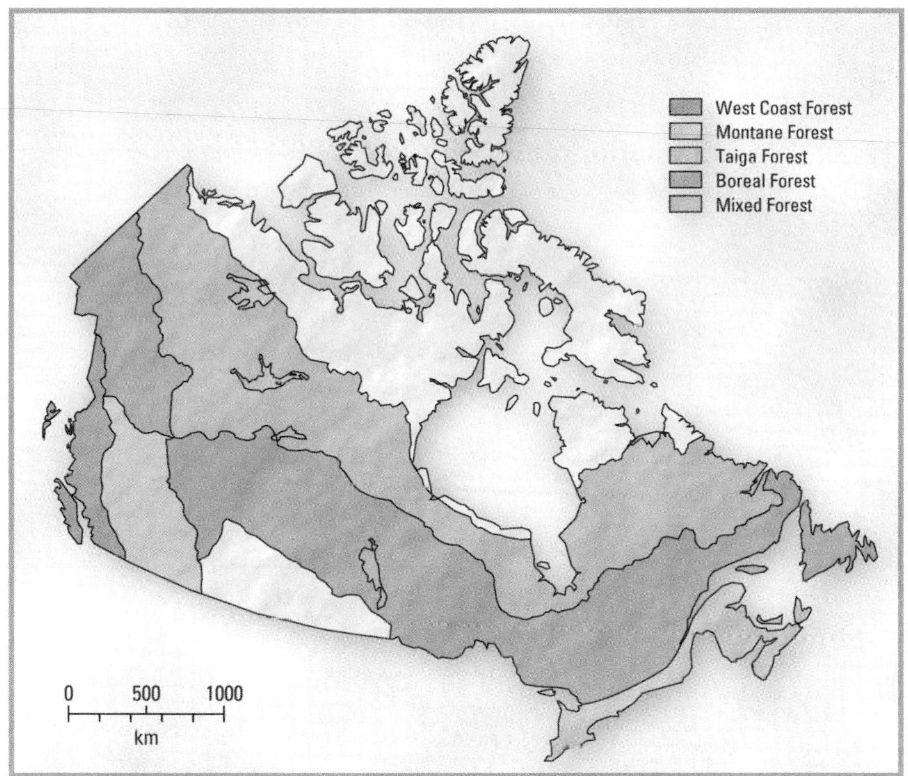

◀ **Fig. 25-3** Forest regions of Canada. In addition, there are relatively small areas of forest in the Arctic and on the Prairies.

You can do this activity with a calculator or a spreadsheet. It may also be completed as a GIS activity if your school has ArcView.

1. In which provinces and territories is each forest region located (see Fig. 25-3)?
2. Answer the following questions using the information in Fig. 25-4.
   a) Proportional circle graphs have circles with areas that are proportional to the values they represent. Draw a proportional circle for the total area of each region on the ecozone map of Canada provided by your teacher.
   b) Within each proportional circle, create a pie graph to show the amount of commercial forest, non-commercial forest, and non-forested land.

If you are using ArcView to do this activity, your teacher will give you complete instructions.

See Chapter 8 to learn about drawing proportional circle graphs.

c) In which regions does the commercial forest occupy more than 45% of the total land area? Suggest reasons for this.

3. Examine the *Commercial Forest* column.
   a) For each forest region, calculate the percentage of the total forest land that is occupied by commercial forest.
   b) In which regions are the highest and lowest percentages located? Suggest reasons for this difference.
   c) Which forest region contains the largest percentage of commercial forest? Explain why.

Forest Regions	Total Area (000 ha)	Total Forest Land (000 ha)	Commercial Forest (000 ha)	Non-commercial Forest (000 ha)	Non-forested (000 ha)
1. Boreal Forest	314 877	229 711	153 808	75 903	85 166
2. Taiga Forest	264 060	117 900	29 411	88 488	146 160
3. Montane Forest	49 211	34 857	32 129	2 728	14 354
4. Mixed Forest	39 818	19 688	18 872	815	20 130
5. West Coast Forest	21 898	10 057	8 563	1 492	11 841
6. Arctic	259 386	3 286	9	3 277	256 100
7. Prairies	47 811	2 085	1 778	307	45 726
TOTAL	997 061	417 584	244 570	173 010	579 477

▲ **Fig. 25-4** Forest statistics

Canada's Commercial Forest Regions

Fig. 25-3 shows Canada's main forest regions. Each is quite distinctive. The following section describes the five regions in which most of Canada's commercial forestry is located.

BOREAL FOREST REGION

(found in Boreal Shield, Boreal Plains, and Boreal Cordillera ecozones)

- by far the largest forest region
- mainly coniferous (softwood) trees of which black spruce is the most common; other important species include white spruce, balsam fir, Jack pine, cedar, and tamarack; deciduous trees such as white birch and poplar are also common
- slow tree growth due to long winters and low precipitation
- since small trees are most common here, pulp and paper production, which uses smaller logs, tends to be more important than lumber production.

Softwood is used for house construction and papermaking.

TAIGA FOREST REGION

(found in the Taiga Plains, Taiga Shield, Hudson Plains, and Taiga Cordillera ecozones)

- stunted trees due to thin soils, cool temperatures, short growing season, and areas of permafrost
- coniferous trees, such as black spruce, white spruce, Jack pine; some deciduous trees such as poplar and trembling aspen
- since most of this forest is inaccessible and far from markets, only small parts are logged, most often for pulp and papermaking.

WEST COAST FOREST REGION

(found in Pacific Maritime ecozone)

- most productive forest in Canada; volume of wood, per hectare, highest in Canada
- temperate coniferous rain forest grows on the western slopes of the coastal mountains
- abundant relief precipitation, moderate temperatures, and long growing season cause Douglas fir, Sitka spruce, western red cedar, and western hemlock to grow larger than any other trees in the country
- because the trees here are very large, the wood is most often used to make lumber, cedar shingles, and plywood; pulp and paper are made from smaller logs.

MONTANE FOREST REGION

(found in Montane Cordillera ecozone)

- volume of wood, per hectare, second only to that of the West Coast Forest region
- lower precipitation levels and shorter growing season than the West Coast Forest region
- smaller coniferous trees such as various spruce, lodgepole pine, and ponderosa pine
- both lumber and pulp and paper are made from the logs cut here.

MIXED FOREST REGION

(found in Mixedwood Plains and Atlantic Maritime ecozones)

- longer growing season and more precipitation than Boreal Forest region
- in the north (near the Boreal Forest), fir and spruce dominate; in the south, coniferous trees such as white pine, hemlock, and red pine grow together with hardy deciduous trees such as maple, beech, and oak

Some hardwoods, such as ash, are used to make baseball bats and hockey sticks.

- conifers are harvested for lumber and pulp and paper; hardwoods for lumber; the sugar maples that grow in the mixed forest provide most of Canada's maple syrup
- in the extreme southern portion of the Mixedwood Plains ecozone—the most southerly part of Canada—mixed forest gives way to deciduous forest; very little of this forest remains because the region is intensively farmed and highly urbanized.
- warmer temperatures, longer growing season, and abundant precipitation allow the growth of hardwood trees such as maple, birch, black walnut, and cherry, which are valued for flooring and furniture-making

Softwood lumber makes up 33% of exports, 20% of newsprint, 18% of wood pulp, and 29% of all other forest products.

Economic Impact of Forests

Forests play an important role in Canada's economy. The forest industry produces lumber, pulp and paper, and other forest products worth about $81 billion per year (2004). Slightly more than half of this amount is exported to other countries.

The industry also provides more than 360 000 direct jobs for Canadians. These jobs are associated with the companies that harvest the timber and operate the saw and paper mills located near the forests (Fig. 25-2). Furthermore, there are almost 500 000 indirect jobs in companies that provide products and services for forestry companies and workers.

Logging Operations

There are several ways to harvest the trees of Canada's forests. We will examine three distinct methods: clear-cutting, shelterwood logging, and selective cutting.

1. **Clear-cutting** This method (Fig. 25-5), which is used in the vast majority of logging operations, is the fastest and cheapest. Loggers remove every tree, leaving a barren landscape behind. Northern forests of pine, spruce, fir, aspen, and poplar are cut in this manner. When the clear-cut area is replanted, the new forest grows up uniformly in species and size. This makes it easier to log this forest in the future when the trees reach maturity. If replanting does not take place, or if it is not successful, less desirable species may grow. As well, the exposed soil may erode, and the land may be damaged.

▼ **Fig. 25-5** Clear-cutting can leave an area looking like this.

2. **Shelterwood Logging** This method involves clear-cutting only part of a forest. Groups of seed-bearing trees are left standing so that

their seeds can **regenerate** the logged area (Fig. 25-6). This is used where tree species, such as white pine, regenerate naturally after major openings in the forest are created. The shelterwood method is often used in forests with trees of **uniform** age and size. Over time, this method will also regenerate a forest that has trees of varying ages and sizes.

regenerate grow again

uniform similar

3. **Selective Cutting** This method consists of harvesting only mature trees of the desired size, type, or quality. This method is much less disruptive to the forest environment. It is used in forests with tree species that need shade to become established. Hardwoods, such as sugar maple, are cut in this manner. Selective cutting tends to be a costly process because of the extra care and time taken to cut down the trees. This method is also costly in the long run because it does not allow the replanting of a new, uniform forest.

Manufacturing Operations

Canada's forests yield products of great value. The two most important are pulp and paper and lumber.

PULP AND PAPER

Canada is the world's second-largest producer of pulp and paper (after the United States) and the largest exporter. The United States buys more

▼ **Fig. 25-6** Three methods of harvesting the forest

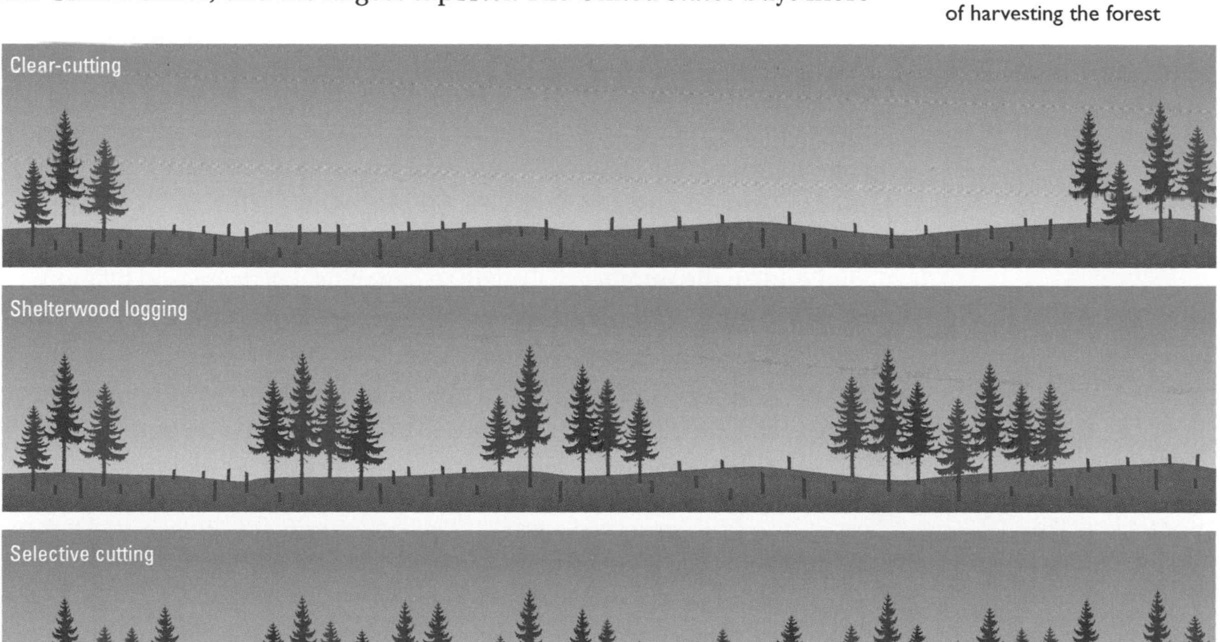

than half of Canada's pulp and paper exports. Although pulp and paper plants are found in every province except Prince Edward Island (Fig. 25-7), they are concentrated in Quebec, Ontario, and British Columbia. Since many of the logs from the trees in these provinces are too small to be used for lumber, they are used for pulp and paper manufacturing instead.

Fig. 25-7 ▶ Value of paper and paper products shipped (2001)

Quebec	Ontario	British Columbia	Other Provinces
$11 993 million	$11 115 million	$6264 million	$13 551 million

LUMBER

particleboard and **chipboard** sheets of building material produced by gluing together particles and small chips of wood under pressure

punitive intended to inflict punishment

Lumber products include raw cut timber, plywood, cedar shingles, **particleboard**, and **chipboard**. One province clearly dominates Canada's lumber industry: British Columbia. Quebec is far behind in second place (Fig. 25-8). In British Columbia, cut timber (also called lumber) is the major product. The province is also Canada's leading plywood producer because its tall, knot-free logs are easily unrolled ("peeled") to make the thin layers that are then glued together to make sheets of plywood. British Columbia's lumber industry has been hurt since the late 1980s by a series of **punitive** US trade measures that are designed to protect the American lumber industry.

Sawmills tend to be much smaller operations than pulp and paper mills. Each mill takes advantage of the unique characteristics of the particular forest that supplies the wood, and specializes in a particular market. A large mill in coastal British Columbia might specialize in producing lumber for house construction in the United States. A small mill in southern Ontario might concentrate on processing valuable hardwood logs to supply fine furniture manufacturers in the region.

Since 1970, the number of Canadian sawmills has decreased by more than 900 to about 850. New, more efficient large mills with better methods for processing small logs have replaced the old-fashioned mills that were designed for sawing large logs. The new mills reduce waste, and parts of the log that were discarded 30 years ago are now made into paper, particleboard, and chipboard. Even the bark and sawdust are burned to help power the mill.

Fig. 25-8 ▶ Value of lumber products shipped (2001)

British Columbia	Quebec	Ontario	Other Provinces
$10 817 million	$8032 million	$5664 million	$5610 million

Recreation

For many Canadians, especially those who live in cities and towns, the forest is important as a place to "get away from it all." Forests, with their lakes and rivers, provide the setting for a wide range of recreational activities, including camping, hiking, canoeing, and fishing.

QUESTIONS

KNOWLEDGE AND UNDERSTANDING

1. a) List two differences between Canada's commercial and non-commercial forests.
   b) The boundary between the commercial and non-commercial forests moves over time. Is it more likely to move north or south? Why?
2. a) Compare the characteristics of the coniferous trees that grow in the Boreal Forest region to those that grow in the West Coast Forest.
   b) Describe the characteristics of Canada's Mixed Forest region.
   c) In what ways are Canada's different forests used for commercial purposes?
3. a) Why is central Canada the leading pulp and paper producer?
   b) Why is British Columbia the leading producer of Canada's lumber?
4. a) Why is the number of sawmills decreasing?
   b) How are new sawmills different from older ones?
5. Copy Fig. 25-9 in your notebook and fill in the information for the three types of logging discussed in this chapter.

THINKING

6. You have 100 logs, each one metre in diameter. You could sell them to either a sawmill or a paper mill. Which would likely offer you a higher price? Why?

APPLICATION

7. Fig. 25-10 gives the total area and percentage of land covered by forest in some of the world's largest forest nations. Draw a circle proportional to each country's area and shade in part of the circle to show the percentage of the country that is forested. See Chapter 8 for instructions on how to draw a proportional circle graph.

▼ **Fig 25-10** Comparison of major forest-producing countries

Country	Area (km^2)	Forest Land (%)
Brazil	8 512 000	59
Canada	9 971 000	42
China	9 597 000	13
India	3 288 000	23
Russia	17 075 000	48
United States	9 373 000	31

▼ **Fig. 25-9**

Harvesting Process	Ease of Logging	Cost	Ecological Protection
Clear-cutting			
Shelterwood logging			
Selective cutting			

8. Those of you who have been paper carriers know how heavy the weekend paper can be. A recent copy of the Sunday *New York Times* (which is made from Canadian trees) weighed 4.5 kg. About 1.7 million copies of this paper were produced.
   a) How many kilograms of paper were used to produce this day's newspaper?
   b) One black spruce tree 13 m high and 20 cm in diameter can produce about 130 kg of newsprint. How many trees were cut down to produce this edition of the *New York Times?*
   c) What are the advantages and disadvantages of this use of our forests?

Threats to the Forests

There is perhaps one obvious reason why we should protect our forests: they provide an essential renewable resource—timber, which is of great economic value to Canada. This timber is constantly threatened by acid precipitation, damage from insect pests, and forest fires. There are, however, other not-so-obvious reasons to preserve our forests. For instance, after a rainstorm or during spring runoff, trees hold water in the soil. This prevents flooding. Forests also provide habitats for a multitude of animals, and they can be important hunting and trapping grounds. They are also important recreational areas.

Environmental Threats

Canadian forests face many environmental threats. **Acid precipitation** is a very serious problem for the forests of eastern Canada. Trees are dying from acid precipitation caused by the emissions from factories in the industrial areas of eastern Canada and eastern United States (Fig. 25-11). The maple syrup-producing forests south of Quebec City have especially suffered from acid precipitation.

Coniferous trees of the southern boreal forest have also been affected by acid precipitation. Many of the trees have weakened and their needles have turned yellow. Those that do not die outright grow much more slowly than normal.

▼ **Fig. 25-11** The influence of prevailing winds on how a forest is affected by acid precipitation can be clearly seen in this photograph.

Insect pests and diseases also pose a serious threat to the health of Canada's forests. The forest area damaged by insects and disease every year is larger than the area harvested annually by forest companies. The spruce budworm, tent caterpillar, and gypsy moth in eastern Canada, and the pine bark beetle in British

Columbia, cause millions of dollars of damage to forests every year. Forestry companies and provincial governments spend a great deal of time and money trying to control these insects and diseases so they will not spread.

Canadian forests are at risk from "imported" insect pests as well. One older and one newer example of this will illustrate the problem. Dutch elm disease is spread by a beetle that arrived in North America from the Netherlands some time before 1930. It has spread throughout much of the United States and Canada since then. The result has been the loss of 35 million elm trees. A newer risk is the Asian longhorned beetle, which was found in 2003 in northwestern Toronto and neighbouring parts of York Region. The beetle was likely brought to Canada in packing materials that were used for imports from China. It can kill virtually all types of deciduous trees and, because it comes from a different continent, it has no natural enemies in North America. To prevent its spread, the Canadian Food Inspection Agency (which is responsible for plant health), has had to take quite extreme measures. They are requiring that all **susceptible** trees in the infected area, along with those in a 400-metre buffer zone around the area, be cut down. In addition, they have prohibited the removal of any wood products from this area. A similar insect threat exists in southwestern Ontario from an insect called the emerald ash borer. As its name suggests, this insect (which also came from Asia) affects only ash trees. To prevent the spread of these insects eastward, an ash-free barrier has been established in this area (Fig. 25-12).

Some elm trees have proven to be naturally resistant to the disease.

susceptible
likely to be affected

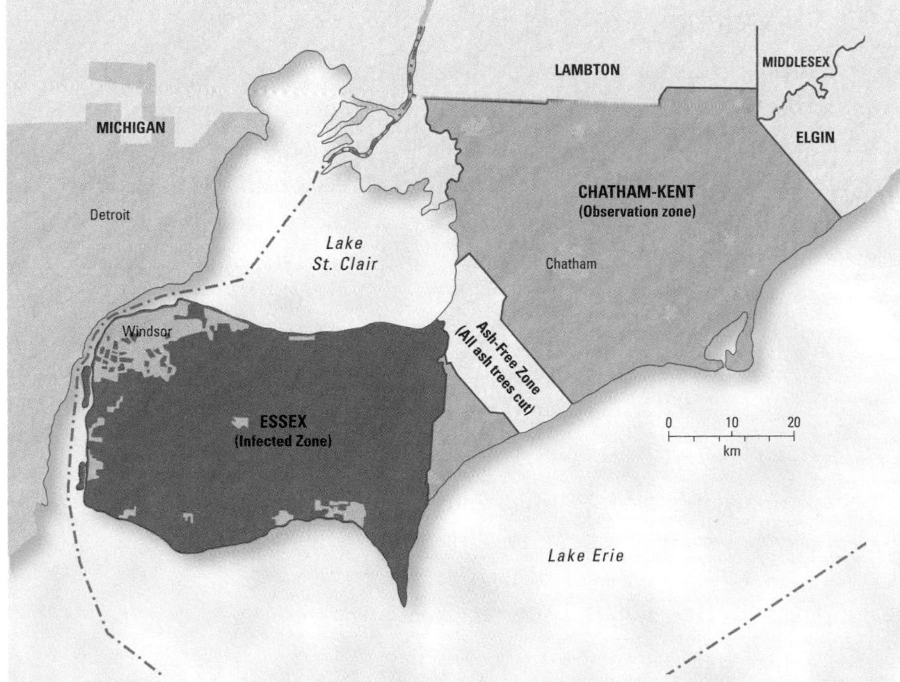

◀ **Fig. 25-12** The emerald ash borer crossed from the United States into Essex County. To prevent its spread to other parts of Ontario, an ash-free zone was created in which all the ash trees were removed. Areas to the east of the ash-free zone (shown in yellow) are inspected to ensure that the insects have not crossed the ash-free zone.

Three Issues, Two Views

Background

CLEAR-CUTTING

Corporate Viewpoint:
Many forests contain trees and other vegetation that naturally regenerate after destruction by fire or insects. Clear-cutting, followed by natural regeneration or by a program of replanting, is similar to what often happens in nature. Furthermore, we determine the size and shape of a clear cut with the preservation of biodiversity and wildlife habitats always in mind. We take great care to cause as little change to the overall forest as possible.

AERIAL SPRAYING OF PESTICIDES

Corporate Viewpoint:
Aerial spraying is an inexpensive and effective technique for killing insect pests such as the spruce budworm (Fig. 25-13). Pests must be killed quickly to protect the forest from extensive damage, and chemical sprays serve that purpose. Today's pesticides require only a few applications, and they have a low toxic effect on birds, fish, and mammals. Many pesticides can be sprayed near peoples' homes without danger. If we stop spraying, insects will kill large numbers of trees. This will damage the forest more than our spraying.

▲ **Fig. 25-13** Aerial spraying to control pests is a common sight in many parts of Canada's commercial forests.

GLOBAL COMPETITION

Corporate Viewpoint:
The Canadian forest industry faces one disadvantage—Canada's short growing season. Most of our competitors have the advantage of warmer weather; this results in faster-growing forests. If we wish to remain competitive, we must do everything possible to produce our lumber and pulp and paper products in the most cost-effective way. Canada also has a difficult time competing with other countries that still allow "cut-and-run" practices. We have two goals when we manage the forests: to achieve sustained yield management—that is, to ensure that for every tree that is cut, steps are taken to help another tree reach maturity—and to minimize costs. If we do not do this, we will lose jobs and valuable income from exports. This would affect the standard of living of Canadians.

Activities

1. Create a graphic organizer summarizing the differing viewpoints on:
   a) clear-cutting
   b) aerial spraying of pesticides
   c) global competition
2. Indicate the arguments with which you agree and explain why.

Environmentalist Viewpoint:
Clear-cutting removes all the ground cover. Soil without ground cover erodes into streams and rivers when it rains. This kills fish and other life in the water. When the forest canopy is removed, changes in temperature occur. Temperature changes disrupt the established ecosystem, and a desert-like landscape results. A forest that has grown up naturally comprises a variety of vegetation, trees of all ages, and wildlife. This diversity is lost when uniform seedlings of tree species are planted.

Environmentalist Viewpoint:
Pesticides endanger wildlife and disrupt the forest ecosystem. Humans can also be affected by insecticides. Aerial spraying has been linked to increased cancers and birth defects in forest workers and in people who live near sprayed areas. Some pesticides and pollution from paper mills seem to be affecting Atlantic salmon so that they are unable to find their way back to their spawning grounds. Research into the use of biological controls should be increased. For example, insects that eat only one thing—a pest insect—could be released into an infected area. After they have eaten the pests, the predators would die off because they would have nothing left to eat. Insects can also be controlled through **silviculture**—the growing and cultivation of trees. By replanting a variety of tree species, logging companies could make the forest less attractive to a single pest.

Environmentalist Viewpoint:
Unfortunately, sustained-yield management is not routine practice for the forest industry in most parts of Canada. The money that would protect our forests as a true renewable resource is not being spent. In many areas we now cut smaller trees because the forests are not given time to grow bigger ones. Our forest stocks are gradually being depleted as loggers travel farther into the forests to find larger trees. This just increases the costs of logging, and makes the industry less competitive on the world market.

GeoLit Reminder

When creating a graphic organizer:

- Identify the information you wish to organize.
- Determine the format that will best display this information.
- Re-read the written text, listing the points you wish to record.
- Organize gathered information into your chosen format. Add column headings, labels, arrows, etc. to clarify relationships.
- Identify any gaps in your information. What additional information do you need to complete your organizer? Where will you find it?
- Revise your work, checking for clarity and completeness.

A wide variety of forest links can be found at www.pearsoned.ca/makingconnections2.

Issues Facing the Forests

In the past, Canada's record of forest management was far below what was needed to maintain harvest levels. Forestry companies have begun to address the problem, but after so many years of abuse, will it be enough?

At the beginning of this chapter, two viewpoints about the use and care of the forests were presented. The Issues feature that follows examines how these differing viewpoints apply to some specific issues.

Forest Fires

Fire is a normal part of the life cycle of forest ecosystems. In fact, new healthy trees regenerate quickly in the burned forest. The cones from some species, such as the Jack pine, require the heat from fire to open. The seeds can then fall to the ground where they begin to grow. Sometimes fires are purposely started in a "controlled burn" to encourage this process. The problem comes when unplanned fires occur in valuable timberland.

On average, 9500 fires burn three million hectares of Canada's forest every year. A fire can create flames over 50 metres high, move faster than a person can run, and create hurricane-force winds. About 48% of all forest fires in Canada are caused by lightning. Many lightning-caused fires are allowed to burn themselves out because they occur in remote areas. The 52% of forest fires caused by people usually occur near settled areas. Since these forests are more easily accessible, they are considered valuable, so costly efforts are made to fight the fires.

A Balanced Approach

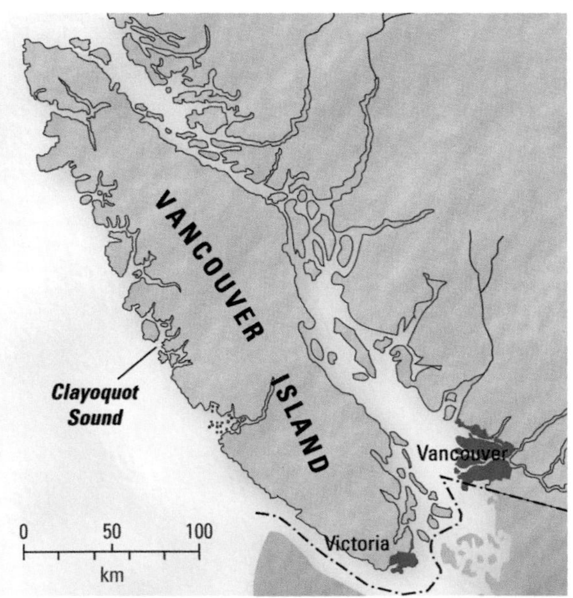

▼ **Fig. 25-14** Clayoquot Sound is the location of an old-growth forest where cooperation between different interest groups may succeed in protecting the environment while providing for economic development.

Canada's forests cannot be regarded as a limitless source of jobs and profits for large corporations and governments. On the other hand, since so many people rely on the forests for their jobs, it is unrealistic to think that the forests should be left in their natural state as habitats for animals and as recreational areas for people. Competing interests need to agree to use the forests in a variety of ways that do not conflict. Perhaps the model for future cooperation can be seen in Clayoquot Sound on the west coast of Vancouver Island (Fig. 25-14).

During the early 1990s, Clayoquot Sound was the site of numerous anti-logging demonstrations. The MacMillan Bloedel Company wanted to log the old-growth rain forest. Environmentalists and the Nuu-Chah-Nulth First Nation objected. In 1993, the government of British Columbia decided that logging would continue in the area, but that it would be highly regulated and would reflect sustained yield forest management. That is, it would be managed to meet current needs without affecting its future productivity, ecological diversity, or ability to regenerate. A panel of scientists, First Nations elders, and Aboriginal experts in traditional ecological knowledge was created to develop a sustainable **stewardship** program.

In 1999, MacMillan Bloedel was bought by the giant American company, Weyerhaeuser. It is now called Weyerhaeuser Canada.

First Nations' traditional ecological knowledge recognizes the relationships among life forms and involves an understanding of the medicinal properties of local plants, animal behaviour, and local weather patterns. Humans, animals, and the land with its forests and plants are viewed as a whole that must be protected. The spiritual and traditional knowledge of First Nations peoples brings a special perspective to sustained yield forest management.

INTERNET

You can learn more about Weyerhaeuser Canada's stewardship policies, including its relationships to Aboriginal groups, through the link at www.pearsoned.ca/makingconnections2.

In 1995, the British Columbia government accepted the panel's recommendations that:

- an ecosystem approach to forest planning be used. Information about the cultural values associated with the forest, as well as information on the forests' biological and physical aspects, should be considered when determining the changes that should take place.
- **Watersheds** (the basin into which surrounding waters drain) and groups of watersheds would be used as the basis for planning.
- First Nations and other local people should be involved in all phases of planning for and managing the land, freshwater, and marine resources in the Clayoquot Sound region.
- important plant and animal habitats and archaeological sites should be mapped and studied.

◀ **Fig. 25-15** Old-growth forest refers to a forest that has never been logged. The largest forest area on Vancouver Island is made up of several old-growth forests around Clayoquot Sound. As of 2005, about 22% of these old-growth forests had been logged.

In 2000, Clayoquot Sound was declared a UNESCO World Biosphere Reserve. These reserves are ecosystems that are internationally recognized for promoting and demonstrating a balanced relationship between people and nature.

Commercial logging activities are still conducted in Clayoquot Sound. Two companies currently have licences: International Forest Products (Interfor), an international firm, and Iisaak Forest Resources, a local firm owned by five Nuu-chah-nulth Central Region First Nations. Both companies are required to operate following sustainable resource guidelines monitored by the BC Government's "Scientific Panel for Sustainable Forest Practices in Clayoquot Sound." Numerous groups and individuals believe commercial logging should be stopped altogether in Clayoquot Sound, and continue to work toward that goal. In the meantime, the cooperation among the various concerned groups may sustain our forests so that all users may benefit from this renewable resource.

QUESTIONS

KNOWLEDGE AND UNDERSTANDING

1. Describe the effect of acid precipitation on Canada's forests. What parts of Canada are most affected? Why?
2. a) What types of insects and diseases affect our forests?
   b) Why do forest companies spend a great deal of time and money to control insects and pests?
3. a) Describe how fire is a normal part of the life cycle of forest ecosystems.
   b) Why are forest fires that are caused by people more likely to be extinguished by firefighters, while those caused by lightning are often left to burn themselves out?

THINKING

4. How are forests like agricultural crops? How are they different?
5. It has been said that Canadians have much to learn from Aboriginal peoples about sustainable development and respect for the land and environment. Do you agree? Explain.

COMMUNICATION

6. a) Using information from sources such as newspapers and magazines, first list the benefits and then the risks of spraying pesticides over insect-infested areas.
   b) What might your reaction to the spraying be if you were
      i. the owner of a forest?
      ii. a fish biologist in the area?
      iii. a person who lives in a community in which the largest employer is a forest company?
   c) Why is this issue so difficult to settle?
   d) Complete research to compare Canada's use of pesticides with pesticide use in two other countries. Which practices are most environmentally friendly?
7. You have been assigned by a newspaper to write a short article about the dispute over logging in Clayoquot Sound. Use the Internet to obtain information. In your article discuss the following:

a) the characteristics of the land and the forest
b) the issues surrounding the dispute
c) how the dispute was resolved
d) what is happening today

8. A forested area of 5000 ha could either be used for logging or could be added to an adjacent provincial park. The park is very heavily used and would benefit from expansion. On the other hand, the local sawmill is gradually running out of local trees to process. What are the arguments that supporters of each side of the issue would put forward? How should the best use for this area be decided?

APPLICATION

9. It is estimated that between 20 and 30 trees are saved for every tonne of paper that we recycle. Although recycling has become a major component in the production of paper in Canada, many Canadians do not recycle as much as they could. How can people be persuaded to recycle and to waste fewer paper products?

10. Most of the time when we use the word "globalization," we are referring to either cultural or economic issues, but globalization also has ecological implications. In this chapter, you had the opportunity to learn about the Asian long-horned beetle (Fig. 25-16) and the emerald ash borer, two insects from Asia that threaten North American forests. However, these are not the only foreign "invaders" to come to Canada. In many cases, the invaders are insects, but they can also be other life forms such as fungi, nematodes, bacteria, and viruses.

a) Movement of invasive species that are a threat to forests is not new. Consider the case of the gypsy moth. For more information on this moth, visit the Web link at www.pearsoned.ca/makingconnections2. Describe the following aspects of the gypsy moth problem:
   i. The damage done by them
   ii. What trees are most at risk
   iii. How and when gypsy moths came to Canada
   iv. What a gyspy moth looks like
   v. How they can be spread by human activity

b) Examine the list of invasive species at the Canadian Nature Federation Web link by going to www.pearsoned.ca/makingconnections2. Some of the species listed affect trees and shrubs while others attack agricultural crops (other than fruit trees). Choose a species that attacks trees or shrubs. You will find a variety of information for your choice. Your job is to create an information poster (or simple Web site, if you know how to create one) to make people more aware of the threat of the insect or pest that you have chosen. You should include the following information:
   i. What does the pest look like?
   ii. (If known) how did it come to Canada?
   iii. What threat does it pose?
   iv. How widespread is it?
   v. What is the government doing to reduce the risk?
   vi. What can the average person do to reduce the threat?

▲ Fig. 25-16

26 Canada's Mineral Wealth

Key Ideas

- What are the major minerals mined in Canada, and how are they used?
- How are minerals found and processed?
- What are the major issues facing the mining industry, and how can the development of Canada's mineral resources be improved?

Key Terms

mineral
metallic mineral
fossil fuel
industrial mineral
mineral reserve
geologist
ore
strip mining
open pit mining
underground mining
milling
smelting

INTERNET

A glossary of mining and mineral terms can be found through the link at www.pearsoned.ca/makingconnections2.

Do you have some Canadian mining products with you today? Chances are that you do. Check in your pocket or wallet for coins. Is your clothing made of a synthetic cloth, such as nylon or fleece? Is there a zipper on your jacket? From what raw materials are these items made, and where did the materials come from? The products of Canada's mining industry are an important part of your life. See Fig. 26-1. Can you match the manufactured product to the mineral?

Types of Minerals

A **mineral** can be defined as a naturally occurring, pure, non-living substance found in rocks. Most minerals have little or no economic value, but some are so valuable and important that it is hard to imagine how we could live without them. The minerals that we think of as valuable today have not always been prized in the past. For example, uranium was not considered a valuable resource until scientists came to understand that it contained enormous energy that they could extract. Perhaps in the future, new uses will be discovered for other minerals that might seem useless today. Then, they too will be seen as valuable resources.

The energy in uranium was initially used to create the atomic bomb. Since then, it has also been used to generate electricity.

Canada's minerals can be divided into three groups on the basis of their composition (Fig. 26-2): **metallic minerals**, **fossil fuels**, and **industrial minerals**. By far, the two most important categories are metallic minerals and fossil fuels.

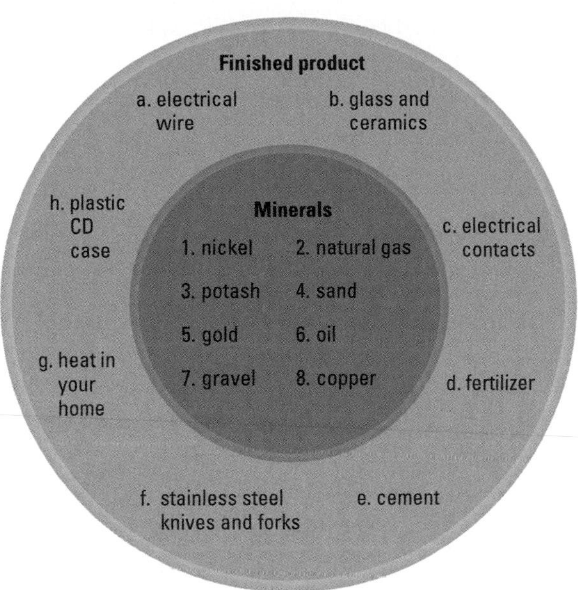

◀ **Fig. 26-1** Can you match the minerals with the finished products they create?

Metallic Minerals

As you might expect from the name, metallic minerals are minerals that, when refined, yield the group of materials that we know as metals. Some metals are valued for their rareness and beauty, for example, gold, silver, and platinum. Others, such as iron, are valued for their strength. Finally, others have a particular property that can be used to meet a human need. Examples include copper, which is well suited for making electrical wiring, and nickel, which can be combined with iron to make steel that is resistant to rust.

All these metals have other uses that are not related to their value as precious metals. For example, platinum is used in the catalytic converters of cars to reduce pollution.

Fossil Fuels

For the last 200 years, fossil fuels have provided most of the energy used by modern society. In the 1800s, coal was the important fuel. In the last

Metallic Minerals	**Fossil Fuels**	**Industrial Minerals**
cobalt	coal	asbestos
copper	natural gas	building stone
gold	oil	clay products
iron	oil sands	diamonds
lead		gravel
nickel		gypsum
platinum		potash
silver		salt
uranium		sand
zinc		soapstone

◀ **Fig. 26-2** These are just some of the minerals mined in Canada. Which ones are part of products that you use?

century, oil and gas replaced coal for most uses, including transportation and heating. In Chapter 27, "Energy: Powering Our Nation," you will have the chance to study fossil fuels in more detail.

Industrial (Non-metallic) Minerals

Because industrial minerals vary so widely in their characteristics, it is very difficult to describe them simply. In fact, it is almost easier to say what they are not—they are all the things that are mined that are neither metallic minerals nor fossil fuels. This is not to suggest that industrial minerals are unimportant. In fact, even common substances such as sand and gravel are critical to our lives and Canada's economy because they are essential in almost any kind of construction.

Here is a list of some of the major industrial minerals, their characteristics, and their uses:

- asbestos is used to protect objects and humans from fire and heat
- potash is a salt-like material used to make fertilizer
- gypsum is a clay-like material used to make sheets of drywall for most interior walls in homes, stores, and offices
- soapstone is a very soft mineral that is carved into sculptures by Inuit and other artists
- diamond is a very hard mineral used to make cutting tools and jewellery
- gravel is a major ingredient in concrete, which is used in the construction of most buildings

Asbestos is used much less often today because it was found that breathing in loose asbestos particles can cause cancer.

Diamonds are the hardest substance on Earth and can be used to cut any other material.

The Ekati diamond mine is the subject of the Case Study that follows this chapter.

Many important industrial minerals are associated with particular regions of Canada. For example, southern Saskatchewan is the world's largest producer of potash (Fig. 26-3), while Quebec is the largest producer of asbestos. Canada's first diamond mines are located in the Northwest Territories. Other industrial minerals, such as sand and gravel, are found in most parts of Canada.

Importance of Mining in Canada

Mining is important to Canada in several different ways. Canada ranks third in the world, behind the United States and Russia, in the production of minerals. We are, however, the largest exporter of minerals. Canada exports about 80% of what it produces because we are able to produce far more minerals than we are able to use. How important are minerals to our economy? In 2001, the total value of all mineral production was about $83 billion. The amount of money from each mineral group is shown in Fig. 26-4. The significance of each mineral category to the incomes of the provinces and territories is shown in Fig. 26-5.

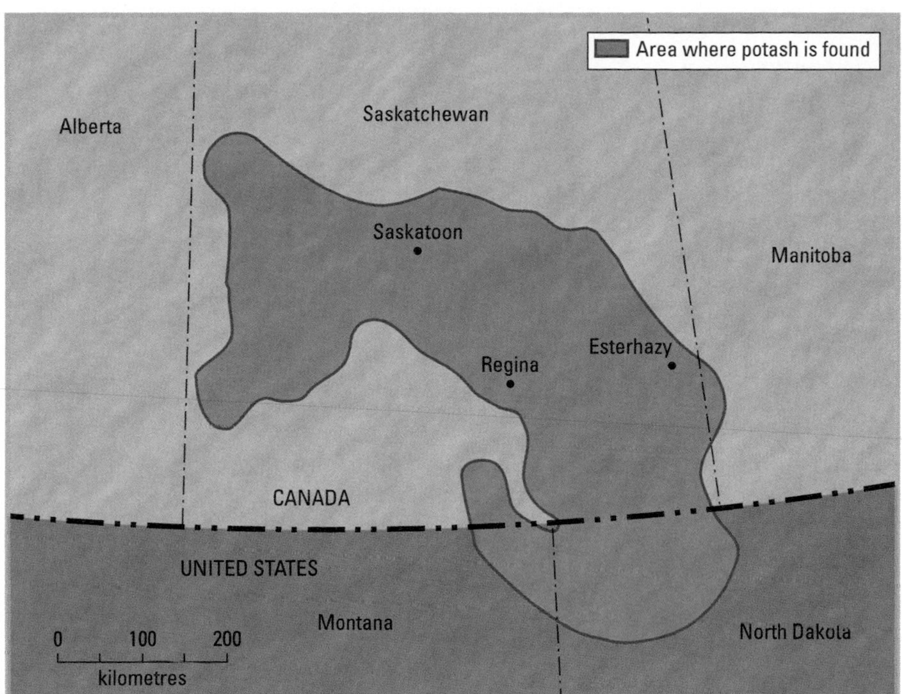

◀ **Fig. 26-3** This area of Saskatchewan is the largest producer of potash in the world.

The mining industry has also contributed greatly to the development of Canada's transportation system. Since the end of World War II, almost all railroad expansion and a considerable amount of road expansion have occurred to allow the development of mining resources.

Federal and provincial governments help the mining industry by offering tax breaks that encourage exploration of new reserves. The programs also encourage research and development to create new mining methods and products. Governments help build port facilities, power projects, roads, railways, and towns. Sometimes, governments even own major mining companies because they are very important to the provincial economy, and the government wants to control them. For example, the Saskatchewan government is a major owner of potash mines, while Quebec owns large asbestos mines.

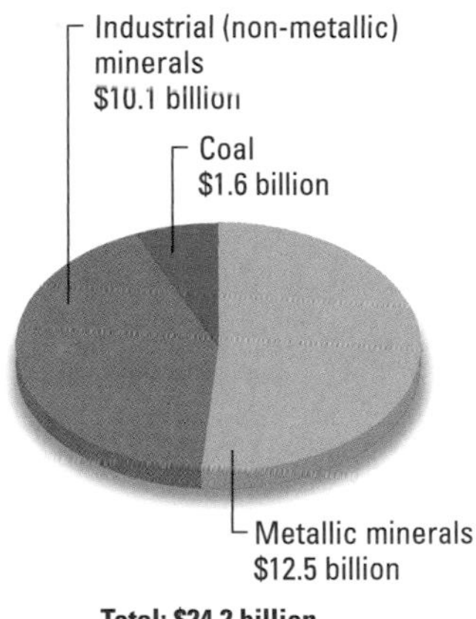

▲ **Fig. 26-4** The value of mineral production in Canada, 2004

Finding Valuable Minerals

Imagine that you are on a holiday somewhere on the Canadian Shield. One day, you are out for a hike and decide to collect some rock samples. Some of the rocks that you find have flecks of gold in them. Should you immediately stake a claim and open a gold mine? Probably not, since it might cost you one million dollars to recover one dollar's worth of gold! This situation points out the fact that a mineral becomes a useful resource only if it makes economic sense to mine it. Mineral deposits become **mineral reserves** once they are judged economical to mine.

Staking a claim is a legal process by which you acquire the right to set up a mine on a piece of government-owned land.

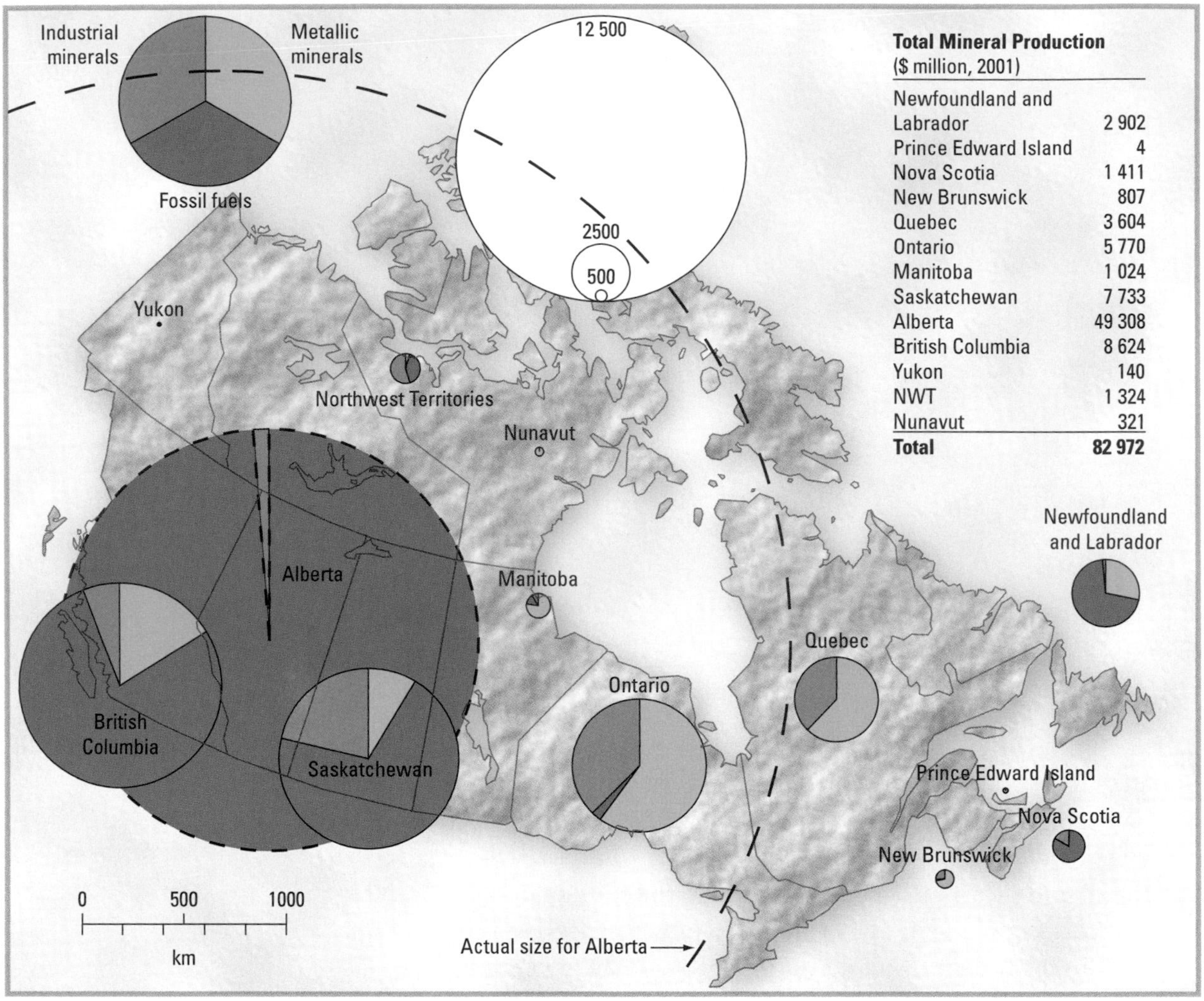

Total Mineral Production ($ million, 2001)	
Newfoundland and Labrador	2 902
Prince Edward Island	4
Nova Scotia	1 411
New Brunswick	807
Quebec	3 604
Ontario	5 770
Manitoba	1 024
Saskatchewan	7 733
Alberta	49 308
British Columbia	8 624
Yukon	140
NWT	1 324
Nunavut	321
Total	**82 972**

▲ **Fig. 26-5** Type of mineral production and total value by province and territory, 2001. Note: Due to the size of mineral production, Alberta's proportional pie graph is shown in outline only.

Canada's mineral reserves decrease each day they are mined. Since it is critical to our economic future that mineral reserves remain at a steady level, Canada needs continuous mining exploration to find new reserves. Finding new reserves is rarely easy because mineral deposits worth mining are found in only a few places in the world. Furthermore, most of the rich deposits in **accessible** areas have already been discovered. In addition, the cost of mineral exploration is very high. To keep costs as low as possible, **geologists** must narrow the search for minerals to areas where they think they have the best chance of finding them. It is their job to know how mineral deposits are formed and which types of rock are most likely to contain a specific mineral.

accessible
easy to reach

To try your luck at starting a mine, check the link at www.pearsoned.ca/makingconnections2.

Answer the questions below based on Fig. 26-6.

1. a) In which ecozones are most of Canada's metallic mineral resources found?
   b) What types of rock are found in that region?
   c) In which ecozone(s) is metallic mineral mining not important?
2. In what ecozones are major non-metallic mineral mines located?
3. All three types of minerals are found in the Atlantic Maritime ecozone. What does this tell you about the types of rock found in this region?
4. Why are both metallic minerals and fossil fuels found in Canada's Arctic ecozones? (See Fig. 27-9 on page 356 for a map of Canada's oil and gas deposits.)
5. This map does not show the location of sand and gravel mining. Why do you think this is so?

Hint: Think about what you learned in Chapters 11 and 12 about Canada's geologic history and landforms.

▼ **Fig. 26-6** Number of mines of various types in each ecozone. Mines shown are currently operating or have operated in recent years.

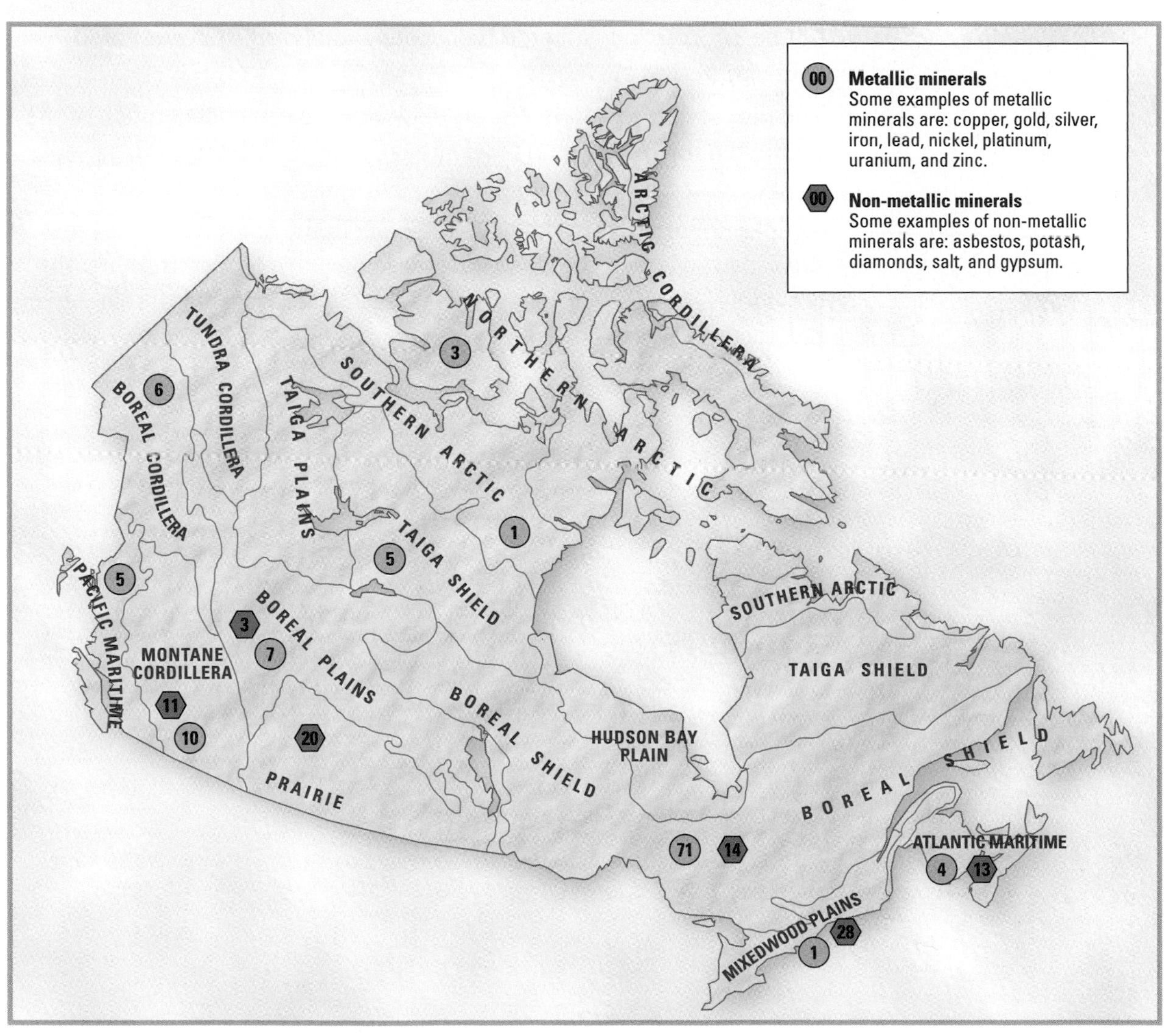

Looking for Metallic Minerals

You now know that metallic minerals are found in igneous and metamorphic rocks of the Canadian Shield and in other regions of Canada. The Canadian Shield is an enormous area; it is actually much larger than most countries. How do geologists narrow their search when trying to locate metals? Here are some of their tactics.

- Some **ore** bodies, such as those containing nickel, iron, and copper, produce a powerful magnetic field compared to surrounding areas where the amount of these metals is low. This magnetic field can be detected by an instrument called a magnetometer, which is towed behind an airplane. A geologist can create a map using magnetometer data that shows the approximate size and shape of the ore body.
- Satellite images and aerial photos tell the geologist a great deal about the geologic structures of an area.
- All the information gathered is collected, analyzed, and presented using a GIS (Fig. 26-7).
- The next step is shown in Fig. 26-8. Geologists can collect much of the required data only by going into the bush or onto the tundra.
- Geologists use a variety of techniques to collect data. They collect rock samples for analysis in the field and back in the laboratory. They test the soil in riverbeds for chemicals that may have eroded from nearby ore bodies. They use a Geiger counter, a special instrument that detects radioactive minerals.

▼ **Fig. 26-7** Geographic information systems (GIS) can organize and present the data needed to evaluate a potential mine. In this example, magnetometer readings (curved lines) and drill sample results (coloured dots) have been related to the topography of an area where copper has been found.

◄ **Fig. 26-8** While a variety of high-tech methods help determine where a mineral deposit might be, geologists and engineers have to go into the field to collect samples to evaluate whether a deposit is worth mining.

- If the findings up to this point look promising, the next step is to drill deep into the ground to get samples of the ore body itself.

Once all the data have been collected, the mining company must decide whether to develop the mine. This decision has the potential of earning or losing many millions of dollars for the company. If a small mining company makes the wrong decision, and the ore body proves too costly to mine, it will probably go out of business. If the company makes the right decision to mine, it can produce a huge profit for its owners.

Canadian stock exchanges list many mining stocks that can be bought for a few cents a share. Most of these companies will go out of business, and those who bought the stock will lose their investment. Some companies, however, will discover a huge deposit, and the stock will rise significantly, making the investors rich.

Mining Metallic Minerals

Many mining sites are located in remote areas, far from existing transportation routes. In these cases, the difficulty and the cost of developing a mine are greatly increased. A road (or, in some cases, railway) must be built to allow the shipping in of equipment and the shipping out of product. The company has to build mine facilities to extract the ore from the ground, and a mill nearby to separate the mineral from the ore. It has to construct housing for the workers. Finally, fresh water, sewage treatment, and electricity must be supplied to the mine and the housing. As you might imagine, the cost of all this development can be staggering, especially in a very remote area.

In the case of a major mine that employs many workers, an entire town may have to be built.

Once all this is in place, it is time to start the actual mining. There are three mining methods: **strip**, **open pit**, and **underground mining** (Fig. 26-9). The selection of any one of these methods depends upon the depth of the ore deposit.

▼ **Fig. 26-9** Strip, open pit, and underground mining

STRIP MINING

– is used to mine oilsands, coal, and other minerals that are located in horizontal layers near the surface.

1. Overburden (trees, earth, rock) is removed.
2. Blasting may be necessary to remove some mineral deposits.
3. Material is loaded onto trucks or conveyor belts by shovel or dragline. A dragline is a large bucket that is dragged to pick up loose material on the ground.
4. Material is taken to a storage area to await processing in the mill or shipment to market.

OPEN PIT MINING

– is used to mine minerals that are found near the surface, but that also may extend deep into the ground.

1. Overburden is removed.
2. Holes are drilled 10–15 m deep and filled with explosives. The rock is blasted apart.
3. Ore is loaded into large trucks (which may carry 90 to 250 tonnes) by huge shovels.
4. Ore is taken to a storage site near the mill to await processing.

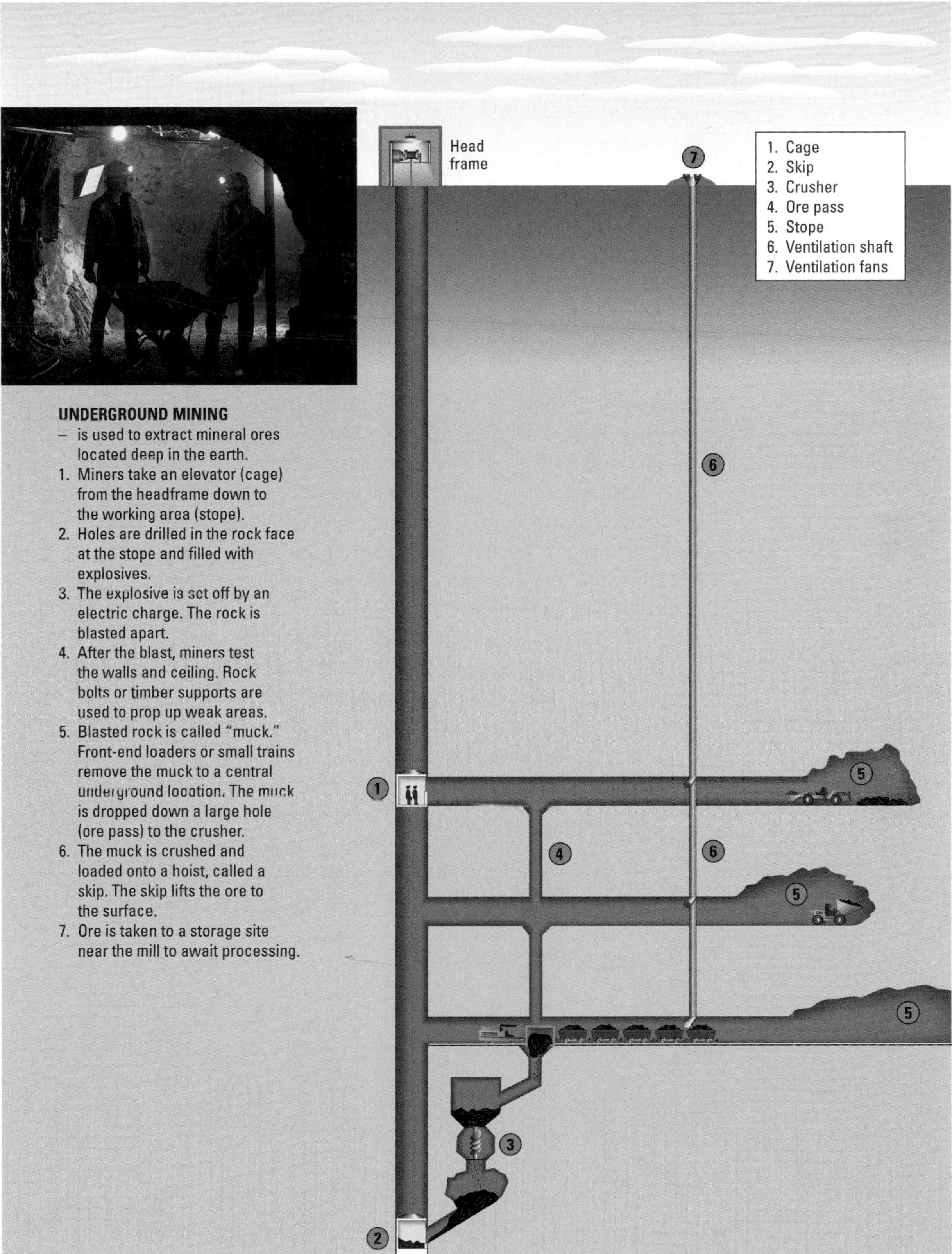

UNDERGROUND MINING

– is used to extract mineral ores located deep in the earth.

1. Miners take an elevator (cage) from the headframe down to the working area (stope).
2. Holes are drilled in the rock face at the stope and filled with explosives.
3. The explosive is set off by an electric charge. The rock is blasted apart.
4. After the blast, miners test the walls and ceiling. Rock bolts or timber supports are used to prop up weak areas.
5. Blasted rock is called "muck." Front-end loaders or small trains remove the muck to a central underground location. The muck is dropped down a large hole (ore pass) to the crusher.
6. The muck is crushed and loaded onto a hoist, called a skip. The skip lifts the ore to the surface.
7. Ore is taken to a storage site near the mill to await processing.

Processing Metallic Minerals

Ore is composed mainly of waste rock. In the case of iron ore, perhaps about half is iron, and the remaining half waste. In the case of gold ore, there may be only a few grams of gold for each tonne of waste. The processing of most ores, including nickel, copper, gold, silver, and zinc, has two steps: **milling** and **smelting**. Milling takes place in a processing plant, or mill, that is usually located near the mine. It is the first step in the refining process that separates a mineral from its ore. Milling separates some of the waste rock from the ore by crushing, separating, filtering, and drying raw ore. Milling produces a concentrated form of ore known as concentrate, although the mineral is still far from pure. For example, a concentrate of copper contains 30% copper and 70% waste rock.

Waste materials, or **tailings**, are a toxic mixture of water, rock particles, and chemicals left over from the milling process. Because they are extremely poisonous, tailings must be carefully handled. They are dumped into tailing ponds that are located near the mill and contained by **dikes**. Tailing ponds and dikes are lined with clay to prevent the waste from seeping into nearby lakes and rivers. The water in the tailings eventually evaporates, leaving solid waste behind. This waste material is then treated with fertilizers and other chemicals to encourage the growth of trees and grasses. As new technology develops, it may be possible to recover more of the mineral from the tailings.

dike
earth walls, often lined with clay, built to hold back a liquid

In iron-ore smelting, the flux is limestone.

Concentrated ore from the mill is then taken to the smelter for further processing. At the smelter, the concentrate and a substance called flux are melted together in a high-temperature furnace. The flux joins with the waste rock to form a liquid waste material called **slag**. Since slag is lighter than the liquid metal, it rises to the top and is skimmed off. The almost pure liquid metal that remains is then poured into moulds, cooled, and sent to customers. When slag is cooled, it has many commercial uses, for example, as fertilizer, as ballast for railway tracks, and in cement. Sometimes it is reprocessed to recover other metals it may contain.

QUESTIONS

KNOWLEDGE AND UNDERSTANDING

1. a) What are minerals?
   b) Name the categories into which minerals may be divided. Give two examples of each type.
   c) Under what circumstances does a mineral become a mineral reserve?
2. Describe the steps used by mining companies to discover and develop an ore body.
3. a) In your own words, describe the steps involved in open pit mining.
   b) In your own words, describe the steps involved in underground mining.
4. Compare milling and smelting in terms of what each does and the location in which each occurs.
5. What is done with the waste products from the processing of minerals? Why must this be done carefully?

THINKING

6. Examine Fig. 26-5. Choose the three most important provinces for each of the following:
   a) metallic minerals
   b) fossil fuels
   c) industrial minerals
7. Copy the organizer in Fig. 26-10 in your notebook and fill in the blanks.

APPLICATION

8. If you were a mining company engineer and had a choice to mine an ore body with an open pit or with an underground mine, which would you choose? Why?
9. a) What conditions must exist before a company will develop a potential mine site? Consider the kind of mineral being mined, the quality of the ore body, the availability of transportation, and the market price of the metal.
   b) How would higher market prices affect the decision in 9a)?
   c) How would changing market prices affect the long-term prospects of a mine?

Metal	Property	Use
	carries electricity well	
		stainless steel
		coins
iron		
		stops steel from rusting jewellery
	light in weight	

▲ **Fig. 26-10**

Issue

CHALLENGES FOR CANADA'S MINING INDUSTRY

◀ **Fig. 26-11** In spite of billions of dollars being spent on pollution control, mine smelters in North America remain among the worst sources of the pollutants that contribute to acid precipitation.

Background

There are several controversial issues related to Canada's mining industry. The most serious concern is the industry's harmful impact on the environment. Over the past 20 years, more than $1 billion has been spent on controlling harmful emissions from mines and processing plants. Despite many successes in this area, millions of tonnes of waste still find their way onto our land and into our air and water. Here are some of the industry's challenges:

- **Acid Precipitation** On a per capita basis, Canada's mining industry produces more of the pollutants that cause acid precipitation than does the United States. Six of the 10 biggest polluters in North America are smelters and refineries in Ontario, Quebec, and Manitoba. In spite of the fact that the mining company Inco has spent hundreds of millions of dollars to control acid precipitation pollutants, the company's smelter in Sudbury is the world's largest single source of sulphur dioxide (Fig. 26-11). Inco's challenge is to control the pollution created by the mine at a cost that allows it to remain competitive in the world market.
- **Abandoned Mines** There are dozens of mines across Canada that were abandoned after the ore ran out. They leave scars on the land and continue as sources of pollution as mine wastes leak into rivers and lakes. Governments now require mining companies to plan what they will do when a mine shuts down. Open pit mines, quarries, and gravel pits can be flooded or filled in and used for recreation. Acidic wastes can be neutralized and then planted with grasses and trees. These **remedial measures** cannot hide the fact that a mine existed. Rather, the purpose is to minimize long-term damage and produce a landscape feature that can be used for other purposes.
- **Exported Jobs** About 50% of the minerals mined in Canada are exported before any smelting or manufacturing is done. This means that we are exporting the jobs that result from the final refining and manufacturing of these minerals.
- **World Events** Canada's mining industry can be damaged by unexpected events in other countries. For example, in 1997 and 1998, the economies of Japan, China, and Taiwan experienced a major slowdown. Since these countries are key customers of our mining

remedial measures
actions to correct a problem

industry, the result was a decline in the demand for Canadian mining products.

- **Depleted Reserves** Many high-quality reserves are being exhausted. In the future, Canada will have to rely on mineral deposits of poorer quality, or those found in areas far from markets and transportation routes. New technologies must therefore be developed to make the mining of lower-grade ores and remote deposits more economical.
- **Foreign Competition** New mineral deposits are constantly being discovered, particularly in the developing countries in Asia, Africa, and South America. Because many of these have lower production costs due to lower labour costs and lower environmental standards, they are able to sell their mineral products on the world market more cheaply than Canadian companies. If Canada wants to compete, it will have to decrease production costs. This will probably lead to more mechanization of the mining and milling processes.
- **One-industry Towns** Mining towns are totally dependent upon their mines for their existence. When a mine closes because the ore runs out or markets disappear, a town may not survive. Schefferville, on the border of Quebec and Labrador, closed down after its iron ore mine shut down in the 1980s. The site was given to the Innu, the Aboriginal people of this remote area. In contrast, the town of Elliot Lake, just north of Lake Huron, managed to survive after its uranium mines closed. It developed an alternative economic base by promoting itself as an inexpensive retirement community for people interested in outdoor activities (Fig. 26-12). It was able to do this because, unlike many other mining towns, it is not located in a remote area of Canada. It also has attractive features such as medical and recreational facilities, and proximity to the Trans-Canada Highway.

▲ **Fig. 26-12** Elliot Lake, once solely dependent upon the mining industry, has successfully re-invented itself as an outdoor tourism centre and retirement community.

Activities

Put yourself in the position of the union president at a mine somewhere on the Canadian Shield. The president of the company that owns the mine has told you that the cost of production must be cut or the mine will be closed, because it will not be able to compete with newer mines in developing countries. In addition, the company must install equipment to meet new environmental regulations. The mine president has said that the workers must accept a 25% pay cut.

1. What alternatives are there for the workers in the mine who belong to your union?
2. What alternative would you recommend to your members and why?

In Closing...

How can the development of Canada's mineral resources be improved in the future? Here are some things to consider:

- Environmental controls on mining should be fine-tuned to protect the environment and at the same time allow Canadian mining companies to operate competitively on international markets.
- Canadian companies should adjust to international competition and pricing.
- Canadian governments should continue to provide substantial financial assistance and other forms of support, e.g., subsidies and tax breaks, to the mining industry to help it remain a world leader.
- Mining companies and governments should consider the land claims of First Nations when deciding when and how mineral deposits will be developed.
- Canadian mining companies should develop new technologies that will make their operations as efficient as possible.
- Companies should continue to explore throughout Canada for new mineral deposits.
- Companies should be encouraged to do more of the processing and manufacturing of Canadian minerals in this country.
- Research and development of new and improved uses for minerals should be intensified.
- With regard to the "boom and bust" nature of a mining-based economy, mining towns whose survival is threatened when the mine closes should be encouraged and assisted in developing a new economic base.

QUESTIONS

KNOWLEDGE AND UNDERSTANDING

1. a) Why should mining companies reduce the environmental damage caused by their mines and smelters?
   b) What makes it difficult to do this?

THINKING

2. It has been suggested that garbage from a southern Canadian city be disposed of in abandoned mines in the north. Consider this idea from the perspectives of city residents and those who live near the mine. Construct a graphic organizer listing the good points and bad points of this plan from both perspectives.
3. Discuss the following statement. Be sure to consider both sides of the issue, and then indicate which side you agree with. "Cleaning up the tailings area of a mine that has shut down is expensive and unnecessary, since such areas cover only a tiny percentage of the countryside."

COMMUNICATION

4. Do this question with a partner. One partner has just been appointed the president of a major mining company. This person is responsible for maximizing the profits and reducing the costs of the company. The other partner is the new mines minister in the government. This person must focus on ensuring that the mining industry is healthy, that new jobs are created, and that the environmental impact of mining is limited. Flip a coin to see who gets which job!
   a) Each partner should look separately at the list of suggestions for the future of Canada's mining industry in the "In Closing..." section of this chapter. From the perspective of your job, rank them in order of their importance.
   b) Compare your list to that of your partner. Explain any significant differences in the two lists.
   c) Work together to create a combined ranking that will reflect the needs of industry and government.
   d) Share your results with the rest of the class.

APPLICATION

5. A company has applied for a permit to extract large amounts of sand and gravel from a glacial deposit at the edge of your town. It expects to operate for 10 to 15 years and provide about 50 full-time jobs.
   a) Describe the effects that this project might have on the local ecosystem (e.g., water table, wildlife, native plants).
   b) Describe the effects that this project might have on people (e.g., economics, noise, appearance, transportation).
   c) Determine a method to evaluate the relative importance of each of the benefits and costs (including non-monetary costs) that you identified in 5a) and 5b).
   d) Apply the approach that you developed above to evaluate a real project in your local area or another part of Canada.

Diamond Mining: Canada's New "Boom" Industry

Key Terms

gemstone diamond
industrial diamond
carat
kimberlite pipe
craton
indicator minerals

Diamonds...the word conjures up images of romance and mystery. Although Canada is one of the world's great mining countries, it has only recently joined the tiny group of countries that are major diamond producers. Botswana is the largest producer, Russia is the second, and South Africa is the third. In 2001, Canada ranked sixth.

The Nature of Diamonds

The world's diamond production is worth about US$8 billion per year. About half this production (by value) goes to jewellers, and the other half to industry. **Gemstone diamonds** are prized for their rarity and beauty. **Industrial diamonds** are valued because they are used as the ultimate cutting tool—no other substance is as hard. Raw gemstones average about US$100 per **carat**, and industrial diamonds about US$10 per carat. Many industrial diamonds are now manufactured in the laboratory, but all genuine gemstones are mined.

One carat equals 0.2 grams. The largest diamond ever found was about 3000 carats.

How Diamonds Were Discovered in Canada

Before diamonds were found in Canada, they had been discovered in the shield areas of southern Africa, Russia, and Australia. Scientists believed that the Canadian Shield contained diamonds, but where?

The Canadian Shield, unlike other diamond-mining regions of the world, was covered by slowly moving glaciers for hundreds of thousands of years. Glaciers picked up diamonds from their source somewhere in northern Canada and then deposited them in many places over the North American continent. In the process, the glaciers did a very effective job of hiding the source. The source of all diamonds are rare geologic structures called **kimberlite pipes** (Fig. 26-13) that exist in enormous masses of ancient rock called **cratons**. Cratons make up the stable cores of the continents. Since kimberlite rock is softer than other rock in the Canadian Shield, the glaciers eroded the kimberlite and left depressions that filled with water to form lakes. The search for diamonds would end under one of these lakes.

Diamonds picked up by glaciers were carried as far away as Indiana.

Canada has five cratons, including the Slave craton, where diamonds are now being mined. Since the Slave craton is as large as the United Kingdom, there are lots of places to look for diamonds.

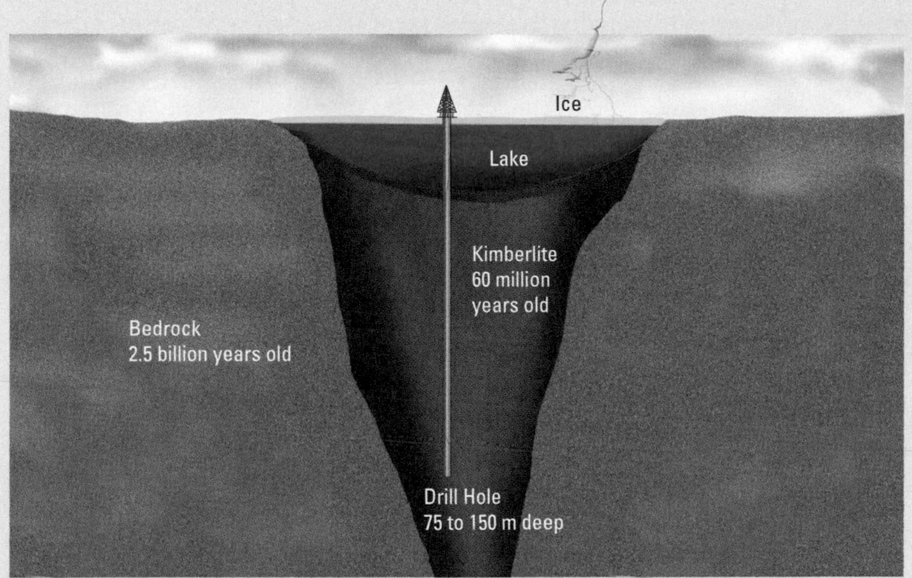

▲ **Fig. 26-13** Perhaps only 100 of the 5000 known kimberlite pipes in the world are close enough to the surface to make mining profitable. Because kimberlite is softer than most other rocks in the Canadian Shield, it was more easily eroded by glaciation. The depressions in the landscape filled with water, forming lakes that covered the kimberlite pipes.

GeoLit Reminder

When reading informational text:

- Use the Case Study title and subheadings as a guide.
- Scan the text for general meaning.
- Look for key terms.
- Examine the margin notes, visuals, and captions for additional information.

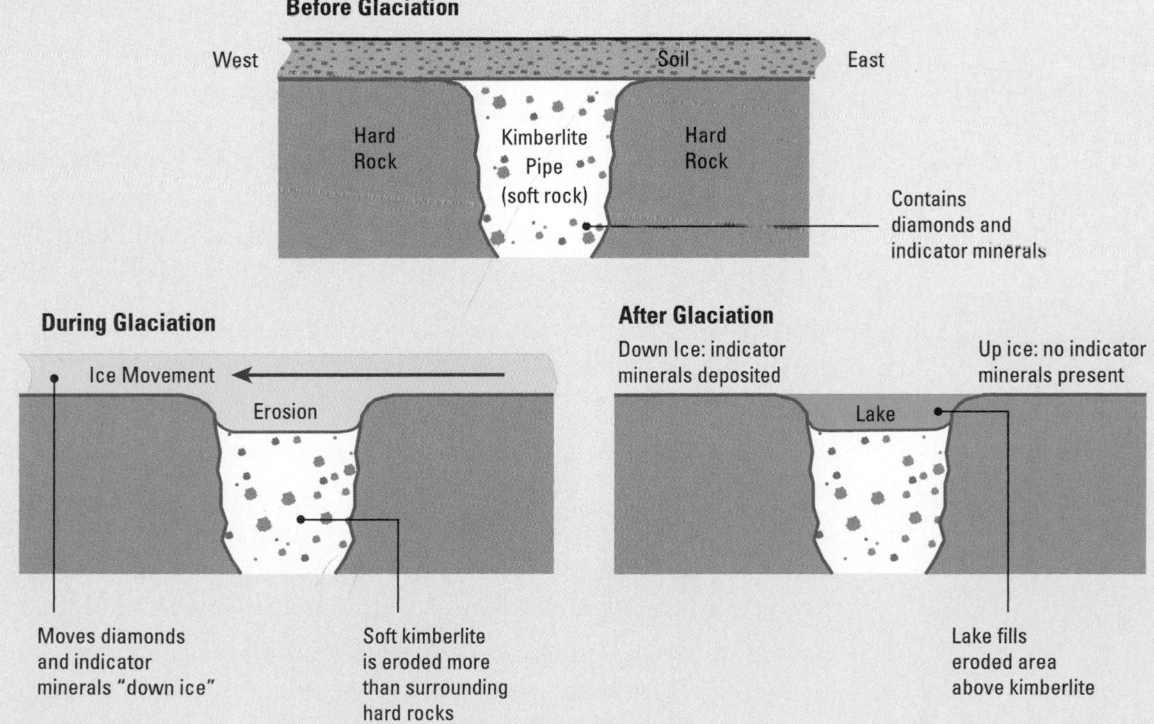

▲ **Fig. 26-14** Glaciers spread the evidence of diamonds over half the continent and hid the sources of the diamonds under lakes on the Canadian Shield.

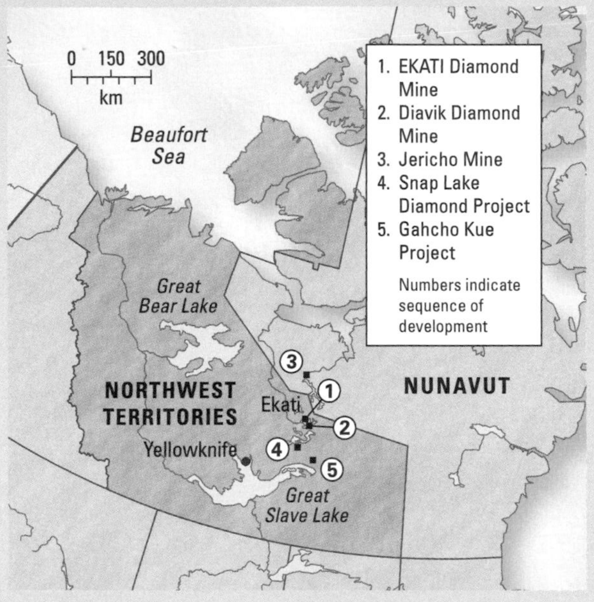

▲ **Fig. 26-15**

Between 1983 and 1989, geologists and prospectors Charles Fipke and Steward Blusson explored for diamonds using a number of techniques. First, they searched for **indicator minerals** that are always found with diamonds. Then, they traced the indicator minerals back to their point of origin by considering the paths of the glaciers. The orientation of glacial features such as drumlins, eskers, and scratches on Shield rock pointed out the trail of the indicator minerals (Fig. 26-14). A geographic information system (GIS) analyzed all the complex data and led the geologists to the Lac de Gras area about 300 km northeast of Yellowknife (Fig. 26-15). There was obviously a kimberlite pipe nearby, but which lake was it under? Geologists began to drill for rock samples from the lake bottoms when the lakes had frozen over in winter.

In late 1991, 81 diamonds in a 60-kilogram rock sample were taken from under Point Lake. Drill sampling continued for the next few years and resulted in the discovery of more than two dozen kimberlite pipes. The quantity and quality of the diamonds were high.

GIS is examined in Chapter 5.

Building the Ekati Mine

Building any diamond mine is a big job, but building the Ekati Mine hundreds of kilometres from the nearest highway or railroad was a gargantuan undertaking (Fig. 26-16). Imagine what was involved in building the following facilities at Ekati.

- dams that drained parts of two lakes to uncover the kimberlite pipes, and a canal through which fish could travel into the undrained portions of the lakes
- a nine-storey processing plant where diamonds are separated from the kimberlite rock
- seven three-storey dormitories plus a supporting complex with kitchen and dining facilities, a full-size gym, squash courts, a simulated golf driving range, a visitor orientation centre, and a diamond exhibit
- a power station, a water processing plant for industrial and personal use, a sewage treatment plant, and two incinerators to burn garbage
- a shop that houses repair bays for excavators and trucks, three overhead cranes, a laboratory, a computerized training lab, and two levels of administrative offices

Ekati is an Aboriginal word for caribou fat, which is highly prized by the local Aboriginal people.

The hard granite surrounding the diamonds grinds down valuable equipment very quickly. Bulldozer blades have a lifespan of only two weeks, and drill bits that cost $1500 each wear out in two hours!

- a gravel airstrip that accommodates Hercules cargo planes and Boeing 737 aircraft
- an explosives manufacturing plant, a fully equipped hospital, an emergency response rescue station with ambulance, fire, and rescue vehicles, and three fuel-storage facilities

Between the summer of 1996 and the summer of 1997, 6500 tonnes of freight were flown into Ekati, and more than 17 000 passenger flights were recorded. Not everything, however, could be brought in by air. An ice road was built, and is still in use today, to transport bulky items during the winter months.

The government of the Northwest Territories is considering a year-round road from Yellowknife to Kinggauk on the Arctic Ocean. This road would replace the ice road. For more information about ice roads, see Chapter 30.

How Ekati Operates

The open-pit mining method proved to be the best way to remove the enormous volumes of kimberlite rock from the Panda pit until it reached its "economic depth" (Fig. 26-17). This is the depth at which the removal of the rock from the pit becomes too great compared to the value of the diamonds that are recovered. Geologists decided that it would be more economically feasible to recover the diamonds in an underground project. An underground operation with a probable lifespan of six years began at Panda in 2005.

▼ **Fig. 26-16** The Ekati mine with its support facilities is a new town in the middle of the wilderness.

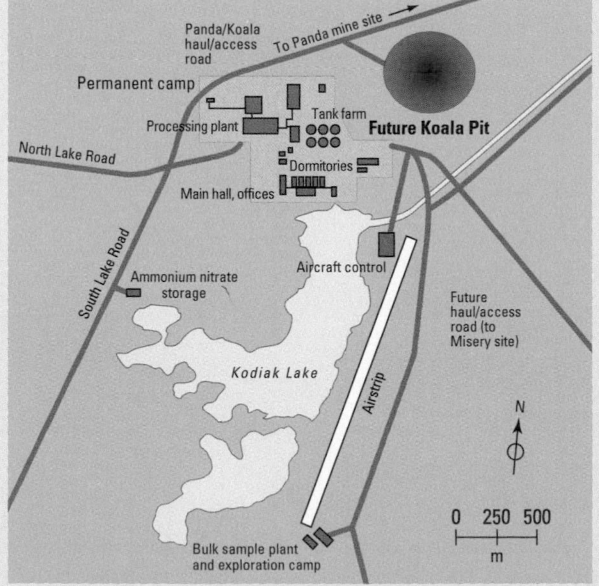

automated
involving machinery rather than people

The rock from the pit is transported to a processing plant where it is crushed and separated from the diamonds. **Automated** processing reduces the need for expensive labour and the likelihood of theft by employees.The raw diamonds are flown to Yellowknife and from there to world markets.

Impact of the Ekati Diamond Mine

In 2004, the average pay for workers in the diamond industry in Canada was $63 000.

The multiplier effect is discussed in Chapter 20.

Economic and Social Impact

It is projected that approximately 5 million carats of diamonds will be recovered each year during Ekati's predicted lifespan of 20 years. These diamonds are worth about US$500 million per year since relatively high proportions are in the high-value category. Because most of the diamonds are exported, Canada's trade balance receives a big boost. The economy of the Northwest Territories also receives a boost because Ekati created 600 new highly paid jobs, plus hundreds of service jobs (as a result of the multiplier effect) in areas such as transportation, housing, and government services.

During the development of the mine, agreements were struck with the local Aboriginal peoples that would minimize the mine's impact on the local environment, but maximize the economic benefits for the people of the area. Approximately 60% of all the mine's jobs must be filled by northern residents, and half of that employment is reserved for Aboriginal workers. To ensure that jobs are shared throughout the Territories, travel assistance is provided for employees from all over the region.

▲ **Fig. 26-17** As the Panda pit at the Ekati mine site became deeper, too much unproductive rock was being mined to make it economically feasible to continue with open pit mining.

Environmental Impact

The Ekati Mine underwent the most in-depth environmental assessment of any mine in Canadian history. The assessment covered many topics, including caribou migration and the handling of the lakes located over the kimberlite pipes. The assessment does not guarantee against environmental damage from the mine, but the environment has a very high priority when mining activities are taking place.

Most metallic minerals are chemically bonded to the ores in which they are found. The two can be separated only through the use of powerful chemicals that are environmentally dangerous. Diamonds, by comparison, can be simply broken away from the kimberlite rock in which they occur and there is no chemical waste.

Five million tonnes of rock are processed to produce one tonne of diamonds per year. This enormous amount of waste rock must be disposed of very carefully so as not to disrupt drainage or cause other environmental damage.

INTERNET

You can learn more about the Ekati mine and its diamonds through the link at www.pearsoned.ca/makingconnections2.

What Is Next for Canada's Diamond Industry?

Ekati's success has sparked a huge surge in diamond mining and exploration in Canada. A second mine, located close to the Ekati, opened in 2002. Nunavut's first diamond mine, the Jericho mine, will begin production in 2006. the Jericho mine is owned and operated by Tahera Diamond Corporation, a Canadian Company. Two more diamond mines, operated by DeBeers, are expected to be in production by 2007. Kimberlite pipes have also been discovered in northern Alberta, Saskatchewan, and Ontario, and exploration is taking place in Manitoba, Quebec, and Labrador.

Canada's legitimate diamond industry stands in contrast to the mining and illegal trade of "conflict" diamonds in African countries such as Liberia, Sierra Leone, and the Democratic Republic of Congo. Rough diamonds are sold on the open market by rebel groups and governments to buy arms, fund conflicts, and carry out atrocities against innocent civilians. In an attempt to stop the sale of uncut stones from conflict areas, the United Nations proposed the Kimberley Process. This program tracks all diamonds from their source to the store where they are sold. Canada has adopted this voluntary program. Each Canadian diamond has an ID number and a tiny Canadian logo engraved on its edge!

The growth of Canada's diamond industry has been phenomenal. In 1995, not a single diamond was produced, but by 2001, diamonds worth $724 million had been discovered. By 2003, this figure had shot up to $1.722 billion—not too much below the value of the gold and nickel mined in the same year. Perhaps some day you will find yourself working in this important new industry.

INTERNET

You can learn more about De Beers Corporation, the world's largest diamond mining company, through the link at www.pearsoned.ca/makingconnections2.

A diamond-cutting and -polishing industry has grown up in Yellowknife and Vancouver to handle a small percentage of the rough diamonds coming out of the mines.

Critics are upset that the Kimberley Process defines conflict diamonds as rough diamonds, not polished stones or pieces of jewellery.

QUESTIONS

KNOWLEDGE AND UNDERSTANDING

1. What is a craton? What is a kimberlite pipe? How is each related to finding diamonds?
2. a) Explain what is meant by the following statement: "Perhaps the surprising thing is not that diamonds were found in Canada, but that it took so long to find them."
   b) How were diamonds eventually found?

THINKING

3. How is diamond mining affecting the Northwest Territories and the Aboriginal people who live in the areas where it occurs?
4. Create a flow chart to illustrate the stages in diamond mining as it is being done at Ekati. Start at the stage where the decision was made to start mining.
5. a) What are the two types of diamonds?
   b) How would each be affected by a weak economy in the world? Why?
6. a) One carat of diamonds was found in one tonne of rock during early tests at the Ekati mine. Express this amount as a percentage.
   b) What does this percentage suggest about the nature of diamond mining?
7. a) Why is theft a greater problem in the diamond mining industry than in other kinds of mining?
   b) What feature of Ekati's operations helps prevent theft?
8. a) In what ways is diamond mining like other kinds of mining that are common in Canada?
   b) In what ways is it different?

COMMUNICATION

9. The United Nations has developed the Kimberley Process to halt the sale of uncut diamonds from conflict areas (so-called "conflict diamonds"). Research this topic. Then conduct a class discussion to examine the process and effectiveness of the UN Kimberley Process.

APPLICATION

10. a) Do you expect to buy one or more diamonds in your lifetime? When? Why?
    b) What roles will tradition and marketing play in your decision?
11. a) Would you like to be a prospector? What would be the advantages and disadvantages of this job?
    b) What training would be needed for this job?

27 Energy: Powering Our Nation

Key Ideas

This chapter helps you investigate these questions:

- How are coal and oil and gas deposits formed?
- What are the different methods for generating electricity, and how is it transmitted to market?
- What methods are used to obtain the oil under the ocean on Canada's east coast?

Key Terms

conventional energy source
alternative energy source
biomass energy
joule (J)
anticlinal trap
secondary recovery
oil sand
hydroelectric generating station
thermoelectric generating station
nuclear-electric generating station
power grid

Canada's Energy Use Today

Depending on which set of statistics you consult, Canadians are either the largest or the second-largest per capita users of energy in the world, for the following reasons:

- we live in a northern climate with very cold temperatures for much of the year
- we have a small population spread very thinly over a huge land mass, which means that we must use a great deal of energy for transportation
- our advanced industrial economy uses a great deal of energy
- energy is relatively cheap in this country, so we tend to waste it

Our energy sources can be divided into the two following categories:

- well-established **conventional energy sources** such as oil, natural gas, coal, hydroelectricity, and nuclear electricity
- a growing number of **alternative energy sources** such as solar, wind, and **biomass energy.**

This chapter will deal **primarily** with conventional energy sources, since they are responsible for almost all the energy used in Canada. We rely mostly on three types of energy that, taken together, account for 98% of our energy use: oil (39%), natural gas (35%), and electricity (24%). This leaves about 2% for other energy sources, including coal, wood, and wind power.

primarily
mainly

Alternative energy sources will be considered in Chapter 37. Our tendency to use our resources in a wasteful manner will be the subject of Chapter 39.

One gigajoule is roughly equal to the amount of energy found in 30 litres of gasoline.

One petajoule would be enough energy to keep about 70 000 average cars going for one year.

Energy Terminology

One difficulty in the study of energy is that we often try to compare litres of gasoline to cubic metres of natural gas and to kilowatt hours of electricity. To compare these forms of energy properly, we need a common unit of measure. The basic unit used to measure energy is the **joule (J)**, but one joule is only a tiny amount of energy. As a result, two large multiples of joules are used: gigajoules and petajoules. One gigajoule (GJ) equals one billion joules. One petajoule (PJ) equals one million gigajoules.

How Energy Is Used

Canada's total supply of energy in 2003 was about 10 000 petajoules. Almost 20% of this total was used by manufacturers as raw material, and by energy producers to get their products to market. This leaves about 8000 petajoules, which were used as energy by businesses and consumers in Canada. Fig. 27-1 shows how this energy was used.

Fig. 27-1 ▶ Energy use in Canada (PJ), 2003

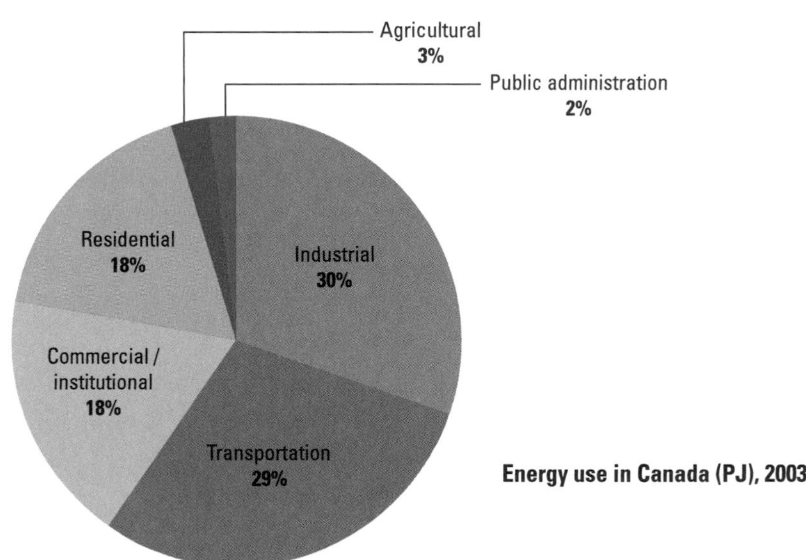

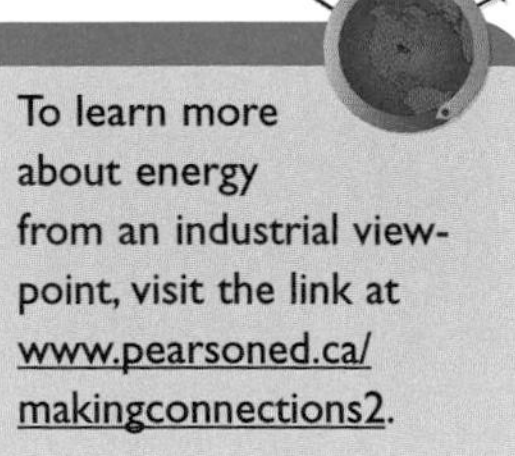

To learn more about energy from an industrial viewpoint, visit the link at www.pearsoned.ca/makingconnections2.

Patterns of energy use vary significantly from one sector of our economy to another. Work with a partner to investigate these differences.

1. Examine Fig. 27-2. You can look at these data in two completely different ways. One is by examining them according to sector (industrial, transportation, etc.). The other is by analyzing them according to type of energy (electricity, petroleum, etc.).

Sector	Electricity	Petroleum	Natural Gas	Other	Total
Industrial	832	271	999	211	2313
Transportation	15	2036	191	0	2242
Agriculture	36	148	28	0	212
Residential	543	123	681	1	1348
Public Administration	48	58	22	0	128
Commercial/ Institutional	426	401	536	0	1363
Total	**1900**	**3037**	**2457**	**212**	**7606**

◀ **Fig. 27-2** Sources of energy and energy use in Canada, 2003 (in petajoules). Note that "Other" for "Industrial" is almost totally coal, but for residential, "Other" is primarily wood.

2. With your partner, create a set of simple bar graphs to show energy use within each sector of the economy. For example, start with a graph that shows the types of energy used in the industrial sector.
3. Write a brief summary of the pattern of energy use in each sector. Why do you think energy patterns vary from sector to sector?
4. Now create a set of bar graphs to show how each type of energy is used. In this case, start with how electricity is used.
5. Write a brief summary of the main uses of each type of energy. Again, try to explain any significant differences in patterns of use between types of energy.

These can be quick-and-simple sketch graphs.

Coal

The Formation of Coal Deposits

Coal formed from the remains of trees and plants that grew in swampy areas 300 to 360 million years ago during the Carboniferous Period. The plant remains did not decay because of low oxygen levels in the swampy water. Layer upon layer of undecayed vegetation formed deep deposits of organic matter that were later covered by sediments. Over millions of years, the weight of the sediments compressed the organic matter and, along with certain chemical changes, turned it into coal. Different amounts of compression formed different types of coal.

- *anthracite coal* formed under great pressure. It is shiny and hard, rich in carbon, relatively clean burning, and used mainly for commercial and residential heating.
- *bituminous coal* formed under less pressure than anthracite. Softer and with more impurities, bituminous coal burns with a smoky flame. It is used primarily as fuel in thermoelectric plants, but substantial amounts are used for heating and for fuel in manufacturing industries.

Coke, a fuel used in the blast furnaces of steel mills, is formed by "baking" bituminous coal at temperatures as high as 1000°C. Coke is known as metallurgical coal because it is used in the production of metals.

- *lignite coal* formed near the surface of Earth where the pressure of overlying sediments was relatively low. Often called brown coal, lignite is soft, inexpensive, and filled with impurities. It is used almost entirely as fuel in thermoelectric plants.

Canada's Coal Industry

Most of Canada's coal is mined in British Columbia, Alberta, and Saskatchewan (Fig. 27-3).

New Brunswick, Nova Scotia, Ontario, Saskatchewan, and Alberta use coal to generate much of their electricity, although Ontario plans to close its plants by 2007.

The coal industry plays a significant role in the country's economy; it contributes about $4.5 billion annually to the GDP and provides over 55 000 jobs to Canadians. In Canada coal is used primarily for fuel in the generation of electricity. In 2004, 93% of the coal consumed in Canada was used in electrical power generation. Most of the remaining 7% of coal consumed in Canada went to steel plants in Ontario and Quebec.

Half of the coal mined in Canada today is exported. This coal, mainly in the form of coke, is exported by ship from ports in British Columbia to steel producers in China, South Korea, and Japan. In 2004, coal exports were valued at $1.9 billion.

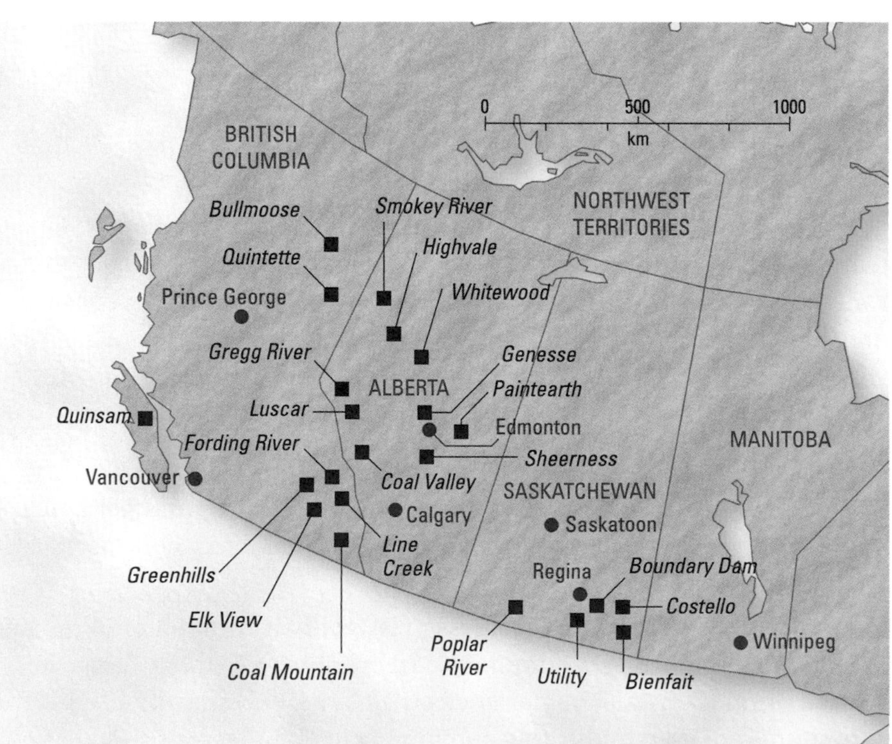

Fig. 27-3 ▶ Coal mines in western Canada

The price of coal rises and falls in a cyclical manner, sometimes encouraging the opening of new mines, and at other times causing mines to close. In 2001, Nova Scotia's coal industry, with a history dating back to 1720, closed. In 2004, however, the rapid economic growth in China and India increased demand and created record high prices for coal. To meet this demand, Alberta and British Columbia began opening new mines, and Nova Scotia considered reopening an old mine with huge coal reserves. As a result, 24 additional coal mines could be in operation in Canada by 2007.

Oil and Gas

The Creation of Oil and Gas

Oil and gas are usually found together. They were formed hundreds of millions of years ago when areas of present-day Canada and its neighbouring seas were covered by shallow oceans. Over a period of millions of years, the remains of marine animals and plants fell to the sea floor. They built up in thick layers and eventually were covered by layers of sand and silt. Over time, the immense weight of all of these layers compressed the lower layers into sedimentary rock. Bacterial action, heat, and pressure converted the remains of the animals and plants into oil and gas.

Oil and gas are found in the geological structures that act as traps, stopping the oil and gas from rising to the surface. These structures have the following characteristics:

- a geologic history that would allow oil and gas to develop
- a layer of porous rock that holds the oil and gas
- upper and lower layers of non-porous rock that form a trap for the oil and gas. **Anticlinal traps** have these characteristics (Fig. 27-4).

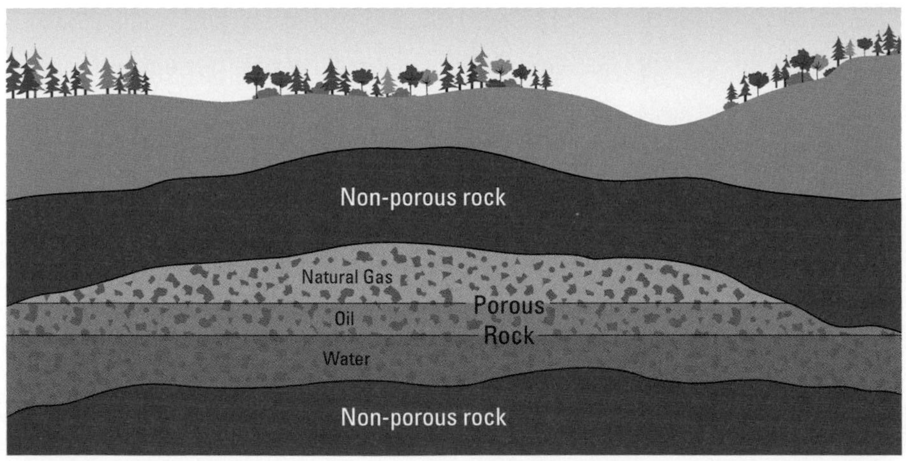

◀ **Fig. 27-4** An anticlinal trap. The dome and lower layer of non-porous rock capture the oil and gas and stop them from reaching the surface. Why does the natural gas rise above the oil? Why do both rise above the water?

Searching for Oil and Gas

Finding oil and gas in amounts that will make their recovery worthwhile is a challenging task. Geologists must look for the special geological structures that have trapped oil and gas. What makes the search difficult is that these structures may be many hundreds of metres underground. Even if the right geological structure is located, there is no guarantee that oil and gas will be found within it.

Geologists use many tricks in their search for oil and gas. These include:

- looking for rocks on the surface that contain traces of oil
- searching for clues, like fossils, in the sedimentary rock that indicate the right conditions for the formation of oil and gas
- using geological information obtained from the drill cores of oil wells in the same general area
- conducting seismic surveys, which use shock waves to locate oil- and gas-bearing rock structures.

elaborate
complex; having many different parts

The presence of oil and gas can be determined only by drilling, a very costly and time-consuming process that involves the use of a specialized drill rig (Fig. 27-5). The drilling process may continue for months.

▼ **Fig. 27-5** An oil rig with an **elaborate** structure is used to turn a long string of pipes that ends in a diamond drill bit. Drill holes can be thousands of metres deep.

Recovering Oil and Gas

The removal of oil and gas from the ground takes place in one of two ways, depending on the nature of the deposit:

- *Flowing wells:* Some wells have enough natural pressure to force the oil or gas to the surface. At the surface, the flow is controlled by a series of valves called a "Christmas tree" (Fig. 27-6).
- *Non-flowing wells:* If there is not enough pressure to make the oil and gas flow to the surface, electric- or gasoline-powered pumps must be used (Fig. 27-7).

As oil is removed from a deposit, the recovery of the oil that remains becomes more difficult. Scientists have created a variety of methods to remove more of the remaining oil from deposits, increasing the total percentage taken from the deposit. This process is called **secondary recovery**. Even with secondary recovery, only about 60% of the oil in most deposits can be recovered. Research is being done to improve this figure, since even an increase of 5% in the amount of recovery would have the same impact as finding many large oilfields.

▼ **Fig. 27-6** A flowing well may need only a Christmas tree valve to control its natural flow.

Sources of Canada's Oil and Gas

Canada's oil and gas production is shown in Fig. 27-8. For more than 50 years, almost all of Canada's oil and gas production has come from the western parts of the Boreal Plains and Prairie ecozones. This has meant that production has been concentrated in Alberta and adjoining parts of Saskatchewan, British Columbia, and the Northwest Territories (Fig. 27-9). Natural gas production has been very much dominated by Alberta and, to a lesser extent, Saskatchewan and British Columbia.

◀ **Fig. 27-7** A "nodding horse," or "grasshopper," pumps oil from a non-flowing well.

The Case Study that follows this chapter looks at Hibernia in more detail.

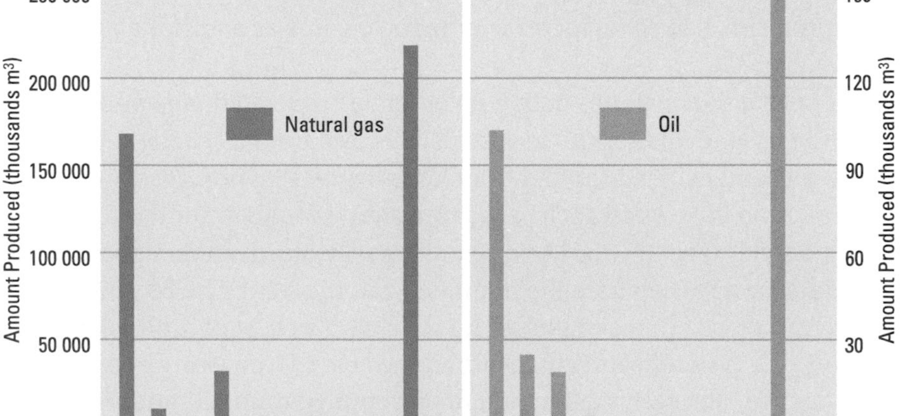

◀ **Fig. 27-8** Producers of oil and natural gas in Canada, 2004

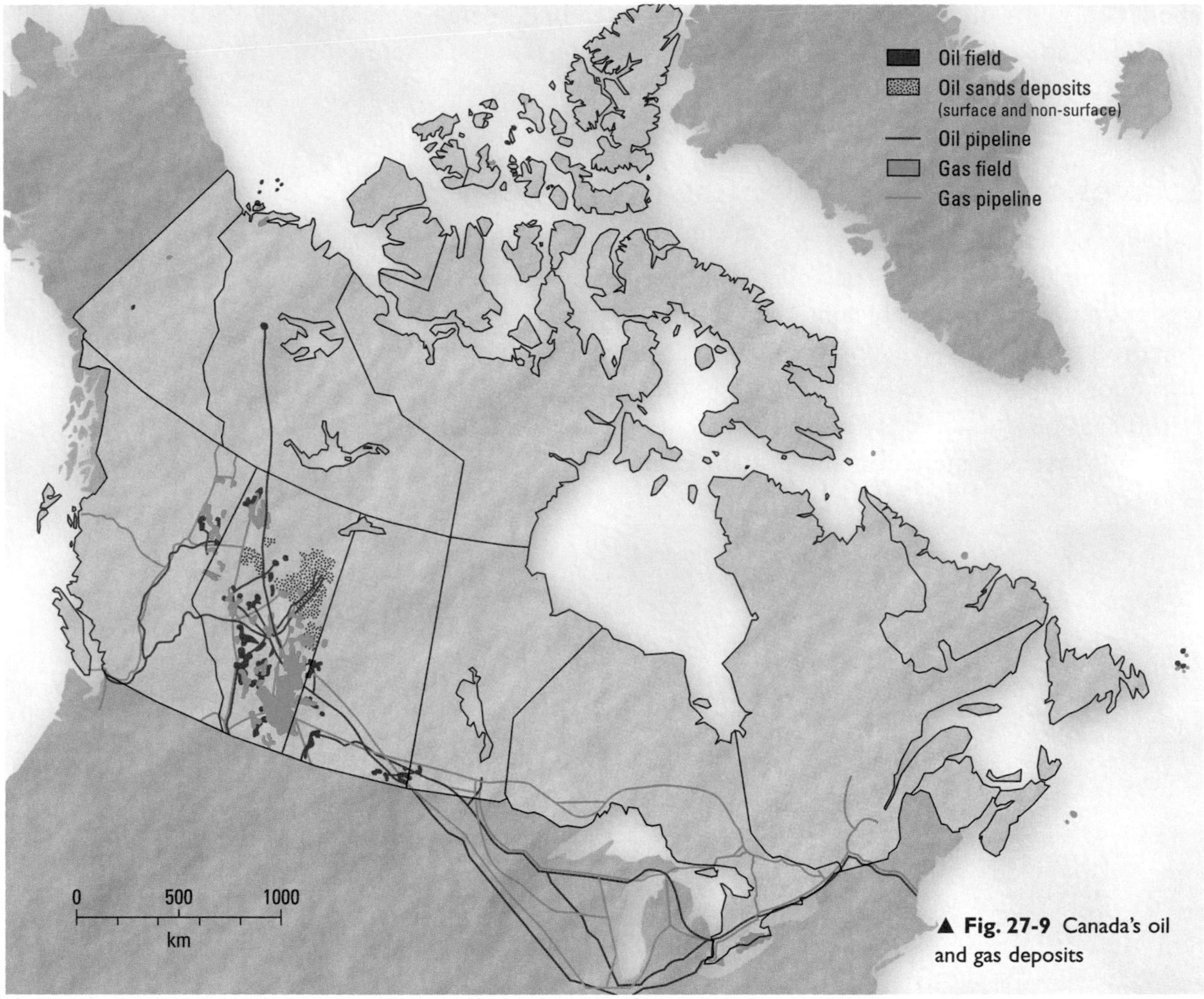

▲ **Fig. 27-9** Canada's oil and gas deposits

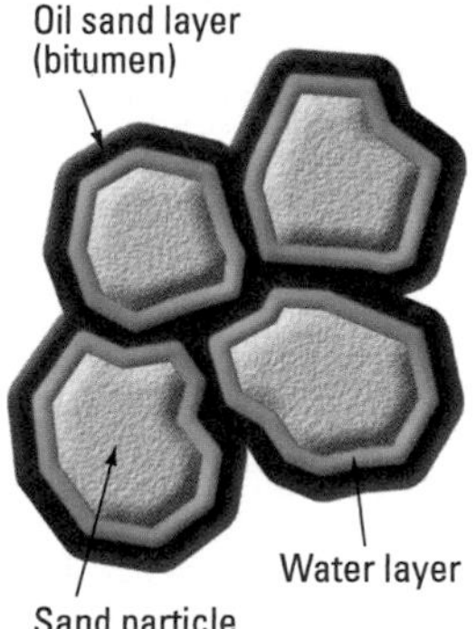

▲ **Fig. 27-10** Cross-section of oil sand particles

Newfoundland and Labrador became a significant producer of oil in 1997 with the opening of the Hibernia offshore oil project. The province's oil production is likely to increase in years to come as additional projects are developed.

Oil production includes both conventional crude oil that is pumped from the ground and synthetic crude oil created from a special substance called **oil sand**, which is mined from huge deposits in northeastern Alberta. An oil-like substance called **bitumen** is found around individual sand particles (Fig. 27-10). The oil sand is easily dug from the ground and then processed to separate the bitumen from the sand. The bitumen is further processed to make synthetic crude oil. The cost of producing synthetic crude is significantly higher than the cost of recovering conventional crude. However, the amount of oil supplied from oil sands will increase as reserves of conventional crude are **depleted** and as the international price of crude oil increases.

depleted
used up

CASE STUDY

The Mackenzie Gas Project

There are an estimated 2.5 trillion cubic metres of natural gas (about 20% of Canada's known reserves) in the Mackenzie River delta and Beaufort Sea area. No pipeline, however, exists to bring this natural gas to markets in southern Canada and the United States.

- In the 1970s, a pipeline down the Mackenzie River Valley was proposed to carry natural gas from the delta and the Beaufort Sea to southern markets. For a variety of reasons, the pipeline was not built then.
- In 2001, four oil companies—Imperial Oil, ConocoPhillips Canada, ExxonMobil Canada, and Shell Canada (Producers)—together with the Aboriginal Pipeline Group (APG) proposed the Mackenzie Gas Project. In 2003, TransCanada Pipelines joined the group with the option to buy into the pipeline when it was constructed.
- The Mackenzie Valley Pipeline (MVP) is the key component of the Mackenzie Gas Project. It would move natural gas 1400 kilometres from three natural gas fields in the Mackenzie River delta and Beaufort Sea area to existing pipelines in northern Alberta (Fig. 27-11). It would take two years for a steel mill to produce enough pipe for the pipeline.
- Total cost of the project is expected to be about $7 billion. Natural gas production facilities, feeder pipelines, compression stations, airstrips, and roads would be built in addition to the pipeline. During its construction phase, the project would require an estimated 1300 workers.

▼ **Fig. 27-11** Proposed route of the Mackenzie Valley Pipeline. The pipeline will be built above ground, in a fashion similar to the Alaska pipeline seen below.

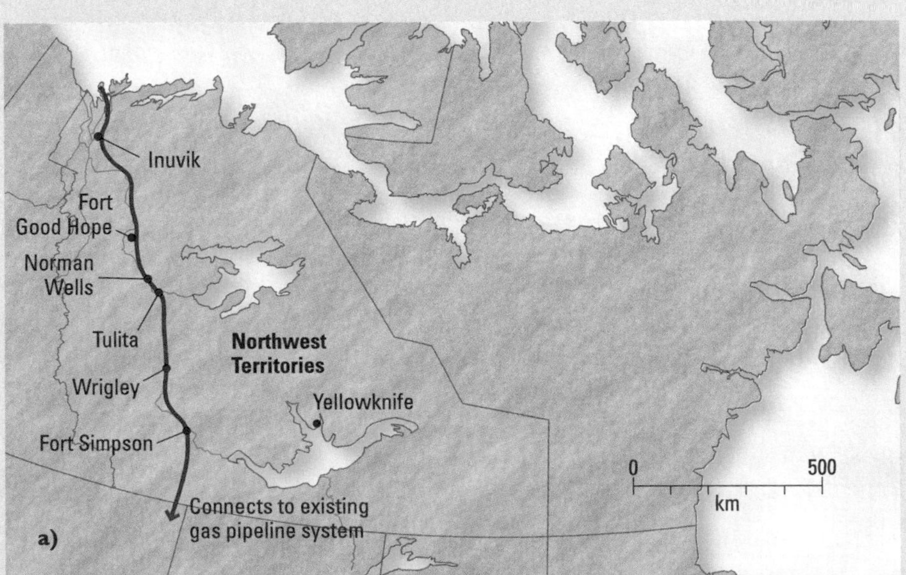

- The Aboriginal Pipeline Group (APG) became a full participant in the project to protect the interests of Aboriginal peoples living along the proposed route. APG will share in the revenue generated by the sale of natural gas and natural gas by-products. It will also ensure that environmental damage and social problems associated with development are limited.
- Although the APG represents the Deh Cho, Sahtú, Gwich'in, Inuvialuit, and other Aboriginal peoples, not all support the project. Some fear they are "selling out" their traditional values by participating. They maintain that the delicate balance between the people and the environment is threatened. There is also concern that the increased flow of workers from the south might create social problems.
- At the time this book was written, the National Energy Board was proceeding with public hearings, scheduled to begin in early 2006 and last about one year. However, the companies had not yet reached an agreement with the APG.
- The companies believed that the communities along the pipeline route wanted too much money for access to their land, and for housing, education, and other aspects of social development. The project was expected to be built by 2010 or 2011. The completion date may be delayed, however, if disagreements among the parties continue.

QUESTIONS

KNOWLEDGE AND UNDERSTANDING

1. Why is a pipeline being proposed for the Mackenzie River Valley?
2. Which companies and groups are involved in the project?
3. Describe the concerns of the Aboriginal people.

THINKING

4. Conduct an Internet search to determine the current status of the Mackenzie Gas Project.

COMMUNICATION

5. a) Research the pros and cons of the Mackenzie Gas Project.
   b) Evaluate the pros and cons. Do you think this project should be developed? Support your position in a short report.

GeoLit Reminder

Developing written ideas:

- Create a graphic organizer listing the pros and cons of the Mackenzie Gas Project. Begin by recording the points discussed in the text.
- Conduct an Internet search to supplement the points gathered from the textbook. Add this information to your graphic organizer.
- Organize gathered information under subheadings.
- Develop each point in a paragraph containing at least three sentences.
- State your position in an introductory paragraph.
- Summarize your main ideas and position in a concluding paragraph.

Electricity

Electricity is produced by generators. A generator may range in size from one you can hold in your hand (for example, to power your bicycle light) to one the size of a large house (for example, to generate electricity in a power station). In both cases, the way the generator works is exactly the same. It converts mechanical energy into electrical energy. In the case of your bicycle light, the turning of the wheel provides the mechanical energy. In the case of the power station, rotating turbines provide the mechanical energy (Fig. 27-12). Power companies in Canada produce massive amounts of electricity as cheaply as possible by using any of three methods to turn turbines that supply mechanical energy to generators:

- moving water in a **hydroelectric generating station**
- expanding steam produced by burning coal, oil, or natural gas in a **thermoelectric generating station**
- expanding steam produced from nuclear fission in a **nuclear-electric generating station**.

Canada ranks second behind Norway in the production of electricity per capita.

Hydroelectricity

Hydroelectric generating stations can be built anywhere there are rivers with significant changes in elevation and large, reliable flows of water. The force of the water moving from a higher to a lower elevation drives the generator (Fig. 27-12).

See Fig. 17-5 in Chapter 17 for a photo of a power dam.

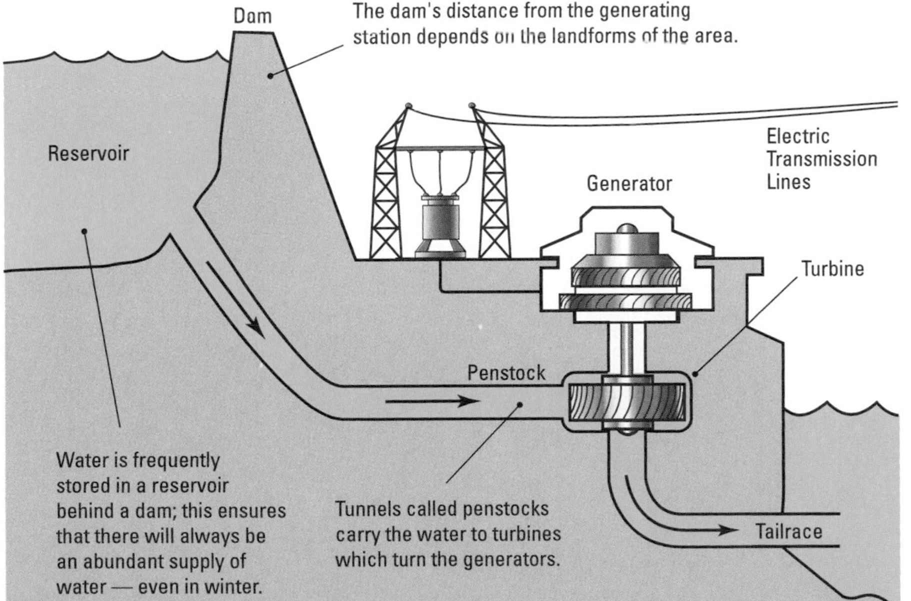

◄ **Fig. 27-12** How a hydroelectric generating station works

ADVANTAGES OF HYDROELECTRICITY

- Plants are cheap to operate since there is no fuel to buy.
- Because the production of hydroelectricity does not require the burning of fossil fuels, it does not produce air pollution or carbon dioxide.
- Hydroelectric power uses a renewable resource—flowing water.
- The reservoir (if there is one) can be used for recreational activities such as fishing and boating.

DISADVANTAGES OF HYDROELECTRICITY

- Plants are very costly to build.
- Suitable sites are often very far from areas where electricity is needed. This means that costly and unsightly transmission lines must be built.
- Practically all large sites near population centres have been developed.
- Dams cause flooding that may destroy animal habitats, people's homes, important historical sites, or even entire towns in the low-lying area behind the dam.
- Flooding may cause the release of dangerous chemicals, such as mercury, from rocks under the reservoir.
- The changed seasonal pattern of water flow of the river below the dam may adversely affect the ecology and animal habitats.

In 2005, when years of drought had lowered the water level in Lake Powell, a dammed lake on the Colorado River in Arizona, Aboriginal peoples could see some of their sacred ancient sites that had been covered with water for over 40 years.

Thermoelectricity

In thermoelectric generating stations, steam, rather than moving water, turns the turbines, and this action causes the generator to turn. The steam can be produced by burning fuel such as coal, oil, natural gas, wood, or even garbage (Fig. 27-13).

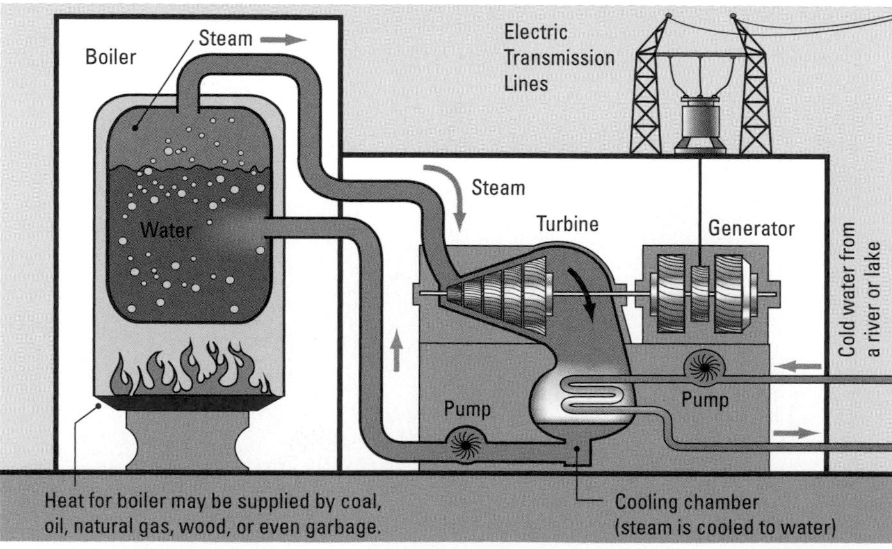

Fig. 27-13 ▶ How a thermoelectric generating station works

ADVANTAGES OF THERMOELECTRICITY

- Plants can be built near population centres where the electricity is needed. This means that shorter transmission lines can be built, keeping the cost of transmission relatively low.
- Plants can be built where fuel is readily available. If the cost of transporting fuel is lower, the cost of producing the electricity will be lower.
- Plants are less expensive to build than hydroelectric or nuclear-electric plants.

DISADVANTAGES OF THERMOELECTRICITY

- Fuel costs, especially for oil and natural gas, are high and are increasing rapidly.
- Oil, natural gas, and coal are non-renewable resources and will run out eventually.
- Coal-burning thermoelectric plants produce a great deal of air pollution and contribute to **global warming.**
- Coal and, to a lesser extent, oil produce the gases that are responsible for acid precipitation.

Chapter 37 focuses on the problem of global warming.

Nuclear Electricity

Nuclear-electric generating stations are similar to thermoelectric plants in most respects except for the source of heat that produces steam. The heat comes from the breakdown (fission) of radioactive uranium atoms. It boils water that produces steam that turns the turbines (Fig. 27-14).

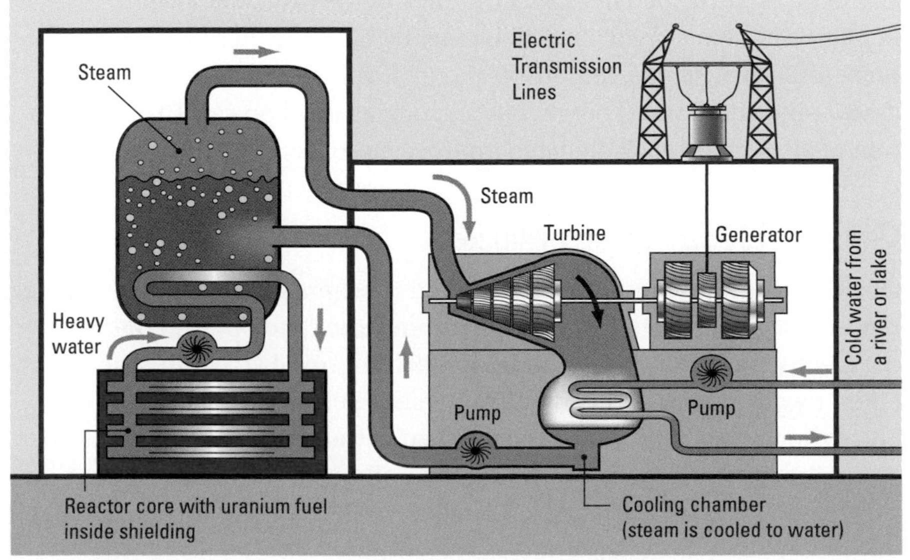

◀ **Fig. 27-14** How a nuclear-electric generating station works

ADVANTAGES OF NUCLEAR ELECTRICITY

- Since plants can be built where the energy is needed, transmission costs are low.
- Operating costs are relatively low, especially in the early years of plant operation.
- Canada has an abundant supply of uranium.
- Plants do not produce air pollution or carbon dioxide.

DISADVANTAGES OF NUCLEAR ELECTRICITY

- Construction costs are very high.
- Radioactive fuel is very hazardous to human health and must be handled with great care; accidents have the potential to harm many thousands of people.
- Waste products from nuclear plants remain dangerous for 100 000 years. No permanent solution has been developed for safely disposing of these wastes.
- As reactors age they become unreliable. The useful life of nuclear plants is much shorter than originally thought, which means that plants will have to be replaced or rebuilt at enormous cost.

Electrical Production in Canada

There is wide variation in the kind of electrical generation used in different parts of Canada (Fig. 27-15). Fig. 27-16 shows the location of Canada's largest electrical generating stations.

Ontario uses large amounts of electricity generated by all three types of plants, including Canada's only large nuclear plants. There are no longer any large undeveloped hydroelectric sites in the province. Future increases in demand will have to be met by building thermoelectric or nuclear-electric plants, importing energy from other provinces, or by developing alternative energy sources such as wind power. The best solution of all, of course, would be to improve energy conservation.

Most of Newfoundland and Labrador's hydro-electric capacity is in Labrador and is not available for use on the island of Newfoundland. Most of the power produced in Labrador is sold to Hydro-Québec, which in turn sells it to customers in the United States.

Getting Electricity to Market

Once produced, electricity is transmitted to where it is needed. A complex **power grid**, into which generating stations direct their power, transmits the electricity, usually over hundreds of kilometres. Large industries, cities, towns, and other major customers take electricity from the grid. Since provincial and state grids are linked within North America, electricity can be moved back and forth between provinces and between provinces and American states as needed. In fact, electricity has become one of Canada's most important export commodities.

In 2005, Hydro-Québec and Ontario Power Generation made a joint $8 billion proposal to build a hydroelectric generating station on the lower Churchill River in Labrador.

	Total Electrical Generation (thousands of megawatt hours)	Percentage That Is:		
		Hydro	Thermal	Nuclear
Canada	561 293	59	28	13
Newfoundland and Labrador	42 039	95	5	0
Prince Edward Island	42	0	100	0
Nova Scotia	12 387	9	91	0
New Brunswick	19 238	17	59	25
Quebec	177 461	96	2	2
Ontario	150 048	24	34	42
Manitoba	21 152	96	4	0
Saskatchewan	18 499	19	81	0
Alberta	56 233	3	97	0
British Columbia	63 051	90	10	0
Territories	1 041	53	47	0

Note: Totals may not equal 100% due to rounding.

◀ **Fig. 27-15** Amount of energy generated, 2003

▼ **Fig. 27-16**

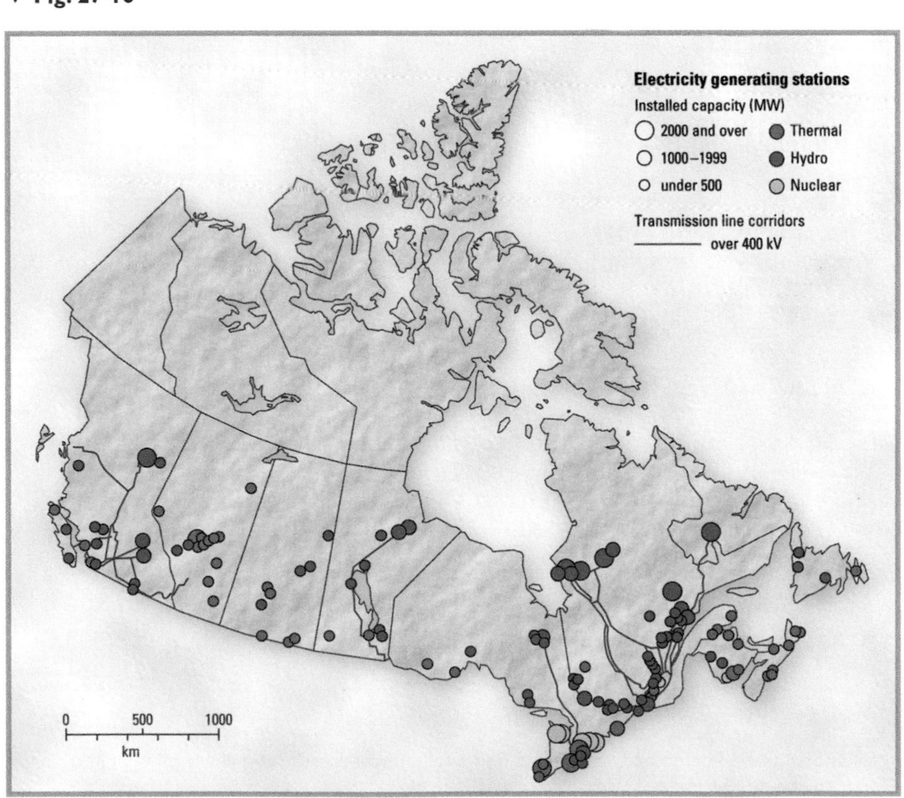

The interdependence of the Canadian and American power grids was illustrated on August 14, 2004, when a failure in a station in Ohio caused a power failure throughout a huge area of the northeastern United States and southeastern Canada. Some areas went days without electricity. This failure points out not only the interdependence of both grids, but also the fact that a grid is only as good as its weakest part.

The Business of Energy

Few people realize that Canada is the largest source of oil for the United States.

Energy industries are a major part of Canada's economy. In 2003 they were responsible for almost 6% of our GDP and provided 230 000 jobs. Investments in energy projects, big and small, made up 16% of all investment in Canada's economy. Energy is also an important element of our foreign trade. Canada has been a net exporter of energy since 1969. More than 90% of all our energy exports go to the United States, which has enormous energy needs. In fact, Canada is a net exporter of every major type of energy (Fig. 27-17).

Fig. 27-17 ► Canada's energy trade in 2004 (in millions of dollars). More than 90% of this trade is with the United States.

Type of Energy	Exports	Imports	Net Trade
Natural gas	26 598	10 861	15 737
Oil	25 159	16 452	8 707
Coal	1 808	3 714	–1 906
Electricity	2 037	1 092	945
Total	55 602	32 119	23 483

	Interprovincial Trade		Trade With the United States		Overall Net Trade
	From other provinces	**To other provinces**	**From the US**	**To the US**	
Newfoundland & Labrador	neg.	30.1	0	0	+30.1
Prince Edward Island	1.1	0	0	0	-1.1
Nova Scotia	0.2	0.5	neg.	0.1	+0.4
New Brunswick	0.6	2.5	0.1	2.7	+4.7
Quebec	34.6	2.9	3.9	10.0	-25.6
Ontario	6.0	3.3	7.4	4.6	-5.6
Manitoba	0.5	3.7	6.0	4.5	+1.7
Saskatchewan	0.4	1.0	0.9	0.7	+0.5
Alberta	1.6	1.3	0.3	0.1	-0.5
British Columbia	1.1	1.0	5.9	8.6	+2.5

neg. = negligible

▲ **Fig. 27-18** Interprovincial and international trade in electricity megawatt hours (all international trade is with the United States), 2003. Totals may not add up due to rounding.

Trade in Electricity

Electricity is moved between provinces and between Canada and the United States by high-voltage transmission lines. It is commonly moved from one area to another to meet varying needs. For example, the United States buys electricity from Canada in the summer when its air-conditioning needs are high. Canada buys power from the United States in the winter when our heating demands are high. Fig. 27-18 shows the movement of electricity between Canada and the United States and among the provinces.

Trade in Natural Gas

The interprovincial and international trade in natural gas relies on the existence of gas pipelines built across provinces and between Canada and the United States. Pipelines are the most economical way to move large amounts of natural gas. They have been built from the main producing areas of Alberta, British Columbia, and Saskatchewan into the United States and across Canada to Ontario and Quebec. New pipelines are being built into the United States because of the development of new gas reserves near Sable Island off the coast of Nova Scotia.

Trade in Oil

Canada imports as well as exports large amounts of crude oil. Supertankers carry crude oil from such oil exporting areas as the Middle East, South America, and Africa to Newfoundland, Nova Scotia, and Portland, Maine. As a result, the market east of the Ontario–Quebec border is supplied mainly with imported oil. On the other hand, pipelines from western Canada enable the export of huge amounts of Canadian oil to the United States as well as supplying Canadian needs from Ontario westward (Fig. 27-19).

EMERGING TRENDS

Supertankers may soon have a role to play in Canadian oil exports, partly because China has expressed an interest in buying Canadian oil. Also, Quebec and Atlantic Canada may find that their reliance on imported oil slowly declines with the continued development of oil resources off the east coast of Canada. Finally, a greater supply of oil from the wells off Newfoundland may mean that Ontario might find it cheaper to buy oil from eastern rather than western Canada.

The crude oil shipped into Portland moves by pipeline to Montreal.

Looking Toward the Future

Much of our prosperity as a nation, and our **affluent** lifestyle, depends on the fact that we have always had abundant energy resources. Will this always be the case? Perhaps not. Consider the simple fact that most of our energy

affluent
well-off

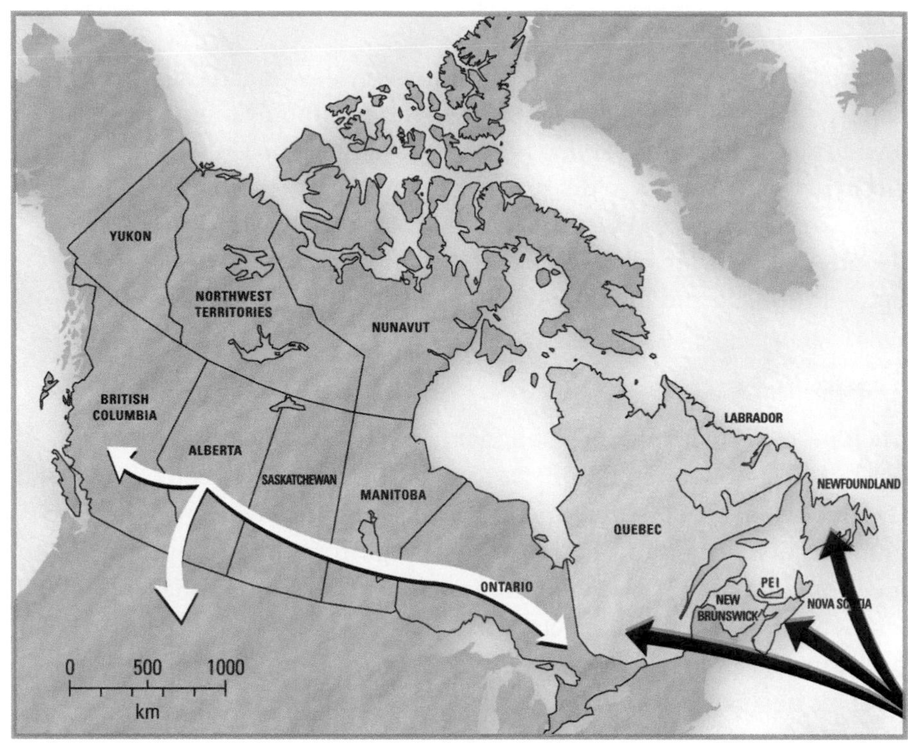

Fig. 27-19 ► Canada's oil market is divided into two parts at the Ontario–Quebec border. Quebec and the Maritimes use imported oil. Western Canada and Ontario use domestic oil. The oil fields off Newfoundland and Labrador are supplying an increasing amount of eastern Canada's oil.

resources are non-renewable and may run out within your lifetime. There are two things we must learn to do: use our energy resources more wisely, and gradually replace our use of non-renewable energy with renewable sources. You can learn more about these two measures in Chapter 39.

QUESTIONS

KNOWLEDGE AND UNDERSTANDING

1. There are three good reasons, and one not so very good reason, why Canadians use a great deal of energy. What are they?
2. a) What is a petajoule?
   b) Why is this unit useful in studying energy?
3. a) Explain how coal is formed.
   b) Why is coal important to the Canadian economy?
4. Describe the three different types of coal.
5. Explain the difference between conventional energy sources and alternative energy sources.
6. a) Describe the geologic characteristics that must exist for oil and natural gas to be trapped in rock.
   b) Examine a geology map in an atlas. Where in Canada might oil and gas be found?
   c) Why have the oil and gas resources of only a few of these areas been developed?
7. What are oil sands and how do they contribute to Canada's energy supply?
8. Complete an organizer like Fig. 27-20 to compare the different methods of making electricity.
9. Describe the steps that the oil industry takes to find and develop possible oil and gas deposits. Be sure to identify the points at which the company must make a decision, and indicate how that decision is made.

	Hydro-electric Power	Thermal-electric Power	Nuclear-electric Power
Source of Power			
Advantages			
Disadvantages			

▲ **Fig. 27-20**

THINKING

10. Use the Internet and your school library to research the following:
    a) the pros and cons of burning coal to produce thermoelectric power
    b) the effectiveness of "clean coal" technology
11. a) Canada's oil market is divided into two parts. Where does the division occur?
    b) Why does this division exist?
    c) How might the expansion of the oil industry off Newfoundland and Labrador change this division?
12. a) What is meant by secondary recovery of oil?
    b) Why is the use of secondary recovery so attractive to the oil industry?
13. a) Every region of Canada relies mainly on one method of producing electricity. Identify regions that depend mainly on thermoelectric power and those that depend primarily on hydroelectric power.
    b) Explain why each region relies on its method. (Hint: Think about the physical geography of these areas.)
    c) Describe the unique situations that exist in Newfoundland and Labrador and Ontario. Why do these situations exist?
14. Why does Canada both import and export energy products? Consider oil and electricity.

COMMUNICATION

15. Alberta's oil sands deposits are Canada's largest source of oil, with reserves estimated at between 1.7 trillion and 2.5 trillion barrels. It may be the biggest petroleum deposit anywhere in the world! Use the Internet to research the oil sands. Imagine you are a newspaper reporter who has been given the task of writing an article that explains the oil sands to readers. Use the following questions as a guide.
    a) Where are the oil sands located in Alberta?
    b) How were the oil sands formed?
    c) How large is the resource?
    d) Explain how the oil sands are removed from the ground and taken to the processing plant.
    e) How is the oil extracted from the sand?
    f) Describe the "in situ" technique for removing the oil.
    g) Explain the upgrading process.
    h) Examine the environmental impact of the oil sands projects:
       i. What is being done to minimize the impact on the environment?
       ii. How successful are these efforts?
    i) Examine the economic impact of the oil sands on
       i. the national economy
       ii. Alberta's economy

APPLICATION

16. As a major exporter of coal, Canada stands to benefit from the rising demand for coal by Asia. The environmental cost to the world of the increasing use of coal, however, could be very dangerous.
    a) Examine the impact of the developing world's growing demand for coal on
       i. global warming
       ii. the success of the Kyoto Protocol.
    b) How do you think developed countries of the world should deal with the dilemma of selling coal to developing countries while protecting the environment?

Offshore Oil: Hibernia

Key Terms

reservoir

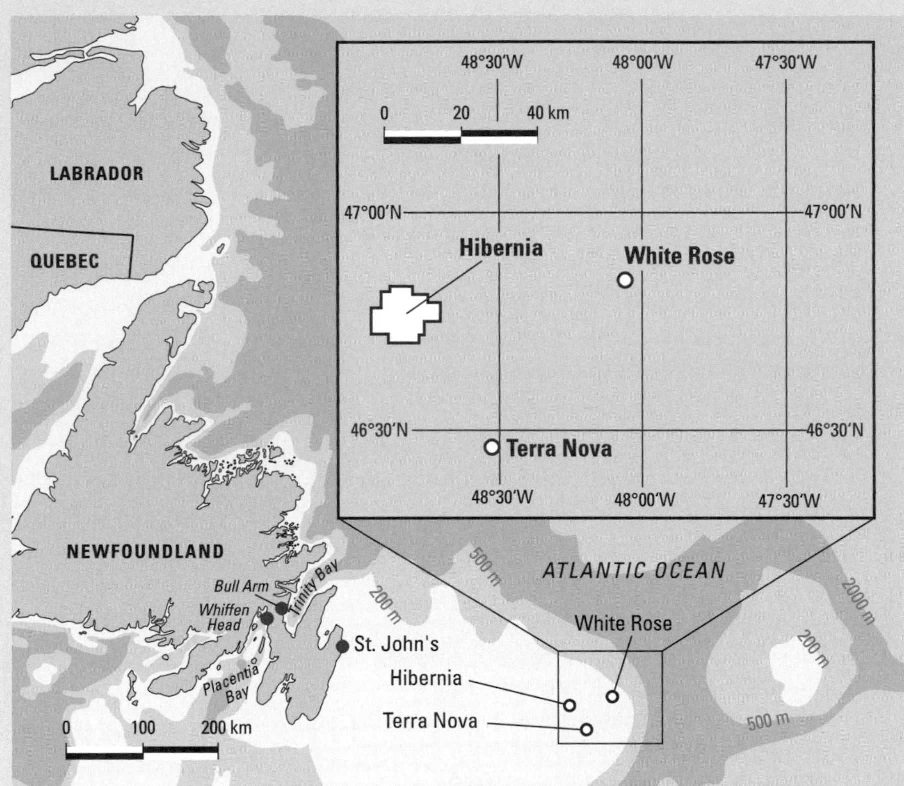

▲ **Fig. 27-21** East coast oil fields

Exploration of the sedimentary rocks that make up the continental shelf off the coast of Atlantic Canada began during the 1960s. Several oil companies began drilling discovery wells into the seabed in search of oil and natural gas. Five major discoveries were made: two gas fields on the Scotian Shelf located 250 kilometres off the coast of Nova Scotia, and three oil fields on the Grand Banks of Newfoundland (Fig. 27-21). Hibernia, the largest oil field on the Grand Banks and the first to be developed, is the focus of this Case Study.

Exploration

In 1979, Chevron Canada Resources drilled a discovery well into the northeastern portion of the Grand Banks. The results of this exploratory drilling were promising. By 1984, Mobil Oil Canada had drilled nine more

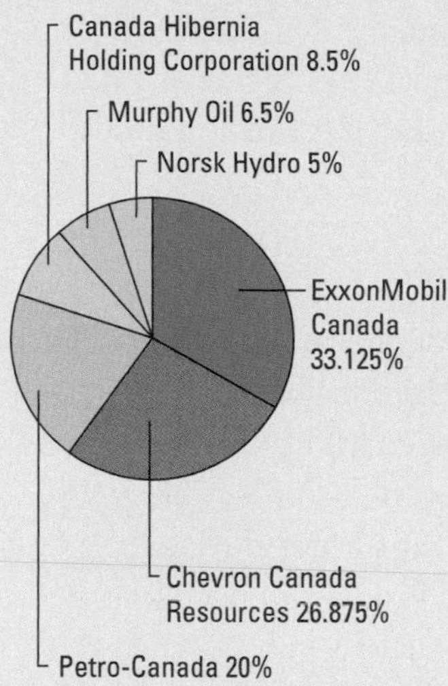

▲ **Fig. 27-22** Hibernia owner companies and their share of ownership as of 2005.

wells in the area. The results of the drilling enabled geologists to map this new oil field and to determine that there were enough oil and gas deposits to make commercial development possible. In 1985, the findings of the geologists were presented to a joint federal–provincial environmental assessment panel. This panel conducted public hearings on whether this mammoth oil-drilling project on the Grand Banks would be good for the environment and the people of Newfoundland and Labrador. By 1990, the project was approved. A 25-year lease was given to the Hibernia Management and Development Company (HMDC), a joint venture of several large oil companies, to construct and operate the Hibernia facilities (Fig. 27-22). Hibernia began producing oil and gas in November 1997.

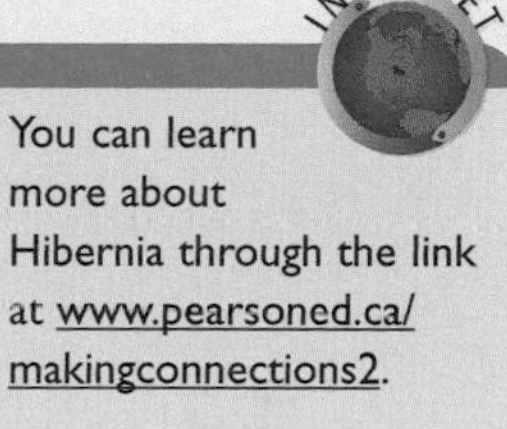

You can learn more about Hibernia through the link at www.pearsoned.ca/makingconnections2.

Geology and Production

The Hibernia oil field is located on the Grand Banks about 315 kilometres southeast of St. John's. The actual drilling takes place in about 80 metres of water. The oil and gas deposits are located in two geologic formations made of sandstone. These formations are **reservoirs** known as the Hibernia and the Avalon sandstones (Fig. 27-23). The total Hibernia field contains about three billion barrels of crude oil. Roughly 900 million

Hibernia is the fifth-largest oil field ever discovered in Canada.

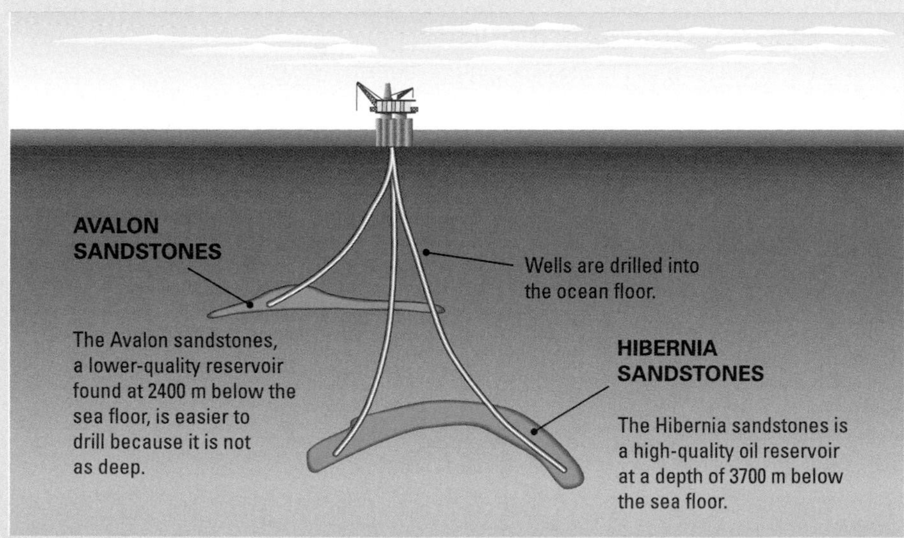

◄ **Fig. 27-23** Cross-section of the Hibernia oil field

barrels of this oil is recoverable with today's technology. The Hibernia oil field will operate for about 20 years. Natural gas is not being recovered at this point because of the difficulty and cost of getting it ashore.

The Drilling Platform

The Topsides portion weighs 37 000 tonnes and the GBS unit weighs 550 000 tonnes. *Time* magazine called the GBS unit the eighth wonder of the modern world.

Dangerous storms, cold temperatures, drifting icebergs, and fog make the waters off Newfoundland and Labrador some of the most dangerous in the world. In 1982, a huge floating drilling platform, the Ocean Ranger, capsized in a fierce storm, killing 84 crew members. To prevent a similar disaster, scientists and engineers designed the Hibernia drilling platform with the utmost care. It consists of two parts: the Topsides Production Facilities and the Gravity Base Structure (GBS) (Fig. 27-24).

The Topsides facilities consist of five super-modules containing the living quarters of the crew and the drilling and production equipment. In addition, there are seven other structures including cranes, lifeboat stations, and a heliport.

Every year between 10 000 and 20 000 icebergs form near Greenland and the Canadian Arctic. About 1000 of them drift into North Atlantic waters. According to computer simulations, a hit from a 6-million-tonne iceberg would damage the structure but would be repairable.

The GBS platform is a concrete structure that cuts into the ocean floor where it is cemented into place. About 400 000 tonnes of iron ore granules are added to compartments inside the platform to give it weight and stability. It is designed to withstand 160-kilometre-per-hour winds and 30-metre waves.

The GBS has four shafts that extend 111 metres from the base slab on the ocean floor to its roof (Fig. 27-25). These shafts support the Topsides facilities. A large tank within the GBS has the capacity to store 1.3 million barrels of crude oil until it can be transferred to a tanker for transport ashore.

An iceberg management program has been developed to detect and track icebergs to reduce the probability of a collision with the GBS. If a

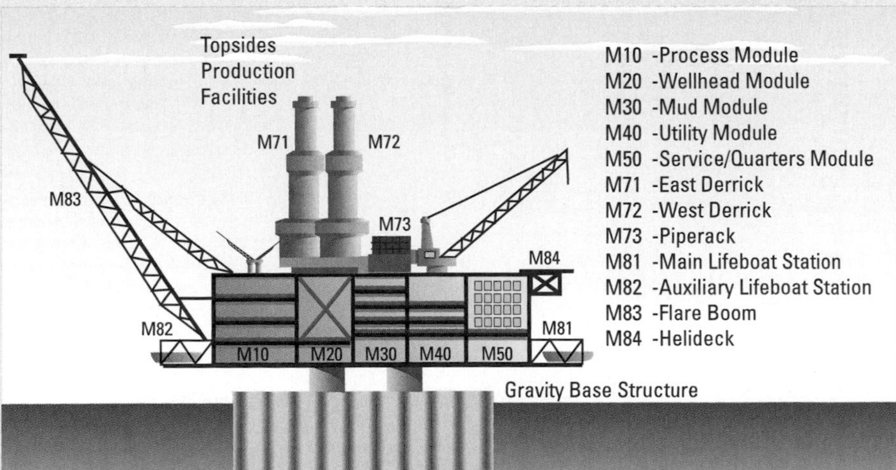

Fig. 27-24 ▶ The Hibernia platform

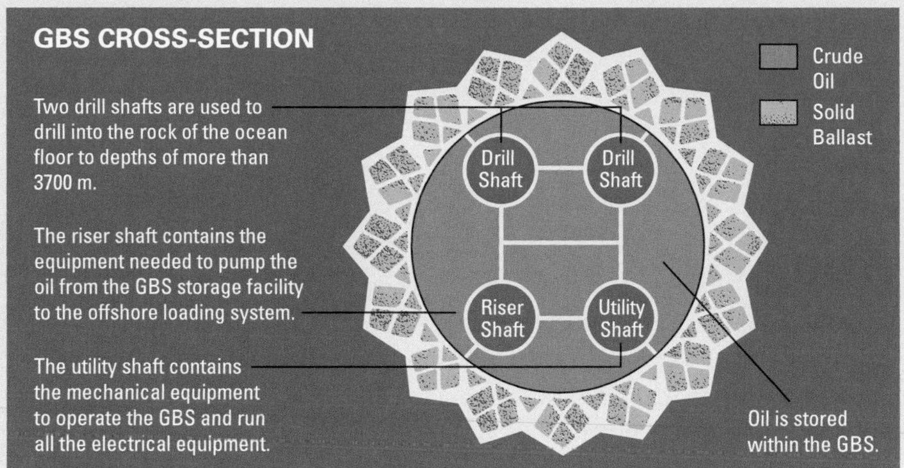

◀ **Fig. 27-25** The teeth of the ice wall are designed to distribute the force of an iceberg hit over the entire GBS. The 1.4-metre-thick ice wall is supported by a set of concrete supports and a 15-metre-thick ice belt filled with iron ore. Each of the four shafts is 17 metres in diameter.

collision seems **imminent**, tugs will try to tow the iceberg away from the platform. The GBS has been designed, however, with the possibility of a collision in mind; it has 16 concrete teeth protruding from its circumference that can absorb the impact of a 1-million-tonne iceberg without suffering damage.

imminent
about to happen

▼ **Fig. 27-26** Anchoring the platform in place

The super-modules and seven other structures of the Topsides facilities were welded together at Bull Arm in Trinity Bay, Newfoundland, and then attached to the GBS unit. The completed platform was subsequently towed out to the installation site on the Grand Banks where it was attached to the ocean floor (Fig. 27-26).

Transshipment of Oil

The crude oil pumped from beneath the sea is stored within the GBS until it can be loaded onto shuttle tankers (Fig. 27-27). Each shuttle tanker carries 850 000 tonnes of crude oil to a newly constructed **transshipment** port at Whiffen Head in Placentia Bay, Newfoundland. The crude oil is then transferred to onshore storage tanks until larger tankers arrive to take it to market. The main markets for this oil are the refineries of eastern Canada, the United States, and Europe. The proximity of these markets keeps transportation costs relatively low.

transshipment transferring from one form of transport to another

After an oil tanker delivers its oil to a refinery, it must return empty to pick up more oil. Since the tanker needs weight to allow it to sail safely, water is pumped into the oil storage tanks as ballast. Many tanker captains dump the oil and water combination from these tanks before reaching port. Much of the oil pollution of our oceans comes from this practice.

Environmental Protection

During the 1980s, several studies were conducted to examine the impact of Hibernia on the biological and physical environment of the Grand Banks. The result was the development of environmental protection plans for all phases of the project. Strict measures have been taken to prevent an oil spill from contaminating the waters. The Hibernia platform has been designed to withstand violent seas that might otherwise threaten leakage of the crude oil stored in the GBS. The ice-resistant features of the GBS ensure that it is able to withstand a collision with a large iceberg. The shuttle tankers have reinforced double hulls and double bottoms as

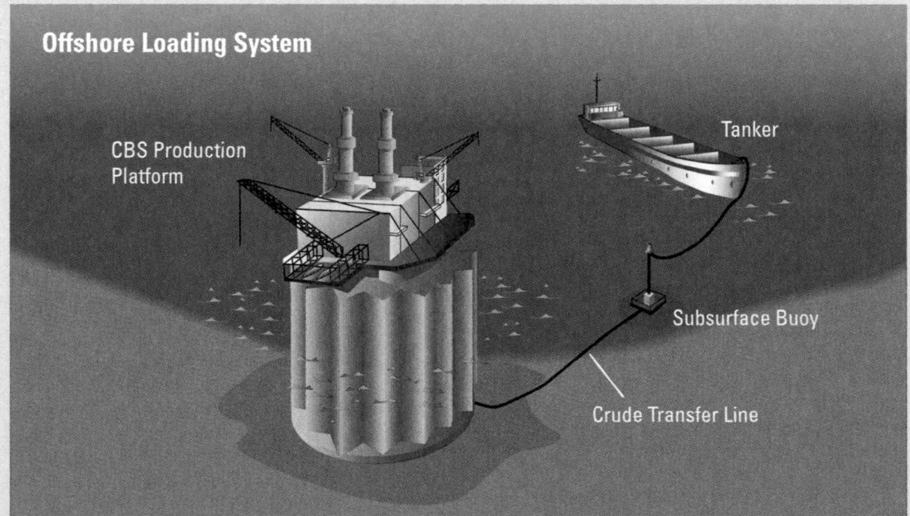

Fig. 27-27 ▶ The crude oil is first stored in the GBS. When a shuttle tanker arrives, the oil is pumped along underwater pipelines to the buoy, which contains flexible loading hoses that are attached to the tanker.

insurance against leakage if punctured. Their ballast and cargo tanks are separate to prevent oil from mixing with ballast water. A computer-based emergency shutdown procedure has been developed to prevent oil spills during loading operations. Canadian crews operate the shuttle tankers under strict Coast Guard regulations, and all Hibernia personnel are required to undergo continual training in the prevention of environmental damage.

Impact on Newfoundland

How are Newfoundlanders benefiting from the development of the Hibernia oil field? Between 1991 and 1995, almost 2500 workers were employed in the construction of the platform, 78% of these at the Bull Arm construction site. Many of these people received training in construction, management, and high technology. Others received an upgrading of their skills as a result of this project. The skills developed by these people are useful in other industries based in Newfoundland and elsewhere. Although fewer jobs are available now than during the construction phase of the project, there are still employment opportunities associated with Hibernia. In the future, royalties from the production of oil could be in the billions of dollars. They will go to the government for use by the people of Newfoundland and Labrador.

Many Newfoundlanders who had moved to Alberta to work in the oil industry were able to return to their home province to use their skills.

In Closing...

The development of the Hibernia oil field was the first step in developing a Canadian offshore oil industry on the Grand Banks. In 2002, oil production began at the Terra Nova site, 35 kilometres southeast of Hibernia. This site is expected to yield about 354 million barrels of oil. The White Rose field, about 350 kilometres east of St. John's, started production in November of 2005. It is expected to yield between 200 and 250 million barrels of oil.

Newfoundland and Labrador has been Canada's poorest province. With the recent loss of the cod fishery, many of the people of Newfoundland have suffered a serious blow to their lifestyle and economy. The offshore oil industry has become a major source of income and jobs for the province. For example, almost 3000 people are employed in the oil industry and in 2005 it is estimated that the government will likely receive between $600 and $700 million in revenues from offshore oil. Newfoundlanders hope that with the development of the Grand Banks oil fields, a new era has begun for their region, in which new job opportunities and oil revenues will lead to increased prosperity for years to come.

QUESTIONS

KNOWLEDGE AND UNDERSTANDING

1. What oil and gas discoveries have been made off Canada's east coast?
2. How do companies determine the size of an oil field?
3. How has the GBS unit been designed to withstand collisions with icebergs?
4. Explain the steps that were involved in building the Hibernia drilling platform.
5. Describe the process of getting the oil from under the sea to market.

THINKING

6. a) Describe the steps that have been taken to protect the environment.
   b) How might large-scale development of oil fields affect the environment and human activities on the Grand Banks?
7. a) What impact has the Hibernia project had on Newfoundlanders?
   b) What types of skills would people have developed by working on this project?
   c) Where else could these skills be used?
8. In spite of the general feeling that Hibernia and neighbouring oil fields are important to the future economic growth of the province, there are critics of this type of development.
   a) Investigate the environmental, economic, and social criticisms that have been made against this project.
   b) How can you compare the benefits and disadvantages of such a project?
   c) Evaluate the differing viewpoints. Which criticisms do you feel are justified? Why?

COMMUNICATION

9. On January 28, 2005, an historic agreement was reached to resolve a dispute between the government of Newfoundland and Labrador and the federal government. It dealt with equalization grants and the sharing of offshore revenues. Research this issue and write a short report in which you answer the following questions.
   a) What were the reasons for the dispute between the two governments?
   b) What events took place during the dispute?
   c) What are the major components of the agreement?
   d) Do you feel the agreement was fair to both sides?
   e) Should other provinces and territories get similar treatment for their natural resources revenues? Explain.

APPLICATION

10. Draw a pie graph to show the amount of recoverable oil compared to the total amount of oil available at Hibernia.
11. Newfoundland and Labrador has been Canada's poorest province. What do you think the provincial government should do with the royalties it receives from offshore oil developments?

28 Location Factors and Manufacturing

Key Ideas

This chapter helps you investigate these questions:

- What factors influence the location of different kinds of manufacturing in Canada?
- What patterns of manufacturing are found in Canada?
- What factors have influenced the location of automobile assembly plants in Ontario?

Key Terms

location factors
raw materials
market
just-in-time (JIT)
labour supply
transportation
political decisions
circumstance
entrepreneur
branch plant
tariff

Imagine that you want to create a new manufacturing business (Fig. 28-1). You must prepare a business plan—a detailed outline that states your goals, estimates how long it will take to reach them, and explains why your company will be successful. One important aspect of your business plan is the **rationale** underlying your choice of location for your new factory.

The bank will want to see your business plan before they lend you the $500 000 (or more) you need to get started.

rationale
reasoning behind a course of action

1. Identify at least four factors that you must consider when deciding where to locate your new factory.
2. Which of these **location factors** are most important for the success of your company? Why?
3. Based on your answer to Question 2, where in Canada does it make sense to locate your factory.

Some day you may have to choose the location for a real manufacturing plant. For most companies, this is a tremendously important decision. In fact, the survival of the company can depend on choosing just the right location for the factory. Fig. 28-2 shows seven important location factors that can affect why manufacturers locate where they do. Let's look at each of these to see how they have played a role in determining the location of specific companies in different parts of Canada. Although all seven factors are likely considered whenever a manufacturer chooses a location, one factor (or maybe two) typically has the biggest influence on the final decision.

▲ **Fig. 28-1** Perhaps your factory will make a revolutionary new product.

INTERNET

More information on RIM is available through the link at www.pearsoned.ca/makingconnections2.

In 2005, the CEO of RIM, Mike Lazaridis, donated $100 million worth of his RIM shares to create the Perimeter Institute for Theoretical Physics. It was the largest gift in Canadian history.

love your wireless, hand-held combination computer, e-mail, cell phone, and Internet browser device (with a full keyboard) that keeps track of your project due dates. You just had a great idea about the project, so you looked it up on the Web while standing in line, and you are now going to send a text message about it to your partner. Science fiction? Science yes, fiction no!

RIM is a designer, manufacturer, and marketer of wireless communication devices. It produces the BlackBerry, along with hardware, software, and other telecommunication services in Waterloo, Ontario, a city located in Canada's "technology triangle." It's the perfect location for a research and development company because Waterloo is home to the University of Waterloo (UW), one of Canada's top universities. UW has the biggest mathematics program in the country and produces many graduates each year with degrees in computer science and engineering. It also has the Institute for Quantum Computing, an institution that applies theoretical physics to the development of computers. RIM draws not only upon the highly skilled workforce in the technology triangle, but also upon the graduates of universities from across Canada and from other countries. RIM had approximately 2200 employees and revenues of US $605 million in 2004.

Transportation

Most manufacturers need access to fast and efficient **transportation** for either raw material or finished products. Two large steel mills in Hamilton, Ontario, were located in that city because essential raw materials can be brought in by ship, which is the cheapest way possible. Companies that have markets all over the world require easy access to international airports or seaports in order to ship their finished products efficiently. Cardium Tool Services uses air freight from Edmonton's airport to ship rush orders of its finished product around the world, while Alcan transports orders of bulk aluminum to customers via ocean freighter. Other companies need access to railroads or national and international highways.

DOW CHEMICAL CANADA INC.

INTERNET

More information on Dow Chemical is available through the link at www.pearsoned.ca/makingconnections2.

Dow Chemical Canada Inc. employs about 450 workers in Sarnia, Ontario. Here, Dow has several manufacturing units that make a variety of polystyrene resins (plastics and synthetic rubbers) whose many end uses include plastic wrap, foam meat trays, CD jewel cases, foam mattresses, bicycle helmets, Styrofoam insulation, and latex house paint. Ethylene gas, the raw material necessary for the manufacture of polystyrene resins, is transported 2000 kilometres from Alberta to Sarnia through the Cochin Pipeline. The Cochin Pipeline transports ethylene, propane, butane, and natural gas liquids (NGLs) from Fort Saskatchewan, Alberta, to the midwestern US and Sarnia, Ontario. The fast and efficient transportation of its raw material through this pipeline is the main reason why Dow is located in Sarnia.

Political Factors

Federal, provincial, and municipal governments often make **political decisions** that improve the business climate and attract new companies. (If they are not careful, they can also make decisions that drive companies away!) Sometimes they make direct political decisions to encourage companies to locate within their **jurisdiction**. For example, they may offer interest-free loans or reduced land taxes for a number of years. They may even provide free land for the factory site. Sometimes governments make indirect political decisions that, although not specifically made to persuade a company to locate or expand in a particular spot, end up doing just that. Highway 407 is a good example of this. The Ontario government built the 407 as an alternative route to the congested Highway 401. Many manufacturers have been attracted to the 407 **corridor** because they can transport their raw materials and finished products efficiently. Auto-assembly and auto-parts companies are especially drawn to the 407 corridor because they are confident that their JIT deliveries can be made when required (Fig. 28-5).

jurisdiction
area over which a government has authority

In 1999, for $3.1 billion, the Ontario government sold a private company a 99-year lease to operate the 407 as a private business.

corridor
land on either side of a highway that provides easy access to it

▼ **Fig. 28-5** Highway 407 is a 108-kilometre toll road that runs just north of the GTA and connects with highways 401, 403, 410, 427, 400, and 404.

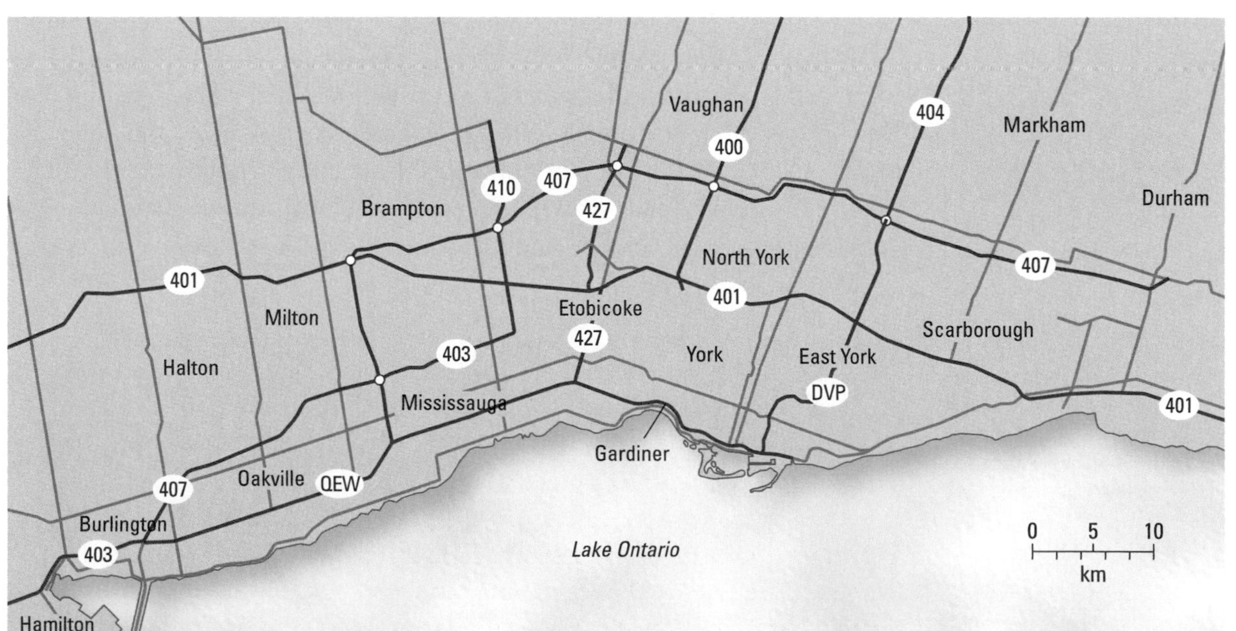

TOYOTA CANADA INC.

In the mid-1980s, the Japanese automaker Toyota decided to expand its North American operations. It's easy to understand why every town and city in Canada and the United States wanted this new assembly plant. Auto-assembly plants provide many secure, high-paying jobs. They also tend to attract other companies, such as parts manufacturers, to locate in the same area. The provincial government and the municipal government of Cambridge, Ontario, offered subsidies and incentives to Toyota to locate in Cambridge. Both governments gambled that the factory would be there for many years and that future expansion in the area was possible. They were right (Fig. 28-6). When Toyota opened in 1988, it employed 1000 workers in a factory designed to build 50 000 cars a year. Since then, employment has grown to more than 4000, and the plant now builds 250 000 cars per year.

INTERNET

You can find more information about Toyota through the link at www.pearsoned.ca/makingconnections2.

More recently, Toyota received additional government incentives to encourage the company to locate a new assembly plant in Woodstock, Ontario. This plant, which involves investments of about $800 million and is to open in 2007, is the first entirely new auto assembly plant to be built in Canada in almost 20 years. It will have a capacity of 100 000 cars per year. Without the help of the federal, provincial, and local governments, it is almost certain that this plant would have been built in the United States.

Circumstance

These high-tech companies did not have demanding raw material, market, or transportation needs that drew them elsewhere. Ottawa's strong technology industry and universities and colleges meant that suitable labour was available locally.

The six location factors mentioned so far are all specific and refer to the needs of particular industries. Other factors that influence the location of companies may be more difficult to measure. These location factors may be referred to simply as **circumstance**. Let's see how circumstance influenced the location of two high-tech Canadian businesses—Newbridge Networks (now owned by the French company Alcatel) and Corel—in Ottawa. Why did they choose this location? Their owners were scientists who originally worked for Nortel, a telecommunications company located in Ottawa, and this is the city in which the scientists

Fig. 28-6 ▶ Newspaper headlines such as this one announced Toyota's decision to locate a new plant in Cambridge, Ontario.

Cambridge, Ontario Wins Toyota Plant

lived. It was not surprising that they opened their new companies where they lived.

Another circumstance that affects a company's location is the influence of the **entrepreneur**. Many people may have seen the potential of frozen French fries, but only the entrepreneurial McCain brothers did something about it. They located their first small company in Florenceville, New Brunswick, because this was their hometown.

Yet another circumstance that has influenced the location of several factories in Canada is the fact that Canada did not always have free trade with the United States. Before free trade, American companies set up **branch plants** that produced and sold products only in Canada. American companies could thereby avoid the **tariffs** payable on goods they would normally have imported into Canada. The branch plants, mostly located in southern Ontario and southern Quebec, were relatively small, independent factories designed to meet the needs of Canadian markets. With the advent of free trade and the disappearance of tariffs, Ford Canada, General Electric Canada, and IBM Canada, already well established in Canada, remain among our most important manufacturers. These branch plants produce goods that are sold in the United States and many other countries.

You can often identify American companies operating in Canada by their names. What is the pattern in their names that identifies them?

GENERAL MOTORS OF CANADA

In 1869, Robert McLaughlin started a carriage-making business in a small village northeast of Toronto. In 1879, he relocated his business to the town of Oshawa on the shores of Lake Ontario to take advantage of the town's port and rail facilities. In 1889, when McLaughlin's factory burned down, the city of Oshawa offered him an interest-free loan of $50 000 with 20 years to repay to remain in Oshawa and rebuild. When the first horseless carriages, or cars, appeared in Canada around 1900, Sam, Robert's entrepreneurial son, realized the limited future of the carriage and the potential of the automobile. In 1907, under Sam's guidance, the McLaughlin Motor Car Company was incorporated in Oshawa and produced 154 McLaughlin Buicks in its first year. The factory, the skilled workers, and the capital to invest in the new venture were already in place, so Sam decided to remain in Oshawa. In 1915, Sam sold the McLaughlin Carriage Company and acquired the rights to manufacture the Chevrolet in Canada. As a result, General Motors of Canada was founded with Sam as its president. This brief history illustrates how circumstance and one person's entrepreneurial outlook combined to make Oshawa the location of one of Canada's most important companies.

INTERNET

More information on General Motors of Canada is available through the link at www.pearsoned.ca/makingconnections2.

In 2004, the value of automotive products (autos, trucks, and buses) and auto parts exports was $62.6 billion and $27.7 billion, respectively.

Canada's Auto Industry

In the 100 years following the creation of General Motors of Canada, southern Ontario became the location for all automobile and most auto-parts manufacturing in Canada. Why did this small region become the location of Canada's number one exporting industry? All seven location factors contributed.

- *Proximity of raw materials:* Steel for vehicle manufacture came from the steel mills in Hamilton, Ontario. Parts and original equipment suppliers located their companies in southern Ontario to supply vehicle assembly plants. This sector of the auto industry was also affected by the seven location factors.
- *Location of markets*: Markets in southern Quebec, southern Ontario, and the northeastern United States were nearby.
- *Availability of fresh water:* Southern Ontario had ample fresh water supplies, necessary in manufacturing for cooling and cleaning.
- *Availability of power:* Southern Ontario had reliable amounts of inexpensive electric power.
- *Availability of labour:* A large, educated population in southern Ontario meant that auto manufacturers could hire workers with the many different skills they needed.
- *Availability of transportation:* A highly developed system of highways and railways in southern Ontario allowed the transport of raw materials to vehicle plants and finished vehicles to market.
- *Political decisions:* Provincial and municipal governments granted tax incentives to car companies to locate in southern Ontario.

You will have the opportunity to learn where auto-assembly plants are located and the reasons they are located in these places. Your teacher will give you detailed instructions.

Auto Pact
agreement signed between Canada and the United States in 1965 that established free trade in autos many years before there was a general free trade agreement. Canada was also guaranteed that at least as many cars would be built in Canada as were sold here.

After the elimination of the **Auto Pact** in 2001, and the advent of free trade with the United States and Mexico in 1994, there was a small decline in the production and sale of vehicles from southern Ontario and a subsequent loss of jobs.

This decline is being addressed in two ways. One is by a greater willingness by government to invest in new and updated assembly plants such as Toyota in Woodstock (new) and Ford in Oakville (updated). The other is by enhancing Canada's position in the high-tech world of new vehicle development.

Some auto-industry experts are convinced that southern Ontario could develop into one of the key research and development (R&D) centres in the world automotive industry. DaimlerChrysler has a billion-dollar R&D lab in Windsor. GM funds a research chair at the University of Windsor, which includes automotive engineering in its curriculum. Ford has its global **casting** technology centre in Windsor. In the 1990s, the number of automotive engineering jobs in the region rose from 100 to over 2000, and the number of skilled trades from 5000 to 10 000.

casting
making a solid object by pouring molten metal into a mould and letting it cool

QUESTIONS

KNOWLEDGE AND UNDERSTANDING

1. a) What is an entrepreneur?
   b) What role do entrepreneurs play in deciding where factories are located?
2. a) What is a location factor?
   b) Name the location factors mentioned in this chapter, and briefly explain each in your own words.
3. Some factories tend to locate close to raw materials and far from markets, while others are far from raw materials and close to markets. Give two examples of each type of factory, and explain why they locate where they do.
4. Why do some auto experts think that southern Ontario could become a global centre for research and development in the auto industry? Why is this a desirable outcome?

THINKING

5. Compare the customers for the products made by Cardium Tool Services and the customers of McCain Foods. How do these different customers affect the location of each company?

COMMUNICATION

6. a) Using an atlas, rank the provinces according to the value of their manufacturing production.
   b) Select a province that does not have very much manufacturing in relation to its population. Explain this lack of manufacturing, using sketch maps together with written text.
7. a) How has the labour supply in Canadian manufacturing changed in recent years? Why?
   b) How might this change affect your educational plans?
8. a) What is a branch plant? Name four branch plant companies that were not mentioned in this chapter.
   b) How have the original advantages of branch plants come to be replaced by different advantages? Is the new location factor likely to be more significant than the original one?

APPLICATION

9. a) List three reasons why a company would be more likely to expand in its current location than to build in a new location.
   b) List three reasons why a company might decide to build a new factory in a different area rather than expand an existing operation.
   c) Compare your answers to 9 a) and 9 b). Is it possible to say which choice would be made in all cases? Explain.
10. The just-in-time (JIT) technique was developed to improve business profitability. Use the Internet and your school library to answer the following:
    a) Outline the history of JIT.
    b) Describe the methods used in JIT manufacturing.
    c) What are the pros and cons of this technique?
    d) How might you apply this technique to your life?

ATI Technologies Inc.

Key Terms

smokestack industries

knowledge industries

tandem engineering

This case study is not concerned with a company in the **smokestack industries**. Smokestack industries were the basis of Canada's economy in the 19th and 20th centuries. Rather, this study looks at a manufacturing company in one of the **knowledge industries**. Knowledge industries will dominate manufacturing in Canada in the 21st century.

You may not have heard of ATI Technologies Inc., but if you use computers, you have probably used its products. ATI makes computer parts that produce the vivid two- and three-dimensional graphic images that we see, for example, on computer and mobile phone screens and on gaming consoles. It is one of the largest manufacturers of 3-D multimedia computer chips and graphics boards in the world. ATI's $2 billion in sales in 2004 made it Canada's third-largest high-tech company after only 19 years in business. Its headquarters is in Markham, Ontario, where approximately 1100 of its 2500 employees work. It has other offices, R&D facilities, and factories in the Americas, Europe, and Asia.

Location Factors and ATI

ATI was co-founded by Kwok Yuen Ho, an electrical engineer educated in Taiwan. Mr. Ho spent 10 years in the information technology industry in Hong Kong before moving to Canada as an immigrant in 1985 to start a business in the computer-graphics hardware industry. Why did Mr. Ho

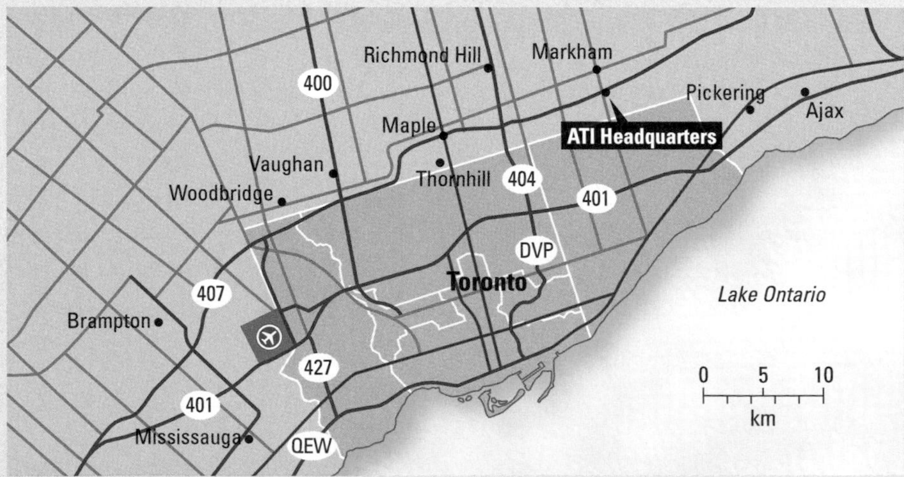

Fig. 28-7 ► ATI's headquarters in Markham

and his partners start up their business in Markham, Ontario (Fig. 28-7)? What location factors affected the selection of Markham as the site of ATI's head office, R&D centre, and manufacturing facility?

Proximity of Raw Materials

Unlike a steel mill or oil refinery, a high-tech computer-parts company such as ATI does not rely on the proximity of large quantities of raw materials. ATI's raw materials are small in volume and light in weight. They can be transported easily by air freight from anywhere in the world, so proximity to raw materials is not a significant factor in the location of ATI's facilities in Markham.

Location of Markets

ATI sells its graphics boards and chips to two kinds of markets. The first is original equipment manufacturers (OEMs). OEMs are companies that make computers, such as Apple and Dell. ATI sells to the 10 largest computer makers in the world, and to many smaller ones. OEMs were ATI's original market. The second market for ATI's products is individual consumers who buy through retail stores. This is a more recent market, and one that is buying an increasing percentage of ATI's product. Both markets are located around the world, with about 35% in North America, 27% in Europe, and most of the remaining 38% in Asia. The location factor is not critical because ATI products are sold worldwide.

Availability of Fresh Water and Power

ATI does not use particularly large amounts of fresh water and electricity, so this is not an important factor.

Labour Supply

Mr. Ho realized that ATI's success would depend on its ability to stay ahead of its competitors in the development, design, and manufacture of new products. He also knew that he would have to meet the needs of customers in the shortest time possible. Mr. Ho achieved these objectives in several different ways.

- The company spends a great deal of money on research and development—for example, about $270 million in 2004. This amount was more than 13% of the total value of sales and much more than most companies would normally spend.

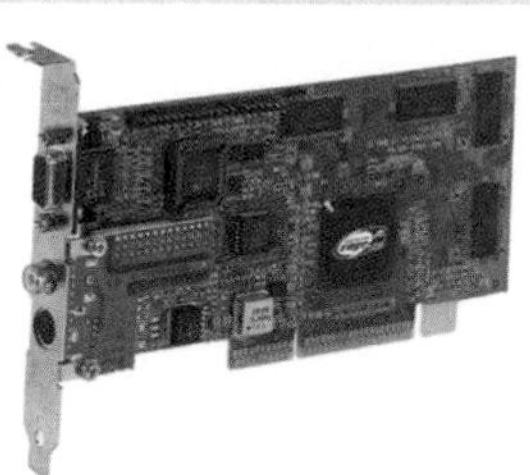

▲ **Fig. 28-8** ATI must always be on the cutting edge of computer graphics hardware. This means new generations of graphics boards come on the market every 6–8 months.

generic
product that does not have a brand name or trademark

- The company instituted **tandem engineering** in 1993, a process that allowed one engineering team to work on a product and a second team to work on the next generation of the same product simultaneously. The research, development, and manufacturing period of the next generation of graphics hardware was reduced from 12–18 months to 6–8 months (Fig. 28-8). Tandem engineering, however, requires a greater number of workers than a regular R&D process.
- Computer chips may be designed for specific uses or for general use. Companies save money by buying cheaper **generic** chips to put into their products, but this practice often results in inferior products. Companies that design and build their own chips inevitably make better products. Since ATI puts its own computer chips into its circuit boards, it avoids the limitations and problems associated with "off-the-shelf" chips. Because it makes chips as well as circuit boards, ATI requires a large and highly skilled labour force.

When Mr. Ho first visited Canada, he was impressed by the number of skilled engineers and scientists in the labour force, due in part to the presence of many universities, colleges, and technical institutions in southern Ontario. He realized that he would be able to hire the workers he needed—a factor critical to ATI's success.

Transportation

ATI's raw materials and finished products are small in volume, light in weight, and high in value, and must be shipped quickly to their destination. Consequently, almost everything ATI needs or produces is shipped by air. ATI's business executives frequently visit customers and suppliers all over the world, while ATI's international contacts regularly visit Toronto to do business. Both freight and people use the facilities of Pearson International Airport in Toronto.

Political Factors

Early in its founding, ATI received financial assistance and advice from Export Development Canada.

Circumstance

In 1984, when Mr. Ho first came to Canada as a visitor, he liked what he saw—wide open spaces and business opportunities. Imagine what might have happened if Mr. Ho had decided to take his vacation in the United States or Australia. ATI might now be located in Boston or Melbourne!

Canadian Business Magazine selected Mr. Ho as Canada's entrepreneur of the year in 1998.

Since most Asian immigrants settle in either Toronto or Vancouver, it is not surprising that Mr. Ho and his partners, as East Asian immigrants, established ATI near Toronto. However, they had the entrepreneurial foresight and drive to recognize and take advantage of a business opportunity that they were convinced existed in the Toronto area. They knew, too, that Markham was home to a significant number of high-tech companies.

All these circumstances influenced the decision to locate ATI in Markham.

Challenges Facing ATI

ATI has an exciting future, but it also faces some serious challenges.

- The computer-graphics field grows and changes very rapidly. To keep abreast of its competitors, ATI must continue to research and develop cutting-edge products quickly and to pioneer new technologies.
- A big breakthrough in a new field could make ATI the dominant player in a huge new market, but will ATI shareholders continue to approve the reinvestment of large percentages of company revenues in R&D?
- Sometimes companies fall victim to their own success. Investors may expect ATI not only to keep up its unprecedented high levels of sales and profits, but also to surpass them. This expectation may be unreasonable, especially when ATI is compared to smaller competitors who can grow, on a percentage basis, much more quickly.
- ATI is an attractive takeover target for other large companies who want the company's advanced technology and share of the market. Although ATI's owners would make a lot of money if this happened, they would no longer control the very successful business that they created and developed.
- ATI must continue to make correct decisions in the unpredictable world of high technology. A right decision makes millions of dollars in just a few months; a wrong decision loses market share and millions of dollars just as quickly.

Because graphics boards are improving so rapidly, computer users are now much more likely to upgrade their computer's graphical capability between computer purchases.

ATI is developing products that are outside its original field of computer graphics. It is now making digital cable-TV terminal boxes that will give us TVs that we can use as computers, or vice versa.

Between 2000 and 2003, ATI acquired five technology companies to expand its technological base and create new market opportunities.

In Closing...

Markham, Ontario, was the right location for ATI at the time of its founding in 1985. Perhaps it was luck, or circumstance, that led Mr. Ho to vacation in Canada more than 20 years ago. His choice of the Toronto area, however, as the site of his new business was strongly influenced by factors that have more to do with good business sense than luck.

INTERNET

You can learn more about ATI Technologies Inc. through the link at www.pearsoned.ca/makingconnections2.

QUESTIONS

KNOWLEDGE AND UNDERSTANDING

1. a) What kinds of products does ATI produce?
   b) Why do ATI's products constantly change?
   c) Are you an ATI customer? How do you know?
2. Briefly describe how ATI came into being and how it became a major high-tech company.

THINKING

3. a) What is a smokestack industry? What is a knowledge industry?
   b) Complete an organizer like the one in Fig. 28-9 to compare the two types of industry.
4. a) In what ways is ATI a typical manufacturing company?
   b) In what ways is ATI **atypical**?
5. From the point of view of ATI, why is it desirable that the graphics ability of computers improve faster than other aspects of the computer's power?

atypical
different

COMMUNICATION

6. Answer this question with a partner. Your teacher will give you the name of a manufacturing company to investigate. Study your company to determine how it has been affected by the seven location factors. Create a poster to illustrate your findings. Find out about your company by:
   - checking the company's Web site on the Internet
   - looking for newspaper and magazine stories about the company
   - phoning the company's public relations department for information or to arrange a visit to the company.

GeoLit Reminder

Creating a poster:

- Gather all visual text (printouts, photographs, news stories) obtained through your research.
- Review any gathered written text to help identify the main idea(s) you wish to convey.
- Select and assemble your visuals, keeping in mind your main idea(s). Move items around until you are happy with the presentation.
- Check to ensure that your poster explains key facts and terms.
- Give your poster a title.

▼ **Figure 28-9**

	Smokestack Industry	Knowledge Industry
Four Examples		
Basis of Industry		
Time Period of Greatest Economic Importance		

29 Services: Where the Jobs Are

Key Ideas

This chapter helps you investigate these questions:

- What range of jobs does the services sector include?
- Why is it highly likely that you will one day work in the services sector?
- Why are basic jobs critical to the economy of a community or region?

Key Terms

tertiary worker
quaternary worker
quaternary industry
research and development (R&D)
basic service
non-basic service
trade
wholesale
retail
call centre
outsourcing

Tertiary and **quaternary workers** do not extract natural resources, manufacture products, or build new buildings. Instead, they supply a wide variety of services to people. Your Geography teacher is a good example of such a worker. Without realizing it, you may be a service provider as well if you have a job in a fast-food restaurant, deliver newspapers, or babysit. Service workers also support workers in the primary and secondary industries. For example, a meteorologist supplies weather reports to fishers, and office personnel prepare the paycheques of factory workers. The number of service jobs has increased tremendously as businesses and governments have become more complex. Today, more than 75% of Canadians are employed in service industries.

The differences and similarities between tertiary and quaternary industries were described in Chapter 22.

Wherever there is a community, there are people working in service jobs. People require services in education, healthcare, planning and management, communications, transportation, sanitation, law enforcement, and road maintenance, among others. Many services are visible. In other words, we can actually see people making daily use of them. Other services, such as computer-related activities, planning and management decisions, scientific research, and communications, may be less visible, although they directly affect our lives (Fig. 29-1).

Fig. 29-1 Service workers are so common in society that we often overlook them. Some are obvious, such as the person who cuts our hair. Others work "behind the scenes," such as the urban planners who ensure that new communities are attractive and function effectively. Some service workers have relatively little formal education, while others must attend university for many years. Some service workers earn minimum wage, while others earn millions of dollars per year. Can you think of examples of each type of service worker?

Quaternary Industries

When Plato and Aristotle spent their days considering the meaning of life, they were "processing information."

Quaternary industries are a special kind of services. Although the term is a relatively new one, people have worked in quaternary industries—highly specialized knowledge-based or technological services—since at least the time of the ancient Greek philosophers. Back then only a few people in the most advanced societies had the opportunity to do this type of work. In most of the world, people were too busy producing the food and other items they needed to survive. As society has progressed and our technology has developed, we have needed more "knowledge workers" and also been able to support them in the work they do.

As mentioned in Chapter 22, it is often difficult to identify separate quaternary industries. It is easier to recognize knowledge-based jobs within primary, secondary, or tertiary industries. For example, the authors of this book could be seen as quaternary workers within a large company whose job it is to produce textbooks (secondary industry). The mining companies that are responsible for the diamond-mining boom in northern Canada are in the primary sector of the economy, but the GIS specialists and geologists who determine where diamonds are likely to be found are knowledge-based workers.

You can read more about Canada's diamond industry in Chapter 26.

Similarly, many manufacturers have invested in extensive **research and development (R&D)** departments to ensure that their products are competitive in the world market. ATI Technologies (see the Case Study in Chapter 28) is a particularly good example of this, because it competes in a field—computer-graphics hardware—where products that are only a couple of years old are considered obsolete.

Another example of a knowledge-based organization is the National Microbiology Laboratory (NML) in Winnipeg, which is part of the Canadian Science Centre for Human and Animal Health. The NML is **unique** in Canada. It is an advanced health-science facility designed to promote public health, perform diagnostic testing, conduct research, and provide training. Its worth has been proven in recent years by the work it has done to fight such public health crises as mad cow disease, West Nile disease, SARS (severe acute respiratory syndrome), and the possibility that terrorists might use bacteriological weapons. Without the NML, Canada would not be prepared to deal with such threats to public health.

unique
existing as the only example

Building a facility like the NML is obviously very costly, as is hiring the highly skilled scientists and technicians to staff it. But this is an investment in Canada's future. Because China, India, and many other countries have the advantage of cheap labour, Canada must find an advantage elsewhere. The best place for Canada to invest is in its large, skilled labour force. The quaternary sector is only likely to grow in the future. That is one reason your parents and teachers emphasize the importance of education.

1. Class members should list on the board the jobs of parents or guardians who are paid for the work they do.
2. a) Within a group assigned by your teacher, categorize the jobs under the headings *Primary* (resource extraction), *Secondary* (manufacturing and construction), and *Tertiary and Quarternary* (services).
   b) Calculate the percentage of parents/guardians in each of the three categories.

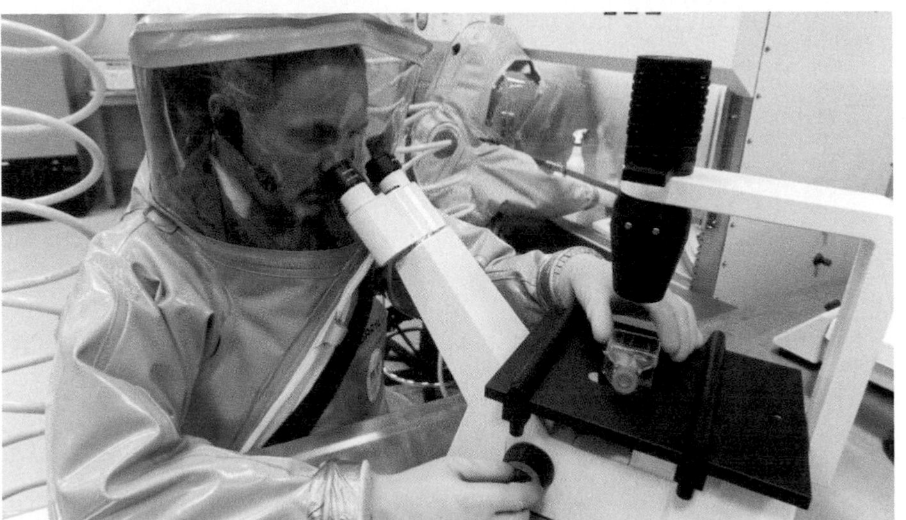

◀ **Fig. 29-2** The CL4 laboratory, where this scientist is working, is in the National Microbiology Laboratory of the Canadian Science Centre for Human and Animal Health, in Winnipeg. This centre is the only facility in the world that has two CL4 labs. One lab is used for studying human pathogens, and the other is used for studying animal pathogens.

c) Compare your percentages with the percentage of employment in primary, secondary, and tertiary industries in Fig. 22-4.
d) How do your percentages compare to the national percentages? Explain why differences may exist. (Hint: Consider the particular characteristics of your community.)

Development of the Services Sector

The number of Canadians employed in service industries has grown tremendously. In 1901, only about 33% of Canadian workers were employed in services; now the figure is about 75% (Fig. 29-3). Why has the tertiary sector of Canada's economy grown so large? Consider the following:

- Throughout the 1900s, greater use of machinery in farming, mining, forestry, and manufacturing reduced the need for workers (Fig. 29-4).

Fig. 29-3 ▶ The percentage of Canadian workers who are employed in the tertiary and quaternary sectors, 2004

Tertiary Sector	2004
Wholesale and retail trade	15.7%
Healthcare and social services	10.9%
Business and professional services	10.2%
Education	6.7%
Accommodation and food services	6.3%
Finance, insurance, and real estate	6.0%
Government services	5.2%
Transportation and warehousing	5.1%
Information, culture, and recreation	4.6%
Other services	4.4%
Total	75.1%

Fig. 29-4 ▶ The use of advanced machinery, like this machine that cuts a tree, removes its branches, and cuts it to length in one operation, has eliminated many jobs in forestry. Similar mechanization in mining, agriculture, fishing, and the oil and gas industry has meant a major reduction in jobs in the primary sector of the economy.

- The growth of Canada's economy has meant that people have more money and enjoy more **leisure**. This improved standard of living has given rise to a greater demand for services.
- Greater educational opportunities have helped people obtain the specialized skills that enable them to offer services to others.
- A growing population has increased the demand for services.
- Technological growth has given rise to a wide variety of new services, such as the Internet and a broad range of banking services.

leisure
time available for rest and recreation

Basic and Non-basic Services

Service industries may be classified into two categories: **basic services** and **non-basic services**. Basic industries provide services to people and businesses outside the community. As a result, they bring money into their respective communities from elsewhere. Without them, communities could not survive. Some examples of basic services:

- The federal government in Ottawa provides services for Canadians throughout the country.
- A university attracts students from outside the community in which it is located.
- An insurance company head office performs services for customers in other parts of Canada or in other countries.

Non-basic industries provide services for people and businesses located within the community. Non-basic services do not generate money from outside sources. Think of some of the non-basic services that you use in your community: public transportation, your high school, your doctor and dentist, and local movie theatres.

Major Categories of Services

Wholesale and Retail Trade

The selling of goods is called **trade**. Trade is divided into two categories: **wholesale**, which is the selling of goods to businesses or stores, not to the public; and **retail**, the selling of products directly to the public in stores, vending machines, over the telephone, through mail order or door-to-door sales, or over the Internet.

SAMPLE OCCUPATIONS

warehouse worker, inventory clerk, merchant, telemarketer, sales representative, cashier, call centre order-taker, marketing expert

The balance of basic and non-basic activities indicated for each category of services is a general guideline and will vary depending on the nature of that community. The balance symbol is, therefore, a general comment that indicates that the category tends to be more basic or more non-basic.

BASIC OR NON-BASIC?

- *Wholesale:* mostly basic, for example, a large Canadian Tire warehouse in Brampton, Ontario, supplies stores in much of Canada
- *Retail:* mostly non-basic because it serves the local area

Healthcare and Social Services

Healthcare services include dental and medical care and medical research. Social services include daycare centres, shelters for the homeless and those escaping violent situations, lunch programs for underprivileged children, and visits by social workers to families in need of counselling.

SAMPLE OCCUPATIONS

doctor, nurse, dietitian, X-ray technician, physiotherapist, psychiatrist, medical researcher, social worker, psychologist

BASIC OR NON-BASIC?

- Most are non-basic because they serve the local community; for example, hospitals, doctors' offices, visits by social workers and nurses.
- Some healthcare and social services are both basic and non-basic because they are specialized and service local as well as non-local people; for example, cancer treatment centres.

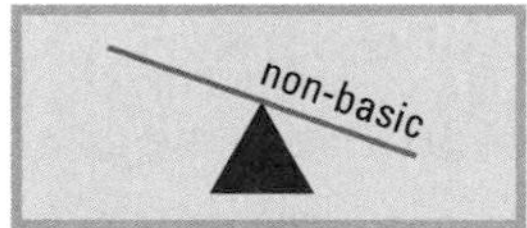

Business and Professional Services

This is the fastest-growing employment area in the economy. It provides services both for companies and for individuals.

SAMPLE OCCUPATIONS

accountant, mechanic, lawyer, secretary, executive, GIS consultant

BASIC OR NON-BASIC?

- Many business and professional activities are local, so they are considered non-basic; for example, a lawyer who helps local residents buy a home in the area is providing a non-basic service.

- Services provided for companies and people outside the city are considered basic activities; for example, a lawyer who works on international trade issues.

Education Services

Education services include elementary and secondary schools, post-secondary education (universities and colleges), vocational training, religious training, and English or French language instruction for new Canadians.

SAMPLE OCCUPATIONS

teacher, principal, secretary, custodian, professor, librarian, teacher's aide

BASIC OR NON-BASIC?

- Elementary and secondary schools: non-basic because they provide services for the local community
- Universities and colleges: a mixture of both

Accommodation and Food Services

This is a rapidly growing part of the economy as people travel more often and as eating meals away from home becomes more common.

SAMPLE OCCUPATIONS

hotel desk clerk, cook, waiter, housekeeper, tour guide, pizza delivery person

BASIC OR NON-BASIC?

- Most accommodation jobs are basic, since workers provide services for visitors from outside the local community.
- Food services jobs can be either basic or non-basic. For example, a Tim Hortons located in the middle of a town will be **predominantly** non-basic—food is provided mainly to local residents. On the other hand, a Tim Hortons located at a service centre along a major highway will be primarily basic. Here, the food is sold mainly to visitors from other places.

predominantly
most commonly

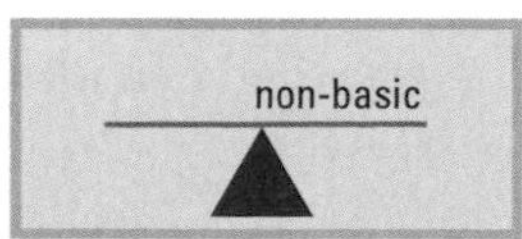

Finance, Insurance, and Real Estate Services

This category includes banks, trust companies, credit unions, stock exchanges, insurance companies, and real estate companies. These institutions range in size from local real estate offices to the head offices of huge insurance companies and banks doing business across Canada and throughout the world.

SAMPLE OCCUPATIONS

bank clerk, investment manager, insurance agent, real estate agent, stockbroker, secretary, credit investigator, financial planner

BASIC OR NON-BASIC?

- This category could be either; for example, the head office of a bank provides services to people across the country (and beyond) and is therefore basic. A local bank branch provides services primarily to those in the community and is therefore non-basic.

Government Services

Federal, provincial, and municipal governments offer a wide variety of services. For example:

Federal: postal service, defence, and Aboriginal affairs

Provincial: health and social services, education, and natural resources

Municipal: police and fire protection, water and sewage services, parks and recreation

SAMPLE OCCUPATIONS

politician, park ranger, jail guard, postal employee, economist, social worker, firefighter, park maintenance worker, planner

BASIC OR NON-BASIC?

- Federal and provincial governments: mainly basic
- Municipal services: almost always non-basic

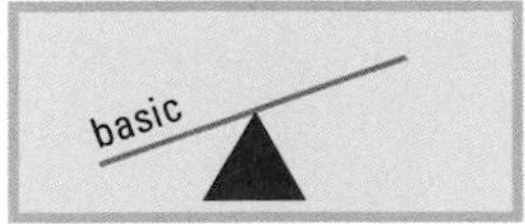

Transportation and Warehousing

Transportation and communication services involve the movement of goods and people.

SAMPLE OCCUPATIONS

truck driver, bus driver, air traffic controller, railway engineer, lift-truck operator, parking lot attendant, telematics programmer

BASIC OR NON-BASIC?

- This category could be either; for example, a shipping clerk at a Canadian Tire warehouse would be basic while a school bus driver would be non-basic.

Information, Culture, and Recreation

This is another area of the economy that is growing rapidly. There are two main reasons for this. One is the explosion in information technologies, for example, the Internet and cable and satellite television. The other is the fact that many people have more money, and often time, to pursue cultural and recreational interests.

The rapid growth in the number of retired people is likely to stimulate continued expansion in this sector of the economy.

SAMPLE OCCUPATIONS

piano teacher, Web designer, actor, golf professional, video game programmer, librarian, pool service representative, cable television/Internet installer

BASIC OR NON-BASIC?

- Can be either basic or non-basic. A piano teacher or cable installer provides services for the local community, while an actor or video game designer provides services for a regional, national, or even international market (Fig. 29-5).

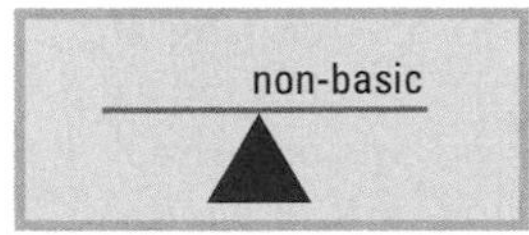

Fig. 29-5 ▶ The production of movies and television shows in Canada has become a major industry in recent years. This photo shows extras and old cars waiting to be called for the movie *Cinderella Man*, starring Russell Crowe and Renée Zellweger, that was made in Toronto in 2004.

Future Trends

What type of work will be available for you when you finish school? Chances are it will be in the services sector. Rapid changes are occurring in the workplace because of the **globalization** of the economy, free trade, and technological advances. These changes may eliminate jobs that we now take for granted, or they may provide you with new job opportunities.

globalization
trend toward a more integrated world; breakdown of barriers among countries

Today, young people can find employment in jobs that did not exist 30 years ago. Internet-related workers and personal trainers in fitness clubs are just two examples. What kinds of jobs will be created in the next 30 years? There is no way to tell, but we can make some informed guesses about the nature of employment in future service industries.

Growing numbers of young **entrepreneurs** will start their own businesses, and most will be in the services sector. Employment in small business is currently rising, and home-based enterprises are increasing. Twenty-five percent of the small businesses in Canada are now owned by people aged 18 to 29. Some young people own businesses because they want to work for themselves; others go into business for themselves because they are unable to find permanent employment in established companies. An example of Canadian entrepreneurship is found in the field of electronic games. Canadian university graduates of computer and related programming courses are producing award-winning games with imaginative stories and **innovative** graphics (Fig. 29-6). They are making their mark in this growing, multi-billion dollar industry.

innovative
new and different

Future growth is expected in jobs that offer services for seniors who are part of the aging "baby boom" generation. These are the people who were born between 1947 and 1966. Today, baby boomers make up about 33% of Canada's population. The needs of these "boomers" are changing as they age. They do not purchase as many manufactured goods as younger people because they already have most of the goods they need. What they do need, however, are increased services in such areas as finance, travel, and healthcare.

Not only is the nature of jobs in the services industry undergoing change, but the jobs themselves can be eliminated by technological change. Consider the following examples:

▲ **Fig. 29-6** Young Canadian entrepreneurs, such as James Schmalz, are producing innovative electronic games. Are creators of electronic games performing a basic or non-basic activity?

- On-line shopping could eliminate many jobs in retail sales.
- Automated checkouts in supermarkets are eliminating some cashier jobs.
- Fax machines, voice mail, and personal computers have reduced the number of secretaries in many offices.
- Internet and telephone banking, as well as automated teller machines, are reducing the need for bank tellers.
- Communications technology is reducing the need for companies to be close to their customers. For example, companies locate their customer service operations in telephone **call centres** located in places where labour costs are lower than in major Canadian cities. Recently, companies have been **outsourcing** their call centres to cities in southern India, where costs are even lower. This can be done only because the cost of communication has been reduced so much that it is no longer a significant factor in the overall cost of doing business. Customers can dial a toll-free number to purchase a product, make a hotel reservation, complain about something, or get help with a problem—and deal with a service worker who may be hundreds or even thousands of kilometres away.

Some call centre workers in India are being trained to speak with a North American accent.

We can only speculate on the number and nature of jobs in the service industries of the future. One thing for certain is that new types of services will develop to meet the changing needs of Canadians.

GeoCareers

Planning and Economic Development

If you were to study accounting in university, chances are good that you would end up working as an *accountant*. If you graduated from community college with an automotive technician's diploma, it is likely you would work as an *automotive technician*. Working in a career that is related to geography, however, does not necessarily mean that you would be called a *geographer*.

Students who study and enjoy geography will find a wide variety of planning and economic development jobs open to them, but from their titles, one might never suspect that these jobs are related to geography. Here are some examples:

- An *economic development officer* for a municipality works to encourage companies to locate in the area.
- A *facility planner* for a school board ensures that there are enough schools to meet demand.
- A *transportation planning technician* for a consulting company plans public transportation improvements in a community.
- A *coordinator of solid waste disposal* for a city plans the disposal of waste in an environmentally and economically sound manner.
- A *health services planner* for a province plans the location of hospital and ambulance services in an efficient manner.

INTERNET

Visit links to Web sites with planning and economic development–related career information at www.pearsoned.ca/makingconnections2.

There are many jobs related to geography, and an equal number of ways to prepare for them. A planning technician requires two or three years of study at a community college. A planner usually requires a bachelor's degree (four years of study) and often a master's degree (one or two additional years of study). These jobs are interdisciplinary. This means that someone thinking of a career in planning will require knowledge in a wide range of disciplines, including geography (and geomatics), economics, politics, engineering, biology, business, and architecture.

Find Out More

1. Investigate planning and economic development–related careers. Begin with a search of post-secondary institutions (community colleges and universities). Then look at other sites that offer information about careers in planning and economic development.

a) List three universities and three community colleges that offer training related to planning.
b) Give the names of the particular departments (or faculties) in each institution that offer training in planning.
c) Briefly describe several of the courses that you would take in the program of one of the colleges and one of the universities mentioned in a).

2. What are the academic requirements for admission to the programs in the college and the university you chose in 1c)? Be specific; list the high school courses you would need and the marks you would need to attain in them.
3. What types of careers do the college and university programs you chose in Question 1c) lead to? List at least three possible careers for each program.
4. Would you need additional training after college or after the first university degree to qualify for the careers mentioned in Question 3?
5. Find at least one career profile of a person who has pursued a planning or economic development career, and write a summary of that person's experience.
6. What aspects of planning or economic development might interest you as a potential career? Explain.

GeoLit Reminder

Conducting an Internet search:

- Review the written text for hints to selecting your key search terms.
- Search using different combinations of key words.
- Use quotation marks for exact phrases, and use the operators AND, OR, and NOT to narrow your search.
- Print any materials relevant to answering the activity questions, or keep a list of the Web sites where you found your information.
- Review the activity questions to ensure that your gathered information covers them. What further information do you need? Where might you find it?

QUESTIONS

KNOWLEDGE AND UNDERSTANDING

1. a) How do service industries differ from primary and secondary industries?
   b) What is quaternary industry?
2. Why has the services sector of the Canadian economy grown so large?

THINKING

3. a) Explain the differences between basic and non-basic service industries.
   b) For each service industry discussed in this chapter, explain how it may have both basic and non-basic characteristics. Give specific examples to explain your answer.

COMMUNICATION

4. Identify examples of service jobs for each category below. Your teacher will tell you whether to answer in brief written form or to create a poster with illustrations of these jobs.
   a) requires limited education
   b) requires a great deal of education
   c) pays at or close to minimum wage
   d) pays millions of dollars per year
   e) requires geographic skills and training

APPLICATION

5. Referring to the changing job market in Canada, a well-known author recently said, "Young people have a choice—they can either see the social and technological changes of the years ahead as a problem or as an opportunity." What did he mean by this? To answer this question, break the statement down into its parts:
   a) What age group would the author have been referring to?
   b) What social changes are occurring? Over how many years will these changes occur? How might these changes **evolve** over this period?
   c) What technological changes are occurring? Over how many years will these changes occur? How might these changes evolve over this period?
   d) What is meant by the changes being seen as a problem or as an opportunity?
   e) What can you do in your life to ensure that these changes are an opportunity for you?

evolve
change gradually

30 Transportation: Canada's Circulatory System

Key Ideas

This chapter helps you investigate these questions:

- What factors are involved in moving people and goods?
- What changes in transportation have taken place in the past, and what changes will take place in the future?
- How will these changes affect your life?

Key Terms

transportation
mobility
commuter
bankruptcy protection
bulk cargo
unit train
piggyback system
container
winter ice road
Pacific Rim
canal
lock

If Canada were compared to a human body, its cities, towns, rural areas, and wilderness would be parts of the body, and its **transportation** system would be the **circulatory system**. Just as a person would suffer ill health with a poor circulatory system, Canada would suffer economic decline without a modern and efficient transportation system.

circulatory system
the heart, blood, and lymph vessels, which together allow blood and lymph to move throughout the body

Introduction

Every day, Canada's transportation system faces an immense task. Millions of people might travel tens of millions of kilometres. Thousands of tonnes of cargo must be moved as quickly and as cheaply as possible. This movement of people and goods must be done in spite of great distances, harsh weather conditions, and some of the most difficult terrain anywhere in the world (Fig. 30-1).

◀ **Fig. 30-1**
This rail line is in the Fraser River Canyon of British Columbia. Imagine the difficulty of building this rail line. Why wasn't a different route chosen?

GeoLit Reminder

Reading photographs:

- What comes to mind as you look at the photographs on this page?
- What do all these photographs have in common?
- How do these photographs differ?
- Do you need further information to answer the question in the caption? Where might you find this information?

▲ **Fig. 30-2** In a country as large as Canada, transportation is critically important. In which decade of the 20th century would each of these transportation methods have become significant to our transportation system?

Examine Fig. 30-3 and answer the following questions.

1. a) Describe the amount and coverage of ground transportation in Zone A. Refer to a transportation map in an atlas.
   b) Why is this pattern not surprising?
2. a) Describe the pattern of ground transportation in Zone B. Why do gaps exist?
   b) With the help of an atlas, explain the kind of ground transportation to each of the following places. If possible, explain why this kind of transportation exists.
      i. Inuvik, Northwest Territories
      ii. Yellowknife, Northwest Territories
      iii. Fort McMurray, Alberta

▼ **Fig. 30-3** Some areas of Canada are very accessible by road and railway, while others are not.

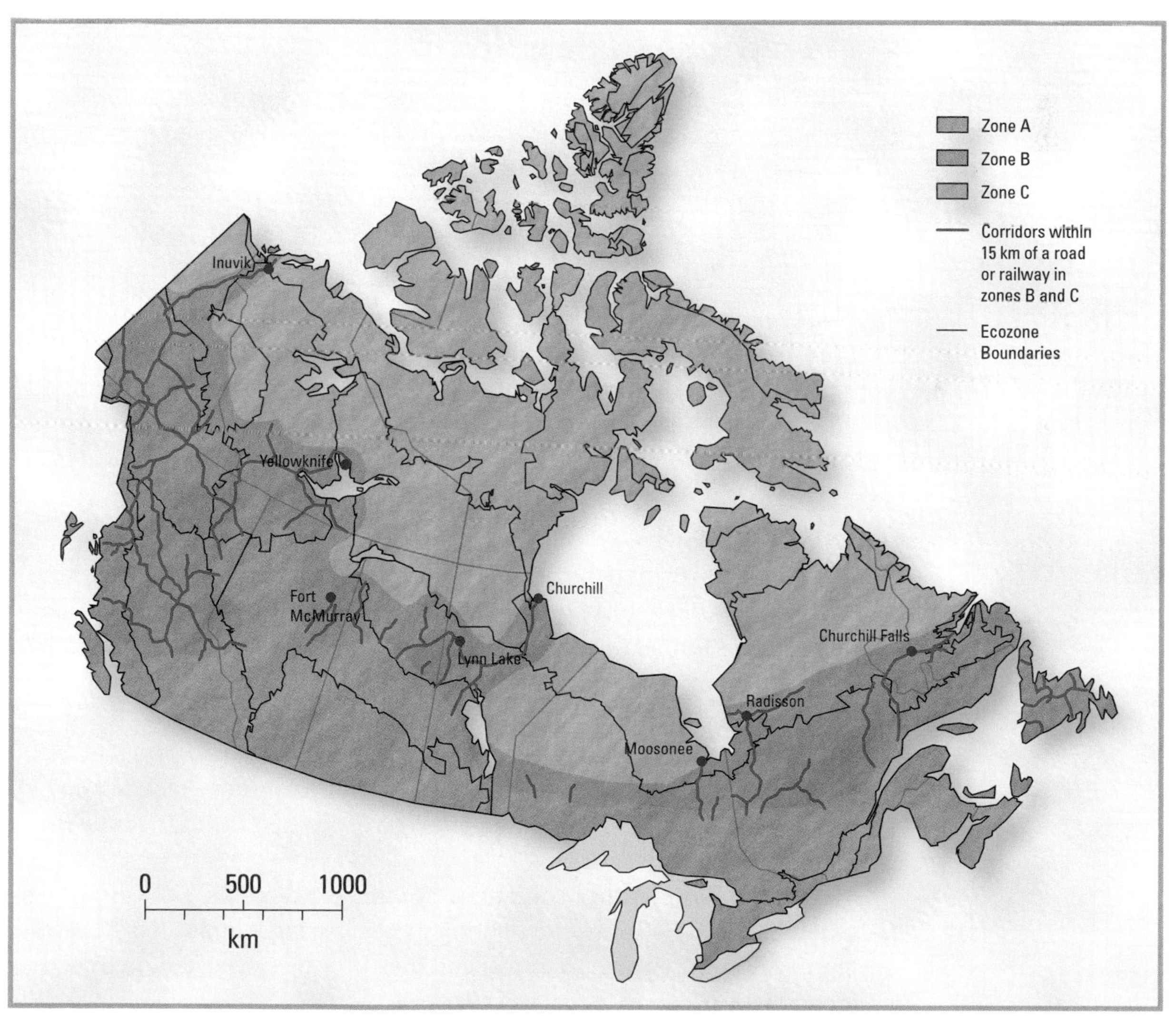

iv. Lynn Lake, Manitoba
v. Churchill, Manitoba
vi. Moosonee, Ontario
vii. Radisson on La Grande Rivière, Quebec
viii. Churchill Falls, Newfoundland and Labrador

c) What would cause the addition of new corridors in Zone B in the future?

3. a) Why does permanent ground transport not exist in Zone C?
   b) What alternative transportation methods must be used in Zone C?
   c) What are the disadvantages of having to rely on these methods?

Hint: Don't forget seasonal differences!

Movement of People

When people plan a journey, they consider a number of things: the distance, the cost, the route, the duration of the trip, and the method of travel. They may choose to travel by road, rail, air, or water.

Road Travel

Roads are the most important means by which people travel in Canada. Every year, governments at all levels spend more than $7 billion combined on the construction, maintenance, and administration of more than 900 000 kilometres of Canadian roads. About 19 million cars, trucks, buses, and motorcycles use these roads.

In spite of this spending, there is general agreement that even more money should be spent to improve Canadian roads.

AUTOMOBILES (CARS AND LIGHT TRUCKS)

Canadians travel more by car and light truck than by any other means of transportation. There are approximately 17.8 million cars and light trucks registered in Canada. The extensive use of the automobile provides the average Canadian with greater **mobility** than ever before, and certainly greater than that of most people in other parts of the world.

The most valuable feature of the automobile is its **flexibility**. It allows people to travel directly from their starting point to their exact destination. Automobiles also allow people to travel on their own schedules, in comfort and in privacy.

flexibility ability to change

Automobiles, however, are not without their problems. They are expensive to purchase, insure, and maintain; they use large quantities of petroleum, a non-renewable resource; and they produce gases that pollute the air and contribute to global warming.

Global warming will be examined in Chapter 37.

BUS

Buses are a major mode of travelling between cities. They are used mainly for trips of less than 1000 kilometres. Each year, more than one billion passengers travel on **intercity** buses. Bus travel has several advantages. It is relatively inexpensive and comfortable. Furthermore, bus operators can establish and change routes and schedules quickly and easily to meet new needs.

intercity between cities

Intracity buses and school buses are used in every city and in many towns and rural areas in Canada. Large cities such as Toronto and Montreal might have thousands of buses, while a small town might have only one. In either case, buses are a key element of the transportation system. They move large numbers of commuters efficiently, and in a typical year, intracity buses in Canada carry about one billion passengers. Compared to automobiles, buses are environmentally sound, as they help reduce traffic, noise, and air pollution.

intracity within a specific city or town

One full bus can replace 40 cars on the road!

Rail Travel

During the first half of the 20th century, travel by train was more common in Canada than travel by any other means. Travel by rail was faster, more reliable, and more comfortable than travel by road or water. In the second half of the century, however, train travel declined dramatically (Fig. 30-4) for a number of reasons.

- Cars were becoming cheaper to buy and own, and intercity highways had improved.
- The rail cars were getting old but because of cost were not replaced.
- Freight traffic—carrying cargo rather than people—was more profitable for the rail companies.
- Travel by airplane became more common and, over the years, less expensive. As a result, automobiles captured much of the short-distance train travel, and airplanes captured much of the long-distance train travel.

Passenger rail service in Canada is now at a crossroads. It will either have to be significantly improved at great cost, or left to decline to the point where it will eventually disappear. There are people who support each view. The president of the Canadian National Railway (CN) said in 1998 that passenger service was a "nuisance" that should be eliminated. Others, however, think that Canada needs a modernized passenger rail system. High-speed train travel between Toronto and Montreal would take less than two hours. The model for such a system exists in Japan and France. Japan's Bullet Train and France's TGV *(Train à Grande Vitesse)* compete effectively with airplanes for trips up to 600 kilometres by travelling at speeds approaching 400 kilometres per hour and by travelling from one downtown core to another.

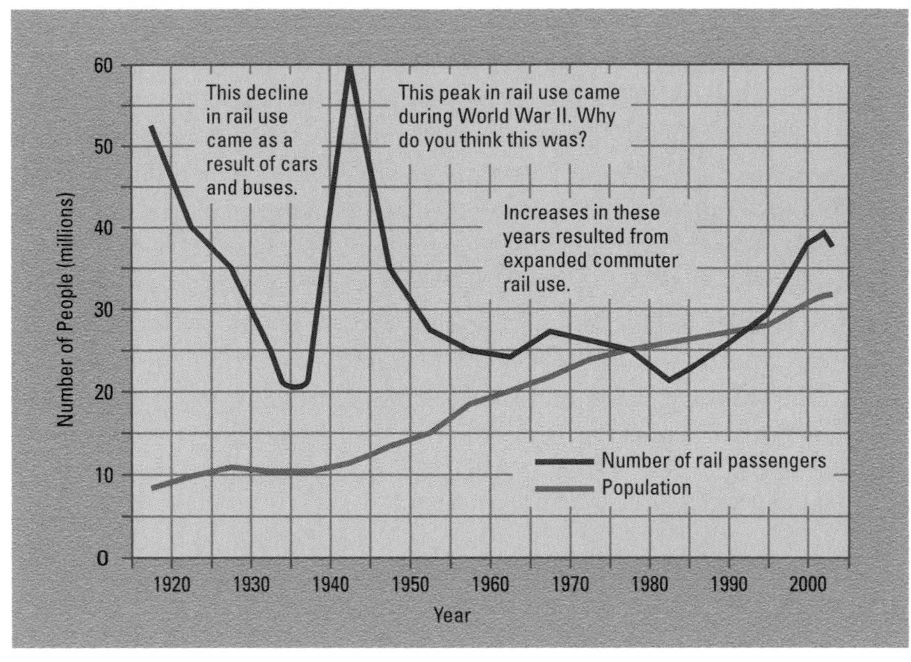

Fig. 30-4 ▶ Rail passengers and population growth, 1919–2003. The decline in rail passengers is even more dramatic if we consider that travel overall has increased tremendously.

Government of Ontario (GO) Transit also uses many buses.

COMMUTER RAIL

There is one exception to the sad state of rail passenger service in Canada. In cities such as Toronto and Montreal, trains move **commuters** to and from work. The largest of these commuter rail systems is GO Transit. It moves commuters into downtown Toronto from surrounding suburbs and nearby towns and cities.

Commercial air travel was not common until the second half of the 20th century.

Air Canada also suffered as a result of reduced air passenger traffic in the wake of the terrorist attacks of September 11, 2001.

Air Travel

Few countries depend on air travel as much as Canada. The great distances between our cities, plus our affluence, combine to make Canadians frequent air travellers. While we might prefer to drive or take the bus or train for shorter journeys, we tend to fly for longer trips. Given the importance of air travel in Canada, you might think that our airline industry is thriving, but this is not the case. In 2003, Air Canada, Canada's largest airline, went into **bankruptcy protection**. Before the 1990s, the air travel industry was highly regulated by government, which determined such matters as the cost of airfares and the routes each airline could fly. These rules changed with **deregulation**, when government no longer controlled fares and routes.

Your view of deregulation may depend on where you live and where you want to fly. If you live in a major city such as Toronto or Vancouver, and you want to fly to another major city in Canada or to a major destination outside the country, you are likely to benefit from deregulation.

Increased competition has driven fares down and given you a wider choice of flights. On the other hand, if you live in a smaller community, deregulation has probably not benefited you at all. You are probably still served only by Air Canada because the competition is not interested in setting up low-profit routes between small urban centres and large cities. Without competition or enough fares to make a profit, you won't see any deals in airfares. Furthermore, there is always the risk that your community may lose its air service if Air Canada cuts back on its operations or goes out of business.

After salaries, fuel is the highest-cost item in airline budgets.

Canada's air travel industry still faces challenges. Increased security procedures have made air travel less comfortable and convenient, and the ever-increasing cost of crude oil makes it more expensive. Nonetheless, air travel will remain a vital method of transportation in Canada. In a country as large as ours, it could not be otherwise.

AIRPORTS

In 2004, a total of approximately 60 million passengers flew into, out of, and within Canada. They flew on a variety of domestic and foreign commercial carriers as well as on private planes. But where did all these passengers take off from, and where did they land? Canada has 330 certified airports, and 26 of them each handle more than 200 000 passengers a year. Of these 26, several are major international airports built in Canada's largest cities. The busiest are Toronto's Lester B. Pearson International (Fig. 30-5), Vancouver International, Calgary International, Montreal's Pierre Elliott Trudeau International, and Winnipeg International Airport. These airports act as **transportation hubs** for international and domestic flights that carry both people and cargo.

Some of Canada's smaller international airports include Abbotsford International, Gander International, Hamilton International, St. John's International, and Saskatoon's John G. Diefenbaker International.

◀ **Fig. 30-5** Pearson International Airport's Terminal 1 was rebuilt and reopened in 2004. Massive luggage carousels and clear signage are just two of the features that help move large numbers of passengers more efficiently.

Travel by Ship

outports
small communities not linked by road to the rest of the province

Travel by ship is not common in Canada, but where it does occur, it is vitally important. Ferries carry residents and tourists across lakes and rivers in Ontario and British Columbia, and across the St. Lawrence River in Quebec. They connect the **outports** of Newfoundland and Labrador. Ferries travel to Newfoundland, Vancouver Island, Prince Edward Island, and to smaller islands along the east and west coasts of Canada. Although costly to operate and often subject to stoppages due to severe weather, ice conditions, and mechanical and labour problems, ferries are essential to the livelihood of many Canadians.

A private company, Strait Crossing Bridge Limited, will manage, maintain, and operate the bridge until 2032, when operations will be transferred to the Government of Canada.

On busy routes or where severe weather is common, ferries are not always the best means of travel. To decrease traffic congestion at ferry terminals and stoppages due to severe winter weather, the Canadian government challenged the private sector to produce an environmentally sound plan for a bridge between Prince Edward Island and New Brunswick. The Confederation Bridge was completed in 1997.

QUESTIONS

KNOWLEDGE AND UNDERSTANDING

1. a) Define mobility.
   b) What factors have allowed Canadians greater mobility over the past 60 years?
2. What is perhaps the most significant drawback of Canada's transportation system?
3. How much do governments spend on roads every year, and why do they spend this much?
4. What is the difference between intercity and intracity buses?

THINKING

5. a) Explain why travel by train has declined in Canada.
   b) Which of these reasons were the fault of the rail industry and which were unavoidable?
   c) What can be done to improve rail travel? Why would this be difficult to do?
6. a) Give two reasons why the high-speed trains of France and Japan can compete with air travel.
   b) What advantages do France and Japan have for building modern rail systems that Canada does not have?
7. a) Describe the changes that have occurred in the airline industry in recent years.
   b) Which of these changes benefited travellers? Have all travellers benefited equally? Explain.
8. Besides Prince Edward Island, what other places in Canada might benefit from a bridge rather than a ferry link?
9. Between the 1800s and today, the importance of different methods of transportation has changed. Copy Fig. 30-6 into your notebook. Name the most important transportation methods in each time period for both short- and long-distance travel.

▼ **Fig. 30-6**

	Short Distances	Long Distances
1800s		
1900–1950		
1950–today		

10. a) List five ways that the automobile has had an impact on the lifestyle of Canadians.
    b) List five ways in which the automobile has influenced the appearance of Canadian cities and towns.
    c) Have the things that you mentioned in 10 a) and 10 b) been beneficial or harmful to the way we live? Explain.
    d) What could be done to reduce the harmful effects of the automobile?

APPLICATION

11. You have just learned that government was highly involved in the airline industry before deregulation, and in the rail industry when railway companies no longer wished to operate passenger service. If a high-speed train link were developed between Windsor and Quebec City, the government would most likely have to subsidize a portion, if not all, of its construction. What role do you think government should play in regulating and financing public transportation systems? Why?

Movement of Goods

You are standing on a train platform in Armstrong, Ontario, 200 kilometres northeast of Thunder Bay. You know that the railway lines run east–west through Armstrong. There are two freight trains in front of you, sitting on parallel tracks but pointing in opposite directions. One train is loaded with wheat, plywood, and television sets. The other is loaded with mining equipment, Canadian magazines, and Toyota Corollas.

1. Which train is heading east and which is heading west? How do you know?
2. Suggest three other cargoes that might be carried by each train.

Every day, Canada's transportation system handles cargo ranging from such goods as 50 000 tonnes of coal to 100 kilograms of live lobsters. It even transports human organs for transplant. Some cargoes are moved as quickly as possible, with little concern for the high cost. Others travel slowly, at a cost that is as low as possible. Some cargoes are frozen. Others are transported with special protection because they are easily damaged. These different cargoes indicate the capabilities of Canada's transportation system.

Moving Cargo by Rail

Trains are very good at moving large amounts of cargo very cheaply. Although they carry many types of freight, trains are particularly good at moving **bulk cargoes** such as coal, grain, wood, and oil (Fig. 30-7). Bulk

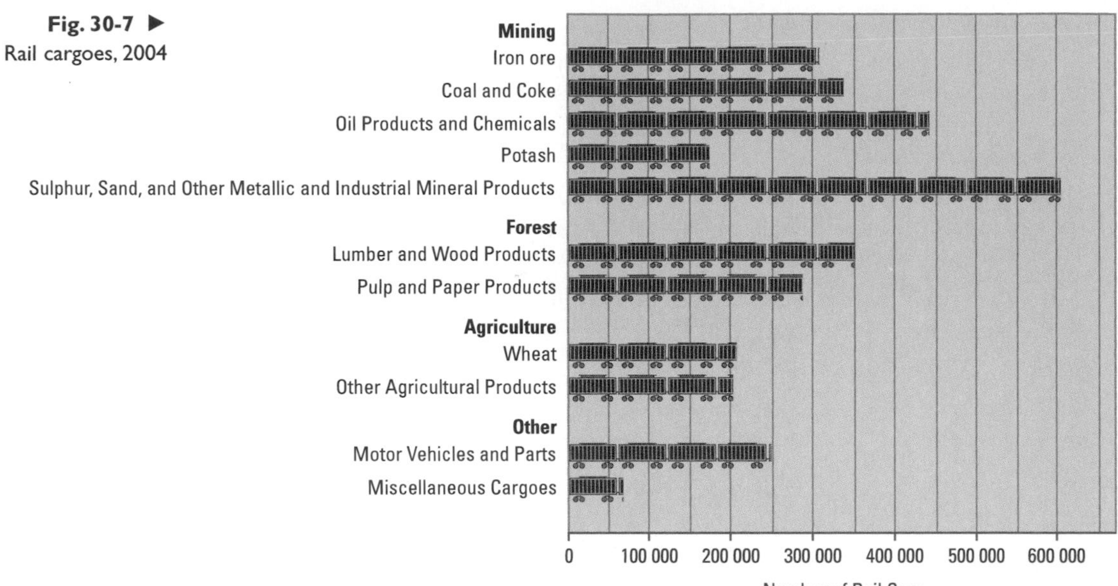

Fig. 30-7 ▶ Rail cargoes, 2004

cargoes have large volume and relatively low value. Consequently, they can be transported as cheaply as possible.

One way to move cargo very cheaply is the **unit train.** A unit train carries only one type of cargo from the cargo's source to its destination. The unit train's cars are identical and specially designed to carry one particular cargo. Since the cars are also designed to load and unload quickly, unit trains are relatively inexpensive to operate. Some of Canada's most important unit-train routes run from:

- the interior of Labrador to ports on the St. Lawrence River (iron ore)
- the Rocky Mountains to Vancouver (coal)
- the Prairies to Vancouver and Thunder Bay (wheat)
- Saskatchewan to Vancouver (potash)

In the 1950s, railways began to face stiff competition from trucks. Trucks have a major advantage over trains in that they are not restricted to fixed routes. They can transport shipments anywhere as long as a network of roads exists. This flexibility allows the transport of cargo from factory directly to final destination. Delays and handling costs are reduced because truck cargo never has to be transferred from one type of transportation to another.

To compete with trucks, which have the advantage of flexibility, the railway came up with two related solutions. The first was the **piggyback system**. Piggyback combines the advantages of trucking with rail. The first five points on the next page explain how the piggyback system works.

- A trailer is loaded at a factory.
- A truck pulls the trailer to a nearby rail yard.
- The trailer is loaded onto a flatcar of a train.
- The train transports the trailer to a rail yard near the trailer's final destination.
- The trailer is unloaded from the flatcar and moved by truck to its final destination.

The second solution is even more flexible and involves the use of **containers**. Containers can be moved by rail, truck, ship, and even air (Fig. 30-8). They are large metal boxes of standard size and shape. The container is filled by the shipper, and then transported by any combination of train, truck, ship, and plane, depending on the type of cargo and its destination. Containers can be moved quickly and efficiently, and theft and damage are unlikely. Before the development of containers, freight had to be loaded and unloaded piece by piece. This was time-consuming and costly.

Moving Cargo by Road

Moving cargo by road has several advantages over rail transport:

- Trucks cost less to buy and maintain than railway cars and engines.
- Truck terminals are less expensive to build than train terminals.
- Trucks are not restricted to fixed routes.
- Trucks are better suited to carrying lighter, less bulky cargo.

◀ **Fig. 30-8** Containers are 2.3 metres wide and 2.3 metres tall. They vary in length, but a common length is about 12.9 metres. These standard sizes make the containers easier to handle and store.

Efficient intercity trucking developed considerably in the last half of the 20th century. Large, reliable trucks and growing networks of high-speed highways allow goods to be moved quickly and dependably.

As the number of trucks on our roads has increased, however, so have problems. Large, heavy trucks damage roads more than other types of vehicles, resulting in the need for costly resurfacing repairs. The high volume of truck traffic leads to increased air pollution and congestion, especially on highways between major cities. Trucks are frequently involved in highway accidents due to mechanical failure or driver fatigue, or because other drivers create dangerous situations that the truck driver cannot avoid.

In the Northwest Territories there are over 1450 kilometres of publicly constructed winter ice roads and a number of privately owned roads to petroleum exploration sites and mines.

ICE ROADS IN THE NORTH

In the winter, road transportation in the Far North takes on a different character from that in southern Canada. **Winter ice roads** play an important role in the transport of cargo to parts of Canada's north. Every winter, a network of ice roads is built through the tundra. These roads are made of a mixture of snow, ice, and soil, and are built across frozen land, muskeg, streams, lakes, and rivers. Road graders build up the roads over the land, and snow plows clear off the routes over the ice. Shipping cargo in trucks over ice roads is an economical alternative to supplying northern communities by air. Fuel, groceries, machinery, and building products are trucked to remote communities and mining operations until road surfaces begin to deteriorate in the spring. Trucks travel 24 hours a day, weather permitting, to take advantage of the short four- to five-month hauling season. Companies that specialize in the planning, construction, and maintenance of winter ice roads carefully regulate the speed of the trucks and the distance between them on the frozen lakes and rivers to avoid wave movement in the ice, which makes the ice unstable and dangerous.

The ice roads have been critical to the development of Canada's diamond mines north of Great Slave Lake.

Moving Cargo by Ship

Ships have moved cargo to, from, and within Canada for more than 400 years. Approximately 150 years ago, ships were the most important form of transportation on all three coasts and in the Great Lakes because transportation on land was slow and **unreliable**. Even though the quality of land transport has improved enormously, ships are still important to Canada's economy.

unreliable not trustworthy

Ships are best suited to the transport of bulky, low-value cargo such as grain, iron ore, coal, crude oil, fuel oil, diesel fuel, lumber, cement, sand, and gravel. Mills, refineries, and factories that produce or use these commodities locate on shipping routes (Fig. 30-9). They save money by taking advantage of shipping by water.

Canada's water-borne freight system can be examined using four categories: the west coast, the east coast, the St. Lawrence Seaway, and the Far North.

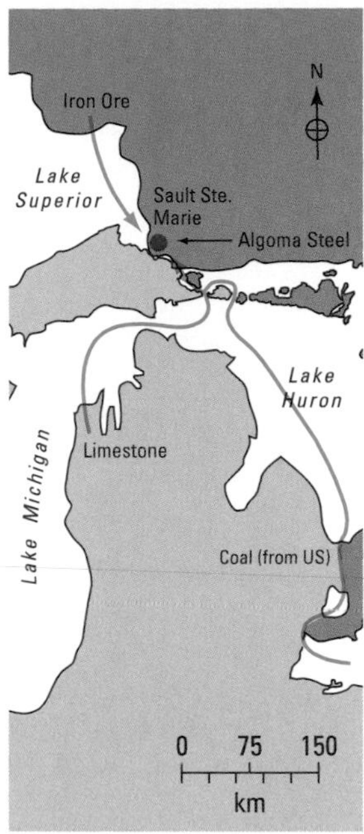

▲ **Fig. 30-9** Algoma Steel is located in Sault Ste. Marie because the raw materials it requires for steel production can be transported by lake freighter to its steel mill.

THE WEST COAST

Enormous amounts of cargo are shipped through west coast ports, and especially through Canada's busiest port, Vancouver. This cargo is shipped primarily to countries along the **Pacific Rim**. A great deal of Canada's lumber, coal, potash, and wheat goes to Pacific Rim countries. Much of the cargo shipped through Canada's west coast ports consists of motor vehicles and manufactured goods packed in containers.

THE EAST COAST

East coast ports such as Halifax, Saint John, and Montreal are the entry points for a wide variety of cargo. These ports handle more container freight and less bulk cargo than west coast ports. For example, manufactured goods from the factories in southern Ontario and southern Quebec are shipped to Europe through east coast ports; European automobiles enter Canada through these ports.

THE ST. LAWRENCE SEAWAY

The St. Lawrence Seaway is a system of **canals** and **locks** (Fig. 30-10) linking the St. Lawrence River and the Great Lakes. The Seaway allows ships to travel 3800 kilometres inland from the Atlantic Ocean to Lake Superior. It is also a vital route for the movement of bulk cargo from one part of the Great Lakes to another.

THE FAR NORTH

Canada's Far North presents special transportation problems. Distances are great, and the climate is harsh. As land transport is generally not

◀ **Fig. 30-10** The operation of a lock: The ship enters the upper lock. The gate behind the ship is closed to lock the ship in. Water is drained from the lock to lower the ship to the level of the water in the lock ahead. The gate in front is opened, and the ship moves forward into the next lock. The process is repeated until the ship has moved through all the locks. The reverse occurs to raise a ship from a lower body of water to a higher one.

available, freight must be moved either by air or by water. Since it is very expensive to ship freight to the Far North by air, it is shipped by water whenever possible. Ships on the Arctic Ocean and barges on the Mackenzie River move bulky cargo such as oil products, building materials, and machinery to northern ports and communities in summer. They also transport many of the groceries that residents will need for a whole year. Because summers are short in the North, the shipping season may be only several weeks in length. Residents must plan very carefully to avoid running out of such items as sugar, flour, and cooking oil before the delivery of supplies the following year. Otherwise, they have to pay high prices for supplies that have been transported to their community by air.

Moving Cargo by Air

Although moving cargo by air is more expensive than other shipping methods, the use of air freight has greatly increased in recent years (Fig. 30-11). The amount of freight moved by air, however, is still small compared to that moved by rail, road, or ship. Moving cargo by air offers special advantages, for which shippers are prepared to pay high prices. In particular, cargo can be moved very quickly, with delivery available the next day. Goods shipped by air have one or more of the following characteristics:

- They are light in weight and small in size, e.g., a shipment of jewellery.
- They are of high value, e.g., electronic equipment.
- They are perishable, e.g., flowers.
- They are required as quickly as possible, e.g., machinery parts to repair construction or manufacturing equipment that is critical to a particular operation.

▼ **Fig. 30-11** Airplanes move almost anything.

Air transport has played an important role in the development of regions in Canada where road, rail, and ship transport are scarce or non-existent. Float planes can fly into areas with lakes and rivers, and small aircraft can fly into communities where small airports have been built.

Moving Cargo by Pipeline

When we think about how cargo is moved, we often overlook the important role of **pipelines.** This is understandable because in most parts of the country, pipelines are generally buried and out of sight. Pipelines transport gases, liquids, and even solids that have been crushed and mixed with water. In Canada, they are vital in moving crude oil and natural gas. A pipeline is built only when these two specific conditions exist:

- The supply of the commodity is large enough to last for many years. Since pipelines are costly to build, a large supply of the commodity makes construction worthwhile.
- It is not possible to transport the commodity by ship. Transportation by ship is usually less expensive than transportation by pipeline.

Fig. 30-12 shows the location of Canada's major oil and gas pipelines. The proposed pipelines on the map may be built if it makes economic

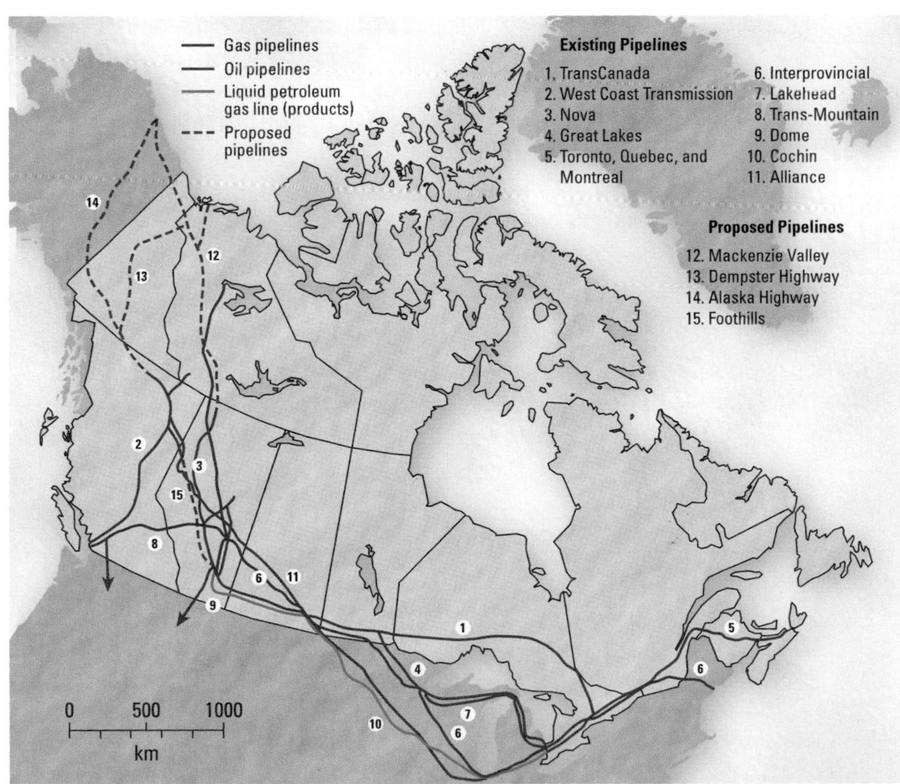

◀ **Fig. 30-12** Major Canadian pipelines. Not shown on this map are hundreds of smaller pipelines that move oil and gas from their source to major pipelines.

sense to do so. They might be built in five years, in 50 years, or perhaps never. As the demand for oil and natural gas rises (along with their price), the likelihood of more pipelines being built increases, particularly to the United States.

In Closing...

Canada could not exist as a modern nation without a complex transportation system that moves people and cargo efficiently to their destination. And yet, Canada's transportation network performs another, perhaps less obvious, task. It connects all our diverse regions, helping Canadians to feel that they are part of one vast country.

QUESTIONS

KNOWLEDGE AND UNDERSTANDING

1. a) What are bulk cargoes?
   b) Rank the various forms of transportation in terms of their suitability to move bulk cargoes.
   c) What is a unit train? Why is it an efficient way to move bulk cargoes?
   d) Give three examples of unit-train routes and cargoes.
2. a) Railways came up with two solutions to compete with trucks. What are they?
   b) Describe how these solutions work.
3. a) Describe winter ice roads.
   b) Why are they important?
4. Describe each of the four different regions in Canada where ships are used to move cargo.
5. What types of cargo are carried by airplanes? Why?

THINKING

6. a) A clothing manufacturer in Winnipeg has sold 10 000 pairs of jeans to a department store in London, England. Complete an organizer like Fig. 30-13 to summarize the manufacturer's choices for transporting these jeans to England.
   b) Which method of transport would you choose and why?

COMMUNICATION

7. Sometimes conflict arises between the movement of goods and the movement of people. For example, freight trains have priority over passenger trains—a passenger train must pull

Transportation Method	Advantages	Disadvantages	Comments
Rail			
Road			
Ship			
Airplane			
Pipeline			

▲ **Fig. 30-13**

onto a siding to allow a freight train to continue on the track. Should the movement of people have precedence over the movement of goods? Why or why not? Express your views in a paragraph.

APPLICATION

8. a) Refer to Fig. 30-7. Calculate the percentage of the total cargo made up by each of the following categories:
   i. mining products
   ii. forestry products
   iii. agricultural products
   iv. motor vehicles and parts

   b) Draw a pie graph to illustrate the types of cargo carried by railways. (See Chapter 8 if you are not sure how to draw a pie graph.)

   c) What similarities do these cargoes have?

9. Which method of transportation would you choose to move each of the following cargoes? Explain your choices.
   a) 100 000 tonnes of wheat from Saskatoon to Vancouver
   b) six pianos shipped from Montreal: four to Ottawa, one to Peterborough, Ontario, and one to Sherbrooke, Quebec
   c) 200 000 tonnes of crude oil from Alberta to Sarnia, Ontario
   d) 50 000 tonnes of iron ore from Sept-Isles, Quebec, to Hamilton, Ontario
   e) 100 kilograms of live daffodils from Victoria, British Columbia to Toronto, Ontario

10. a) Fig. 30-14 shows the traffic trend on the Welland Canal over 45 years. Calculate the average tonnage carried by each ship in 1959 and 2004.

    b) What has happened to the
    i. total tonnage?
    ii. number of ships?
    iii. size of ships?

    c) If a large transport truck can carry 50 tonnes of cargo and a freight train with 60 cars can carry 4000 tonnes of cargo, calculate
    i. the equivalent number of truck- and trainloads of cargo that went through the Welland Canal in 2004
    ii. the number of truck- and trainloads that are equal to the average ship's cargo

    d) How do these figures help explain why bulk cargo is shipped by water whenever possible?

	1959	2004
Number of ships	7500	3185
Cargo tonnage (tonnes)	27 000 000	34 300 000
Average tonnage (tonnes)		

▲ **Fig. 30-14** Traffic flow, Welland Canal

31 Communications: Canada's Nervous System

Key Ideas

This chapter helps you investigate these questions:

- How does communications technology affect your daily life, and how might it affect you in the future?
- Will changing communications technology have a favourable or unfavourable effect on your life? Explain.

Key Terms

communications

global village

convergent technologies

If we compare Canada to the human body, we could say that the country's communications system is like the body's nervous system. The nervous system carries information to all parts of the body so that it may function properly; Canada's **communications** system carries information to all regions of the country so that the country may carry out its day-to-day operations. While studying the communications system, you will see that communications technology changes very rapidly. Each new change has a major geographical effect: it decreases the **relevance** of distance in communications.

relevance
importance

Marshall McLuhan, a famous Canadian philosopher and communications theorist, stated in the late 1950s that the world is becoming a **global village.** He meant that technological improvements are making communications throughout the world as easy as if they were taking place in a small village. While the world is not yet a global village, it is rapidly moving in that direction. Complete the following activity to see how this trend is occurring.

You will need the following items for this exercise: a phone book that provides international calling information, a globe, a piece of string, and graph paper. You will also need the following information:

- Long-distance calls to destinations in Canada and the United States are made by dialing 1 + area code + local number.
- Long-distance calls to other countries are made by dialing 011 + country code (2–3 digits) + city code (1–5 digits) + local number (2–9 digits).

City codes are not required for all countries. In some countries, city codes are not required because the country code covers all places.

Column A	Column B
1) Canada's prime minister in Ottawa	a) 011-57-1-35-50-**
2) *The New York Times* newspaper in Manhattan, New York City	b) 1-403-247-****
3) Sydney Opera House in Australia	c) 1-613-992-****
4) Calgary Tower and Canada Olympic Park in Alberta	d) 011-44-171-930-****
5) Buckingham Palace in London, England	e) 1-213-956-****
6) Paramount Studios in Los Angeles, California	f) 011-27-12-319****
7) Canadian Embassy in Bogotá, Colombia	g) 1-212-556-****
8) *The Globe and Mail*'s bureau in Beijing, China	h) 011-86-10-8526-****
9) South Africa's president in Pretoria	i) 011-61-2-9250-****

◀ **Fig. 31-1** Can you match the phone number to the location?

INTERNET

An on-line distance calculator is available through the link at www.pearsoned.ca/makingconnections2.

1. Examine the telephone numbers in Column B of Fig. 31-1. Using the area codes and country codes listed in the long-distance section of your phone book, match each place in Column A to its telephone number in Column B.
2. Calculate and record the distance from Toronto to each city in Column A. You can do this with a globe and a piece of string.
3. Do you think that the cost to phone each city from Toronto is tied to its distance from Toronto? Why or why not? To help you answer these questions, construct two scattergraphs that relate the cost to distance from Toronto for the years 1984 and 2005. The cost data for this exercise are given in Fig. 31-2. Construct a scattergraph for each year with *cost per minute* as the vertical scale and *distance* as the horizontal scale.
4. Look at the two scattergraphs you have created, and answer the following questions:
   a) What has happened to the cost of making long-distance calls over the years? Why?

GeoLit Reminder

Constructing a scattergraph:
- Label the dependent variable on the vertical axis and the independent variable on the horizontal axis.
- Choose scales for the vertical and horizontal axes.
- Record data using dots, small x's or circles.
- Draw the line of best fit.
- Give your graph an appropriate title.

Destination of Call	1984 cost (in 2005 $)	2005 cost ($)
1) Canada's prime minister in Ottawa	1.15	0.039
2) *The New York Times* newspaper in Manhattan, New York City	0.71	0.049
3) Sydney Opera House in Australia	3.11	0.059
4) Calgary Tower and Canada Olympic Park in Alberta	1.77	0.039
5) Buckingham Palace in London, England	2.26	0.059
6) Paramount Studios in Los Angeles, California	1.13	0.049
7) Canadian embassy in Bogotá, Colombia	2.83	0.18
8) *The Globe and Mail*'s bureau in Beijing, China	3.11	0.35
9) South Africa's president in Pretoria	3.11	0.15

◀ **Fig. 31-2** The price of a one-minute phone call from Toronto in 1984 and 2005. The 1984 prices have been adjusted to reflect the amount of inflation that occurred between 1984 and 2005. This allows a direct comparison between the amounts shown. The 2005 prices are from a discount provider of phone services. Companies like this did not exist in 1984.

b) Have changes in cost been more significant for calls to less distant places or for calls to more distant places? What does this finding suggest?
c) How significant was the relationship between distance and cost in 1984? in 2005? Describe any trends (and major exceptions) that you see.
d) Why do you think this change has occurred?

The Nature of Communications

revolutionize
cause a major change

The invention of the printing press extended the power of writing, since information could now be mass-produced and widely distributed.

Communications is the transfer of information from one place to another. The nature of communications has changed greatly since the invention of writing thousands of years ago. Written language **revolutionized** communications because people were able to transfer and store information that could be read in a different place at a different time. Writing—and much later, print—were enormous advances in communications, but they still had major shortcomings. For example, the treaty that ended the War of 1812 was signed in Europe in December 1814. Unfortunately, it took many weeks for the news to reach North America. During this time, the war continued, and hundreds of people were killed in battles that would not have occurred if communication had been speedier.

Clearly, there was a need for faster communications over long distances. The first breakthrough was the invention of the telegraph in the mid-1800s. Since the telegraph required wires, there were some obvious limitations to its use. The next invention was the "wireless," better known today as the radio, in the early 1900s. In the decades that followed came television and enormous advances in both wired and wireless communication, including satellite communications and the Internet. Today, people around the entire world are linked as a result of these communications advances.

INTERNET

Learn more about SETI, the Search for Extra-terrestrial Intelligence, through the link at www.pearsoned.ca/makingconnections2.

We humans even have a desire to communicate with others who may live beyond our planet. We have sent messages to those who might live elsewhere in the universe (Fig. 31-3) and have listened for communication from other galaxies by means of the SETI Project. The Pioneer 10 spacecraft holds the record for the most distant human communication yet. Its last message to Earth was received in January 2003, more than 31 years after its launch. By that time, the spacecraft was more than 121 billion kilometres from Earth.

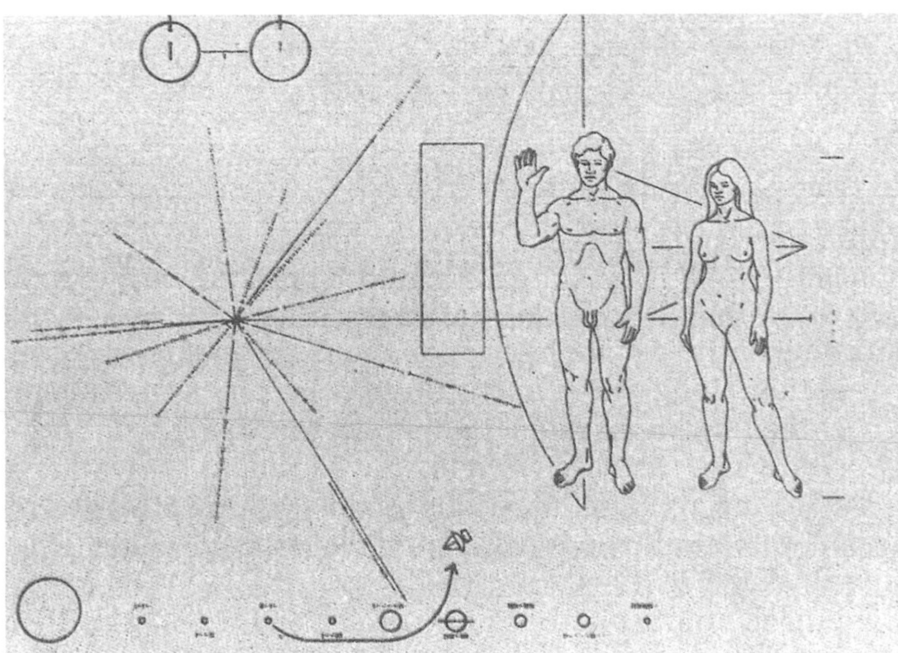

◀ **Fig. 31-3** We are already trying to communicate with beings beyond our own solar system. This plate was attached to the Pioneer 10 spacecraft, which was the first object designed to leave the solar system. Try to figure out the message on the plate. What information would you have sent?

INTERNET

You can learn about what this message means through the link at www.pearsoned.ca/makingconnections2.

Communications: Existing and Emerging

Existing Communications Technologies

Canadians exchange information by

- talking to one another
- listening to the radio—More than 99% of Canadian households (and almost every car and truck) have a radio.
- watching television—More than 98% of Canadian households have television. More than 75% have cable or satellite service that gives them access to perhaps hundreds of different stations.
- using the telephone (Fig. 31-4)—As of April 2005, there were approximately 19.4 million fixed telephone lines and 15 million mobile phone subscribers in Canada.
- sending e-mails over the Internet and visiting Web sites
- mailing letters to one another
- reading—Canada has over 100 daily newspapers and more than 1500 magazines. Some magazines, such as *Maclean's* and *Chatelaine*, are read by hundreds of thousands of people, whereas others are published for fewer readers with specific interests.

Between 1999 and 2003, the number of mobile phone subscribers almost doubled.

Canadian Coin News and *Sweep! Curling's Magazine* are examples of specialized magazines.

Most of us are familiar with these forms of communication, but few of us think about what happens behind the scenes to allow such communication to occur. What allows you to read your morning newspaper, receive

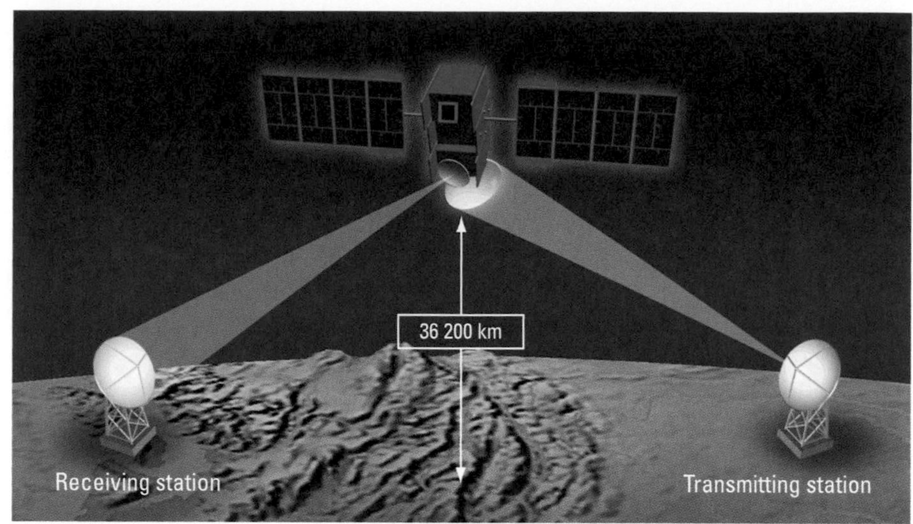

Fig. 31-4 ▶ Satellites are used for both telephone and television communications. Communications satellites are in **geostationary** orbit, moving at the same speed as Earth's rotation.

Communication occurs in ways that you might not always be aware of. For example, when you use a bank machine (ATM), messages are sent back and forth between the machine and your bank's computer.

a long-distance call, or watch the Olympics broadcast on television from a distant country? Examine Figures 31-5, 31-6, and 31-7 to discover the answers to this question. Remember that a communication consists of two parts: the message itself and the technology that delivers the message.

Canada has a highly developed communications system. This system has evolved partly because of the nature of Canada's human and physical geography. A modern and efficient communications system was, and remains, essential in unifying a relatively small population spread out over many thousands of kilometres.

Our advanced communications system has also developed because we have a body of scientists and engineers with the education and imagination to tackle our communications challenges. These talented

▼ **Fig. 31-5** Each form of communication technology consists of two parts.

Form of Communication	Message	Technology to Carry Message
newspaper	news stories	digital transmission of information, fully automated printing press
long-distance telephone call	words said by each person	phone system including satellites and microwave network (Fig. 31-6)
television	pictures and words	TV production facilities (Fig. 31-7), satellite/undersea cables, antennas, and cable TV distribution system
e-mail	pictures and words	transmission of information over phone lines, cable systems, and computer networks
text message	words	transmission of information over cell-phone lines

▲ **Fig. 31-6** Microwave transmission can be used where a cable network could never be built.

▲ **Fig. 31-7** Engineer at a television production facility

people have enabled Canadians to be among the first in the world to have access to new methods of communication. They have enhanced Canada's reputation in the communications field, thus encouraging other countries to buy Canadian **expertise**. For example, a Canadian telecommunications company provides high-speed fibre optic technology to a major telecommunications company in Argentina and a digital cable television system (for TV, data, video, and multimedia services) to parts of China.

expertise knowledge and skills

Emerging Communications Technologies

Communications technologies are changing rapidly, and new technologies often become **obsolete** before many people even know they exist! In this section, we will look at the changes that are occurring in a number of communications technologies.

obsolete outdated

DEVELOPMENTS IN THE TELEPHONE SYSTEM

Perhaps the most dramatic change in Canada's telephone system is the recent growth of wireless phone service. For a century after its **inception**, phone service was provided by telephones that were connected by wires. These telephone wires, or land lines, linked one place to another. In the mid-1980s, wireless (also called cellular or mobile) phone service became available. Another, more fundamental development is taking place in the telephone system. As you learned in the long-distance activity earlier in this chapter, distance is becoming a less important factor in communications.

inception beginning

In 1999, the number of residential Internet connections was 3 367 000. By 2003, the number of connections had more than doubled to 7 013 000.

DEVELOPMENTS IN THE INTERNET

The Internet has become such an important part of our lives that it is easy to forget how new it is and how quickly it is developing and changing. Every month, the number of Internet users in Canada grows dramatically. Today, the most important elements of the Internet are e-mail, on-line discussion capabilities, and the World Wide Web.

E-mail has already had a profound impact on the way people communicate. E-mail messages, whether to someone in the next office or on the other side of the world, make communication cheaper and faster.

On-line discussions on the Internet have many purposes. Sometimes their purpose is recreational—you can play games with other Internet users or chat with the star of a new television show. At other times, their purpose is more serious. For example, you can take university or college courses on-line, and have on-line discussions with your classmates. While this might be a convenience for someone living in a city with a college or university, for someone living in a remote area, it is a revolution. People now have access to higher education without having to travel great distances to obtain it.

Perhaps the most important element of the Internet is the World Wide Web (WWW). There are millions of Web sites all over the world that have as many purposes as the human imagination can create. It is rapidly becoming the meeting place for people who have access to the necessary computer technology. Here are a few current uses of the WWW:

- a large library of knowledge (Fig. 31-8)
- a centre for the exchange of entertainment and cultural information
- the ultimate shopping mall, with on-line stores

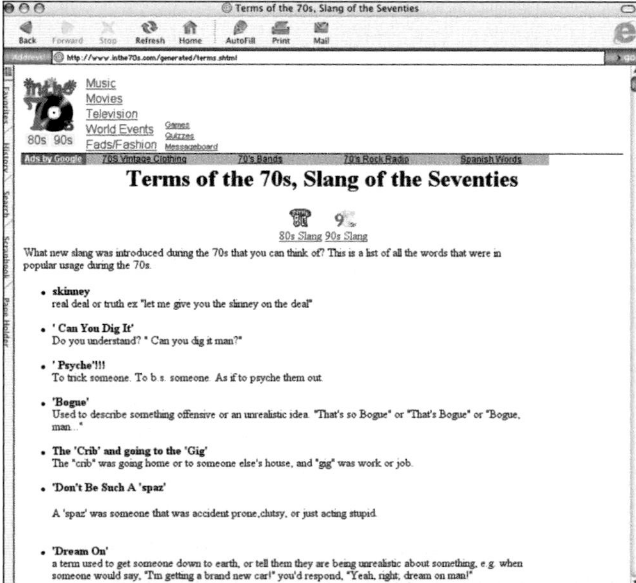

Fig. 31-8 ▶ Just as you would consult the references in a library, you may now consult references on the World Wide Web. This particular Web site is a dictionary of 1970s slang!

- a banking centre
- a centre for personal expression. Weblogs (blogs) are Web-based communications in which people and organizations publish everything from personal diaries to political commentary.

DEVELOPMENTS IN TELEVISION

Before the 1980s, Canadians had very few television stations to watch. Television signals were received by rooftop antennas, and in some areas only one or two stations were available. Today, by comparison, Canadians can choose from dozens of stations broadcasting from locations across the country—and, indeed, from across the continent—because of the development and growth of cable and satellite television.

Cable and satellite television companies have traditionally used **analog transmission**. Many are now using **digital transmission**. Digital transmission has two huge advantages. First, it gives viewers better quality pictures and sound. Second, it is much more efficient. One analog channel can be used to carry as many as eight digital channels. For example, a cable company that had 77 analog channels now offers a total of almost 300 analog and digital channels combined. Cable TV service providers now enable access to the Internet via the television, and offer interactive TV, movies on demand, and personal video recorders.

Digital technology is also used for radio transmission.

Convergent Technologies

Until recently, communications technologies were completely independent. Television, radio, newspapers, movies, magazines, and the Internet each worked separately and differently. The people who worked in these media, and the people who used them, thought more about their differences than their similarities. Now, however, the independent nature of each communications technology is disappearing as one technology merges with another. Distinctions among various communications technologies are becoming blurred. This complex and exciting change, known as **convergent technologies,** may be the most important of all.

Communications companies are battling each other for supremacy in the war of convergence. Each company wants to be able to deliver telephone, radio and TV broadcasting, and Internet services all at the same time. Consider the following examples of technological convergence:

- Telehealth Networks have been developed throughout Canada. In Ontario, for example, over 100 of the province's public hospitals are connected through networks of regular phone lines and fibre optic cables that allow video conferencing among healthcare professionals for the diagnosis and treatment of illnesses. It allows patients in their local hospitals to consult with specialists elsewhere, eliminating the

The first photos available of the terrorist bombings in the London underground (subway) in July 2005 were taken by video cell phones.

need to travel long distances to obtain care. This technology also gives doctors in remote areas access to continuing medical education.

- Interactive TV may be used for accessing the Internet, playing games, distance learning, home shopping, voting, and telebanking.
- Newspapers and magazines are available on-line.
- Internet telephone services or VoIP (Voice over Internet Protocol) allow people to make phone calls over a broadband Internet connection on their computers. This technology eliminates long-distance charges.

In Closing...

Geography is all about places and distance. Rapid changes in technology, however, are making distance irrelevant in many of our day-to-day communications and, in a sense, making communications less "geographic." Convergent technologies are giving us new and exciting ways to transfer and use information. These revolutionary changes in communications have made your life very different from that of a young person in your parents' generation.

QUESTIONS

KNOWLEDGE AND UNDERSTANDING

1. What is the major geographical impact of new communications technology?
2. a) Define communications.
   b) Name four important advances in the historical development of the world's communications system.
3. Canada has one of the world's most advanced communications systems. Give at least two reasons why this is not surprising.

THINKING

4. a) Each form of communication technology consists of two parts. Name these parts.
   b) Describe these two parts for the following forms of communications: a television broadcast, an Internet Web page, and a conversation.
5. a) What is the global village?
   b) Give three specific pieces of evidence from this chapter that suggest the world is becoming a global village.
   c) Give two additional pieces of evidence from your own life that suggest that the world is becoming a global village.

COMMUNICATION

6. It is time to put on your "futurist" hat. Predict how Canada's communications network will be different in 20 years as a result of convergent technologies. (You might want to brainstorm ideas with a group of classmates.) Compose your answer in a five-paragraph essay.

APPLICATION

7. a) Why is distance a less important factor in communications today than in the past?
   b) Why is this fact of particular interest to geographers?
8. a) What is meant by *convergent technologies*?
   b) Give four examples of how technologies are converging.

Locating a New Business

◀ **Fig. CA5-1** In October 2005, Toyota broke ground for its newest automobile assembly plant in Woodstock, Ontario. Canadian-made RAV 4s will start rolling off the assembly line in 2008.

When you look around your community, what types of businesses, industries, and transportation systems do you see? If you walk around your local shopping mall or your community's downtown core, which retail businesses appear successful, and which do not? This activity gives you the opportunity to work in small groups to decide where to locate a business of your choice. You will also create a promotional item explaining the location's benefits that could be used to attract other businesses to your chosen location. Your group can choose any business, and any Canadian location, but you must be able to justify your choice on the basis of the location factors listed in Fig. CA5-2. These location factors are also discussed in detail in Chapter 28.

Activity

1. Work in groups of four or five students. Review the information on location factors in Chapter 28. As a group, decide what type of business you will choose: primary, secondary, tertiary, or quaternary.
2. Brainstorm questions you will need to ask before you can decide in which part of Canada to locate your business. (Hint: base your questions on the location factors you have learned about.)
3. Conduct research to answer the questions you have identified. Use a fishbone organizer to record your information. Identify the location factors that are absolutely necessary ("musts") versus those that are desirable ("wants"). Figure CA5-3 shows a completed organizer that

▼ **Fig. CA5-2**

7 Location Factors
- Proximity of raw materials
- Location of markets
- Availability of fresh water and power
- Labour supply
- Transportation
- Political factors
- Circumstance

answers why Toyota selected Woodstock, Ontario, as the location for its newest automobile assembly plant.

4. Based on the information you have collected in your fishbone organizer, choose a suitable location for your new business.
5. Use the information in your organizer to create a promotional item such as a newspaper ad, a brochure, or a poster. Each group member should provide an idea for the promotional item. Your promotional item will
   - clearly identify the business and its location
   - describe the business (e.g., types of products, services)
   - summarize your reasons for choosing the location
   - include a map of the region showing the business's location in relation to major transportation routes and nearby communities (e.g., for labour supply)
   - include other visuals (e.g., photographs with captions, charts or graphs, a logo) related to the business and the community
   - include a catchy slogan to attract future industries (Most towns have a slogan. For example, Streetsville's slogan is "The Village in the City," and Milton's is "Gateway to the GTA.")
6. Individually, write an opinion paragraph outlining why the community you have chosen would be a great place for similar industries to locate. Support your selection with specific information and examples stemming from your business's location factors.

▼ **Fig. CA5-3** This diagram explains some of the reasons why Toyota chose Woodstock as a site for the new factory.

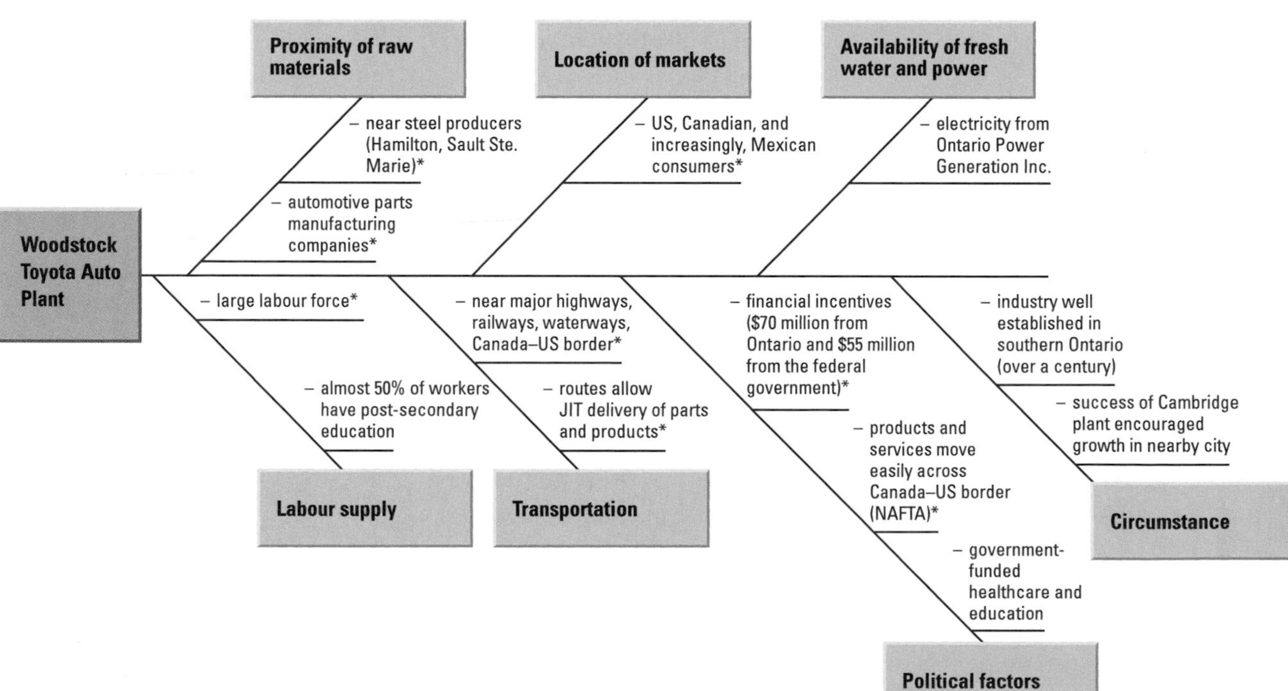

* Necessary requirement ("must" factor)

UNIT 6

Canada's Global Connections

Approximately 90% of Canadians live within 160 kilometres of the Canada–US border. However, physical location is only one aspect of Canada's place in the world. With your classmates, brainstorm a list of ways Canada is connected with the world community. For example, do you have friends or relatives living abroad? Does a member of your family, or someone you know, work for a company that exports goods or services abroad? How are you, your school, or your community, involved in helping people in other countries when disaster strikes? Are you aware of any disputes Canadians have with other countries in the areas of trade or of sovereignty? How do we resolve disputes with other countries? In this unit, you will learn about the many ways Canadians participate in the global community.

32 Canada and the World Community

Key Ideas

This chapter helps you investigate these questions:

- Why is it helpful to be able to study the world's countries in groups rather than to study each country individually?
- What methods can be used to group countries?
- In what group is Canada?

Key Terms

global village
developed countries
newly industrializing countries
developing countries
life expectancy
GDP per capita
foreign aid
cash crops

INTERNET

To examine maps of individual countries, check www.pearsoned.ca/makingconnections2.

Most often when Canadians see a map of the world, it is like the one shown in Fig. 32-1: it is centred on the Atlantic Ocean. A map organized in this way reflects Canada's history for most of the last 300 years. During this time, thousands of settlers came across the Atlantic Ocean from European countries and, as a result, Canada had strong political, military, and cultural ties with Europe.

Fig. 32-2, on the other hand, reflects a newer reality for Canada. It is centred on the Pacific Ocean and shows Canada in relationship to its neighbours on the Pacific Rim. This second map makes sense since most immigrants to Canada now come from Asian countries, and a growing percentage of our trade is with this region.

Many people would suggest that the growing interconnectedness is making the world a "smaller" place.

The final map (Fig. 32-3) is a view of the world that we rarely see. It shows the world with Canada at its centre. Looking at the world in these ways encourages you to ask some very important questions: What is Canada's place in the community of nations? How does Canada compare with other nations? In what ways is the world becoming a more interconnected place? Is being more interconnected a good thing or a bad thing?

There are several reasons for the increase in international connections.

- More people are travelling to more places. They are more likely to visit foreign countries than were any previous generations.
- Communication by phone and the Internet allows a level of contact in the world that is faster, easier, and cheaper than ever before. The result is a more closely connected **global village**.

Of course, many people in the world are not able to take advantage of these new travel opportunities or forms of communication.

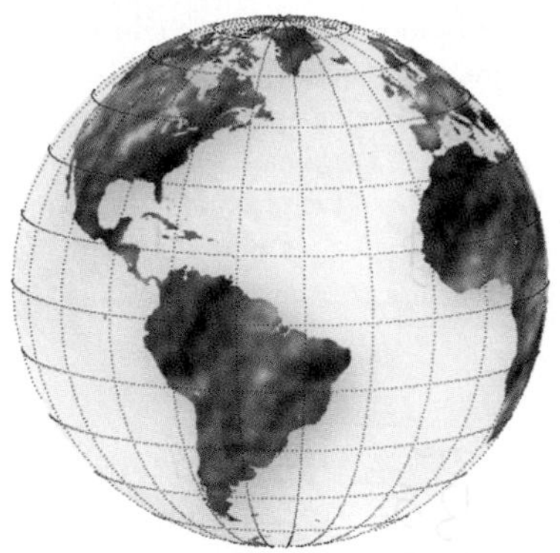

▲ **Fig. 32-1** This Atlantic-centred view of the world is the traditional one that Canadians have been used to seeing for more than a century. The centre of this map is at 10°N and 50°W.

▲ **Fig. 32-2** In recent years, Canadians are more likely to have a view of the world that is focused on the Pacific. The centre of this map is at 10°N and 160°W.

▲ **Fig. 32-3** Rarely do Canadians take a Canada-centred view of the world. How does looking at the world in this way change our perspective? This map is centred at 60°N and 95°W.

- International trade grows enormously every year. The economies of the world's countries are becoming more closely linked.
- Although the peoples of the world still exhibit considerable diversity, they increasingly share a common culture.
- Natural hazards, wars, and terrorism also link nations—often in ways we would not choose.

GeoLit Reminder

Interpreting diagrams:

- What type of visual text is shown in Figs. 32-1, 32-2, and 32-3? What is the purpose of these diagrams?
- What do the captions tell you about these visuals?
- State the main idea of the visuals, giving evidence to support your answer.
- How might these diagrams express bias? Explain your answer.

Grouping Countries

Understanding the connections among countries is not an easy thing to do. In fact, there is no clear agreement about what a country is. A commonly used way of identifying the world's countries is to consider the membership of the United Nations. In 2005, the United Nations had 191 members. Each country has a unique combination of culture, history, government, and economic development. One way to simplify our view of the world's countries is to group them according to their similarities. The most frequently used method is by comparing them on the basis of their economic and social development. Using these two measures, we can divide countries into three groups: **developed countries, newly industrializing countries**, and **developing countries** (Fig. 32-4).

Countries can be grouped together on the basis of several criteria. Complete the activity on page 436 to learn about these criteria and to see how countries are grouped together into one of the three groups.

Other methods of grouping involve as few as two groups, five groups, or as many as nine groups.

▼ **Fig. 32-4** This map identifies developed, newly industrializing, developing, and Communist and former Communist countries. The Communist and former Communist countries are gradually evolving to become more like their neighbours. For example, countries in Eastern Europe like Poland and Hungary have joined the European Union and are slowly developing economies and social systems like their European neighbours: They now operate under the same economic rules, share a common currency, and have eliminated duties (taxes) between member countries. Countries like Kazakhstan and Vietnam are each becoming like their neighbours in Central and East Asia.

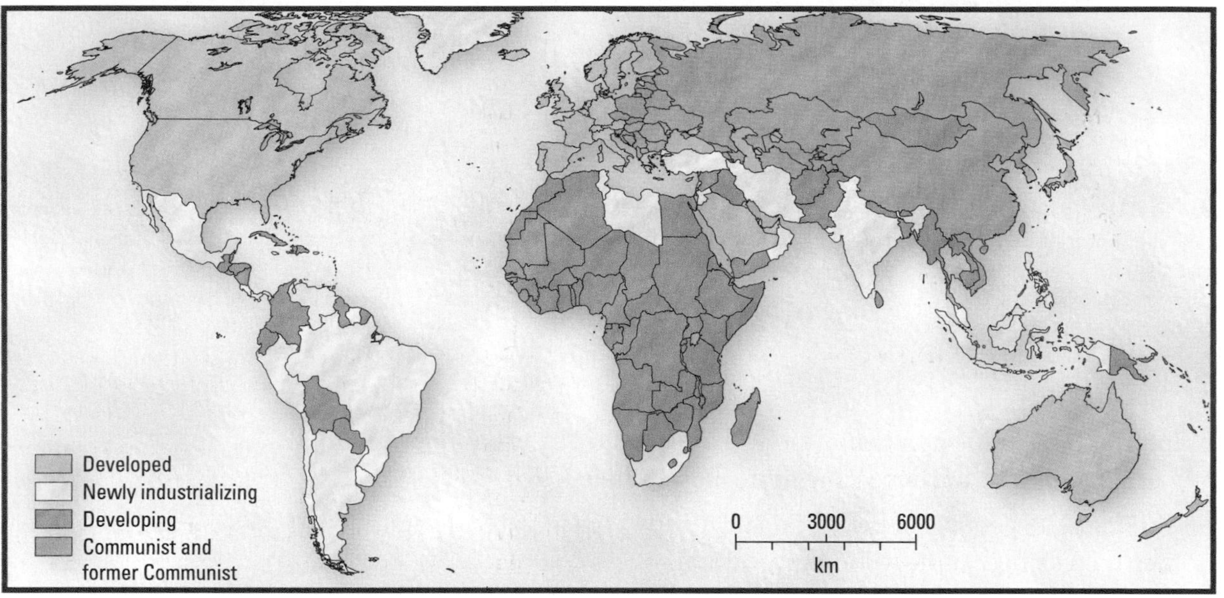

LIFE EXPECTANCY

How long a country's people can hope to live is an indicator of development of a country's healthcare and social system. Fig. 32-5 shows how long a person can expect to live in 18 different countries. As you can see, there are large differences in **life expectancy** among these countries. Fig. 32-6 rearranges the same data to show life expectancy from shortest to longest. We can see that countries such as Canada, Japan, and Germany have much longer life expectancies than countries such as Nigeria, Bangladesh, and Kenya.

The HIV/AIDS epidemic in Africa has caused the life expectancy in some countries to drop below 40 years.

1. a) Use the information in Figs. 32-5 and 32-6 to rank the countries from 1 to 18, with 1 being the longest life expectancy.
   b) Average the rankings for any countries that are tied. For example, since Australia and Japan are tied for first and second place, give each a ranking of 1.5 [(1 + 2)/2 = 1.5]. The United States, Germany, and Singapore are tied for fourth, fifth, and sixth place so each should have a ranking of 5 [(4 + 5 + 6)/3 = 5)].
   c) Copy the organizer in Fig. 32-7 into your notebook. List the countries alphabetically in the first column. Transfer the rankings of life expectancy from the list you created in 1a) and 1b).

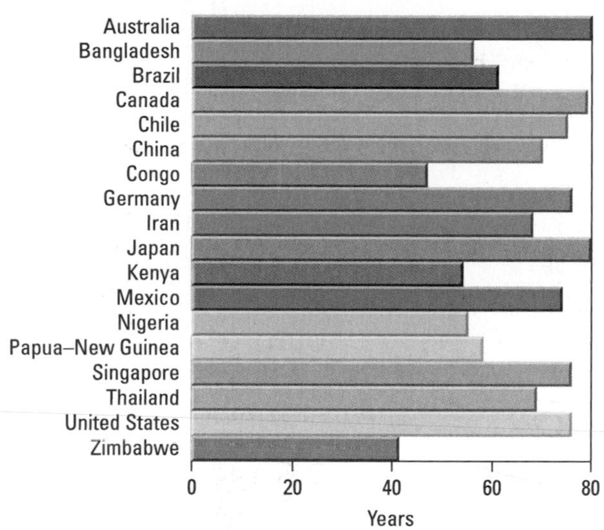

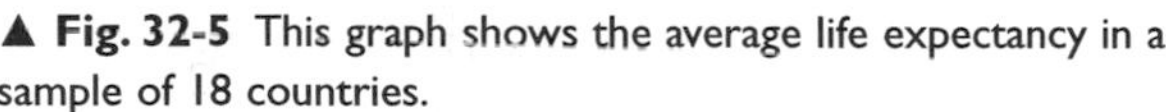

▲ **Fig. 32-5** This graph shows the average life expectancy in a sample of 18 countries.

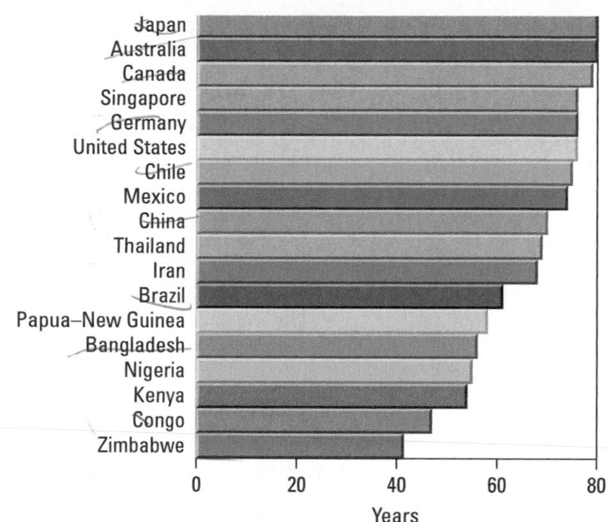

▲ **Fig. 32-6** If we sort countries according to life expectancy (from longest to shortest), it becomes easier to see that certain countries can be grouped together. If we had data for all of the countries in the world, we would follow the same process—it would just be a lot more work. Note that it would be much faster if we could find a data source that already gave us the statistics sorted from high to low (or low to high) rather than sorted alphabetically. Many on-line data sources give the user the option to display the data in various ways.

▼ **Fig. 32-7**

	Life Expectancy (years)	GDP per Capita (US$) PPP	Natural Increase Rate %	Undernourished People as % of Total	Literacy Level (%)	Doctors per 100 000 People, 2004	TOTAL
Australia							
Bangladesh							
Brazil							
Canada							

WEALTH

GDP per capita (PPP) is the most commonly used measure of a country's wealth. It measures the total value of goods and services a country produces in a year on a per person basis. In developing countries, even the basics of life—food, shelter, and clothing—may not be available to most people. On the other hand, in developed countries, new products are constantly being created for people to purchase. More powerful video game systems, designer clothing, and the latest athlete-endorsed running shoes are just a few of the non-essential items that some people in developed countries may feel they "need." You can probably think of other examples.

The Purchasing Power Parity (PPP) version of GDP per capita is used here. It is more accurate than the simple GDP per capita measure since income is related to the cost of living in the country.

	GDP per Capita (US$), PPP, 2004	Natural Increase Rate (per 1000), 2005	Undernourished People as % of Total, 1998–2000	Literacy Level (%), 2003	Doctors per 100 000 People, 2004
Australia	30 700	4.8	neg.	100	240
Bangladesh	2 000	21.6	35	43	23
Brazil	8 100	10.7	10	86	206
Canada	31 500	3.1	neg.	97	209
Chile	10 700	9.7	4	96	109
China	5 600	6.2	9	86	164
Congo, Dem. Rep.	700	29.9	73	66	7
Germany	28 700	−2.2	neg.	99	362
Iran	7 700	11.3	5	79	105
Japan	29 400	0.5	neg.	99	201
Kenya	1 100	25.5	44	85	13
Mexico	9 600	16.2	5	92	171
Nigeria	1 000	23.5	7	68	27
Papua–New Guinea	2 200	22.6	27	66	5
Singapore	27 800	5.3	neg.	93	140
Thailand	8 100	8.7	18	95	30
United States	40 100	5.9	neg.	97	549
Zimbabwe	1 900	5.1	38	91	6

neg. = negligible

▲ **Fig. 32-8** Use these data to complete the activity.

2. Fig. 32-8 shows the GDP per capita for the sample of 18 countries. Sort these statistics from high to low GDP per capita. The highest GDP per capita would be ranked 1 and the lowest 18. Add the rankings to your organizer.

Natural Increase Rate = Birth Rate – Death Rate

You can learn more about the natural increase rate in Chapter 16.

NATURAL INCREASE RATE

As a country develops, it is typical for the natural increase rate to decrease. There are many reasons for this. For example, in a developed country most women have control over how many children they will have. In addition, people in countries with pension systems and effective health care do not feel the need to have large families to support them in their old age.

3. Using the data in Fig. 32-8, sort the statistics from low to high natural increase rates for the 18 countries, with 1 being the lowest population growth rate. Add these rankings to your organizer.

FOOD SUPPLY

Food supplies energy to the human body. The amount of food energy needed to survive varies from country to country. This is because of differences in average body size, the age composition of the population, and the climate. Generally speaking, people in tropical regions need less food energy than those in colder climates. Canada, for example, has an average daily requirement of 11 172 kJ (kilojoules), while Indonesia has an average of only 9072 kJ. In this study we measure food supply by examining how many people in the country are undernourished, i.e., do not have enough to eat based on what is needed in that country.

Why do people in cooler countries like Canada need to eat more than those in warmer countries?

4. Use the data in Fig. 32-8 to sort the countries' food supply from high to low, with 1 being the highest level of food supply. (Assume that **negligible** is equivalent to zero.) Transfer the ratings to your organizer.

negligible insignificant

EDUCATION LEVEL

Many experts would suggest that the best way to advance a country's economic and social development is to improve the education of the country's citizens. Educational achievement can be measured in many ways. One of the simplest is to determine the **literacy** level, that is, the percentage of the population that can read and write. Experts know that if literacy is higher, it is easier to spread information about such things as better farming methods and health issues.

5. Sort the literacy levels in Fig. 32-8 from high to low, with 1 being the highest literacy level. Place the rankings in your organizer.

HEALTHCARE

You may have suffered from diarrhea on occasion. Your parents probably had measles when they were children and had to stay home from school for a few weeks. In developed countries, we assume that we will recover from what we think of as minor illnesses like diarrhea, and we are able to eliminate diseases like the measles almost entirely. In developing countries, though, thousands of children die each year from illnesses like these.

You almost certainly have not had measles, formerly a common childhood disease, since you likely received vaccines to prevent it.

An effective healthcare system is an important indicator of a country's level of development. One way to measure the quality of the health care system is to know how many people, on average, each doctor must look after.

6. The final column of data in Fig. 32-8 shows the number of doctors per 100 000 people for the 18 countries. Rank these from lowest to highest, with 1 having the highest number of doctors per 100 000 people. List the rankings in your organizer.
7. For each country, total the rankings for the six measures used. Based on these totals, divide the countries into three groups of six, from most to least developed. These three groups of countries represent different levels of development: developed countries, newly industrializing, and developing countries.

INTERNET

To get detailed information about countries, check www.pearsoned.ca/makingconnections2.

The Three Levels of Development

Developed Countries

Countries classified as "developed" are at the highest level of economic and social development. What are the characteristics of developed countries?

- Citizens of the developed countries have the highest standard of living in the world. Even the poorest people in these countries live well compared to many people in developing countries.
- Their economies are based increasingly on the service sector. They have well-developed services such as education, healthcare, banking, transportation, and information technologies.
- While most of these countries developed because of advanced manufacturing, manufacturing is a less important economic activity today than in the past.
- Primary industries, while highly efficient, are the least important part of the economy in terms of value and providing jobs.

See Chapter 22 for more information on primary industry.

The wealth and high living standard of developed countries have been achieved at great cost. Despite the fact that they have only about 20% of the world's population, they use most of the world's resources and produce most of its pollution. In the years to come, it will be a great challenge for these countries to maintain their standard of living while reducing their impact on the world's environment.

See Chapter 39 for more information on the ecological cost of development.

Developing Countries

Of the three groups, "developing countries" have the lowest levels of economic and social growth. Most of the countries of Africa and many countries in Asia are members of this group. They tend to share the following characteristics:

- In contrast to the developed world, developing countries have economies that are dominated by primary industries and, in particular, by agriculture (Fig. 32-9). In most developing countries, the majority of people are farmers who consume most of what they produce.
- Much new development is focused on manufacturing since these countries often have raw materials that can be used in manufacturing. Furthermore, their rapidly growing populations need manufactured goods of all types.
- The service sector of the economy tends to be poorly developed since most people have little money to spend on services such as telephones, movies, schools, and restaurants.
- Citizens earn little cash income. Most of their production is for their own use or is traded to supply their needs.
- Since citizens earn so little, they do not pay taxes. As a result, the government is not able to provide money for education, healthcare, or economic development. Frequently, developing countries have to rely on **foreign aid** to pay for such things.

▲ **Fig. 32-9** The economy of developing countries is dominated by agriculture.

Not enough foreign aid is available to meet all of these needs.

Newly Industrializing Countries

Different countries in many parts of the world are moving from the category "developing countries" to the category "newly industrializing." The economies of these countries were once based mainly on agriculture. Over time, different manufacturing industries became established.

As the industrial base grows and diversifies, the service industry will also increase in size, and this will help improve the standard of living. This process takes many years to occur. Perhaps the best examples of this change in the last 60 years or so have occurred in southeast Asia, especially in the "Four Dragons": Taiwan, South Korea, Hong Kong, and Singapore. Each has progressed from the developing stage to the developed stage since the end of World War II. They progressed by achieving economic growth rates much greater than those that were occurring in developed countries. The enormous changes involved in becoming developed are currently occurring in other countries of Asia such as China and Malaysia, and in Latin America countries such as Brazil and Chile.

Limitations of Grouping Countries

While there are some obvious and important advantages to grouping countries as we have done here, there are also some problems with this method.

- One problem is deciding what "progress" and "development" really are. For example, by the definition we have used here, a country can be seen to "develop" when it increases its GDP per capita, even if this increase may not improve the quality of life for the country's citizens. For instance, if a country spends a great deal of money on its military or on industrial development that causes major environmental damage, it will increase its GDP but might cause harm to its citizens.

Remember that high military expenditures might be used to keep a dictator in power.

- Consider what isn't revealed in GDP statistics. In some countries, most people produce their own food. This fact would not be reflected in GDP statistics since this food was not sold to anyone. On the other hand, farmers may grow **cash crops** like coffee and sugar, which they sell and thus add to the GDP. However, the land used for cash cropping is no longer available for growing food and the coffee and sugar workers may not earn enough to provide their families with adequate healthcare, education, or even food.

When the farmer buys food and other items this increases the GDP as well.

- A third problem is that there are only three groups. This means that each group contains countries that can be very different from each other. For example, compare Bangladesh and Nigeria. Bangladesh has a huge population and few marketable natural resources, while Nigeria has vast **reserves** of natural resources like oil and natural gas.

reserves
amounts

- A fourth problem is that this approach assumes that a country's level of economic and social development is the same throughout the population. Clearly this is not the case. In Canada, we have people who are billionaires and others who live on the street. In countries such as China and India, some people drive luxury automobiles and live in fancy homes while hundreds of millions struggle to feed their families. Each group gives only a broad picture of the level of economic and social development of the countries within it.

Cuba, for example, has levels of economic development that you would expect to find in a developing country, but levels of social development typical of a developed country.

- Not all countries fit neatly into one or another of the three groups. You have seen that countries with the most advanced economies usually have the most highly developed social programs. Countries that were once allies of the Soviet Union or part of the Soviet Union itself, however, had more highly developed social programs than economic development. So, in which group do they belong? The level of economic development in the former Soviet bloc countries is beginning to match that of their neighbours. Former Soviet **bloc** countries such as Estonia, Hungary, and even Russia itself, may move into the developed countries category. Others, such as Kazakhstan and Uzbekistan, may fall into the newly industrializing category.

bloc
group of countries with a shared aim such as the group of eastern European communist countries formerly controlled by the Soviet Union

- A final problem is that these groupings are only a snapshot of the situation at a particular time. They do not reflect the fact that rapid changes may be occurring.

QUESTIONS

KNOWLEDGE AND UNDERSTANDING

1. Describe the characteristics of developed, developing, and newly industralizing countries. Give two examples of each that are not listed in Fig. 32-8.
2. a) Copy Fig. 32-10 into your notebook and complete it using the information from Figs. 32-6 and 32-8. The first row has been completed for you.
   b) Briefly describe the importance of each characteristic to a country's well-being.

▼ **Fig. 32-10**

Characteristic	Developed	Newly Industrializing	Developing
Life Expectancy (years)	76–80	61–78	41–56
GDP per Capita			
Natural Increase Rate (per 1000), 2005			
Undernourished People (%)			
Literacy Level (%)			
No. of Doctors per 100 000 People			

THINKING

3. a) Using Fig. 32-4, identify the parts of the world where most of the developed and developing countries are located.
   b) Sometimes these two groups of countries are called the North and the South. What is meant by this, and what significance does it have?

COMMUNICATION

4. What do you think are the two most serious problems facing most developed countries? How should we deal with them? Share your ideas with a partner. Then, as a class, reach a consensus on what the two most serious problems are and create a master list of ideas for dealing with them.

APPLICATION

5. a) Assume that you thought that using three groups of countries was too complicated. How would you divide the world into only two groups? What would be the main advantage and main disadvantage of having two groups?
   b) It is possible to criticize the three-country group model for being oversimplified—consider the problem of having countries like Nigeria and Bangladesh in the same group or Chile and China together. Assume that you decide to have more than three groups, how many additional groups would you add? What would be the distinctive characteristics of each of these groups? What would be the main advantage and main disadvantage of having more than three groups?

33 Canada's International Relationships

Key Ideas

This chapter helps you investigate these questions:

- What connections do we have with other countries, as individuals and as a nation?
- What roles does Canada play in the world?
- What impact is globalization having on Canada?

Key Terms

peacekeeping

peacemaking

foreign aid

official development assistance (ODA)

non-governmental organizations (NGOs)

globalization

multinational corporations (MNCs)

The relationships that exist among the world's countries and, in particular, the relationships between Canada and other countries take many forms. Some relationships are very formal—for example, treaties between the governments of Canada and other nations—while others are informal, for example, when we holiday in another country.

- Canada belongs to a wide variety of international organizations in which countries work together to make the world a safer, happier, and healthier place in which to live.
- The world's economies are so closely linked that you may see the same movies, wear the same brands of clothing, and eat many of the same types of food as teenagers who live on the other side of the world.
- Every day, Canadians have cultural contacts with the world through television, movies, books, magazines, the Internet, and family connections. The most important athletic competitions, such as the Olympics and World Cup of soccer, are worldwide in scope.

Despite differences in their standards of living, culture, language, and lifestyle, the people of the world must learn to cooperate with one another. Because we all share one planet, problems that affect people in one part of the world sooner or later affect people in another part of the world. We all have more similarities than differences, and yet, for the last century, conflict has been much more common than cooperation. Two devastating world wars and dozens of smaller wars claimed millions of lives. Furthermore, much of the world has experienced poverty and environmental damage. In recent years, a major increase in violent terrorism has occurred in many parts of the world. Canada has been a leader in trying to find ways to eliminate conflict, poverty, and environmental problems and to minimize the damage they cause.

INTERNET

To learn more about Canada's foreign policy, check www.pearsoned.ca/makingconnections2.

Canada and the United Nations

When the United Nations was formed in 1945 to promote world peace and to help poorer countries develop economically and socially, Canada was one of the 50 founding members. Since 1945, the UN has grown to include more than 190 countries. Unfortunately, the UN often has difficulty resolving major international crises because of political differences among its members. It does, however, provide a forum for discussions and may have helped to prevent a third world war since it was established over 50 years ago.

When people think about the UN, they tend to focus on its political activities, which are centred at the UN headquarters in New York. The activities of the UN go far beyond settling political and military conflicts. Fig. 33-1 outlines just a few of the specialized UN agencies that have quietly cooperated in solving international problems for many years. One UN organization has its headquarters in Canada. The International Civil Aviation Organization (ICAO), located in Montreal, has responsibilities such as coordinating air traffic control and setting standards for air-flight security.

In 1957, Lester B. Pearson, who later became Prime Minister of Canada, was given the Nobel Peace Prize for proposing the first UN peacekeeping operation. This operation resolved the Suez Canal crisis in the Middle East.

The UN sometimes acts as the world's peacekeeper. It organizes military and police forces made up of troops from member states. Canada has been involved in more peacekeeping operations than any other country. Peacekeepers are sent to scenes of conflict to make sure that truces are being observed. In some cases—for example, Cyprus—UN peacekeeping forces have been in place for more than 30 years with no indication that they will be withdrawn soon. Over 90 000 Canadian armed forces personnel (along with a much smaller number of Royal Canadian Mounted Police and other police officers) have served as peacekeepers in Eastern Europe, Cyprus, the Middle East, Africa, Southeast Asia, and Latin America (Fig. 33-2).

▼ **Fig. 33-1** These are just a few of the specialized organizations that are part of the United Nations. You may have raised money to support UNICEF activities at Halloween.

Program/Organization	Purpose
• United Nations International Children's Fund (UNICEF)	• to provide emergency relief aid and promote the role of children
• Food and Agriculture Organization (FAO)	• to raise levels of nutrition, improve production, and distribute food
• The World Health Organization (WHO)	• to direct and coordinate activities, promote research, and supply drugs and equipment where needed

Fig. 33-2 ▶ These Canadian peacekeepers are wearing the distinctive blue helmets of UN peacekeeping forces.

Issue

PEACEMAKING EFFORTS OUTSIDE THE UN

◀ **Fig. 33-3** These naval officers are serving on *HMCS Winnipeg*, shown here in the Persian Gulf, where the Canadians are part of the US-led coalition campaign against the terrorism mission known as *Enduring Freedom*.

Background

United Nations peacekeeping operations must be agreed to by the Security Council. This powerful body is dominated by its five permanent members: China, France, Great Britain, Russia, and the United States, each of which can **veto** any motion that is being considered by the Council. Often vetoes are cast because these countries have conflicting political needs. As a result, the UN often failed to resolve armed conflicts that were devastating to the populations of many countries. Since the early 1990s, Canada, along with many of its traditional allies, has been less involved with UN-led peacekeeping missions. Instead, we have been involved in a number of peacemaking missions. These missions have been led by other countries (principally the United States) instead of by the United Nations. The difference between peace*keeping* and peace*making* is a critical one. **Peacekeeping** occurs where the parties in a conflict have agreed to work toward peace. The role of the peacekeeper is to support the peace on the ground—often acting as a police

veto
power to reject

force or conflict mediator. **Peacemaking** occurs where there has been no peace agreement and military operations may be necessary to create peace. Peacemaking thus can be much more difficult and dangerous.

The first of these peacemaking missions was Operation Desert Storm in 1991. Desert Storm involved a major coordinated military operation by many nations to drive the Iraqi army out of the neighbouring country of Kuwait, which they had occupied in 1990.

The second mission was in Bosnia in eastern Europe starting in 1992. Here, there was an existing UN peacekeeping force (including Canadians) but it was not nearly large enough to cope with the vicious conflict that was occurring. The North Atlantic Treaty Organization (NATO) organized a powerful military force to deal with the situation. Again the Canadian Forces were involved in this effort.

A third peacemaking effort was the invasion of Afghanistan that occurred in 2002. The government of Afghanistan had been offering a safe home for the terrorist organization that launched the devastating attacks on the United States on September 11, 2001. A NATO military force, led by the United States and including the Canadian Forces, entered Afghanistan to overthrow this government and capture terrorist leaders.

Canada has not always chosen to be part of American-led military operations. In 2003, the Canadian government decided not to be involved in the American invasion of Iraq. Some of our traditional allies, like Great Britain and Australia, chose to join the American military force, while others, like France and Germany, did not.

INTERNET

There are many reasons why Canada chose not to get involved in Iraq. Visit www.pearsoned.ca/makingconnections2 for detailed information.

Activities

1. Investigate how the Security Council works and the efforts that have been made to reform its membership and operation. Assume that you have been given the job of improving the Security Council. What changes would you make?
2. What factors should be considered by the Canadian government when we are asked to be involved in a US-led international military mission?
3. a) Canada was a leader in UN peacekeeping efforts for more than 40 years. Consider Canada's history and current situation, and then suggest why Canada was more involved in peacekeeping than the following countries.
   i. United States
   ii. United Kingdom
   iii. Bangladesh

   b) Give two reasons not mentioned in 3a) that would explain Canada's long-standing commitment to peacekeeping.

   c) Since 1991, Canada's role has been one of peacemaking rather than peacekeeping. Why has this change occurred?

To learn more about peacekeeping, check www.pearsoned.ca/makingconnections2.

INTERNET

Want to learn more about Africa's needs? Go to www.pearsoned.ca/makingconnections2.

Your teacher will give you instructions for a GIS activity that examines Canada's foreign aid.

INTERNET

To learn more about *Free The Children* and *Help Lesotho*, and to link to dozens of Canadian NGOs who work in the developing world, visit www.pearsoned.ca/makingconnections2.

Foreign Aid

In July 2005, an estimated three billion people watched a series of nine televised concerts that were held to pressure the governments of the rich nations of the world into giving more support to poor nations, especially Africa (Fig. 33-4). A major part of this support would involve increasing the amount of foreign aid given. The target for such aid is 0.7% of each country's gross national income (GNI) (Fig. 33-5). Only a few countries, particularly in northern Europe, have hit this target (which was originally suggested by former Prime Minister Lester B. Pearson).

Much of Canada's **foreign aid** is managed by the Canadian International Development Agency (CIDA). CIDA follows four principles in its operation:

- deal with poverty first
- help people to help themselves
- promote development
- build partnerships

Government-provided foreign aid, or **official development assistance (ODA)** as it is formally known, is only one of the ways in which Canada and Canadians help those in poorer countries. Canadians also give their time and money to a wide range of **non-governmental organizations (NGOs)**. Some NGOs, such as the *Red Cross*, provide a wide range of aid around the world and have existed for more than a century. Others are much smaller and have been started in recent years by Canadians to meet the specific needs of one group or one country. Examples are *Free The Children* (Fig. 33-6), which was created to help children in developing countries, and *Help Lesotho,* which was created to provide aid to a tiny country in Africa.

◄ **Fig. 33-4** Canada's Live 8 concert was held in Barrie, Ontario. Concerts were also held in the United States, Britain, France, Italy, Germany, Japan, Russia, and South Africa.

	1990 Amount (US$ billion)	1990 % of GNI	2004 Amount (US$ billion)	2004 % of GNI
Canada	2.47	0.42	2.54	0.26
Australia	0.96	0.34	1.46	0.25
Denmark	1.17	0.93	2.03	0.84
Sweden	2.01	0.90	2.70	0.77
Switzerland	0.75	0.31	1.38	0.37
United Kingdom	2.64	0.27	7.84	0.36
United States	11.39	0.21	19.00	0.16

◀ **Fig. 33-5** Foreign aid in billions of US dollars by a number of developed countries in 1990 and 2004. GNI—Gross National Income—is a measure used by organizations such as the World Bank and the Organisation for Economic Co-operation Development. GNI is very much like GDP.

◀ **Fig. 33-6** *Free The Children* was created by Craig Kielburger and 11 of his friends in 1995, when they were 12 years old. Their goal was to fight against child labour in the world. Here, Craig speaks with children in Manila, Philippines, to learn what *Free the Children* can do to help them spend their time at school, instead of foraging through a garbage dump trying to find items they can sell to help feed themselves and their families.

GeoCareers

International Development

As you have learned in this course, Canadians are very lucky. We live in a wealthy, safe country that provides enormous opportunities to its people. Most of the world's people, however, are not nearly so fortunate. They live in poverty, in places with terrible health conditions, often without enough to eat and too often in fear for their lives. Increasing numbers of Canadians are choosing their careers in the growing field of international development (ID) because they want to do something to help people in need.

ID workers are involved in an enormous range of activities because developing countries need help in so many areas. Some of these areas are entirely obvious: education, healthcare, agriculture, water purification, sewage treatment, and economic development. Assistance is required from educational experts, healthcare professionals, agricultural specialists, engineers, and economic development specialists. Other international development opportunities are not so obvious. For example, a recent ID job listing included a position for someone with expertise in running a community radio station for Indonesia and one for a honey advisor to help with the development of a beekeeping industry in the Solomon Islands.

There are two very different ways to prepare for an ID career. One is to study international development in university. Most undergraduate (bachelor's level) programs in ID are fairly general in nature. Students gain a wide knowledge of how development works and how development problems can be solved. In most of these programs, students have opportunities to gain practical experience by working in a developing country for a period of time. Some graduate (master's level) programs, however, are very specific. For example, some programs offer courses that focus on issues in developing countries and develop student expertise in such fields as small-scale farming techniques, government management, and urban and rural planning. Community colleges also offer training in specific fields that can be applied to developing countries. Courses in radio station management, computer repair and maintenance, and the various trades—electrical, plumbing, and building—give students the skills necessary to work in ID.

Find Out More

Investigate international development-related careers.

1. Begin by examining the types of careers that are available in ID. A good starting place is www.pearsoned.ca/makingconnections2. You might also want to talk to a guidance counsellor for help with this.
   a) Identify five careers for which university studies in ID would be required. Does each of these require a bachelor's degree or a graduate degree? What additional experience does each require?
   b) Identify five careers for which specialized job training and experience would be needed. How would someone gain the experience needed for this type of job?
2. Do a search of universities that offer undergraduate international development degrees. A good starting point for this is www.pearsoned.ca/makingconnections2.
   a) List three universities that have such programs.

b) Give the names of the particular departments (or faculties) in each institution that offer this education.
c) Briefly describe the kind of courses that you would take in one of the universities mentioned in a).

3. What are the academic requirements to gain admission to the universities you chose in 2a)? Specifically, what high school courses would you need and how high would your marks have to be?
4. Find information about at least one person who has pursued an international development career, and write a summary of that person's experiences.
5. What aspects of international development might interest you as a potential career? Explain your answer.

Canada's Economic Links

International relationships are becoming more and more important as we move into a period of increased **globalization**. What globalization means is that borders between countries are becoming less important as the world operates increasingly as one unit. This can be seen in a number of areas, most noticeably in the economic world. In the past, companies operated primarily in one country or one small region. Now, large companies called **multinational corporations** (**MNCs**) operate across the entire world. Examples of MNCs are given in Fig. 33-7.

Some MNCs are larger, economically, than many countries. For example, Shell Oil's revenues in 2004 were about US$268 billion, equivalent to the value of all production (GDP) in Turkey in that year. Toyota's revenues of US$173 billion were slightly more than the GDP of Finland. Because of their enormous size and worldwide operations, MNCs are able to move their operations from place to place as they see opportunities emerge. This can mean that a decision made outside Canada may cause joy in a Canadian community where an MNC opens a new mine that provides employment. It also can mean sadness when an MNC closes a factory and people lose their jobs.

Economic globalization brings both risks and opportunities for Canada. If the international business community feels that Canada has a **competitive advantage** over other countries, then it will expand its operations here. The advantage could be that our country has a highly educated labour force, cheap raw materials, or a stable society. If international businesses expand their operations in Canada there will be more jobs created

competitive advantage If it is cheaper to operate a business in Canada, then Canada has a competitive advantage. A competitive advantage allows the company to compete more effectively with companies in other countries.

and our economy will grow. On the other hand, if the international business community decides that other countries have an advantage, then it will move jobs out of Canada and our economy will be hurt. In recent years, many Canadian jobs have been "outsourced" to countries like China and India where labour costs are much lower than here. In particular, manufacturing jobs have gone to China and information technology jobs have gone to India. It is almost impossible for Canada to compete with these countries on labour costs—we have to find our competitive advantage elsewhere.

Fig. 33-7 ▶ Examples of multinational corporations

Company	Home Country	Type of Business
Walt Disney	United States	Entertainment
Shell Oil	Netherlands	Oil
Bata	Canada	Shoes
Toyota	Japan	Automobiles
Microsoft	United States	Computer software
Bombardier	Canada	Aircraft and trains
Panasonic	Japan	Electronics
Adidas	Germany	Athletic clothing and footwear

Canada's Cultural Links

Globalization is also important in the cultural field. Increasingly, the cultures of the world seem to be losing their distinctiveness. There are a number of reasons why this is happening. Television, movies, popular music, professional sports, and the Internet all provide opportunities for people to be exposed to the cultures of other countries. The result is that teenagers in Senegal, Sri Lanka, Peru, and Canada may watch the same television shows and movies, listen to the same music, have the same sports heroes, and wear the same clothing styles.

However, many people say that this is not a question of globalization. Instead, they say that it is really the Americanization of the world's cultures since the United States is the source of most of the entertainment and styles that influence the rest of the world. In some areas of the world, this Americanization or globalization (if you prefer that term) is happening with little objection, while in others, there is a violent reaction against this cultural change.

The cultural influence of the United States on Canada is considered in more detail in Chapter 35.

QUESTIONS

KNOWLEDGE AND UNDERSTANDING

1. Identify and describe, with examples, three different types of connections that Canada and Canadians have with other countries.
2. a) Describe three main roles played by the United Nations in the world.
   b) Describe one key role that Canada has played within the UN.

THINKING

3. a) List the four principles that govern the activities of CIDA.
   b) Discuss why these principles were chosen. Can you suggest any other principles that might have been used instead of, or in addition to, these?
4. a) Select an international organization to which Canada belongs and identify its purpose (e.g., Commonwealth, La Francophonie, NATO, G8, International Olympic Committee).
   b) Evaluate its effectiveness in addressing global concerns.
5. Many people have petitioned the governments of the G8 countries to forgive the debts of developing nations. Give arguments that support, and arguments that oppose, this idea.

GeoLit Reminder

Revising your work:

- Have you answered the assigned question?
- Does the introduction outline your main ideas?
- Is your supporting information accurate, well organized, and on topic?
- Have you checked spelling and grammar?
- Have you included a proper bibliography?
- Have you asked a classmate to edit your work?

6. a) The amount of money that Canada has for foreign aid is much less than is needed to meet all the needs of developing countries. Name three factors that Canada should consider when deciding which countries should get the most aid.
   b) Using the factors identified in (a), make a list of the 10 countries on which you think Canada should focus its aid effort. Map and label these on a world map with a light shading of one colour.
   c) Go to www.pearsoned.ca/makingconnections2, where you will find a link to a list from the Organisation for Economic Co-operation and Development (OECD) of the 10 countries that get the most aid. Map these with a light shading of a different colour. Remember to add a title and legend to your map.
   d) Is the list you made for (b) similar to the OECD's list? Suggest reasons for any differences between the two lists.

COMMUNICATION

7. Research the purpose and operations of one international development–related NGO that has a Canadian connection of some sort. Present your findings as a bullet chart with appropriate illustrations added.
8. In a group of three or four students, discuss the following questions. Summarize your discussion in your notebook.
   a) How might the world be different today if the UN had not been created after World War II?
   b) One example of an international problem that requires the united action of many countries is international terrorism. Describe three other international problems that require united action for their resolution.
   c) Would you expect international agencies related to the UN to solve these problems? Check to see if such agencies exist.
   d) What contribution could Canada make to help solve the problems you identified in (b)?

APPLICATION

9. "Because we all share one planet, problems that affect people in one part of the world sooner or later affect people in another part of the world. We all have more similarities than differences, and yet, for the last century, conflict has been much more common than cooperation." This statement was made in reference to the need for people across the world to work together to solve the problems they face.
   a) Describe the nature of the similarities and differences among people in the world.
   b) Give at least two examples of problems in one part of the world that eventually affect people elsewhere.
10. Consider the meaning of the term *world power*. On one hand, Canada is not as economically, militarily, or politically powerful as the United States, but on the other hand, we have more international clout than countries like Senegal or Honduras. Where does Canada rank as a world power? Give evidence to support your answer.
11. Here is one person's opinion: "Canada should not give away more than $2 billion per year in foreign aid when we have such serious economic and social problems at home."
   a) Give arguments supporting this position.
   b) Give arguments opposing this position.
   c) What is your personal belief? Why?
12. Put yourself in the place of the prime minister of Canada or the premier of a province. You realize that MNCs are not choosing to expand in Canada as much as you would like. These companies feel that wage rates are too high here and environmental standards are too tight. Would you support changing Canadian laws to allow lower labour costs and relaxed environmental standards? If you would, explain why. If you would not, what alternative strategies would you suggest to encourage MNCs to invest in Canada?

34 Foreign Trade: The Foundation of Canada's Economy

Key Ideas

This chapter helps you investigate these questions:

- What are Canada's most important import and export goods and services?
- With which countries do we trade most?
- How has Canada been affected by free trade?
- What issues are there for the future of Canada's trade?

Key Terms

imports
exports
trade surplus
trade deficit
net exports
net imports
import substitution
tariff
protectionism
free trade

What do all of the objects in Fig. 34-1 have in common? If you guessed that all of the objects shown are typical **imports** to Canada, then you would be right. Canada also **exports** a wide range of products. A picture of these would include such things as crude oil, minivans, giant rolls of newsprint, airplanes, natural gas, wheat, and coal. A comparison of the items Canadians import with those we export shows significant differences between the kinds of things that Canada buys from others and what we sell.

More than 300 years ago, a famous English poet named John Donne wrote, "No man is an island, entire of itself." He meant that no person

◀ **Fig. 34-1** These items represent Canada's four major import categories: motor vehicle parts, goods produced only in warmer climates, high-technology products, and low-cost goods. Can you identify the category each item belongs to, and the possible country of origin? (Some items may have more than one answer.)

To help you understand more clearly what $363 billion is, this means that Canada imports about $11,500 worth of goods per second for the entire year. Remember that we export even more than this!

Examples of specialized manufactured goods exported from Canada in 2004 include $19 billion worth of computers, telecommunications, and related equipment. In the same year, Canadians also exported almost $11 billion worth of aircraft.

Your teacher may give you instructions to complete a GIS exercise on motor vehicle production in North America.

GeoLit Reminder

When checking your finished graph:

- Have you given your graph a title that clearly reflects the topic?
- Is your graph legend useful to the reader and properly positioned?
- Are your labels correctly spelled and properly aligned?
- Have you used colour appropriately?

could exist without others. A similar situation exists for countries. No nation can survive independent of other countries, and with globalization, this interdependence of countries will only increase. This chapter explores the complex and fascinating business of international trade and why it is so important to all Canadians.

In 2004, Canada imported goods worth more than $363 billion. Our exports were $429 billion. When the value of exports is greater than the value of imports, a **trade surplus** exists. When imports are higher than exports a **trade deficit** occurs. Our trade surplus in *goods* is vital since Canada imports more *services* than it exports. Our trade deficit for services in 2004 was $13 billion. In this year, our trade surplus in goods was $66 billion. Combining these two, our net surplus was $53 billion.

The whole question of trade could affect you personally in the years to come. Right now, one out of every five jobs in Canada is tied to exports, and this fraction is growing. With globalization, countries will tend to produce and export only a few specialized commodities, and they will have to import many other products they need. Keep the export/import field in mind when you start looking for a job in a few years.

Analyzing Canada's Trade

While Canada's pattern of trade is very complex, it is relatively easy to understand if we remember a few simple facts.

- Canada trades with countries all over the world, but our trade with the United States far exceeds our total trade with all other countries.
- In general, Canada's imports fall into four categories:
  - high-technology products
  - motor vehicle parts
  - goods produced only in warmer climates
  - low-cost goods
- Most of our exports fall into only three categories:
  - products based on our natural resources
  - motor vehicles
  - specialized manufactured goods

ACTIVITY

1. Figure 34-2 lists our top 10 trading partners for 2004 and the value of the export or import trade with each.
   a) Create a bar graph that shows the countries that bought Canada's exports and the value of the exports that each country bought. (Hint: put the $ on the horizontal axis and use the entire width of the page for your graph.)
   b) Create a second bar graph showing our top 10 import partners and the value of the imports from each.

Imports	2004	Exports	2004
Country	**Amount ($million)**	**Country**	**Amount ($million)**
United States	208 954	United States	348 142
China	24 098	Japan	8 557
Mexico	13 409	United Kingdom	7 745
Japan	13 368	China	6 653
United Kingdom	9 657	Mexico	2 994
Germany	9 415	Germany	2 667
South Korea	5 824	France	2 377
France	5 334	South Korea	2 266
Norway	4 955	Belgium	2 223
Italy	4 569	Netherlands	1 922

◀ **Fig. 34-2** Canada's top 10 trading partners, 2004

2. Fig. 34-3 shows some important export items for Canada. When you compare the amount of these goods that we export to the amount we import, you can see that these are important sources of wealth for our economy.
   a) For each, calculate the amount by which our exports exceed our imports. These could be described as **net exports**, since the export amount is greater than the import amount.
   b) Into which category of exports does each of these items fall?
   c) Name three other commodities that you think would be significant net exports for Canada's economy.

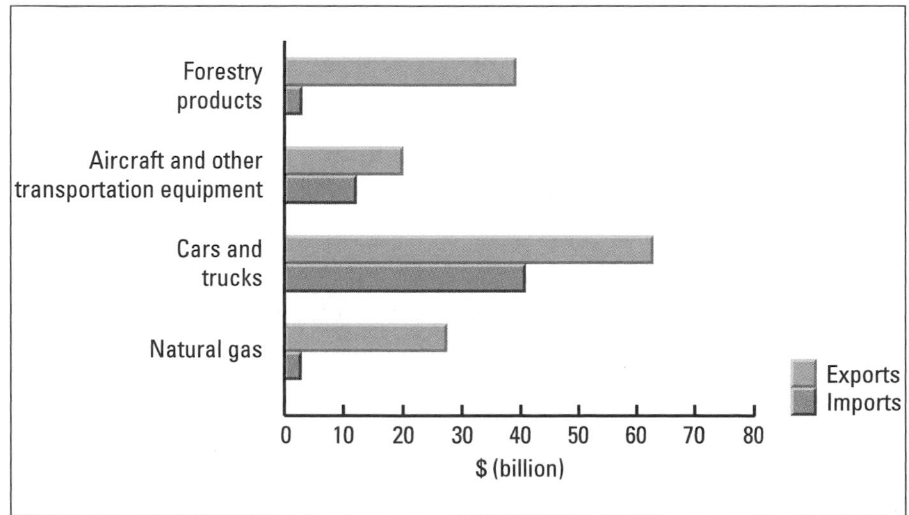

◀ **Fig. 34-3** Some important net export items for Canada, 2004

3. a) Fig. 34-4 shows some important import items for Canada. In contrast to the net exports mentioned in Question 2, these items could be described as **net imports** for Canada. Why?
   b) For each, calculate the amount by which the imports exceed the exports.
   c) Into which category of imports does each of these commodities fall?
   d) Name three other commodities that you think would be significant net imports for Canada.

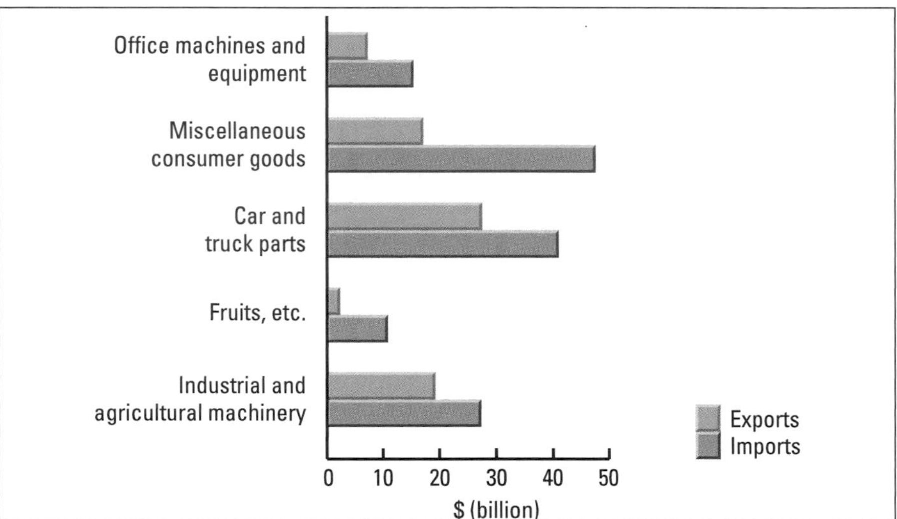

Fig. 34-4 ▶ Some important net import items for Canada, 2004

The "miscellaneous consumer goods" category includes clothing, footwear, sporting goods, household goods, and photographic equipment. The "fruits, etc." category includes fruits, vegetables, cocoa, coffee, tea, and sugar.

Note that "plastics" does not refer to articles made of plastic, but to the actual plastic itself.

4. Other types of goods are also important to Canada's trade but are neither important net exports, nor important net imports. Fig. 34-5 shows this situation very well for the wide range of goods that make up the chemicals and plastics category. Trade in this sector of the economy is huge—almost $54 billion in 2004—but it is almost evenly divided between imports and exports. Name three other commodities for which you think the amount of imports and exports would be almost balanced.

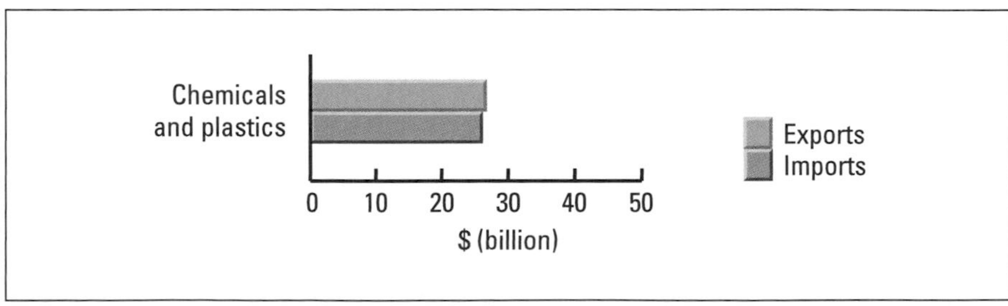

Fig. 34-5 ▶ Trade in chemicals and plastics, 2004

Issue

SHOULD WE—CAN WE—REDUCE OUR IMPORTS?

◀ **Fig. 34-6** Even when you buy fresh produce, sometimes you can choose to buy Canadian over other sources. Will you buy apples from the United States, or New Zealand, or Canada?

When you decide to buy a CD player made in China, a pair of jeans from Bangladesh, orange juice from Brazil, or a minivan made in the United States, you are making a decision that causes money to leave Canada. Can you do anything about this? In some cases you can, in others you have little choice. For example, you could choose to drink Canadian-made apple juice instead of imported orange juice. Your family could choose to buy a Honda Pilot made in Alliston, Ontario, or a Chrysler Grand Caravan made in Windsor instead of an American-made minivan. When you choose to buy a Canadian-made product instead of a foreign one, you are practising what is called **import substitution**.

Activities

1. What are the benefits, for Canada and Canadians, of import substitution?
2. Identify two different kinds of costs to Canadians that occur when we practise import substitution. Note that one of these costs is monetary and one is not.
3. Can we always find ways to practise import substitution? Why or why not?
4. Why has much manufacturing that used to be done in Canada been moved to China and other low labour-cost locations? What does this say about the likely willingness of Canadians to "buy Canadian"?
5. What choices will you, personally, make about practising import substitution?

Importance of Exports

Why must Canada export? There are three major reasons:

1. *To pay for the things that we import*—Canadians import both necessities and luxuries from other countries. If we want to continue to enjoy these products, we must be able to pay for them. The obvious way to do this is by selling our goods and services to other countries.
2. *To keep our economy healthy*—Almost 50% of the goods and services that Canadians produce are exported. With fewer exports, unemployment would be higher and most of us would be poorer.

Fig. 34-7 ▶ Bombardier, maker of the CRJ700 aircraft, manufactures a variety of products for the aerospace (aircraft) and transportation (railway cars) markets. Most of its products are sold outside of Canada.

3. *To lower the prices of Canadian-made goods for Canadians*—Keep in mind that the cost per unit of something (a pair of skates, for example) is lower if you make one million pairs of skates than if you make 10 000 pairs. A Canadian company that produces for export as well as for the Canadian market can keep the price lower for everyone.

INTERNET

Bombardier is also the world's largest producer of trains and subway cars. To access their home page, go to www.pearsoned.ca/makingconnections2.

Trade in Services

Most often when Canadians talk about trade, they are thinking only of trade in goods. If we consider trade in goods only, the economic picture looks very rosy. In 2004, for example, we had a trade surplus for goods of about $66 billion.

However, trade involves services as well as goods and here the picture is not quite so bright. In 2004, we had a deficit in services of over $12 billion. The largest part of this deficit comes from travel and transportation services (Fig. 34-8). There are more Canadians who travel to other countries than there are foreign visitors to Canada. Plus, the amount of money the average Canadian traveller spends in other countries is greater than the amount spent by the average visitor to Canada. Another portion of our deficit arises from the import of many business services.

Fig. 34-8 ▶ Canada's international trade in services, 2004 ($ million)

	Imports	**Exports**	**Balance**
Travel	16 709	20 839	–4 130
Transportation services	11 053	15 844	–4 791
Business services	32 540	36 857	–4 317
Government services	1 513	950	+563
Total	**61 815**	**74 490**	**–12 675**

You contribute to Canada's deficit every day! Consider how money leaves Canada in each of the following situations and how this relates to your life:

- A Canadian television station shows *The Simpsons,* which is produced in the United States.
- American-produced advertisements for Pepsi appear in a Canadian magazine.

Free Trade versus Protectionism

Free trade versus protectionism has been a recurring theme in Canada's history for more than a century. It continues to be an important issue for Canadians. Before discussing this issue, a few terms need to be explained: tariffs, protectionism, and free trade.

Tariffs: A **tariff** is a tax on an import. What role do tariffs play in trade? Consider the example of the blue jeans described in Fig. 34-9. Clearly,

	Without Tariffs		With Tariffs	
Cost in your local store	**Canadian-made jeans $60**	**Foreign-made jeans $45**	**Canadian-made jeans $60**	**Foreign-made jeans $75**
Results	Few sold • factory closes • unemployment higher • money leaves Canada to pay for foreign jeans	Many sold • imports of jeans higher • balance of trade hurt	Many sold • Canadian industries and jobs protected • money stays in Canada	Few sold • imports of jeans lower • balance of trade improved

	For Tariffs	Against Tariffs
Student A: wants the best price when buying jeans in the store	?	?
Student B: parent works in a jeans factory	?	?
Student C: parent sells new cars in a town that has a large jeans factory	?	?
Student D: cousin operates a foreign jeans factory	?	?

▲ **Fig. 34-9** How tariffs work. Which of students A, B, C, and D would likely favour tariffs, and which would oppose them?

tariffs make it more costly to buy foreign goods. As you can see, tariffs can seriously affect trade, particularly if you remember that other countries could also have tariffs that could keep out Canadian products!

Protectionism: **Protectionism** is a government's policy of using tariffs and having rules that limit imports. Canadian companies gain an advantage over foreign competitors who can produce things more cheaply.

Free Trade: **Free trade** is a government policy that eliminates tariffs and other laws designed to restrict trade. The basic idea of free trade is that enhanced trade among nations is good for everyone.

WORLD TRADE ORGANIZATION (WTO)

After World War II, major trading countries, including Canada, realized that they had to avoid the trade protectionism that had proved so disastrous during the Depression of the 1930s. To avoid protectionism, they agreed on a set of rules to govern and encourage trade. This agreement, the General Agreement on Tariffs and Trade, or GATT, came into effect in 1947 and now includes more than 120 countries.

The latest additions to the GATT came into effect in 1995 with the creation of the World Trade Organization (WTO), which was designed to resolve disputes under the rules of the GATT. The WTO's dispute resolution process can be very slow and uncertain. A good example of this is the softwood lumber dispute between Canada and the United States. In 1986, the United States charged that Canada was providing unfair subsidies to producers of softwood lumber (which is used mainly in house construction). As a result, they put tariffs on imports of Canadian wood. This benefited American lumber producers but harmed Americans who bought Canadian lumber since prices became higher. Over the years, Canada has appealed to both the WTO and NAFTA (see next section), and both groups have repeatedly judged that Canada does not have unfair subsidies. In 2005, the US decided to substantially reduce the tariffs on softwood lumber.

NORTH AMERICAN FREE TRADE AGREEMENT (NAFTA)

While the GATT has done much to promote free trade across the world, Canada has also pursued freer trade directly with the United States and, more recently, with other countries. Free trade with the United States is of particular significance because we have an enormous amount of trade with our southern neighbour.

This move to increase free trade started in 1988 with the creation of a free trade agreement with the United States. In 1993, the arrangement was expanded to include Mexico under an agreement called the North American Free Trade Agreement or NAFTA. It would be very hard for Canada to move away from free trade since its economy has changed enormously to reflect a

There are other free trade areas of the world. The largest is the European Union. The EU has gone much farther than NAFTA in breaking down the barriers between the economies of nations. For example, the EU created a common currency, the euro, for the region.

free trade environment. More recently, there have been discussions to have a free trade agreement for the Americas and one for the Pacific Rim. Much work remains before either of these becomes a reality.

The Future of Canada's Trade

International trade allows most Canadians to enjoy a relatively high standard of living. To maintain this in the future, we will have to find satisfactory answers to several critical trade-related questions.

- *Can we maintain our traditional markets?* Most of our exports are related to our rich natural resources. Developing countries rich in resources such as Brazil, Congo, and Papua–New Guinea are competing with Canada to provide cheap forest, mineral, and fish products to our traditional customers such as the United States, Japan, and the European Community.
- *Can we export more manufactured goods? Can we develop new products to create new markets?* Over the years, Canadians have invented many products that we take for granted today: the telephone, snowmobile, zipper, snowblower, hydrofoil, and newsprint. We must continue to create new products and then develop export markets for them.

Have you thought about a career that might involve creating new products?

- *Can we increase our exports of services?* Yes we can, and in a wide variety of fields. For example, we could continue to increase our production and international sale of movies, television shows, and music. Or, Canadian airline companies could expand their international service.
- *Should we (can we?) decrease our trade reliance on the United States?* No two nations have ever had so much **bilateral trade**. This trade relationship has contributed much to our standard of living, but there are dangers in relying so heavily on one trading partner. We are easily harmed by downturns in the American economy or by protectionist policies from the American government. If we could expand our trade with other countries, we would not have to depend so much on the United States.

bilateral trade
trade between two countries

- *Can we compete effectively within NAFTA and beyond?* Our NAFTA partners each have strong advantages: huge American companies have enormous economic power and Mexican companies have lower labour costs. How do we respond to the enormous economic (and trade) growth in China and India?

To learn more about Canada's trade, go to www.pearsoned.ca/makingconnections2.

QUESTIONS

KNOWLEDGE AND UNDERSTANDING

1. a) How important is trade to Canada? Consider the impact on our lifestyle, jobs, and economy.
   b) Why must Canada export?
   c) Why must we import?
   d) How are our imports and exports related?
2. a) What is "trade in services"? Give a definition and at least three specific examples from different aspects of Canadian life.
   b) How do you contribute to Canada's deficit in trade in services?
3. a) What is the GATT?
   b) What is its purpose and how has it changed over the years?
4. a) What is the difference between total imports and exports and net imports and exports?
   b) Consult a table of total imports and exports in an atlas. Compare this information to Figs. 34-3 and 34-4. What differences do you see between total and net trade?
   c) Which figures describe Canada's trade best? Why?

THINKING

5. Each of the following statements describes one aspect of Canada's international trade. Briefly explain why each is true. Why is it not surprising that...?
   a) Most of Canada's trading partners are in the developed world rather than among the developing and newly industrializing countries.
   b) High-technology products (especially consumer electronics such as TVs and DVD players) are produced in only a few countries.
   c) Canada builds and exports only smaller (up to about 100 passengers) aircraft.
   d) Canada has a large trade deficit in services.
   e) Much of Canada's export trade involves our natural resources.

COMMUNICATION

6. a) Define trade surplus and trade deficit.
   b) People can decrease a trade deficit (or increase a trade surplus) by practising import substitution. In a paragraph, describe how you could do this with any five imported products you normally purchase.
   c) How could import substitution be applied to trade in services?

APPLICATION

7. Should ethics (moral standards) play a role in Canada's trade policies? Consider the following cases:
   a) Canada's tobacco farmers have suffered financial setbacks in recent years as fewer Canadians smoke. At the same time, demand for tobacco products is increasing in developing countries. Should the Canadian government promote the sale of Canadian tobacco in other countries?
   b) The governments of many countries of the world violate the human rights of their citizens. It has been suggested that Canada should try to discourage these abuses by tying trade to human rights. For example, imports from a country would be stopped if that country did not respect human rights. Should human rights and trade be linked? Do you think such methods would be successful? Explain.

ANSWERS TO FIG. 34-1

A. High-technology products (South Korea)
B. Low-cost goods (Mexico)
C. Goods produced in warmer climates (India)
D. Motor vehicle parts (United States)
E. Low-cost goods (China)
F. Goods produced in warmer climates (Colombia)
G. High-technology products (Japan)

How many countries did you identify correctly?

35 Our Cultural Connections with the United States

Key Ideas

This chapter helps you investigate these questions:

- How much do you know about Canada's culture?
- What are the different meanings of the term *culture*?
- What are the arguments in favour of protecting Canada's culture, and what are the arguments opposing protection?

Key Terms

culture
ecumene
nationalist
continentalist

Former Prime Minister Pierre Trudeau described Canada's relationship with its American neighbour in the following way:

> Living next to the United States is in some ways like sleeping with an elephant. No matter how friendly and even-tempered is the beast...one is affected by every grunt and twitch.

While this statement could apply to many aspects of our relationship with the United States, perhaps it applies best to our cultural connections with our huge neighbour. **Culture** is what makes a nation unique, and many Canadians feel that our culture is influenced too much by the culture of the United States. But what exactly do we mean by culture? The term has two different meanings (Fig. 35-1).

What exactly do we mean by "culture"? The term has two distinct meanings.

In the broad sense...

Culture includes all the characteristics of a way of life:

- language
- religion
- values
- behaviour
- education
- clothing styles
- food
- the arts
- media
- entertainment
- healthcare system
- nature of government

When all these characteristics are put together, they form a "culture."

In the narrow sense...

Culture includes only the following characteristics:

- the arts
- media
- entertainment

◀ **Fig. 35-1** Consider how these two definitions of culture apply to you.

Complete the following quiz to discover if you are more familiar with American or Canadian culture.

You and Canadian Culture

1. Name the last novel you read (a) in English class, and (b) for enjoyment.
2. Name the members of the Group of Seven.
3. List your five favourite television shows.
4. List your five favourite singers or groups.
5. List the last five movies you have seen.
6. List three magazines you read regularly.

Now work out your score. Your teacher will help you. Give yourself one point for each of the following:

a) each Canadian novel in Question 1
b) every correct answer in Question 2
c) every Canadian answer in Questions 3, 4, 5, and 6

Add up your points.

21 to 27 points: You are a Canadian culture vulture!
11 to 20 points: You take advantage of Canadian culture.
6 to 10 points: Living in Canada makes little difference to your cultural life.
0 to 5 points: You might as well live in St. Louis!

Consider the following factors that contribute to the similarities between our culture and that of Americans.

- The Canadian **ecumene** contains over 95% of Canadians and is located within 600 kilometres of the United States border (Fig. 35-2).
- Travel between the two countries is routine. In 2004, about 14 million overnight trips were made by Canadians visiting the United States. In the same year, more than 15 million overnight trips were made by Americans visiting Canada.
- Many Canadians have relatives and friends who live in the United States.
- Cable and satellite television offer a vast selection of American television programs and news to Canadians in even the most remote parts of the country.
- The vast majority of movies shown in our theatres come from American studios such as Universal, Paramount, and Disney.

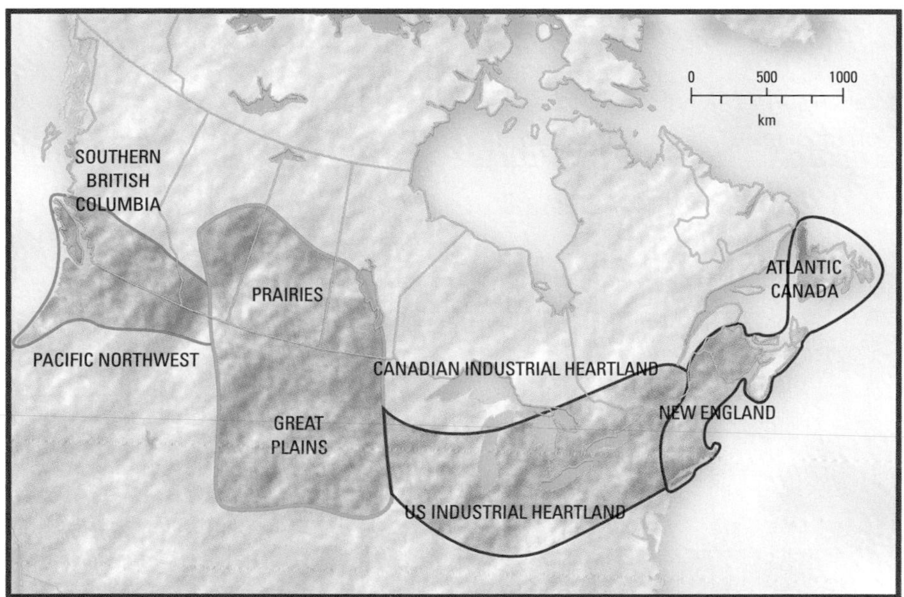

▲ **Fig. 35-2** Canadians sometimes identify more closely with Americans who live near them than with Canadians who live thousands of kilometres away because they are more likely to share a common economy and lifestyle with their American neighbours.

▲ **Fig. 35-3** Consider Wal-Mart, Canadian Tire, Home Depot, Loblaws, GAP, Roots, and Sears. Which are Canadian and which American? Many Canadians do not know. Do you?

- Many of the most popular books and magazines in Canada are published in the United States.
- Most of the fast-food chains and retail chains in Canada are American-owned.

Given the enormous influence that American culture has on Canadian culture, it might be hard to imagine how our culture could be distinctive (Fig. 35-3). Evidence of the uniqueness of Canadian culture is **subtle**, but is easier to see when the Constitution of Canada and the US are compared. A nation's founding documents express the most important values upon which that nation is based. In Fig. 35-4, the most significant founding principle of Canada's *Constitution Act, 1867,* is compared with that of the American Declaration of Independence, 1776. It also shows the different impact each governing principle has on two issues in each country. Comparisons of the two governing principles and their effect on gun control and healthcare illustrate the fundamental difference between the cultures of the two countries: in Canada, the rights of society as a whole usually take precedence over the rights of the individual. In the United States, the reverse is true. There is little evidence today that this fundamental difference is becoming less pronounced.

subtle
not obvious

Key phrase in…	
American Declaration of Independence, 1776 "Life, Liberty, and the pursuit of Happiness."	*Canadian Constitution Act, 1867* "Peace, order, and good government"
What it focuses on…	
United States Rights of the individual	*Canada* Role of the individual as a member of society
Significance of this on…	
gun control	
United States • Lax gun control laws (Americans own 1 handgun for every 4 people.) • Constitution specifically talks about the right to "bear arms" • Governing principle reflects the idea that the right of the individual to own a firearm is more important than the collective right of the society to restrict gun ownership	*Canada* • Strict gun control laws (Canadians own 1 handgun for every 27 people.) • Gun control laws reflect the idea that fewer guns will make a safer, more peaceful and orderly society. The individual's right to own guns is therefore limited. • In recent years, with the support of most citizens, gun laws have become more strict.
national public healthcare	
United States • Healthcare is a private responsibility. • Most people get health insurance through their employer but about 45 million people have no health coverage. • In 1993, President Bill Clinton tried to introduce a modest national healthcare system. He was unsuccessful partly because the prevailing attitude is that individuals should be responsible for themselves and their families.	*Canada* • All citizens are covered by government-paid healthcare, which has existed since 1961. • Most Canadians passionately defend their healthcare system. They think that it unites the country and is an important part of Canadian culture. • The prevailing attitude is that Canadians have a collective responsibility for the provision of healthcare to all citizens. Canadians accept this responsibility by authorizing government to pay for all healthcare services with money collected through taxation.

▲ **Fig. 35-4** The American Declaration of Independence and the Canadian Constitution each contain a key phrase that helps to explain important differences in the attitudes and culture of the two countries.

Issue

IS THERE HOPE FOR CANADA'S CULTURE?

◀ **Figure. 35-5**

Background

Because we live next door to a country 10 times our size in population, which also happens to be the richest nation in the world, Canadians find it challenging to preserve our national identity. Is there hope for a distinct Canadian culture in the face of the powerful influences of American TV, radio, publishing, movies, and music?

Television

Most Canadians watch a lot of American shows. Canadian networks carry many American programs because they can buy them for much less than it costs to produce their own programs in Canada. As a result, few Canadian-made shows become favourites of Canadian viewers.

INTERNET

You can see what the most popular English language television shows are for any given week through the link at www.pearsoned.ca/makingconnections2. You will see that almost all the shows listed come from the US.

Radio

Most Canadian radio stations sound the same as American stations because they buy prepackaged formats from American companies. These formats include jingles, station nicknames, contests, and station advertising. A station purchases the format and then personalizes it with its frequency, local advertising, and some Canadian music. An exception to this growing continental uniformity is the Canadian Broadcasting Corporation (CBC), which provides unique, Canadian-focused programming. For example, the CBC has a northern service that provides programming to First Nations in their own languages. This is possible only because the CBC is funded by the federal government.

Movies

Every year, the Genie Awards are presented to Canada's outstanding movies. Most Canadians look at the list of winners and ask, "Why haven't I heard of most of these movies?" The reason they haven't heard of them has nothing to do with the quality. Rather, it is related to the way in which movies are distributed. Canadian movies are rarely shown in the large theatres owned by companies such as Famous Players and Cineplex Odeon. These American companies feel they will make more money showing American movies with big-name stars. Interestingly enough, many of these "big name" movies are made in Canada because production costs are lower here than in the US. Vancouver often stands in for Seattle, and Toronto for New York or Chicago.

▲ **Fig. 35-6** In 2004, Denys Arcand won Genies for best film, best director, and best screenplay for *The Barbarian Invasions.* The film also won an Academy Award for best foreign film.

INTERNET

You can check this week's most popular movies through the link at www.pearsoned.ca/makingconnections2. For information about Canadian films, from Genie Award nominees and winners to which Canadian films are playing in your neighbourhood, browse the Academy of Canadian Cinema and Television Web site through the link at www.pearsoned.ca/makingconnections2.

Popular Music

Many Canadian popular music performers enjoy success within Canada despite intense competition from American performers. You can probably name quite a few Canadians who have even achieved international reputations. In part, they succeeded so well because government regulations require that Canadian radio and TV music stations broadcast a certain percentage of Canadian music. Music is defined as Canadian based on the nationality of the performer, composer, and producer, or if it was recorded in Canada. As the demand for Canadian "content" increased, more Canadians were offered recording contracts. Without Canadian content rules, the Canadian music industry would not be as healthy as it is today. Many people feel that similar rules should exist for movies.

▲ **Fig. 35-7** The Canadian rock group Nickelback, established in 1996, scored a North American hit in 2001, when "How You Remind Me" hit the top of the charts in Canada and the US.

Should We Protect Our Canadian Culture?

Americans who are in the business of exporting television shows, movies, and music disagree with any attempts to protect and enhance Canadian culture. They believe their cultural industries are just that—industries that exist to make money. In contrast, some Canadians and some people in other countries believe that culture is much more than just a business. They believe that their culture is a critical part of their identity as a nation, and that American cultural exports are a threat to this identity. As a result, they have decided to do what they can to protect their culture. For example, France tries to stop English words from being adopted into the French language (e.g., "microcomputer" and "slamdunk."). Another example is Iran, which banned satellite dishes to try and keep American television and movies out of the country.

Here in Canada, the federal government supports Canadian writers and artists with grants from the Canada Council. It also funds CBC, Canada's national radio and TV network. Telefilm Canada sponsors filmmakers, encouraging the production of films with Canadian points of view. The National Film Board is federally funded to produce and distribute films with a distinctive Canadian perspective.

Despite these efforts, some Canadians feel that English-Canadian culture is swamped with American cultural "products." Those who feel that we will have a better future by remaining as independent of the United States as possible, especially in the area of culture, are called **nationalists**. Others feel that the two cultures are so much alike that we should stop worrying about it. People who take this view are called **continentalists**.

Do you support the continentalist view or the nationalist one? The attitudes of young Canadians like you will determine the nature of Canada's culture in the future.

Activities

1. List three reasons why American culture has such a great influence on Canadians.
2. Canadian English language differs from American and British English. Create a list of 10 examples of Canadian English. Consider unique words and words with different spellings and pronunciation. Consult the *Canadian Oxford Dictionary* for help with this task.
3. You are a consumer of culture. You watch television and movies, read books and magazines, and listen to music. Analyze your attitudes to Canadian culture by answering these questions.
   a) Canadian commercial radio stations must play at least 10% Canadian music. Do you support this rule? Do you think the percentage should be higher?
   b) Should movie theatres be required to show Canadian movies for a certain number of weeks each year? Why or why not?
   c) Should the government, through agencies like the ones mentioned above, support cultural activities?
   d) CBC television currently airs both Canadian and non-Canadian programs. Should the CBC be allowed to air non-Canadian programs? Why or why not?
4. Do you consider yourself a cultural nationalist or continentalist? Explain.

QUESTIONS

KNOWLEDGE AND UNDERSTANDING

1. In your own words, state the two definitions of the word *culture*.
2. What is the fundamental difference between Canadian and American culture as illustrated by the basic governing principle of each country's constitution?
3. What does the Canadian government do to support and protect Canada's culture?
4. Many Canadians who work in the arts have had considerable international success. Make a list of Canadians who "have made it" in the United States and in other parts of the world. You may want to consider Grammy Award winners, actors, directors, writers, artists, and TV personalities. In your list, describe the achievements of each individual or group.

THINKING

5. For each definition of culture you provided in Question 1, give evidence that there is a distinctive Canadian culture.
6. With the help of atlas maps, identify natural factors or human activities that
   a) make North America a north–south-oriented continent
   b) make Canada an east–west-oriented country
   c) contribute to the strength of the regional cross-border relationships shown in Fig. 35-2
7. You have probably heard the story about the American tourist arriving at the Canadian border in July with skis on the top of the car, eager to see the igloos and polar bears. Although an unfair exaggeration, this story illustrates the fact that many Americans know very little about their northern neighbour. Does it surprise you that so many Americans know relatively little about Canada? Why or why not?

COMMUNICATION

8. Is there a need to protect Canada's culture in an age of globalization? Conduct a class debate in which one side supports the view that Canada's culture should be protected because it is distinct and constantly threatened by cultural influences from other countries. The other side should take the position that Canada's culture should not be protected because Canadians benefit from the cultural influences of other countries.
9. Chapter 35 began with a quotation from a former Canadian prime minister about the United States. The following quotation about Canada is from the American president of the early 1960s, John F. Kennedy.

   > Geography has made us neighbours. History has made us friends. Economics has made us partners. And necessity has made us allies. What unites us is far greater than what divides us.

   a) Explain each leader's quotation in your own words.
   b) Which view—nationalist or continentalist—does each quotation express? How did you decide?

APPLICATION

10. a) In groups of 4 or 5, develop a list of characteristics that express Canadian identity in each of the following areas. Give examples of that characteristic in appropriate areas. An example is provided to get you started.
    i. social programs (e.g., characteristic: universality; specific example: healthcare)
    ii. bilingualism
    iii. multiculturalism
    iv. contributions of Aboriginal peoples and immigrants
    v. the narrow view of culture

    b) Each group presents its list of characteristics and examples to the class. After all the presentations have been made, produce a set of characteristics agreed upon by the class as representative of the Canadian identity.

Beyond Our Borders

▲ CA6-1

Background

In this unit, you learned about some of Canada's involvement in the global community. The images above document some of the roles Canadians play—peacekeeping in Afghanistan; providing aid to countries devastated by natural disasters, and enforcing international law at the International Court of the Hague. Now you will have a chance to express your views about how Canada should participate in the international community.

GeoLit Reminder

Evaluating bias in the media:

- Who wrote this item?
- Who was the intended audience?
- Why did the author write this item?
- Does the headline contain words that trigger emotion?
- Has the author made unwarranted or unsupported assumptions?
- Has the author used facts selectively or omitted important details?
- If there are visuals, do these support the author's argument with facts, or do they play on the reader's emotions?

Activity

1. Find a recent newspaper story, magazine article, or blog entry that deals with Canada's involvement with another country (or countries) in some way. As you read the article, think about the following questions.
   - What is the issue, e.g., natural disaster, trade dispute?
   - What is the exact nature of Canada's involvement, i.e., what are we doing? (For example, are we providing financial aid, arguing about trade matters, sending medical supplies or personnel, offering or refusing military assistance?)
   - What impact does Canada's action (or decision not to act) have on the other country (or countries) involved?

- What impact does this action or decision have on Canada?
- Do you agree with Canada's action or decision in this situation, or not? Why?

2. Next, write a concise and convincing letter to the editor of a newspaper in which you express your opinion about Canada's response to the particular international issue discussed in the article you chose. Before you write the letter, you need to gather background information. First, check your textbook for any information about your issue. Then, conduct an Internet search of national and international news sources to learn more about Canada's involvement in the issue you have selected. Your school and community libraries will also have additional periodical resources and reference materials.

   As you draft your letter to the editor, make sure that it follows these guidelines:
   - no more than one page in length (about 250 words)
   - provides a brief summary of the issue you are writing about
   - presents your views (i.e., agree/disagree) with Canada's international involvement, and supports your viewpoint using information from your article as well as from your research
   - concludes with a one- or two-sentence statement that highlights your opinion
   - ends with your name and where you are from

INTERNET

Start your research at the Internet sites available through the links at www.pearsoned.ca/makingconnections2.

3. Share your letter to the editor with three or four members of your class. Get feedback from each other and revise your letter as needed. Then post your letter on a class bulletin board under one of these four categories:
   - Humanitarian Involvement/Disaster Relief (e.g., helping communities in Africa cope with HIV/AIDS, sending medical personnel and financial aid to hurricane or earthquake victims)
   - Military Matters (e.g., UN peacekeeping, increasing or decreasing our involvement in NATO, lending or refusing to lend military assistance to American-led efforts like Afghanistan and Iraq)
   - International Trade (e.g., disputes with trading partners, membership in international trading organizations such as APEC and NAFTA)
   - International Organizations (e.g., UN, G7/8, International Olympic Committee, International Criminal Court)
   - Which category drew the most attention from students?
4. Participate in a class discussion. Be prepared to provide your response to one of the letters you read (not yours or one you peer-edited). Does the author of the letter you chose believe Canada responded appropriately to the described situation? Do you agree with the author's opinion? Why or why not?

UNIT 7

Future Connections

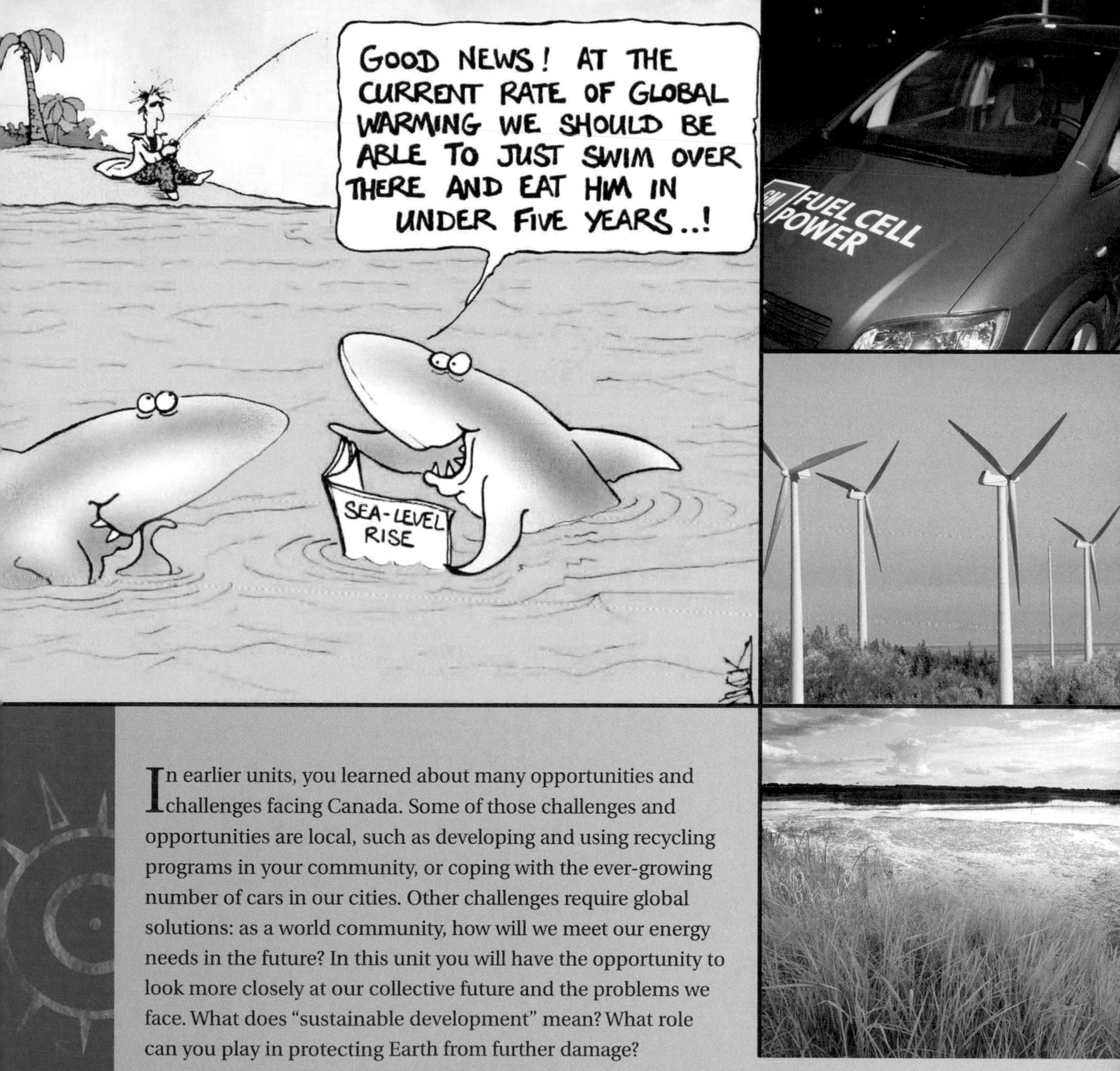

In earlier units, you learned about many opportunities and challenges facing Canada. Some of those challenges and opportunities are local, such as developing and using recycling programs in your community, or coping with the ever-growing number of cars in our cities. Other challenges require global solutions: as a world community, how will we meet our energy needs in the future? In this unit you will have the opportunity to look more closely at our collective future and the problems we face. What does "sustainable development" mean? What role can you play in protecting Earth from further damage?

36 Water: The Most Basic Resource

Key Ideas

This chapter helps you investigate these questions:

- How much water does your family use each day?
- How extensive are Canada's water resources?
- What water issues affect Canada today?

Key Terms

runoff
groundwater
hydrologic cycle
wetlands
drainage basin
tributary
watershed
discharge rate
water table
instream use
withdrawal use
toxic chemicals

Activity	Use
Clothes washer	230 L/use
Bath	130 L/use
Dishwasher	65 L/use
Shower	25 L/min
Toilet flush	20 L/use
Water from a faucet	12 L/min

▲ **Fig. 36-1** Average water use for various activities. Your appliances and water fixtures may have higher or lower rates of flow. Many newer toilets use only 5 L/use.

How much water do you and your family use each day? To find out, record the amount of water used in your home for one day. For some activities, you will have to estimate how much you use. Here are some figures to help you (Fig. 36-1). Don't forget to record water lost because of dripping faucets. Studies suggest that as much as 10% of the water piped into a home disappears this way. For each dripping faucet in your home, add 75 L/day. After you have collected the data, form groups to compare your family's use of water to that of your classmates.

1. Construct a graph like the one in Fig. 36-2, and complete it using information provided by each student in your group.
2. What is the relationship between the number of people in a household and the amount of water used?
3. a) Divide the total water consumption of each household by the number of people in that household. This will give the consumption per person within each household.
   b) Make a list of ways your family consumes water.
   c) Compare this list with those of other group members. What similarities and differences exist?
   d) Compare your list to one prepared by the City of Toronto (Fig. 36-3). (Note the amounts shown on this graph represent a typical winter day so there is no water used for lawn watering, car washing, and swimming pool use.)

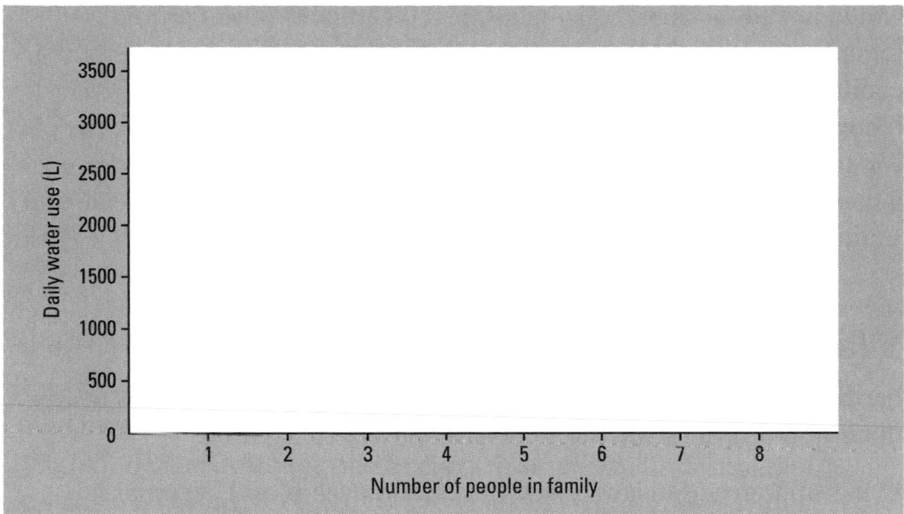

◄ **Fig. 36-2** Graph showing the relationship between water use and family size

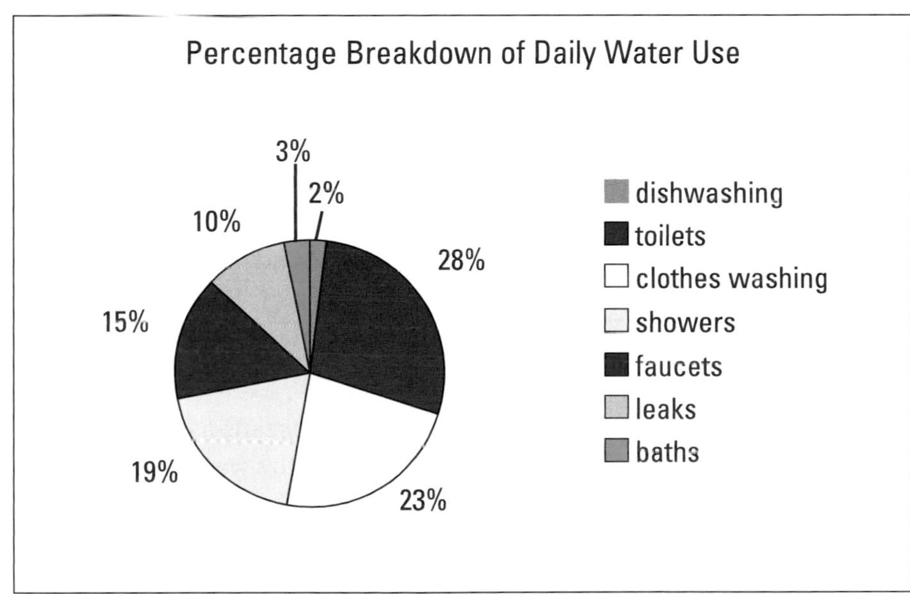

◄ **Fig. 36-3** A typical Torontonian's water use during the winter of 2004

4. What steps could you and your family take to reduce the amount of water you use?

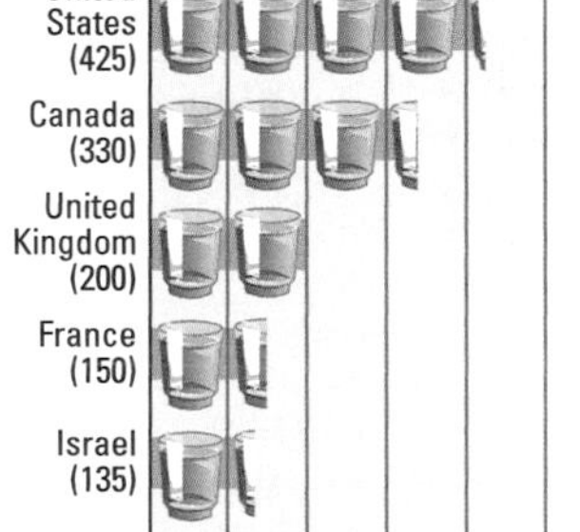

▲ **Fig. 36-4** Canadians are the second largest per capita users of water in the world.

In Canada, most people take water for granted. Studies show that the average Canadian uses about 330 L/day for personal use (Fig. 36-4). How does this figure compare to the one that you calculated in question 3a)?

We could calculate the personal amount of water used daily by all Canadians by multiplying 330 by the population of Canada, but this

QUESTIONS

KNOWLEDGE AND UNDERSTANDING

1. "The fact that we use water does not mean that we actually consume it." Explain this statement.
2. Explain, using your own words and a diagram, how the hydrologic cycle works.
3. What are the advantages and disadvantages of using groundwater as a source of fresh water?
4. Compare instream uses of water with withdrawal uses.
5. List four reasons why the demand for water will probably increase in the future.

THINKING

6. a) Define the terms *drainage basin* and *watershed.*
   b) On a drainage map of Canada (provided by your teacher), draw the borders of the five major drainage basins in Canada (Fig. 36-5). Shade in each with a different colour.
   c) Label each drainage basin with its name, area (km^2), and mean discharge (m^3/s).
   d) Rank the drainage basins by
      i. area
      ii. mean discharge
      Explain the difference between your two rankings.
   e) i. In what direction does most of Canada's water flow?
      ii. What percentage of the total flow goes in this direction?
   f) Where is most of Canada's population located? Compare the pattern of population with the pattern of water flow. What does this suggest about our ability to meet growing water needs in the future?

APPLICATION

7. a) Where does your water come from?
   b) Where is it treated?
   c) Where does it go after you have used it?

Water Issues

Pollution

Many Canadian cities have old sewage systems. During heavy rainfalls, these systems cannot handle the volume of water, and raw sewage flows into rivers, lakes, and oceans. These systems are currently being updated—a long and costly process.

The three main types of water pollution are physical, biological, and chemical. Perhaps the least harmful, but most obvious, is physical pollution. Floating garbage, old tires, paper litter, pop cans, and bottles are not pleasant to look at, but we can easily spot these things, making cleanup and even prevention relatively simple.

Biological contamination refers to bacteria and viruses that enter lakes and rivers from a variety of sources. The sewage of cities and towns is the largest source of biological contamination. Most sewage is treated, but not all treatment does the job adequately. Some human sewage enters water bodies without any treatment at all. About 20% of Canadian cities put their raw sewage into lakes and rivers without treatment.

The most serious incident of biological contamination in Canadian history occurred in Walkerton, Ontario, in 2000. Two factors combined to kill seven people and make more than 2000 ill. First, a large herd of cattle grazed near one of the town's wells. The groundwater that fed the well became contaminated with a dangerous bacterium called *E. coli* from the animal manure. Second, because the water purification system was improperly run, the *E. coli* bacteria in the water were not eliminated. Since the Walkerton incident, more rigid controls ensure that a similar problem does not happen again.

The most dangerous form of water pollution results from chemicals in our lakes and rivers. These usually colourless, odourless, and tasteless wastes can be deadly. Unfortunately, the water bodies containing these chemicals are often the source of drinking water for millions of people.

Some people say that no safe level exists for these chemicals in our water supplies because many of them build up in our bodies over time.

Two important sources of chemical pollution are pesticides and herbicides. These chemicals, which protect our food supply from animal pests,

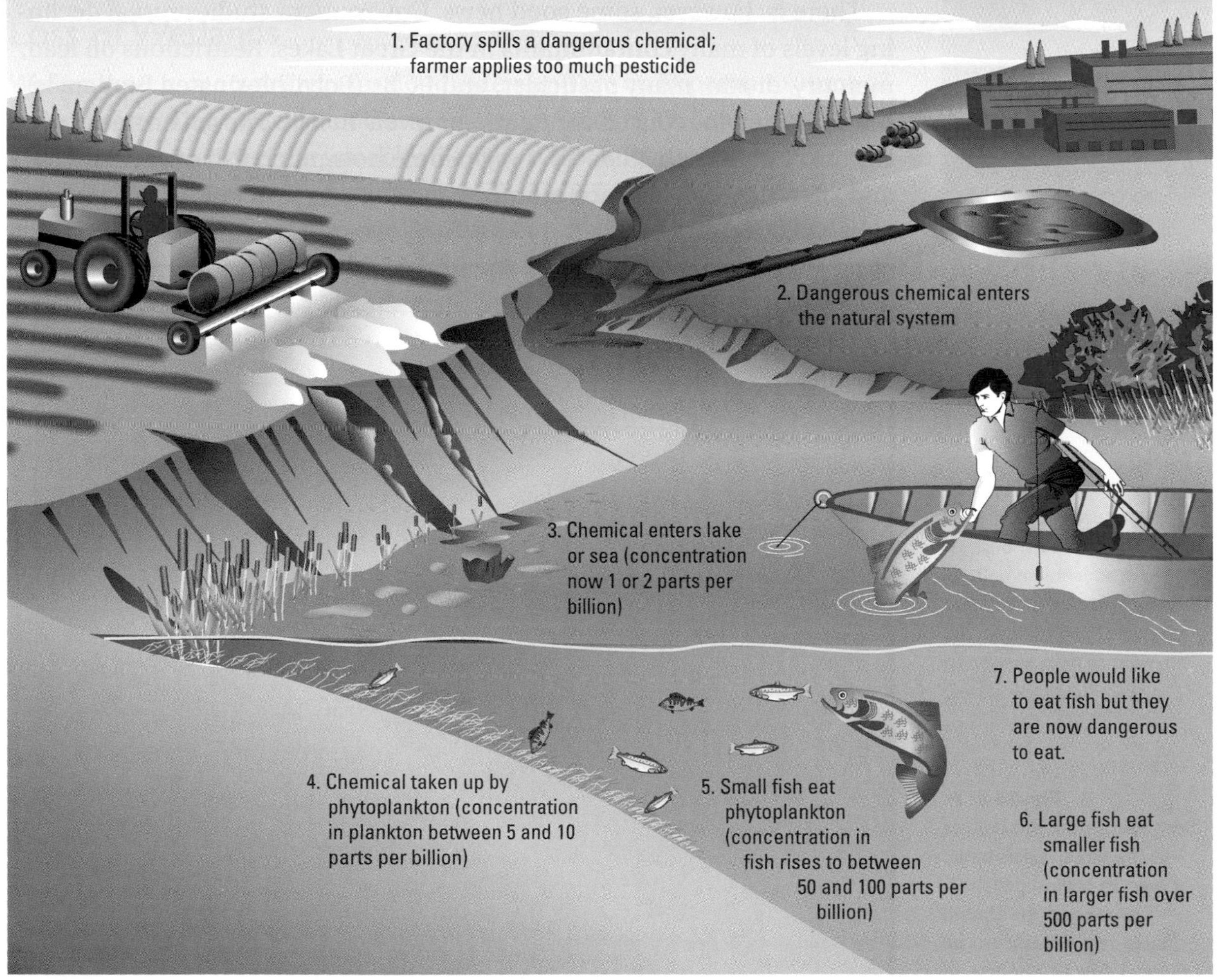

▲ **Fig. 36-7** How toxic wastes move through the food chain

37 Global Warming: Living in a Greenhouse

Key Ideas

This chapter helps you investigate these questions:

- What is global warming, and why does it occur?
- What can or should be done about it?
- What can YOU do to limit your contribution to the greenhouse gases that cause global warming?

Key Terms

global warming
greenhouse effect
greenhouse gases (GHGs)
carbon dioxide
carbon sink
phytoplankton
carbon source
zooplankton
carbon fixation
Kyoto Protocol
One-Tonne Challenge

The five hottest years on record are
1. 1998
2. 2002
3. 2003
4. 2004
5. 2001

In February 2005, scientists from NASA (National Aeronautics and Space Administration) predicted that 2005 would be the hottest year on record. Did this happen? What are the five hottest years now?

In recent years, the weather has seemed warmer than usual to many Canadians. In fact, since 1861 when global temperatures were first recorded, nine of the ten hottest years have occurred between 1995 and 2004.

CBC News: Ontario heat wave to continue until August 16/11/2005 12:15 PM

CBC.CA | RADIO | TELEVISION | LOCAL | CBC.CA | THE WEB | SEARCH

CBC News

NEWS
Indepth »
Viewpoint »
BUSINESS
SPORTS
ARTS & ENTERTAINMENT
WEATHER
HEALTH & SCIENCE
CBC ARCHIVES
KIDS
TEENS
PROGRAM GUIDE
E-MAIL NEWSLETTERS
SERVICES
CONTACT US
ABOUT CBC

SUBSCRIBE TO E-MAIL NEWS:
DAILY NEWS DIGESTS
NEWS ALERTS

RADIO-CANADA
shop

Ontario heat wave to continue until August

Last Updated Wed, 13 Jul 2005 20:46:56 EDT
CBC News

A heat wave that's been scorching Eastern Ontario will stay with little relief until at least the end of July, Environment Canada says.

- INDEPTH: Heat waves and how to protect yourself

Average daily temperatures will be between a half and a full degree higher than normal with few breaks until at least the end of July, the agency says.

This is partly due to high temperatures through the nights, on top of blazing afternoon heat.

"We're not really getting cooler nighttime temperatures," said an Environment Canada meteorologist, Geoff Coulson.

CHOOSE YOUR MEDIA
VIDEO: Ron Charles reports for CBC-TV (Runs 2:13) RealVideo Quicktime
Download Players

EXTERNAL LINKS
- Forecasts on Environment Canada's Weather Office

(Note: CBC does not endorse and is not responsible for the content of external sites - links will open in new window)

FEEDBACK
Send your feedback
Read your letters
Report a typo or inaccuracy

TOOLS
Printable version
E-mail this story

Fig. 37-1 ▶ Canadians have seen many on-line and newspaper stories like this one in recent years.

Some scientists say that we should not read too much into higher temperatures because the next few years might be colder than normal. Other scientists say that warmer conditions reflect natural long-term cyclical changes in Earth's climate. Still others say that human activity has caused the trend to higher global temperatures, and unless human behaviour changes, Earth's climate will continue to get warmer. How might a long-term change in Earth's climate affect Canadians and people in other countries?

1. Complete an organizer like the one in Fig. 37-2 to explore how warmer temperatures might affect your life.
2. Did you find it easier to think of positive effects or negative effects of warmer temperatures? Do you think that your list of positive and negative effects would apply to most Canadians? Why or why not?
3. Would warmer temperatures affect people in other countries in similar ways? Why or why not?

Positive Effects of Warmer Temperatures	1.
	2.
	3.
	4.
Negative Effects of Warmer Temperatures	1.
	2.
	3.
	4.

◀ **Fig. 37-2**

In this chapter, we will look at **global warming**, the rise of world temperatures. We will consider changes in the world's climates and the reasons for those changes. We will also consider how global warming will affect us, and what we can or should do about it.

Climate Changes and Why They Matter

Geological evidence shows that the climate has changed many times throughout history, and that these changes have had an enormous influence on Earth's topography and human life. Here are two examples:

- *Colder times:* Until as recently as 10 000 years ago, great ice sheets called continental glaciers covered much of Canada. Scientists have calculated that glaciation occurred because the average temperature dropped by as little as 4C°.

You can learn more about glaciation in Chapter 12.

The Viking village at L'Anse aux Meadows was the earliest known European settlement in the New World. In 1978 it was declared a UNESCO World Heritage Site.

- *Warmer times:* Historical climatologists suggest that an earlier period of global warming caused an important event in Canada's human geography. Around the year 1000, the Vikings built several settlements in Greenland and at least one at L'Anse aux Meadows in northern Newfoundland. Scientists think that warmer-than-normal temperatures permitted the Vikings to establish these settlements (Fig. 37-3). By the early 1400s, the Vikings had abandoned the settlements in Greenland and Newfoundland because average temperatures had fallen.

Although climate variations may still occur naturally, most scientists agree they may also occur as a result of human activity. This chapter focuses on how human activities may cause rapid and damaging increases in temperatures around the world. To understand this connection, we must first look at the role played by carbon dioxide and other gases in controlling temperatures on Earth.

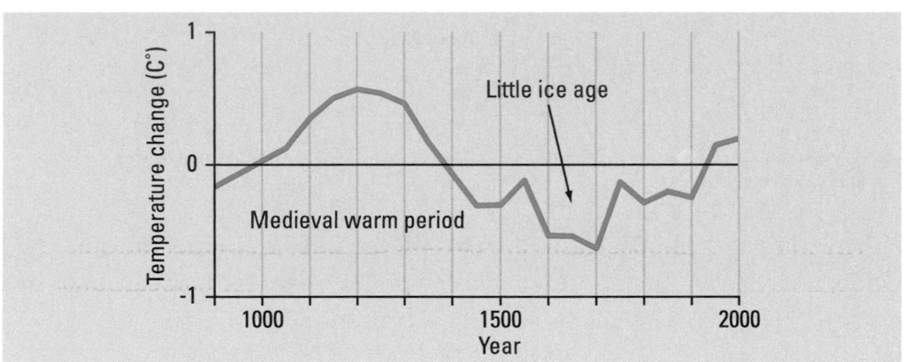

Fig. 37-3 ▶ Natural temperature fluctuations have occurred throughout history.

Life in a Greenhouse

Nitrogen (78%) and oxygen (21%) make up 99% of Earth's atmosphere but do not act as greenhouse gases.

Have you ever sat in a parked car on a sunny day in winter? If so, you probably noticed that the car's interior became hot in spite of the freezing temperature outside. You may have had to open a window to cool the car down. What you experienced is called the **greenhouse effect** (Fig. 37-4). The greenhouse effect exists within Earth's atmosphere (Fig. 37-5) and makes the presence of life on the planet possible. Tiny amounts of different **greenhouse gases (GHGs)** in the atmosphere absorb some of the heat reflected from Earth's surface before it can escape into space. Without greenhouse gases, the world's average temperature would drop by about 33C°, and Earth would be a cold, lifeless planet like Mars. On the other hand, if greenhouse gases increased substantially, they would trap too much heat and cause the temperature of Earth's atmosphere to rise. Some people fear that this is happening today. Strong evidence suggests that global warming occurs as a result of increased greenhouse gases produced by human activity.

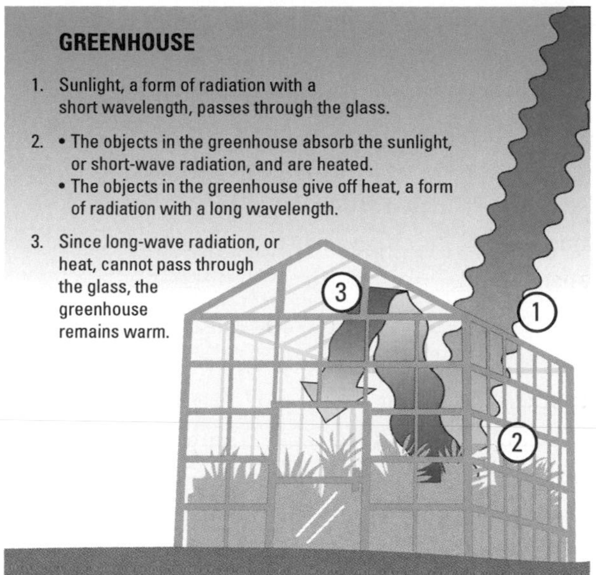

▲ **Fig. 37-4** The space within a greenhouse heats up in much the same way as the atmosphere surrounding Earth.

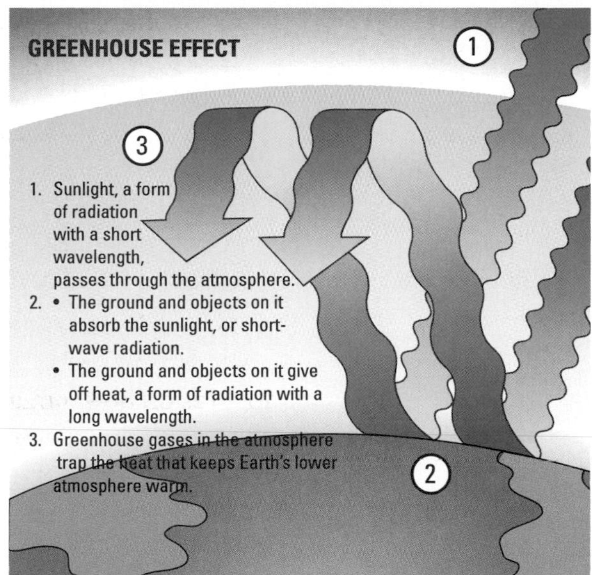

▲ **Fig. 37-5** Without this natural greenhouse effect, temperatures would be so low that life as we know it would not be possible. The problem today is that human activities have increased the amount of greenhouse gases, trapping more heat in the atmosphere.

The main greenhouse gases are **carbon dioxide, methane**, nitrous oxide, **halocarbons**, ozone, and water vapour. Except for halocarbons, these gases and chemicals occur naturally in the atmosphere. They make possible the favourable greenhouse effect that allows life on Earth to exist. In recent decades, however, a heightened greenhouse effect has occurred because of an enormous increase in the production of greenhouse gases. Most scientists believe that these gases occur in greater amounts as a result of human activities. This enhanced greenhouse effect likely has a number of harmful impacts on human life and the natural world.

The increase in greenhouse gases has several sources, including the burning of fossil fuels that produce carbon dioxide. Since carbon dioxide is the most important greenhouse gas, this chapter will concentrate on its role in global warming (Fig. 37-6).

Carbon Cycle

Carbon in its various forms is constantly cycling through Earth's environment. The **carbon cycle** describes the movement of carbon through plants, animals, water, soil, air, and rock. Here's how it works.

When carbon is removed from the atmosphere and stored for a period of time, we have a **carbon sink**. Consider the following: a carbon dioxide molecule in the atmosphere is absorbed by the ocean. Then through the

Fig. 37-6 ▶
Carbon dioxide is the most important greenhouse gas. Study the graph. When did the amount of carbon dioxide in the atmosphere start to increase? Why? (Hint: Consider the technological changes occurring at this time.)

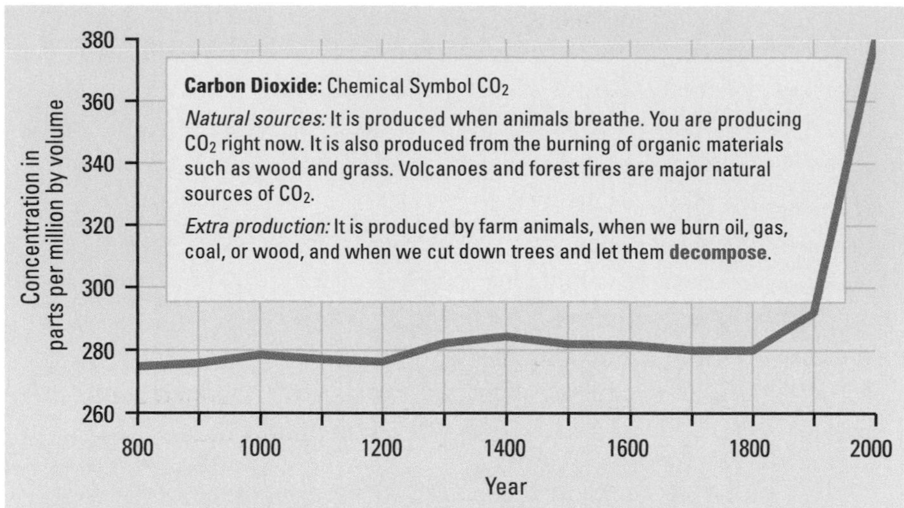

decompose
decay

process of photosynthesis, it becomes part of a tiny ocean plant called **phytoplankton**. A few days later, the phytoplankton dies, and the carbon dioxide molecule is recycled into the atmosphere. Both the ocean and the phytoplankton are carbon sinks because they remove the carbon dioxide from the atmosphere and store it for a period of time in a different form.

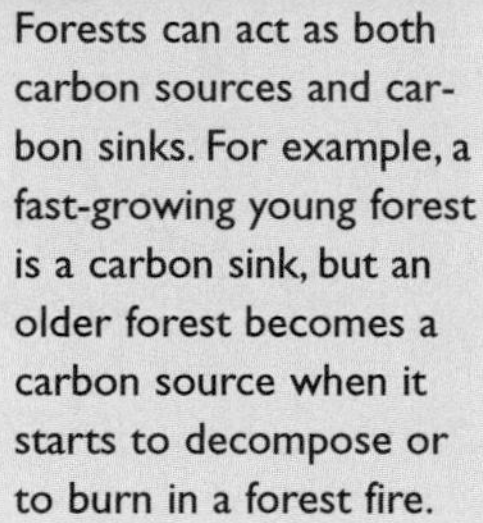
Forests can act as both carbon sources and carbon sinks. For example, a fast-growing young forest is a carbon sink, but an older forest becomes a carbon source when it starts to decompose or to burn in a forest fire.

When carbon is added to the atmosphere, we have a **carbon source**. Consider the following: a blade of grass (a carbon sink) eaten by a steer on the Prairies is digested in the animal's stomach. The carbon molecule in the grass becomes part of a methane gas molecule that the steer then recycles into the atmosphere. This is an example of a carbon source. The burning of fossil fuels and other organic matter, and the weathering of limestone (which releases CO_2) are other examples of carbon sources.

Sometimes carbon is removed from the atmosphere for a very long time. Think for a moment about a carbon dioxide molecule in the atmosphere that became part of a tiny animal called a **zooplankton** in the ocean 100 million years ago. The zooplankton died, fell to the bottom of a shallow sea, and became part of a crude oil deposit. This process, which tied up carbon for a very long time, is called **carbon fixation**. When the oil was recovered, refined, and burned as gasoline, the carbon was recycled into the environment as a carbon dioxide molecule.

The carbon cycle moved carbon through its many forms without human interference for millions of years. As a result, the amount of CO_2 in the atmosphere stayed more or less the same, and the greenhouse effect remained relatively stable. Things have changed, however. The amount of carbon dioxide in the atmosphere has increased. Scientists believe that this is the result of certain human activities, but especially those that release fixed carbon that has been out of circulation for perhaps hundreds of millions of years. The increased carbon dioxide has accelerated the greenhouse effect. How has fixed carbon been released?

- From 1888 to 2005, the world's population grew more than four times larger—from 1.6 billion to more than 6.5 billion. If you assume no other changes in people's lifestyles, you may say that four times as much carbon dioxide entered the atmosphere. Carbon dioxide escaped as fossil fuels were burned for heating and cooking, and as forests fell to create space for farming and urban growth.
- People's lifestyles changed between 1888 and 2005. Today's Western lifestyle includes individual ownership of cars, large centrally heated and air-conditioned homes, and a broad range of travel and recreation options. All these factors produce much more carbon dioxide per person than in previous generations. The problem of too much carbon dioxide will only get worse as more people in rapidly industrializing countries such as China and India **aspire** to a Western lifestyle.

aspire
work to attain

The Impact of Global Warming

Scientists predict that average temperatures in the next 100 years will increase by 1 to 5.8C°. The greatest increases will occur in polar areas, especially in the winter months. Some areas of northern Canada can anticipate winter temperature increases of as much as 10C°. This warming would have a number of effects on the world and on Canada.

Flooding caused by a cyclone (hurricane) in the Indian Ocean killed 500 000 people in Bangladesh in 1970.

Potential Effects on the World

- One of the most serious impacts of global warming is the melting of the polar ice sheets of Antarctica and Greenland. Such melting would increase the world's sea levels by perhaps one metre. An increase in sea level would have an enormous impact on people living in distant low-lying coastal regions. For example, increased sea levels would have a great effect on Bangladesh, a country with a population of more than 120 million people. Bangladesh often floods during tropical storms, and higher sea levels would make this flooding worse (Fig. 37-7). Canada would not be significantly affected by higher sea levels because it does not have many low-lying coastal areas.
- The world's total amount of precipitation would increase because higher temperatures would cause more evaporation from the oceans. Precipitation, however, would not increase evenly everywhere on Earth. Areas

▼ **Fig. 37-7** One of the most serious impacts of global warming is an increase in sea levels because of the melting of much (or even all) of Earth's glaciers and ice caps. Parts of the world close to sea level, like Bangladesh, could suffer devastating floods.

These temperature changes may not seem very large until you remember that a cooling of only 4C° caused glaciation.

that now receive abundant rainfall would receive even more; dry areas would receive even less. In Canada, for instance, the eastern and western coastal areas, which today receive enough rain for good farming, would flood because of too much precipitation. The country's valley areas would also flood during times of heavy rainfall. On the other hand, drought would become even more common in the dry areas of Canada. Most at risk would be the southern parts of Alberta and Saskatchewan—already the driest areas of southern Canada.

- The world's forests would suffer as a result of changes in precipitation caused by higher temperatures. Forests would die as regions became too dry to support tree growth. Fewer and smaller forests would make the problem of global warming worse because forests are important carbon sinks. Global warming would have a massive impact on Canada's forests. More forested areas would appear, but with completely different distribution (Fig. 37-8). As a result, forest industries and towns would have to make enormous adjustments. For example, Flin Flon, a papermaking town in Manitoba, would find itself in the middle of the expanded grassland. Towns like Flin Flon would have to develop a new economic base.
- Glaciers would get smaller, and many would disappear completely. Canadian glaciers are already shrinking. The front of the Athabaska Glacier in Alberta has **receded** 1.5 kilometres since 1890, about the time carbon dioxide and methane levels started to increase in the atmosphere.
- Some agricultural regions would become more productive as a result of greater levels of precipitation and longer, warmer growing seasons. Others would become less productive as levels of precipitation declined and temperatures rose. Although some agricultural regions

recede
retreat

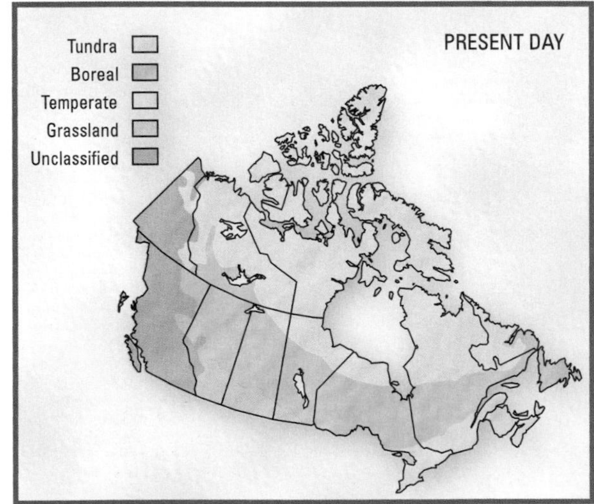

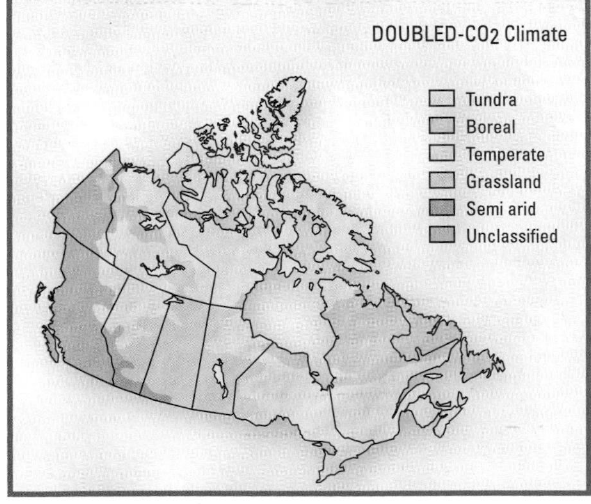

▲ **Fig. 37-8** Canada's vegetation regions and ecozones could change dramatically because of global warming.

might disappear as a result of global warming, others might develop. For example, farming might become possible in areas of Canada currently too cold for agriculture. A century from now, Grade 9 Geography students might learn about wheat farming near Yellowknife or raising livestock near Hudson Bay—areas without commercial farming today.

- The world would have to deal with millions of "climate change refugees"—people who would have to abandon their homes because of adverse weather conditions or higher sea levels. Canada would feel pressured to accept millions of these refugees from around the world.

Successful commercial agriculture needs good soil as well as suitable climate conditions. Most of the northern parts of Canada that might become warm enough for farming in the future have poor soil conditions or very little soil at all.

QUESTIONS

KNOWLEDGE AND UNDERSTANDING

1. Make a fully labelled sketch to illustrate how the greenhouse effect works in
   a) a car or greenhouse
   b) Earth's atmosphere
2. Compare the possible effects of global warming in Canada to those in other parts of the world in terms of the following: sea level, precipitation, forests, glaciers, agriculture, human health, and refugees.
3. Define the following terms in your own words and give two examples of each: *carbon sink*, *carbon source*, and *carbon fixation*.

THINKING

4. Fig. 15-3 shows Canada's ecozones. If global warming occurs, suggest how the following ecozones would change: Prairies, Mixedwood Plains, Boreal Plains, Taiga Shield, and Boreal Shield.
5. Describe the impact that global warming might have on each of the following:
   a) the size of Canada's areas of permafrost (check an atlas to see the current extent of permafrost)
   b) the operations of the St. Lawrence Seaway
   c) the popularity of various outdoor recreational activities
   d) the need for air conditioning and heating in our homes, schools, and businesses
   e) Canada's fishing industry

COMMUNICATION

6. a) What are *climate change refugees?*
   b) Examine the pros and cons of accepting climate change refugees in Canada.
   c) Imagine that you are a Member of Parliament. Write a bill to submit to Parliament that deals with
      i. the criteria used to determine which climate change refugees (if any) to accept
      ii. how they would arrive in Canada
      iii. what services Canadian agencies would offer them
      iv. any conditions placed on them, such as where they would live in Canada and how long the state would support them.

   (Hint: Consult with a teacher of Civics to find out how to write a parliamentary bill.)

APPLICATION

7. a) Today's lifestyles mean that we produce much more carbon dioxide per person than in the past. Suggest a few lifestyle choices we make today that cause this increased production.
   b) How might you reduce your production of carbon dioxide?
   c) Would you be willing to make these changes to your lifestyle? Why or why not?
8. a) Conduct an Internet search to determine whether the number of extreme weather events, such as hurricanes, droughts, and severe thunderstorms, has increased.
   b) If extreme weather events have increased, what causes do scientists suspect?

The Dilemma of Global Warming

Global warming could be the greatest problem facing humanity in the 21st century. Unfortunately, we don't have conclusive evidence that this is the case. The weather in recent years has been abnormally warm, but we do not know whether this trend will continue, or if it is merely a short-term variation in climate.

dire
disastrous

If global warming is a long-term trend, it will have **dire** consequences for people all over the world. To avoid global warming, we must drastically change the way in which we live. The longer we delay, the more serious the problem (if there is a problem!) will become. Global warming is a **dilemma** with conflicting issues that make it difficult to know what actions to take to stop it.

dilemma
problem having no easy solution

How Can We Reduce Global Warming?

We must reduce the amount of carbon dioxide that we release into the atmosphere, and we must find ways to remove some of the carbon dioxide that already exists. To accomplish these two tasks, we must minimize the activities that release fixed carbon (created by carbon fixation) into the air, and we must protect and expand carbon sinks.

We could also use nuclear power, but growing concern suggests that the environmental cost of nuclear power may exceed that of carbon-based energy.

Minimizing the Release of Fixed Carbon

Global warming might be controlled if we could minimize the release of fixed carbon into the atmosphere. The burning of enormous amounts of fossil fuels causes the release of fixed carbon. The carbon in these fuels, which has been fixed for millions of years under the surface of Earth, enters the atmosphere with the burning of every gram of coal, oil, or natural gas.

An important way to cut back on the amount of fixed carbon entering the atmosphere is to expand the use of new types of fuel and alternative energy technologies that are not carbon-based. For example, we could generate electricity using wind power (Fig. 37-9), hydroelectric power, solar power, or geothermal power. The electricity produced can replace power from stations that burn coal, fuel oil, or natural gas—all of which release large amounts of CO_2 into the atmosphere. We could also use energy-efficient devices (Fig. 37-10). For example, some motor vehicles use one-third the amount of energy used by standard vehicles—and release only one-third the amount of carbon dioxide into the atmosphere.

New types of fuel, alternative energy sources, and energy-efficient vehicles and appliances help to prevent the release of more fixed carbon. Perhaps more important, however, people must develop new knowledge and attitudes about energy use.

◀ **Fig. 37-9** Windmills built on the Gaspé peninsula harness the power of the area's strong winds.

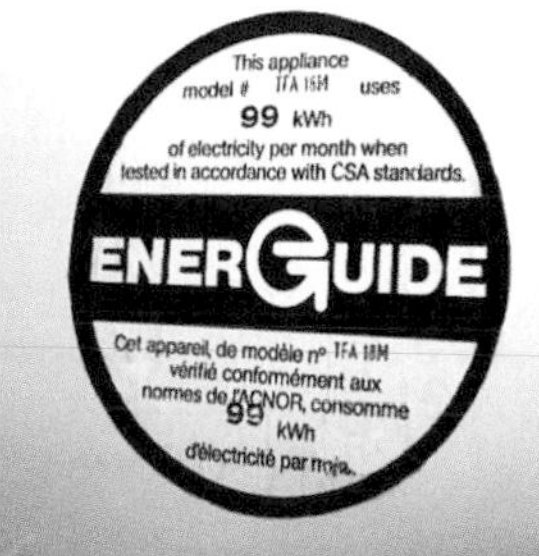

▲ **Fig. 37-10** Labels like this on major appliances tell how much energy the appliance uses. Similar labelling appears on new cars. Knowing how much energy something uses helps consumers reduce greenhouse gas emissions and also save money.

Protect and Expand Carbon Sinks

The most obvious carbon sinks that we can protect and expand are Earth's forests. For centuries, people cut down enormous tracts of forest all over the world. This practice accelerated in the 20th century, particularly in the tropics, as the world's population and level of economic development grew rapidly. People cut down forests for several reasons:

- to obtain wood for lumber or papermaking (two of Canada's most important industries)
- to clear land for farming
- to obtain wood for fuel for cooking and heating.

In the future, we will have to do three things to protect and expand forests as carbon sinks. First, before we cut down a tree, we should be absolutely sure that we need too. Second, we must use the wood from each tree as efficiently as possible. Third, we must plant trees in as many places as possible, including recently cut areas.

Many elementary and high schools have built carbon sinks by "greening" at least part of their grounds by planting trees and bushes (Fig. 37-11). This increases absorption of carbon dioxide because plants need CO_2 for photosynthesis. Do you think your school could build a carbon sink?

Think of the huge forest clearances in North America over the last two centuries by pioneers who settled southern Ontario and Quebec.

OCEANS AS CARBON SINKS

We tend to take the oceans for granted—out of sight, out of mind—but they have a critical role in preventing global warming. Oceans and their plant life (phytoplankton) are the most important carbon sinks of all. We must try to protect the oceans as carbon sinks by preventing ocean pollution that damages phytoplankton.

▲ **Fig. 37-11** Every time a tree is planted, the world's carbon sinks are increased.

Perhaps you have noticed fewer bubbles in an open can of pop that was left standing in a warm room than in one from a cold fridge. A warmer liquid cannot hold as much CO_2 as a cooler one.

Unfortunately, the effects of global warming on the oceans have set a vicious cycle in motion. As global warming occurs, ocean water becomes warmer. As ocean water warms, it becomes less efficient as a carbon sink because it releases more carbon dioxide than colder water. More carbon dioxide in the atmosphere speeds up the greenhouse effect, which in turn causes further global warming.

In the following sections, you will learn about international efforts to limit global warming.

International Efforts to Limit Global Warming

Scientists and politicians held the first international conferences on global warming in the late 1980s. The purpose of these conferences was to share information about the newly discovered problem of global warming, not to solve it. The participants negotiated a treaty in which they agreed to limit the production of greenhouse gases and promote the increase of carbon sinks. In 1992, more than 160 countries at a conference in Rio de Janeiro, Brazil, signed it. By signing the treaty, countries agreed to stabilize greenhouse gas concentrations in the atmosphere at a level that would prevent harm to Earth's climate. Developed countries agreed to a target of reducing their greenhouse gas (GHG) emissions to 1990 levels by the year 2000, and developing countries agreed to pursue sustainable development. Since the treaty was a framework convention, it did not include legally binding commitments on emission levels or penalties for countries that failed to meet their goals.

The treaty was called the United Nations Framework Convention on Climate Change (UNFCCC). The word "Framework" meant that the treaty provided a structure within which more specific agreements could be reached.

The Rio treaty recognized that all nations should take responsibility for solving the problem of global warming. It put emphasis, however, on the role played by developed countries in creating global warming. On a per-person basis, developed countries have produced far more than their fair share of greenhouse gases. For example, India produces about twice as much greenhouse gases as Canada, but it has a population more than 20 times larger. This means that the average Canadian produces about 10 times more carbon dioxide than the average Indian.

Treaty negotiations continued over the next five years. At the climate conference in Kyoto, Japan, in 1997, 180 countries accepted an **amendment** to the Rio treaty. Thirty-eight developed countries, including Canada, agreed to reduce their emissions of six greenhouse gases between 2008 and 2012 to levels 5.2% below 1990 levels. Under the **Kyoto Protocol** (treaty), the reductions in greenhouse gas emissions are legally binding. The Kyoto Protocol came into force on February 16, 2005.

The United States, the world's largest emitter of greenhouse gases, did not sign the treaty. It said the Kyoto reductions would cost too much for the US economy. The US also felt that the agreement favoured developing countries such as China (the world's second-largest emitter), India, and Brazil, which did not have to meet specific targets.

amendment modification

What You Can Do To Limit Global Warming

The fight to reduce global warming has to spread beyond UN conferences; it needs to occur at an individual level. Consider two teenagers on holiday. One spends a day riding a personal watercraft for a few hours; the other spends a few hours windsurfing. There is a considerable difference in each activity's impact on global warming. One hour of personal watercraft use releases many kilograms of carbon dioxide (from a fixed source) into the atmosphere. One hour of windsurfing releases none at all.

This example illustrates that we have some choice in preventing global warming and other environmental problems. Each of us creates an **ecological footprint (EF)** on Earth. This is a somewhat poetic way of saying that everything we do has an impact on the environment. Most of us do not think about this impact as much as we should, but if you think about the size of *your* ecological footprint, you can make lifestyle choices that help limit global warming.

You can learn more about the concept of the ecological footprint in Chapter 39.

The One-Tonne Challenge

Individual Canadians personally produce about 25% of the country's emissions. The average Canadian releases about 5 tonnes of greenhouse gases (GHGs) into the atmosphere each year. The remainder comes from industry and government.

We are not meeting our Kyoto targets. In fact, our GHG emissions today are considerably higher than 1990 levels. We will therefore have to reduce our emissions by about 26% to reach the level we pledged in the Protocol. How are we going to do this?

INTERNET

To learn more about federal energy initiatives, go to the link at www.pearsoned.ca/makingconnections2.

Fig. 37-12 ▶ Average personal greenhouse gas emissions

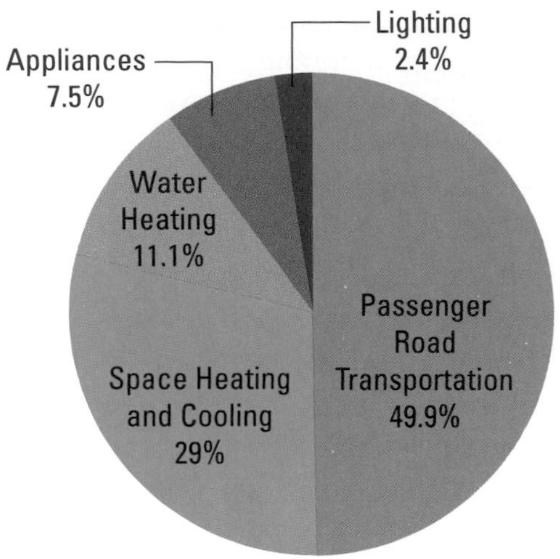

INTERNET

Find out more about the One-Tonne Challenge through the link at www.pearsoned.ca/makingconnections2.

The federal government has put energy-reduction programs into practice for itself and for various industries. In 2003, the Canadian government launched the **One-Tonne Challenge** to encourage individuals to reduce their personal GHG emissions (Fig. 37-12). One tonne represents about 20% of your annual GHG emissions from energy use.

How can you and your family reduce your GHG emissions and contribute to Canada's effort to meet its Kyoto Protocol commitment? You can turn off lights, televisions, and computers when not in use. You can walk, ride, or carpool to school instead of driving. You can turn down the thermostat in winter to make your home a little cooler, and you can turn the air conditioner down in summer to make your home a little warmer. These measures may not seem like much, but if all Canadians reduced their GHG production by one tonne, we could help reduce the impact of global warming and get closer to meeting our Kyoto commitments.

INTERNET

To learn more about global warming, check the government and business Web site links available at www.pearsoned.ca/makingconnections2.

In Closing...

We have to choose a course with respect to global warming. One path will lead to a solution; the other will lead to continued emissions of GHG and accelerated global warming. Which path will Canadians choose? Those who think that scientists have exaggerated the potential impact of global warming will suggest that we do nothing without clear proof of the problem. Those who believe the threat of global warming will insist that we take drastic action now before it is too late. Where do you stand?

QUESTIONS

KNOWLEDGE AND UNDERSTANDING

1. a) What two basic actions can humanity take to reduce global warming?
   b) What two specific actions can individuals take to minimize the release of fixed carbon into the atmosphere?
2. a) Identify three ways in which we can protect and expand forests as carbon sinks.
   b) What are the world's most important carbon sinks and how can we protect them?

THINKING

3. a) A carbon tax is a special tax tied to any product or activity that causes a release of carbon into the atmosphere. Give five examples where it might apply.
   b) Do you think that a carbon tax is a fair and effective way to fight global warming? Explain.
4. a) Canada might experience some benefits from global warming. Describe three possible benefits.
   b) Canada might gain from global warming while some countries might suffer. In light of this possibility, do Canadians have a responsibility to change the way in which they live in order to minimize the effects of global warming? Why or why not?
5. It has been said that global warming is a 100-year problem facing four-year governments. What does this statement mean?

COMMUNICATION

6. a) One of the worries that scientists have about global warming is the impact that "feedback loops" will have on making the problem worse. (In a feedback loop, when condition A increases, it causes condition B to increase. In turn, this causes condition A to increase even more, which causes condition B to . . . well, you get the idea.) Use the Internet to determine the impact of three feedback loops that increase global warming. In your notebook, use your own words (and possibly simple diagrams) to explain how these feedback loops might occur.
   b) Scientists have also been considering the possibility of feedback loops that might *lessen* the impact of global warming. In a paragraph, identify and explain at least one of these loops.
7. a) What is the purpose of the One-Tonne Challenge?
   b) What can you do to reduce your GHG emissions?
   c) i. With your family, develop an action plan to meet the One-Tonne Challenge.
      ii. Form a group with three members of your class. Discuss your family's action plan with your group.
      iii. Revise your family's action plan based on your group's discussion.
   d) i. With your group, develop an action plan for your school to meet the One-Tonne Challenge.
      ii. Share your group's action plan for your school with the rest of your class.
      iii. Together as a class, develop a final version of a school action plan using the best ideas from each group's plan.
      iv. Discuss the action plan for your school with the school's Environment Club (if it has one) or the school administration. Set up a committee to present and administer the plan.
      v. At the end of the school year, evaluate your successes and failures. Then, modify the plan for the next school year.

APPLICATION

8. Your rich Uncle Charlie wants to buy you a car for your not-too-distant 16th birthday. You want to choose a vehicle that expresses your personality and how you think. Which car would you choose (Fig. 37-13)? Explain.

Fig. 37-13

	Full-size SUV	Compact Fuel-efficient Vehicle
List price (approx.)	$78 000	$22 000
Cost of fuel (based on 20 000 km/year @ $1.00/L)	$4 000	$800
CO_2 emissions (kg/yr)	8 449	2 291
"Coolness" factor	??? You decide	??? You decide

9. Research information about the Kyoto Protocol on the Internet.
   a) What did developed countries agree to do?
   b) What responsibilities do developing countries have?
   c) How does Canada plan to meet its obligations under the treaty?
   d) What is meant by "emissions trading"?
   e) What penalties does a country face if it fails to meet its emissions target?
   f) i. Summarize the arguments put forward by the United States to explain its refusal to sign the treaty.
      ii. Do you agree or disagree with the US's arguments? Explain.
10. Your teacher may give you instructions for a global warming exercise that you can do using ArcView.

CASE STUDY

The Impact of Climate Change on the North

▲ **Fig. 37-14** Scientists say that global warming affects polar regions more dramatically than other parts of the globe.

During the 1990s, in the community of Sachs Harbour on the shores of Banks Island in the western Arctic, people began to see insects for which they had no names! The people had no names for these insects because they had never seen them before. Thunder and lightning also occurred for the first time. What is happening in the Arctic to cause the appearance of "new" insects and unknown weather conditions?

The insects were wasps and sand flies.

In the Arctic, the average temperature is rising at almost twice the rate of the average global temperature. Changes that occur in the Arctic as a result of rising temperatures will have an impact in other parts of the world. For example, the melting of Arctic ice will lead to a global rise in sea levels around the world (Fig. 37-14).

Scientists predict that during the 21st century, the global temperature will increase by between 1.4C° and 5.8C°.

In November 2004, a report known as the Arctic Climate Impact Assessment (ACIA) was published to shed light on environmental changes occurring in the Arctic. The Arctic Council, a group made up of members from eight Arctic nations and six Aboriginal peoples' organizations, commissioned the assessment. The ACIA resulted from a four-year effort by nearly 300 scientists from different countries to chronicle the effects of global warming on the Arctic. The researchers received help from the

A study released in 2005 stated that the area covered by sea ice in the Arctic had shrunk for four consecutive years. The ice now covers 20% less area than the average extent of sea ice between 1978 and 2000. Scientists calculated the rate of shrinkage at 8% per decade. If this rate continues, the ice may disappear by the year 2060!

Aboriginal peoples of the Arctic, who contributed their special knowledge about the changes taking place in the environment.

The Arctic includes Iceland and Greenland (a territory of Denmark) and portions of Norway, Sweden, Finland, Russia, the United States, and Canada. It can be defined by any one of several boundaries: the Arctic Circle (66.5° N), the treeline, the extent of permafrost on land, or the extent of sea ice on the ocean. The ACIA, however, uses a boundary that includes subarctic areas vital to the functioning of the Arctic system. It presents the beneficial and harmful impacts of climate change on the people of the Arctic and subarctic areas. Some of the findings of the ACIA are summarized below.

Decline in Food Supply and Loss of Hunting, Fishing, and Gathering Culture

Aboriginal peoples make up about 10% of the total population of the global Arctic but about 50% of the population of Canada's Arctic.

It is feared that climate warming causes a decline in the food supply of the Inuit and other Aboriginal peoples of the Arctic and subarctic. This, in turn, leads to the loss of their hunting, fishing, and gathering lifestyle. This lifestyle forms the basis of their culture.

- Warmer temperatures melt the sea ice—the habitat of numerous marine animals. Polar bears hunt seals on the ice, and seals and walrus bear their young there. These animals are declining in numbers and may become extinct if their habitat continues to diminish.
- Warmer temperatures have increased the frequency of freezing rain and have disrupted the freeze–thaw cycles in the Arctic and subarctic.

Fig. 37-15 ▶ Two Inuit hunters eat fresh seal meat to stay warm during a traditional polar bear hunt. Aboriginal peoples depend on seals, polar bears, and caribou for food, but hunters now find it dangerous to venture onto the thin ice in search of prey.

These changes have affected the growth of vegetation that provides caribou, musk ox, and other wildlife with food. Land animals upon which Aboriginal people depend for food are declining in number as a result of climate change.

- A warmer climate has caused a decline in several northern freshwater fisheries. Arctic char and whitefish, major components in the diet of indigenous peoples, are among those species threatened. The loss of traditional foods such as fish has led to greater dependence upon a diet typical of southern Canadians. Non-traditional diets increase indigenous peoples' risk of diabetes, obesity, and cardiovascular disease.
- Warmer temperatures in the Arctic have already allowed the northern migration of certain insects. This may also permit the northern migration of southern species that will compete with local species for food. Such migration may cause a decline in local species.

New species may introduce previously unknown diseases into the environment that could have adverse effects on people and animals.

Thawing Permafrost

In recent decades, the temperature of the ***permafrost*** *has risen by up to 2C°. In many areas of the North, the layer of Earth that thaws each spring above the permafrost becomes deeper. The water from the melting permafrost changes the pattern of freshwater lakes, wetlands, and drainage.*

- The changes in these patterns alter animals' access to breeding grounds and historic migration routes.
- Some freshwater lakes, formed as a result of the **impermeable** layer of permafrost beneath them, disappear because the water seeps away through the melted permafrost layer.
- Permafrost has the ability to stabilize the soil. In some northern forests, certain tree species, such as the black spruce, need firm soil in which to root. When the permafrost thaws, the soil loses its solidity. The trees, lacking a firm base in which to spread their roots, lose support and lean over, or fall down and die.
- Thawing of the permafrost has affected transportation in the North. Residents, as well as oil, gas, diamond, and forestry companies, have always relied on the cold climate and the permafrost to maintain the roads built over frozen lakes and tundra. The warming climate has shortened the winter season during which much transportation occurs over these "ice roads."
- Thawing of the permafrost affects the infrastructure of northern communities (Fig. 37-16). Buildings shift and crack, and the runways of airfields break up. Even sewage pipes bend, break, and spill raw sewage as the ground beneath them thaws and slumps. Gas pipelines and water lines suffer a similar fate.

impermeable
not permitting the passage of a liquid

When large numbers of trees start to lean, they are referred to as a "drunken forest."

For more information about winter ice roads, see Chapter 30.

Fig. 37-16 ▶
This building, constructed in 1901 in Dawson City, Yukon, shows how structures shift as permafrost thaws.

Reduced Sea Ice

As greater areas of the Arctic seas become ice-free for longer periods, marine transport in the North will expand.

- Transportation on water may become more important than transportation on land as new waterways open up. Increased marine transport may lead to increased industry and tourism, but the **influx** of non-Aboriginal people may create social, cultural, and environmental problems for the Inuit and other Aboriginal peoples.
- The world's maritime nations will gain greater access to the shipping channels of the Northwest Passage, and to the Arctic's natural resources of oil and gas, as the sea ice melts. This situation will increase the risk of oil spills in a fragile environment. It may also lead to sovereignty issues, since many countries do not recognize Canada's jurisdiction over some areas of the Canadian Arctic.

influx
sudden arrival

Impact of Warming Climate on Coastal Communities in the Arctic

In communities located on low-lying seacoasts, such as Tuktoyaktuk on the Beaufort Sea, the thawing permafrost weakens the shoreline, making the land vulnerable to erosion.

- Coastal communities and industrial facilities may face the threat of higher sea levels, and perhaps may even have to relocate.
- Higher waves and stronger storm surges will disrupt Aboriginal peoples' hunting and fishing practices and may cause damage to homes and boats, as well as erosion along the coasts. They may also cause changes in animal habitats, or alter the fragile natural ecology of terrestrial and marine wildlife.

Enhanced Marine Fisheries

As the climate warms, the Arctic marine fisheries, which include herring and cod, will likely become more productive. Freshwater fishing of Arctic char and whitefish may decline.

- In total, warmer sea temperatures may increase fishing opportunities for Canada's northern residents.
- Warmer temperatures may also attract fishing fleets from other countries that do not abide by the laws protecting fish stocks.

Enhanced Agriculture and Forestry

Climate warming in the North will cause longer, warmer growing seasons, and will increase precipitation.

- Longer growing seasons open up new opportunities for agricultural and forestry operations. Food and wood production will be possible in areas that were once too cold for growing certain types of food and trees.
- Although a warmer climate may better suit agriculture, Arctic soils are not very fertile and would not be very productive.

Observed Changes in the Weather and Environmental Conditions

Residents across northern Canada and in other Arctic nations have noticed changes in the weather and have made the following observations.

- Weather patterns have become more variable and unfamiliar. For example, storms often occur without warning, and wind directions change suddenly. Experienced indigenous hunters and elders who can predict the weather using traditional techniques now often find it difficult to do so.
- Freezing rain occurs more often.
- The characteristics of the snow are changing. For example, the snow may be more hard packed, making it unsuitable for building igloos during hunting trips (Fig. 37-17). Unusually loose snow often occurs and makes travel more difficult.
- Because the arrival of spring has become unpredictable, even experts find it difficult to tell when the ice on rivers will break up.

These changes to weather patterns, wildlife, and environmental conditions affect the ability of Aboriginal peoples to hunt, fish, and maintain their traditional way of life and culture. Whether Canada's Arctic peoples can adapt to these changes or take advantage of them has yet to be determined.

Fig. 37-17 ▶ Global warming may affect snow conditions, making it difficult to build igloos for shelter during travel.

QUESTIONS

KNOWLEDGE AND UNDERSTANDING

1. What is the ACIA, and who initiated the project?
2. a) Make a list of the beneficial impacts of climate change in the Arctic.
   b) Make a list of the harmful impacts of climate change in the Arctic.

THINKING

3. In general, do you think that climate change will bring more beneficial than harmful impacts in the Arctic, or vice versa? Explain.

APPLICATION

4. Conduct research to determine the *global* consequences of climate warming in the Arctic.
5. The changes taking place in the Arctic result from activities occurring outside this region. Conduct research to find the answers to these questions:
   a) What human activities and natural events cause climate change globally and in the Arctic?
   b) What steps are governments and others taking to correct the human activities that cause climate change?
   c) What steps would you agree to take to limit climate change?

GeoLit Reminder

When answering questions about informational text:

- Scan the written text, noting headings, subheadings, and key words.
- What additional information can you gather from the margin notes and visuals?
- What further information would help you better understand this Case Study? Where might you find it?

38 Measuring Environmental Sustainability

Key Ideas

This chapter helps you investigate these questions:

- Is the quality of the environment getting better or worse? How can we measure the improvement or deterioration of the environment?
- How does Canada compare to other countries in terms of improving environmental quality?
- Which countries do a good job of environmental protection? Which countries do not?

Key Terms

Environmental Sustainability Index (ESI)

index

variable

indicator

component

environmental stresses

The Environment: Who Is Responsible?

> The responsibility for environmental damage ultimately belongs to every individual and not to companies or governments.

Discuss the above statement in a group of four or five classmates. On a large sheet of paper, list arguments both in support of the statement and in opposition to it. Try to come up with a conclusion that everyone in the group can agree on, and then write it at the bottom of your sheet. Your teacher may want you to explain your conclusion to the class—so be prepared!

Measuring Environmental Sustainability

Discussion of environmental problems surrounds us. Newspapers, television, and the Internet feature stories about global warming, air and water pollution, forest destruction, the problem of nuclear waste, and other issues. Some of these stories tell us that we face environmental ruin; others point out progress in cleaning up the environment. Until recently, we couldn't track environmental progress very effectively. The creation of a measure called the **Environmental Sustainability Index (ESI)** has changed this situation.

In 2005, a Google search for "environmental problem" yielded about 26 million hits.

Fig. 38-1 ▶ Former US President Bill Clinton and Microsoft Chairman Bill Gates attended the 2005 World Economic Conference in Davos, Switzerland. They, along with other conference attendees, including British Prime Minister Tony Blair, U2 lead singer Bono, President Thabo Mbeki of South Africa, and President Olusegun Obasanjo of Nigeria, took part in a panel discussion calling for increased aid to Africa.

INTERNET

You can check out this report through the link at www.pearsoned.ca/makingconnections2.

Scholars at Yale and Columbia universities in the United States produced the 2005 ESI Report for a very influential organization called the World Economic Forum (WEF) (Fig. 38-1). The WEF believes that we can solve global problems only by coordinating the efforts of government, corporations, and non-governmental organizations (NGOs). The WEF includes representatives from all of the world's 1000 largest companies, from government, from the intellectual community (universities and **think tanks**), and from non-governmental organizations.

think tanks
organizations of experts who do research

The ESI Report calculates the level of environmental sustainability in 146 countries. It considers each country's current environmental conditions and **sustainability** over the next several decades. The report rates each country by using 76 **data sets** that include such measurements as the amount of fresh water, the amount of waste recycling, and the number of people who attend college or university.

data set
numerical information on a specific topic

What Is Environmental Sustainability?

Before we compare the levels of environmental sustainability achieved by different countries, let's make sure we know what environmental sustainability means. According to a major UN report on environmental health and economic development, "sustainable development seeks to meet the needs and aspirations of the present without compromising the ability to meet those of the future."

This definition comes from *Our Common Future: The World Commission on Environment and Development*. Gro Harlem Brundtland, former prime minister of Norway, headed this commission (1983–1987).

1. Give at least five examples of how we might use Earth's resources today without compromising future generations' ability to meet their needs.
2. Give at least five examples of non-sustainable use of Earth's resources.
3. Assume that you want to create an international **index** of sustainability. An index is a number, expressed without a unit of measurement, used to make comparisons between and among countries. Comparisons are possible because the index for each country is calculated using the same data sources. From the following list of data sets, select the 10 that would *most help* in calculating a sustainability index.
   a) *number of barrels of crude oil used per capita per year*
   b) *number of migrating birds passing within 10 kilometres of your home*
   c) *total fertility rate*
   d) *percentage of the population that graduates from college or university*
   e) *number of visitors to Disney World from different countries*
   f) *death rates from cancer*
   g) *people's attitudes toward protecting the environment*
   h) *percentage of a country's land protected in national/provincial parks*
   i) *number of Internet users per 1000 people*
   j) *number of people convicted of polluting*
   k) *number of newspapers sold per year per capita*
   l) *cost of gasoline compared to world average cost*
   m) *change in the amount of forested land in the country*
   n) *amount of corruption in the country*
   o) *renewable energy production as a percentage of total energy production*
   p) *number of new golf courses in the country in the past five years per 100 000 people*
   q) *percentage of the population with access to safe water supply*
   r) *rate of waste recycling in the country*
   s) *another data set of your choice*

   Explain why each data set that you choose would help in measuring progress toward environmental sustainability. You may summarize your answer using a simple graphic organizer of your choice.

You learned about a variety of useful indexes in Chapter 1 of this book.

See Chapter 16 for a discussion of fertility rate.

You might wish to consider some data sets that do not specifically refer to the environment. For example, a wide variety of economic and social conditions relate to environmental sustainability.

The data sets that you suggest must be easily accessible from a reliable source and be available for most of the world's countries.

What Does the ESI Report Include?

Visit www.pearsoned.ca/makingconnections2 for a list of the variables included within each component.

The authors of the ESI Report had the same problem you faced in the activity above: which data should they use to measure sustainability? They faced an additional challenge because they actually had to calculate an index.

How did they use their data sets to create an accurate and easily understandable numerical index? First, from the 76 data sets, or **variables**, they created 21 **indicators** that combined similar variables. (Each indicator contains between 2 and 12 variables.) Then, they sorted the 21 indicators into five groups or **components**. Averaging the scores of the indicators within each component produces the ESI.

These are the five components:

- *Environmental Systems:* This component measures the country's current environmental health. It considers the wealth of the country's natural resources and the impact that people have on the environment.
- *Reducing Environmental Stresses:* This component measures the severity of the country's environmental problems. These problems range from deforestation and air pollution to overfishing and inadequate waste disposal. This component also looks at the country's success in dealing with these **environmental stresses** compared to other nations.
- *Reducing Human Vulnerability:* This component measures the security of the country's people. For example, it measures the amount of available food and access to basic healthcare. It also considers whether

▼ **Fig. 38-2** Non-sustainable and sustainable development: a) Smoke billows from the chimneys of China's largest iron and steel works at Anshan, in the province of Liaoning. Rapidly industrializing countries such as China will place increasing strain on the global environment. b) Kenyan environmentalist and human rights campaigner Wangari Maathai (centre, front) won the 2004 Nobel Peace Prize "for her contribution to sustainable development, democracy, and peace." In 1977, she founded the Green Belt Movement, a grassroots non-governmental organization that has mobilized poor women to plant 30 million trees.

a)

b)

people are at particular risk from natural hazards such as hurricanes and droughts, and from human-made hazards such as air pollution.

- *Social and Institutional Capacity:* This component measures the ability of the country's government, people, and corporations to respond effectively to environmental challenges. It considers such factors as educational standards, effectiveness and honesty of government, and the willingness of companies to behave in an environmentally responsible fashion.
- *Global Stewardship:* This component measures "good global citizenship,"—the country's impact on the environmental health of other nations. It examines contributions to international efforts to promote sustainability. It also considers the extent to which the country "exports" environmental damage to other countries—for example, by importing goods whose production causes environmental problems elsewhere.

ESI—The Global Picture

ESI values range from 0 to 100, with a high score indicating a good level of environmental sustainability. In the 2005 survey, North Korea had the lowest ranking with an index of 29.2; Finland had the highest with an index of 75.1. When we examine a list of the 10 countries with the highest ESIs (Fig. 38-3), we can see some interesting patterns. Seven of the top ESI countries—Finland, Norway, Sweden, Iceland, Canada, Switzerland, and Austria—also have positions in the top 14 nations on the UN's Human Development Index. This suggests a strong, and perhaps not surprising, relationship between high levels of wealth, education, and life expectancy (factors measured in the HDI) and environmental sustainability.

The Human Development Index has often been used to identify the "best country in the world in which to live." It includes measures of wealth, health, and education. See the UN Human Development Index mentioned on page 16 for more details.

But countries with high ESI rankings do not always have high HDI levels. Uruguay, which has a high ESI ranking at #3, has a **mediocre** HDI ranking (#46). Guyana, relatively high at #8 on the ESI list, has a very low HDI level (#104). The small African nation of Gabon, which ranks #12 on the ESI list, slips even farther down to #122 for the HDI.

mediocre
neither good nor bad

Rank	Country	ESI
1	Finland	75.1
2	Norway	73.4
3	Uruguay	71.8
4	Sweden	71.7
5	Iceland	70.8
6	Canada	64.4
7	Switzerland	63.7
8	Guyana	62.9
9	Argentina	62.7
10	Austria	62.7

◄ **Fig. 38-3** ESI values: 10 highest-ranking countries, 2005

Furthermore, when we look at the other countries in the top 10 for the HDI, we see that their ESI scores may not rank very high (Fig. 38-4). Being a wealthy, highly developed country is helpful in working toward environmental sustainability—but it is not always enough to achieve similar rankings in each index. However, the top 10 countries in the ESI do share two important characteristics: all have rich resource bases and relatively low population densities.

▼ **Fig. 38-4** Comparison of ESI and HDI rankings, 2005

a) ESI and HDI Rankings Both High

Country	ESI Ranking	HDI Ranking
Finland	1	13
Norway	2	1
Sweden	3	2
Iceland	5	7
Canada	6	4
Switzerland	7	11
Austria	10	14

b) ESI Ranking Much Higher Than HDI Scores

Country	ESI Ranking	HDI Ranking
Uruguay	3	46
Guyana	8	104
Argentina	9	34
Gabon	12	122

c) ESI Ranking Much Lower Than HDI Scores

Country	ESI Ranking	HDI Ranking
Australia	13	3
Japan	30	9
United States	45	8
Belgium	112	6

Let's now look at the countries that rank lowest on the ESI (Fig. 38-5). We can see, once again, that the level of environmental sustainability tends to relate to the level of development as indicated by the HDI. Yemen, Sudan, Haiti, and North Korea, all countries at the bottom of the ESI ranking, rank among the least advanced countries in the world. Others at the bottom of the ESI, however, have average HDI rankings, for example, Kuwait and Trinidad and Tobago. The countries at the bottom of the ESI list share two characteristics: all face serious environmental stresses and all have shown only very limited willingness and ability to deal with these stresses.

Kuwait is #44 and Trinidad and Tobago is #54 in the HDI.

Fig. 38-5 ► ESI values: 10 lowest-ranking countries, 2005

ESI Ranking	Country	ESI
137	Yemen	37.3
138	Kuwait	36.6
139	Trinidad & Tobago	36.3
140	Sudan	35.9
141	Haiti	34.8
142	Uzbekistan	34.4
143	Iraq	33.6
144	Turkmenistan	33.1
145	Taiwan	32.7
146	North Korea	29.2

The ESI and Canada

The ESI report produces a "report card" for each country. Each of these reports features a unique and useful kind of graph (Fig. 38-6) called a "sustainability **pentagon**." The meaning of the pentagon is simple: the larger the shaded (inner) area of the pentagon, the higher the country's level of sustainability. A quick comparison of the pentagons for Finland and North Korea shows you immediately that one country has very high sustainability and the other very low sustainability (Fig. 38-7).

pentagon
five-sided figure

The shape of the pentagon gives the reader a quick, visual sense of the country's sustainability strengths and weaknesses. Canada's sustainability pentagon (Fig. 38-8) is quite large, but irregular in shape when compared to Finland's. Canada has high scores for three components: *Environmental Systems*, *Reducing Human Vulnerability*, and *Social and Institutional Capacity*; a mediocre score for *Reducing Stresses*; and a low score for *Global Stewardship*. To understand the reasons for the shape of Canada's graph, we need to look at the scores for the variables that were used to calculate the component scores. The bar graph in Fig. 38-9 compares Canada's indicator scores with those of other wealthy countries.

For purposes of this comparison, Canada's "peer group" consists of those countries with the highest GDP per capita in the world. One-fifth of the countries in the world belong to this peer group.

Most of Canada's scores are not surprising:

- Our high *Environmental Systems* score reflects our generous resource base—land, water, biodiversity, and air quality.
- Our high *Reducing Human Vulnerability* score reflects the rich and secure life that Canadians enjoy.

▼ **Fig. 38-6** The sustainability pentagon is really five graphs—one for each component—joined together. These graphs all start at a value of 0 in the centre of the pentagon and radiate outward to a value of 100.

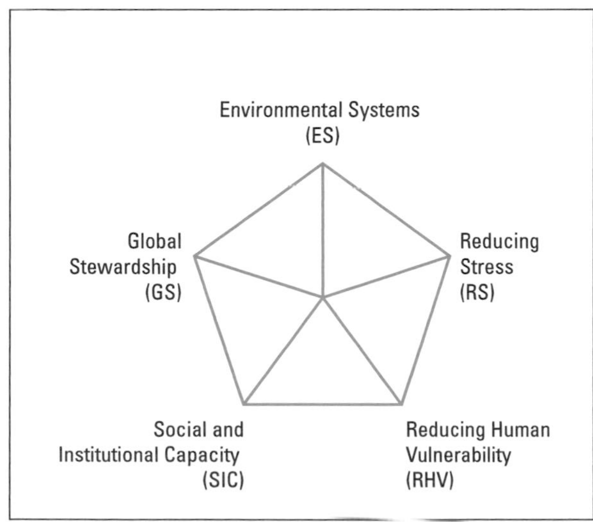

▼ **Fig. 38-7** Environmental sustainability graphs for (a) Finland and (b) North Korea

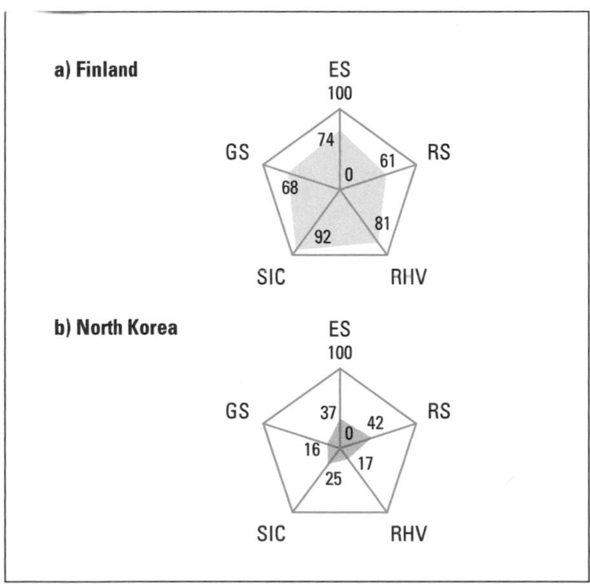

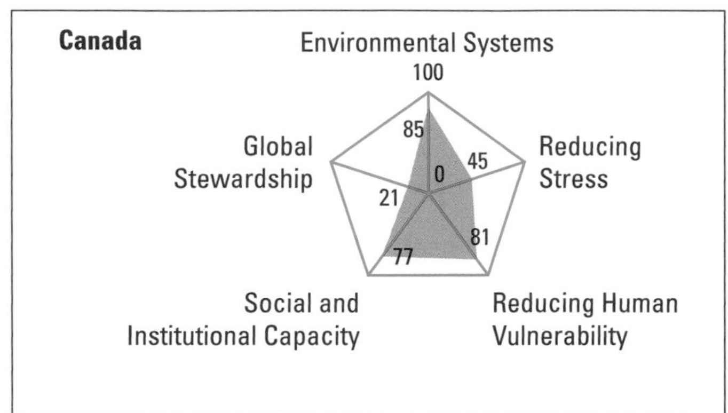

Fig. 38-8 ▶ Environmental sustainability graph for Canada

- Our high *Social and Institutional Capacity* score indicates that we have effective governments and private sectors, along with advanced science and technology.
- The situation for the *Reducing Stresses* indicator is mixed. While we have low population stress and little water stress, we have very poor scores for reducing air pollution and minimizing waste.
- For *Global Stewardship*, our score falls because of our willingness to export the environmental impact of our lifestyle to other countries. For example, we rank 144th in the world for *Reducing Transboundary Environmental Pressures*—out of 146 countries in the study!

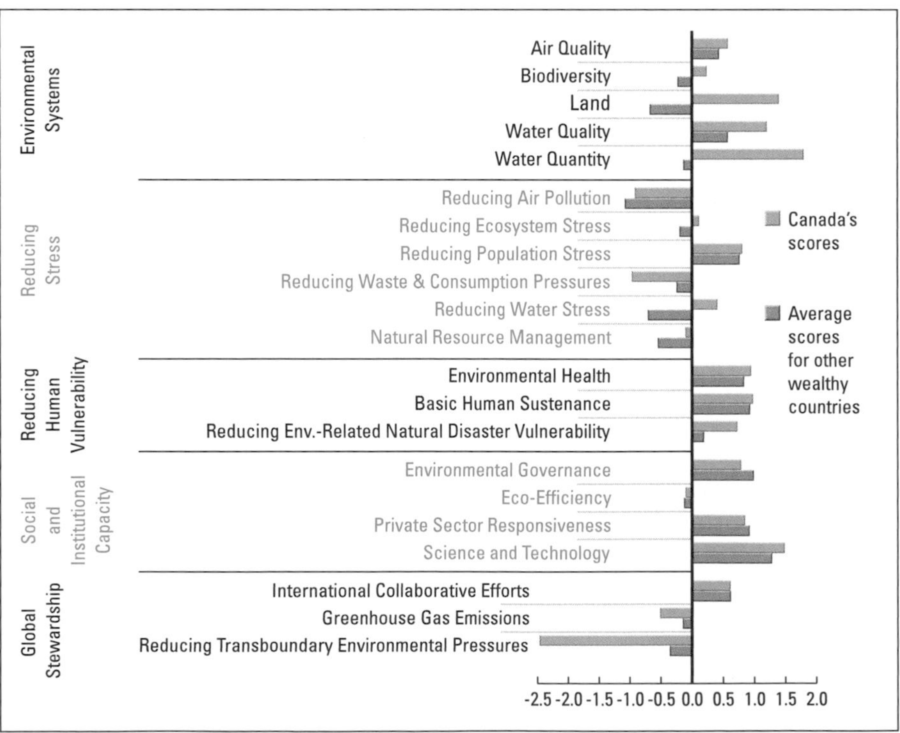

Fig. 38-9 ▶ Canada's indicator scores, compared with those of other wealthy countries

The ESI—Why It Matters

After reading about the ESI and learning how Canada compares with other nations, you will likely begin to ask such questions as, "How can Canada do better?" Governments and business leaders have begun to ask questions like this because the ESI Report is published by a respected and influential group and enjoys wide readership. You may even be asking yourself whether your personal decisions have an impact on Canada's ESI. As future ESI reports become available, we will watch with interest how Canada's progress compares with that of other countries.

QUESTIONS

KNOWLEDGE AND UNDERSTANDING

1. a) Who produced the ESI Report? For whom was it produced?
   b) Compared with other environmental reports (for example, from governments or environmentalists), why is the ESI Report important?
2. a) What is an index?
   b) Besides the ESI, name two other indexes mentioned in this book. (Hint: Refresh your memory by scanning the Glossary and Index.)
3. In your own words, define a variable, an indicator, and a component.
4. Describe, with specific details and in your own words, how Canada did on the ESI. Indicate areas in which we do well and those where we need to improve.

THINKING

5. Relate Canada's ESI to the characteristics of our physical geography, population, economic development, and trade.

COMMUNICATION

6. Write a letter to your Member of Parliament on the subject of the ESI and, in particular, Canada's rating. In your letter, you should provide a brief explanation of the ESI in case your MP is unfamiliar with it. (MPs receive an avalanche of information on virtually every subject imaginable.) You should provide a Web site where the ESI is explained. Tell your MP your concerns about Canada's scores and how we might improve them. If you decide that you actually want to send your letter, have your teacher or parent check it first.

GeoLit Reminder

When writing a letter to a government representative:

- Clearly state your opinion early in the letter.
- Back up your opinion with as many points of fact as you are able to gather.
- Organize supporting information in a logical sequence.
- Ensure that all information is relevant and accurate.
- Use proper letter format and formal language.
- Provide your full name and address.

Remember that you do not need a stamp on a letter sent to Parliament.

APPLICATION

7. a) Discuss how your lifestyle relates (or does not relate) to Canada's ESI.
   b) What lifestyle changes can you make that would contribute to improving Canada's ESI:
      i. at this stage of your life?
      ii as an adult?

39 Reducing the Size of Your Ecological Footprint

Key Ideas

This chapter helps you investigate these questions:

- What is an ecological footprint?
- How does an increase in the global ecological footprint affect you?
- What role can you play in reducing the size of Canada's ecological footprint?

Key Terms

ecological footprint (EF)
carrying capacity
fair earthshare
sustainability
ecological overshoot
Industrial Revolution

▼ **Fig. 39-1** How often do we think about the ecological impact of modern life?

In *Making Connections*, we have often looked at how people use resources and how this use affects the world's environment (Fig. 39-1). For example, in Chapter 24, you learned that despite Canada's great size, it has only a very small amount of excellent farmland—and yet we continue to expand our cities onto this land. In Chapter 27, you learned that most of our oil and gas reserves will run out in the 21st century, and yet we do little to reduce our use of these vital, non-renewable resources. In Chapter 38, you learned how the environmental sustainability index attempts to measure national success (and failure) in promoting sustainability. But what does this mean to individual Canadians?

Measuring and comparing the impacts of different activities on the environmental health of Canada and the world is a difficult task (Fig. 39-2). We sometimes end up trying to "compare apples to oranges." For example, we can easily compare the impact of living in a house in the suburbs to that of living in a downtown high-rise. We have more difficulty, however, comparing the environmental impact of riding a snowmobile to that of buying a new pair of jeans. How can we decide which activity causes less harm to the environment? How can we measure and compare the different environmental impacts of such diverse human activities? The answers lie in the concept of the **ecological footprint (EF)**.

▲ **Fig. 39-2** How can we determine the *combined* ecological impact that all our activities place on the environment?

The ecological footprint measures the ecological impact of a person's activities by determining the amount of biologically productive land and water (in hectares) required to support that person and to dispose of his or her wastes. The EF does not represent a single, specific area of land and water because people use resources from all over the world and create waste both close to home and far away. Rather, the EF represents many small pieces of land and water all over the world. We can calculate the EF of one person, or the average EF of that person's city or country. We can even measure the average EF of the entire world.

INTERNET

For more on the ecological footprint, read the book *Our Ecological Footprint: Reducing Human Impact on the Earth* by Mathis Wackernagal and William Rees, who developed the concept. Or, visit the Web link at www.pearsoned.ca/makingconnections2.

How Big Is the Average Canadian's Ecological Footprint?

In 2004, the World Wildlife Fund (WWF) published a detailed look at the ecological footprint of every country in the world using data from 2001. Examine Fig. 39-3 to learn about the ecological footprint of an average Canadian.

Under the Energy Footprint, *CO_2 from fossil fuels* refers to the amount of forested land needed to eliminate (through photosynthesis) the carbon dioxide that we produce by burning fuels such as gasoline, natural gas, and coal. This approach is used because the environmental cost of fossil fuel use is much greater than just the small amount of land that is actually required to produce the energy—for example, at the oil well or coal mine. Although this calculation does not reflect all the environmental costs related to energy use, it does at least consider the critical impact of fossil fuel use on global warming.

INTERNET

You can read the WWF report that includes the ecological footprint data at http://www.pearson.ca/makingconnections2.

More information on global warming can be found in Chapter 37.

Fig. 39-3 ▶ How the ecological footprint of the average Canadian was calculated. The ecological footprint consists of three main parts: the *food, **fibre**, and timber footprint*; the *energy footprint*; and the *built-up land footprint*.

Item Required to Support One Average Canadian	Area in Hectares	Total Area in Hectares
Food, Fibre, and Timber Footprint		
Cropland	1.09	
Forest	1.45	
Grazing land	0.39	
Fishing grounds	0.11	
Total Food, Fibre, and Timber Footprint		**3.04**
Energy Footprint		
CO_2 from fossil fuels	2.70	
Fuelwood	0.02	
Nuclear energy	0.51	
Hydroelectric energy	0.12	
Total Energy Footprint		**3.35**
Built-up Land Footprint		**0.06**
TOTAL ECOLOGICAL FOOTPRINT		**6.45**

Notes
The values in this column have been rounded to two digits. This results in an EF of 6.45 instead of the WWF's calculation of 6.4.

fibre
substances like cotton, wool, and linen

INTERNET

If you want to calculate your own ecological footprint, go to the link at www.pearsoned.ca/makingconnections2.

Fig. 39-3 shows that when we measure the different environmental impacts of all aspects of our lives (using hectares as the common equivalent measurement) and then combine the measurements, we get an ecological footprint of 6.4 hectares. This represents the amount of productive land needed to support the lifestyle of the average Canadian.

1 ha = 10 000 m^2
(100 m × 100 m)

WHAT ABOUT MY 6.4 HECTARES, ANYWAY?

Answer the following questions to gain a better understanding of the concept of your ecological footprint.

1. a) Identify the three parts of the ecological footprint listed in Fig. 39-3.
   b) We calculate the ecological footprint using only productive land. Why does this approach make sense?
   c) Name two examples of non-productive land.
2. a) To appreciate just how much land actually makes up the average Canadian's EF, do the following calculation:

   Convert 6.4 hectares to square metres. Now take the square root of this number. This will give you the length of each side of a square with an area of 6.4 hectares. Try to visualize the size of this area—remember that a Canadian football field is about 100 metres long. That area you imagine is the amount of land needed to support the lifestyle of an average Canadian—you, for example.

b) Your EF occupies more than one piece of land because you rely on products that come from many places in the world, both local and distant. Your EF consists of a great many small pieces of land in various locations that add up to 6.4 hectares. Give an example of parts of your ecological footprint that would be located
   i. in your community
   ii. in a nearby part of Canada
   iii. in a distant part of Canada
   iv. in a foreign country

3. How much productive land would all the people of Canada need? Multiply 6.4 hectares by Canada's population (32 300 000). This calculation provides the total amount of productive land needed to support all of Canada's population.

Rounded numbers may be used in this kind of analysis.

4. Does Canada have enough productive land to support our current population? Canada has about 434 477 000 hectares of productive land. Compare this number to your answer to Question 3, and then determine the surplus, or deficit, of productive land.
5. Next, calculate Canada's **carrying capacity**—the number of people that could be supported at current living standards by Canada's productive land. Do this by dividing the total amount of productive land by 6.4 hectares. How many people could Canada support?

LOOKING BEYOND CANADA'S BORDERS

6. So far, it appears that Canada could support substantially more people than it does. However, other factors affect Canada's carrying capacity.
   a) Explain how Canada's exports use up large parts of Canada's carrying capacity.
   b) Give one favourable impact and one unfavourable impact of these exports on Canadians.
   c) Identify one piece of evidence that suggests Canada may be exporting too much. (Hint: Think about the impacts of some of Canada's primary industries.)
7. a) Canadians do not exist in isolation from the rest of the world. Consider the following: Earth's biologically productive areas total about 11 300 000 000 hectares. About 6 500 000 000 people populate the world. If you divide the land by the people, you will get the **fair earthshare**. Calculate this figure. This represents the

amount of Earth's productive land that each person would have if all the world's productive areas were shared equally. How does the fair earthshare compare to the EF of the average Canadian?

b) Earth's population grows by about 75 million people per year. What happens to the fair earthshare as the world's population increases?

8. Now calculate Earth's carrying capacity, assuming that everyone lives at the average Canadian's standard of living. To do this, divide the amount of Earth's productive land by Canada's average ecological footprint. What did you discover?

Many calculators will not handle numbers this large. You may have to drop several zeroes from the amount of productive land, and then add them to your answer.

What Does It All Mean to Canadians?

What do all these facts and figures about fair earthshare and the carrying capacity of both Canada and Earth tell us? They tell us that we must remember that Canada is only one country, and that we must take into account the needs and living standards of people elsewhere in the world. We must not be **complacent** about the size of our ecological footprint: if everyone in the world lived at the same standard of living as the average Canadian (and who says they shouldn't?), we would need TWO additional Earths!

complacent self-satisfied

Examine Fig. 39-4 to see some specific comparisons among Canada, the United States, India, and the entire world. Notice that the worldwide ecological footprint of 2.2 hectares per person exceeds the fair earthshare you calculated in Question 7 of the previous activity by about 6%.

Fig. 39-4 ▶ Consumption and ecological footprints in developed countries differ considerably from those in other parts of the world.

	Canada	United States	India	World
CO_2 emissions, 2003 (tonnes per year per 1000 people)	15.9	19.5	0.9	3.6
GDP per capita, 2004 (PPP basis)	31 500	40 100	3 100	8 800
Vehicles per populated km^2, 2001[1]	35	47	2.5	17
Newspaper consumption, 2001 (per person per year)	57	61	11	25
Oil use, 2001 (mJ per person per day)	428	428	12	61
Freshwater use, 2001 (m^3 per year per person)	1410	1950	620	650
Ecological Footprint, 2001 (ha per person)	**6.4**	**9.5**	**0.8**	**2.2**

[1] populated km^2 represents the area of the country with a population density of at least 5 people/km^2

Region	Population (millions)	Average Ecological Footprint (ha)	Ecological Load (million ha)
Africa	810	1.2	972
Middle East and Central Asia	334	2.1	701
Asia Pacific	3407	1.3	4429
Latin America	520	3.1	1612
North America	319	9.2	2935
Western Europe	390	5.1	1989
Central and Eastern Europe	337	3.8	1281

◄ **Fig. 39-5** Ecological load values were calculated by multiplying the population of the region by the average ecological footprint for the region.

Issue

CONSIDERING THE IMBALANCES

Background

In Fig. 39-4, you saw some comparisons among Canada, the United States, India, and the world as a whole that suggested ecological footprints (and the lifestyles they reflect) vary enormously from place to place. Complete the activities below using the statistics in Fig. 39-5 to better understand the world pattern of ecological footprints.

Activities

1. On the world base map provided by your teacher, create two proportional circles for each region: one to show the size of the population and the other to show size of the ecological load. Make the population circles one colour, and the load circles another colour. Hints: If you are not sure about how to create proportional circles, check page 79. When determining a suitable scale, look at the highest and lowest values for each item so that you can create circles that are as large as possible but do not overlap too much.
2. Which regions appear to put a disproportionate load on the Earth and which do not?
3. Should all regions have a load that is in proportion to their populations? If North Americans had to bring their ecological footprint in line with population, how could they do this? What would be the impact on your lifestyle?

Clearly, Canadians use much more than their fair share of Earth's resources. As India and other developing countries become wealthier (which is happening quite quickly), their citizens too will use more resources, live better—and, of course, have a larger EF. If the world's EF already exceeds the fair earthshare, how can Earth support even more consumption of its resources and the production of even more waste? The serious problems of global warming, pollution, and resource depletion suggest that Earth has already surpassed its carrying capacity and that Canadians contribute more than their share to the problem. This situation poses some clear **moral** and practical choices for Canadians.

moral
ethical

You can read about the One-Tonne Challenge in Chapter 37.

People in developed countries such as ours can take action. Reducing our consumption of resources and production of waste by a significant amount will allow people in the rest of the world to expand theirs. We can start by recycling waste and taking up the One-Tonne Challenge, but even more fundamental changes in how we live will be necessary in the future.

While the current situation regarding carrying capacity is unhealthy, what may happen in the future is particularly disturbing. Let's examine the concept of *load*—the demand that a population exerts on its environment. Load is the product of two factors: the size of population and the rate of consumption:

$$\text{Load} = \text{Size of population} \times \text{Rate of consumption}$$

Gross world product is the value of the total goods and services produced annually in the world. Dollar amounts here have been adjusted to eliminate the effects of inflation.

We can use the per capita **gross world product (GWP)** to represent the rate of consumption when calculating the load using the formula above. In 1950, the world's population was about 2.5 billion, and the per capita gross world product (GWP) was about $1520. By 2003, the population was 2.5 times as much (2.5 billion × 2.5 = 6.3 billion). The per capita GDP was 3.1 times as much at $4700 ($1250 × 3.1 = $4700). If we combine these two increases, we can see that the load on the world's environment was 7.75 times (2.5 × 3.1) as much. This pattern continues today, since both the population and the per capita GWP continue to grow.

Toward Sustainability

The graph in Fig. 39-6 shows the relationship between Earth's carrying capacity and the load that human activities place on the environment. Read the following notes to help interpret the graph. (Each number in the list on page 527 corresponds to a number on the graph.)

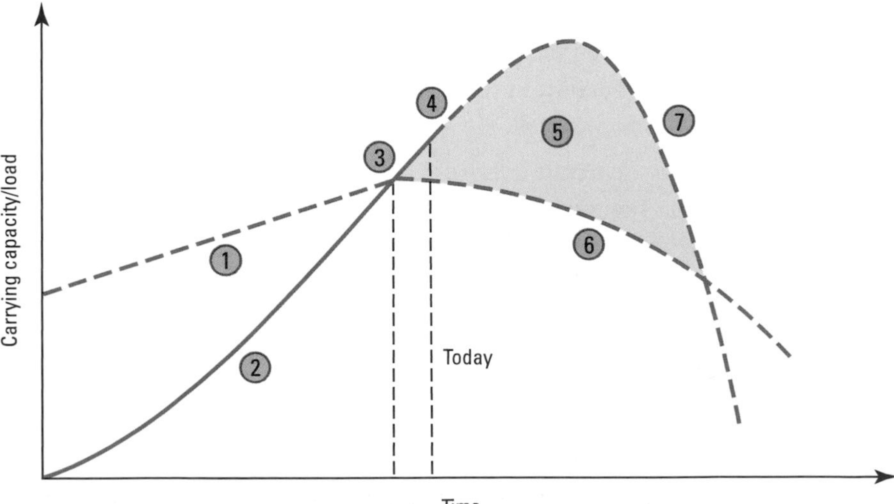

Fig. 39-6 ▶ This graph shows the critical relationship between the carrying capacity of Earth and the environmental load that people put on it.

1. The carrying capacity of Earth has increased only slightly over the last two centuries, as people have found uses for parts of the environment they didn't use before. For example, we now use various chemicals to improve crop yields and uranium to make electricity.
2. The load that the world's population places on Earth has grown substantially because the population has increased along with the rate of consumption.
3. This marks the final point of **sustainability**. Beyond this point, the load on Earth exceeds its carrying capacity.
4. This indicates the point where Earth is today. We are in a situation called an **ecological overshoot,** in which the worldwide ecological footprint exceeds Earth's carrying capacity. Global warming, loss of topsoil, shortage of fresh water, destruction of forests, loss of fisheries, depletion of the ozone layer, and many other problems all reflect the fact that we have reached an overshoot condition.
5. Earth can operate temporarily in an overshoot only by using up its supply of non-renewable resources.
6. Earth's carrying capacity will start to decline as we deplete the supply of non-renewable resources, and as renewable resources deteriorate through overuse.
7. The load on Earth will decline sharply as the population drops dramatically. This decrease in population will occur when the resources no longer exist to support it at its former size.

Earth's carrying capacity increased significantly twice in human history. The first increase occurred when humans developed agriculture, about 8000 years ago; the second occurred with the Industrial Revolution, which started about 1750.

GeoLit Reminder

Interpreting a graph:

- What kind of graph is shown in Fig. 39-6?
- Examine the caption, labels, and numbered notes.
- Why are scales not given on the vertical and horizontal axes?
- In your own words, describe the trend outlined in the graph.
- What additional information would help you better understand this graph? Where might you find it?

You will notice that the graph's time axis has no numbers because at this point, no one knows for sure how far we have overshot sustainability or when a collapse might occur. In fact, opinions differ greatly with regard to sustainability and collapse because there are two completely different ways to view the problem. Some people think that a collapse will never happen because the twin problems of too few resources and environmental damage will have a *technological solution*. Other people say that we have already reached the point where Earth can no longer sustain its human population and we must therefore adopt a **behavioural** solution.

behavioural
pertaining to human actions

The Technological Solution

People who believe in technology's ability to solve problems think that we will find ways to **eradicate** environmental problems and increase Earth's carrying capacity. They argue that technology greatly increased the world's carrying capacity in the past, and will do so again. The best example of this, they say, is the **Industrial Revolution**, which began more than two centuries ago. Supporters of the technological view defend their stance by saying that 300 years ago, people did not predict, and, in fact,

eradicate
get rid of

The Industrial Revolution is the basis of the wealth that exists in developed countries today.

▲ **Fig. 39-7** Growing our own food represents just one step we might take toward solving the environmental problem.

could not have predicted, the coming of steam power, and yet it revolutionized the world. In the same way, we cannot predict what technological breakthroughs will revolutionize life in the future. Nor can we predict when this might occur.

The Behavioural Solution

The first step in finding a behavioural solution is to recognize that we are dealing with a single, huge, all-encompassing problem rather than many smaller problems. To correct our overshoot condition, we must fundamentally change the way we live (Fig. 39-7). One of the most important things we can do is to change the way we measure "progress."

In *Making Connections*, we have used the idea of per capita gross domestic product (GDP) to measure wealth and progress. In fact, this commonly used measure has some serious shortcomings. The GDP assumes that more economic activity means progress and a better quality of life for people. However, the very activities that increase the GDP often increase our ecological footprint and do little to increase human happiness. For example:

- GDP is increased by the building and operation of cars, but gasoline-operated cars greatly increase global warming and use non-renewable fossil fuels
- catching too many fish off our Atlantic and Pacific coasts has helped Canada's GDP but has contributed to the collapse of fish stocks
- making weapons increases the GDP, but results in many deaths in war, violent crimes, and terrorism

We need a measure of progress that combines both economics and ecology. The ecological footprint provides a very useful step in this direction. The next step is to determine how we can live in a more ecologically responsible way in order to reduce our EF, while at the same time living happy and satisfying lives.

GeoCareers

Looking to the Future

This final GeoCareer Activity asks you to search out a career that interests you, and that is related to the topics presented in this unit. Now that you know something about water resources, global warming, and environmental sustainability, what kind of work in these fields appeals to you? Perhaps you're interested in monitoring water quality with the Ministry of Natural Resources, or in studying climate change as a meteorologist. Or, maybe a career with an NGO such as Pollution Probe or with a company engaged in the production of renewable energy interests you.

Find Out More

Check out the career opportunities related to challenges facing Canada and the world.

1. Select one career related to the subject matter in three different chapters in this unit. To find information on a career in each field, research university and college courses, examine Web sites that post job opportunities, or talk to your guidance counsellor.
2. a) Select one of the three careers that looks interesting.
   b) Do a search of universities and community colleges for courses that lead to the career you selected. A good starting place is the Association of Universities and Colleges of Canada found through the link at www.pearsoned.ca/makingconnections2.
3. a) List three universities and/or colleges that have programs related to your career.
   b) Give the names of the particular departments (or faculties) in each institution that offer this education.
   c) Briefly describe the kind of courses that you would take in one of the universities or colleges mentioned in (a).
4. What are the academic requirements for admission to the university or college you chose in 3c)? Specifically, what high school courses would you need, and how high would your marks have to be?
5. Find at least one career profile of a person who has pursued a career in the field you are interested in. Write a summary of that person's experiences.
6. What are the aspects of work in this field that interest you? Explain why.
7. What other geography course(s) offered in your school might help you decide which career appeals to you?

In Closing...

In spite of knowing that we need to control our resource use and the size of our population, we humans have shown little ability to do so. The EF gives us a basis for understanding how we affect our environment and Earth's ability to sustain our population. It also gives us a basis for planning our activities and measuring the impact we have on our planet.

QUESTIONS

KNOWLEDGE AND UNDERSTANDING

1. a) What is an ecological footprint?
   b) Describe how to calculate an ecological footprint.
2. In your own words, explain the meaning of each of the following:
   a) food, fibre, and timber footprint
   b) energy footprint
   c) built-up land footprint
3. a) Define sustainability.
   b) Name two factors that contribute to the load a population puts on the environment.
   c) How do the factors mentioned in the answer to Question 3b) contribute to the problem of achieving sustainability in the future?

THINKING

4. The ecological footprint calculation uses amounts of productive land. Is non-productive land the same as useless land? Explain your answer.
5. Look at Fig. 39-6. Consider the point on this graph where Earth's carrying capacity starts to decline and the population drops. What kinds of events would indicate the occurrence of these two conditions?
6. You can test your understanding of the EF concept by explaining how you might reduce your own EF. Examine Fig. 39-3. It shows nine individual EF values. Describe how you might significantly reduce any five of these, either in terms of how you live now or the lifestyle choices you will make as an independent adult.

COMMUNICATION

7. The EF represents only one of a number of attempts to measure human progress. Use the Internet to research
   a) the Genuine Progress Index
   b) the Canadian Index of Well-being
   c) Gross National Happiness

   Determine how you would go about explaining each of these to your parent or another adult. You should also explain why each could be considered an improvement on GDP measurements and what (if any) shortcomings each of these measures has.

APPLICATION

8. The use of paper can serve as one indicator of consumption. Canadians use far more paper than people in developing countries. What benefits does having access to all this paper have for you? What do young people from very poor countries miss out on because they do not have easy access to as much paper?
9. a) Do you think that all people in the world have the right to enjoy a standard of living similar to that of the average Canadian?
   b) Would you be willing to reduce your own EF to allow this to happen? Explain.
10. a) Some people in our society tend to equate consumption of more goods and services with increased happiness. Give three examples of how this assumption might be true. Give three examples that suggest it is not true.
    b) Because reducing our EF would require reducing our consumption, do you think that you could maintain (or perhaps even increase) your happiness while significantly reducing your consumption? Explain.

CULMINATING ACTIVITY

Living Today and Planning for Tomorrow

The world community faces enormous environmental challenges in the 21st century. For example, how can we prevent the following?

- By 2025, two out of three people on Earth may not have enough fresh water because of misuse and over-consumption.
- Approximately 60% of Canada's wildlife species face possible extinction. Mining, forestry, and the construction of roads and homes have taken over their habitats.
- Our daily activities deplete non-renewable energy resources. Sometimes we get a drive to school instead of walking, or we keep our homes warmer in winter and cooler in summer than they really need to be.
- Increased average temperatures around the world have caused significant changes to coral reefs, polar regions, forests, weather, and agriculture.
- Humanity's ecological footprint is about 20% larger than the planet can support. According to one study, Canadians contribute heavily to this **ecological overshoot** with an ecological footprint of 6.4 hectares per person versus the world average of 2.2 hectares per person.

▲ **Fig. CA7-1** UNESCO has declared 2005–2014 the Decade for Education on Sustainable Development (DESD).

These examples illustrate how our actions at the local, national, and international levels connect socially, environmentally, and economically. Can these warnings stir us into action to improve the health of our planet?

On a global scale, many initiatives promote sustainable development. One important one is UNESCO's Decade of Education for Sustainable Development (DESD) 2005–2014. The DESD views sustainable development as a critical goal for all humanity. It focuses on the important role that education plays in understanding, promoting, and implementing the values, behaviours, and lifestyles required for a sustainable future. UNESCO has chosen to base its decade-long program on the principles of the **Earth Charter**, which provides a framework to help us work toward achieving the DESD goals. The Charter is based on these four interdependent principles:

- Respect and Care for the Community of Life
- Ecological Integrity
- Social and Economic Justice
- Democracy, Non-violence, and Peace

INTERNET

For further information on UNESCO's Decade of Education for Sustainable Development, go to the link at www.pearsoned.ca/makingconnections2.

INTERNET

For more information about the Earth Charter, visit the link at www.pearsoned.ca/makingconnections2.

Fig. CA7-2 ▶ What can you do to meet the environmental challenges of the 21st century?

How can we, as individuals, contribute to meeting the goals of the Earth Charter and the environmental challenges of the 21st century? We can start by using our resources more sustainably, without jeopardizing nature's ability to provide them for future generations. We can personally do such things as taking public transit, using energy-saving light bulbs, recycling our pop cans and newspapers, and buying locally produced goods.

Activity

Obtain a copy of the Earth Charter online through the link at www.pearsoned.ca/makingconnections2 or from your teacher.

1. a) Work in a group of four. Read the Earth Charter carefully. Assign a different Earth Charter principle to each group member.
   b) Summarize the information about your principle in point form, and then share the information with your group.
   c) With your group, complete the Benefits and Drawbacks organizer (Fig. CA7-3) for each of the four principles.
2. a) With the help of the Benefits and Drawbacks organizer, select one of the four principles to present orally to the rest of your class. (Later,

Earth Charter Principle	Benefits (i.e., what can be achieved)	Drawbacks (i.e., what will be difficult to achieve)	Additional information
I. Respect and Care for the Community of Life			
II. Ecological Integrity			
III. Social and Economic Justice			
IV. Democracy, Non-violence, and Peace			

◀ **Fig. CA7-3** Benefits and Drawbacks Organizer

in Step #3, your group will try to convince your classmates that your principle should be promoted in your school to raise student awareness of global sustainable development.)

b) With your group, record the information about your chosen principle in point form. Outline the environmental, social, and economic benefits of your principle and make sure that you can explain clearly why it should be promoted in your school.

c) Suggest a strategy to promote your principle effectively in your school. Include a visual example if possible.

d) Organize your presentation so that it has an introduction, main arguments, and a conclusion.

e) Rehearse your presentation and ensure that all group members have significant speaking roles.

3. a) During the group presentations, remember to listen actively by recording any new information about the Earth Charter principles under the "Additional Information" column of the organizer.

b) After each group presents its chosen Earth Charter principle, class members should ask at least two questions about the principle and why it should be promoted in the school.

c) Have a class discussion in which groups question each other about the principles they selected. The class then decides which Earth Charter principle and strategy to promote in the school.

d) As a class, develop a plan to generate support for the chosen principle and implement the plan. Consider starting by educating your fellow students about the Earth Charter, the DESD, and global sustainable development.

4. Write a one-page letter to your Member of Parliament that briefly summarizes the purpose of the Earth Charter, explains its importance to Canadians, and outlines at least three ways that Canadians can implement aspects of the Earth Charter in their daily lives. Use information from the presentations as support and remember to check your letter for spelling and grammar. Ask your teacher for assistance if you choose to send your letter.

Glossary

Aboriginal peoples descendants of Canada's first inhabitants

absolute measure type of measure that does not consider total amounts in relation to population sizes

acid precipitation rain, snow, or fog created after sulphur dioxide and nitric oxides mix with water vapour in the atmosphere. Acid precipitation kills vegetation and turns lakes acidic, causing fish to die and wildlife to disappear.

active layer upper layer of permafrost that thaws only briefly in summertime

aerial photo photograph taken from the sky instead of the ground

agribusiness agricultural business. Operations include growing, storing, processing, and distributing food, and may be owned by a large corporation, a family, or an individual.

air mass large body of air having the same moisture and temperature conditions throughout

air pressure weight of air

alphanumeric grid grid that uses letters and numerals to identify squares of a grid pattern on a map

alternative energy source non-conventional energy source such as solar, wind, and biomass energy

analog transmission transmission of a continuously variable signal as compared to a discrete (digital) one. The problem with analog transmissions is that they are subject to signal loss and distortions.

anchor large store, such as a department store or grocery store, that is located one at each end of the shopping mall and attracts great numbers of customers

anticlinal trap dome-shaped structure of rock layers created by folding. Oil and gas are often found in these traps.

aquaculture production of fish and other marine products on fish farms

ArcView GIS program especially designed for map-making

area symbol coloured pattern representing a feature on a topographic map

assimilate to lose your culture and adopt the culture of the larger group within which you live (e.g., First Nations adopting broader Canadian culture)

average annual temperature monthly average temperatures added together and divided by 12

balance of trade difference between value of exports and value of imports. If exports exceed imports, there is a trade surplus. If imports exceed exports, there is a trade deficit.

band an Aboriginal group that is recognized by the Canadian government. The government sets aside money and land (reserves) for use by the band. There are almost 600 bands in Canada.

bankruptcy protection a legal action that gives companies and individuals time to reorganize their operations and stops creditors from taking action against them

banks shallow areas of a continental shelf

barren without trees

base map map providing only an outline of the most basic features of the mapped area

basic industry industry that sells its products outside the community, bringing money into the community

basic service service provided by basic industries to people and businesses outside the community, thereby bringing money into the community from the outside and ensuring its survival

bedrock solid rock beneath the soil

bias distorted or misleading

big-box store very large store, often specializing in one kind of merchandise

biomass energy energy produced by combusting biomass materials such as wood, peat, and manure

birth rate number of births per 1000 people

bitumen in oil sand deposits, each grain of sand is covered by a layer of water and a heavy oil or black tar called bitumen. Processed into synthetic crude oil.

boreal and taiga forest coniferous (needle-leaved) forest that stretches from east to west across Canada, south of the tundra but north of the grasslands and mixed forest

branch plant Canadian company controlled by a foreign company

BSE (mad cow disease) bovine spongiform encephalopathy forms holes in the brains of infected animals, crippling and eventually killing the animal. BSE is believed to be caused by contaminated feed made from a diseased animal.

bulk cargo things like wheat, coal, gravel, and iron ore shipped in loose form rather than in packages. They are usually of low value and must be shipped as cheaply as possible.

calcification process by which, in dry climates, water carrying dissolved minerals moves upward through the soil. At the surface, the water evaporates, leaving the minerals behind. The surface soil is then considered calcified.

call centre place of business where customer service telephone calls are received

Canadian Shield large area of Precambrian rock that forms the core of Canada

canal waterway dug across land on which boats and ships travel

capillary action movement of water upward through small spaces, as in soil

carat unit of mass of precious stones, especially diamonds, equal to 200 milligrams

carbon cycle movement of carbon through plants, animals, water, soil, air, and rocks

carbon dioxide greenhouse gas composed of one carbon atom and two oxygen atoms in each molecule, otherwise known as CO_2

carbon fixation the process whereby carbon is trapped in fossil fuels or sedimentary rock for millions of years. Fixed carbon does not contribute to global warming if we prevent its release into the atmosphere.

carbon sink a reservoir that stores carbon. The build-up of CO_2 in the atmosphere is moderated by carbon sinks, which remove carbon from the atmosphere and store it for a period of time. The oceans, growing vegetation, soil, and some sedimentary rock (e.g., limestone) are carbon sinks because more carbon moves into them than out of them.

carbon source an activity or location that gives off more CO_2 than it absorbs. Examples of carbon sources include volcanoes, burning forests, limestone weathering, decaying organic matter, the burning of fossil fuels, and breathing, all of which release CO_2 into the atmosphere.

carrying capacity number of people that could be supported at current living standards by Canada's productive land

cash crop crop that is grown by a farmer to be sold

Cenozoic era most recent era of geologic time, which began about 66 million years ago. See geologic time.

census tract smallest urban area used for census data collection

Central Business District (CBD) downtown area of a city or town, where most of the important commercial and government activities take place

central place village, town, or city that exists primarily to provide goods and services for a surrounding hinterland

circumstance in manufacturing, particular influences on the location of factories that are more general and difficult to measure

clear-cutting logging method whereby all trees in an area (except for very small ones) are cut at one time

climate weather conditions of a place averaged over a long period of time

climate station place where climate information is gathered

commercial forest part of a forest that has large enough trees and is close enough to a market to allow it to be harvested by the forest industry

communications transmission of information, especially by electronic or mechanical means

commuter person who travels daily between home and a place of work

compass bearing degrees on a compass, measured in clockwise direction from 0° (North) to 360°

compass point direction on a compass, such as north and south

compass rose diagram, in the shape of a flower, showing directions (compass points) and bearings (measured clockwise from north) used to indicate direction on maps

component one part of a program or system; in the Environmental Sustainability Index, one of five categories that measures the health of the environment, i.e., reducing human vulnerability, social and institutional capacity, global stewardship, environmental systems, and reducing environmental stresses

comprehensive claim claim available to First Nations not based on treaties or other means, dealing with many issues, including land ownership, self-government, ownership and control of resources, hunting/fishing/trapping rights, and financial compensation

comprehensive treaty First Nations land treaty negotiated in an area where no other treaty has ever been signed, i.e., the first treaty for that area

concession system type of survey system used in southern Ontario, whereby land is divided by concession roads and side roads into squares and rectangles of varying sizes

condensation process whereby water vapour is cooled and changes from an invisible gas to liquid water. Condensed water vapour is what forms clouds.

coniferous trees trees with cones and often needle-like leaves; evergreen

container metal box of standard size (2.4 m × 2.4 m × 4.9 m or 9.8 m) used for moving freight. The container is loaded at the point of shipment and remains sealed until it reaches its destination. Along the way, it may be moved by truck, train, plane, or ship.

contaminant substance that pollutes air, water, soil, or food

continental climate climate type that develops away from the influence of the ocean. The annual temperature range tends to be large and precipitation is low.

continental drift theory by German scientist Alfred Wegener stating that 300 million years ago all of Earth's land masses, which were in constant motion, collided to form one supercontinent called Pangaea. About 200 million years ago Pangaea broke apart and the continents have drifted apart to their present locations. According to his theory, only continents drifted.

continentalist A person who believes that Canadian and American cultures are so similar that there is no need to protect Canadian culture from American influences

continental shelf gently sloping outer edge of a continent that extends below the surface of the ocean to a maximum depth of about 200 metres

convection current circular movement in a gas or liquid created by uneven heating

convectional precipitation precipitation caused on hot summer days, when heated land causes the air above it to rise by convection. As the air rises, it cools and condensation occurs. Rain or hail may fall from thunderclouds that build up.

conventional energy source well-established source of energy such as oil, natural gas, coal, hydro- and nuclear-electricity

convergent technologies the merging of various communication technologies, such as the Internet and telephone communication

craton ancient geologic feature formed in Precambrian era, largely undisturbed by mountain-building for one billion years, containing kimberlite pipes in which diamonds are found

culture the characteristics of a way of life that, when put together, make a nation or people unique

database table of information in a computer program that can be searched for particular values or rearranged in a variety of ways

death rate number of deaths per 1000 people

deciduous trees broad-leaved trees that shed their leaves annually in the fall

demography study of population numbers, distribution, trends, and issues

dependency load portion of the population that is not in the workforce; total people under 14 and over 65

dependent variable (graphing) variable that goes on the vertical axis of the graph and is, to a greater or lesser extent, caused or influenced by the independent variable

deregulation removal of regulations controlling certain parts of an industry. For example, deregulation of the airline industry removed rules controlling routes travelled and the price of seats.

developed country country with a highly developed economy. Its citizens have high incomes, abundant food, good housing, and can afford many luxuries. Sometimes called "industrialized."

developing country country with a poorly developed economy. Its citizens have low incomes, shortages of food, poor housing, and cannot afford luxuries. Sometimes called "less developed."

differential erosion process whereby softer sedimentary rocks erode more quickly than harder rock, shaping the surface of the landscape (e.g., three different levels of elevation on the prairies)

digital mapping the location of geographic data (lines, points, areas, elevations, and numerical data such as census information) is digitized, placed in databases, and used in various combinations to create maps.

digital transmission a method of transmission that uses binary bits (zeroes and ones) to increase television picture quality and the number of signals that can be carried per channel

direct statement scale words are used to describe the relationship between a distance on a map and a specific distance on Earth's surface (e.g., 1 cm to 10 km)

discharge rate amount of water that flows through a drainage basin. The discharge rate of a drainage basin may vary greatly from season to season depending on the weather conditions.

diversified urban centre town or city that has a variety of basic urban functions

doubling time (demographics) how long it would take for a country's population to double at the country's current rate of population growth

drainage process whereby water is removed from an area by flowing out of depressions in the land such as lakes and rivers

drainage basin area drained by a river and its tributaries. One drainage basin is separated from another by an area of higher land called a watershed.

Earth Charter a UN document that lists values and principles that are thought to be necessary for creating a just, sustainable, and peaceful future for the Earth. It was developed through international consultations and based on the four interdependent principles of Respect and Care for the Community of Life; Ecological Integrity; Social and Economic Justice; and Democracy, Non-violence, and Peace. The document has not been endorsed by the UN because of some concerns by a number of countries.

easting first three figures in a map reference giving the east–west location

ecological footprint (EF) measure of total human impact on an ecosystem

ecological overshoot the amount by which our resource demands exceed Earth's supply

economic base economic activities that allow a community to exist. For example, a town might exist because a mineral resource in the area is being developed.

economic immigrant category of Canadian immigrant that includes two groups: (a) skilled workers and (b) individuals with the ability to make a significant financial contribution through the establishment or purchase of a business or the making of an investment that creates jobs

ecotourism tourism industry promoting travel for the purpose of observing ecosystems

ecozone region based on its ecological characteristics

ecumene occupied areas of a country or settled area

emigrate to leave your country of origin to live permanently in another country

emigration rate number of people per 1000 population in one year who emigrate

entrepreneur person who takes a risk by setting up a business in order to make a profit

environmental stresses those factors that combine to cause the environment to deteriorate, such as pollution, overfishing, and deforestation

Environmental Sustainability Index (ESI) measurement, devised by the World Economic Forum, of current and future levels of environmental sustainability in each of 146 countries

eras major divisions of geologic time (for example, the Paleozoic era). *See* geologic time.

erosion wearing away of Earth's surface followed by the movement to other locations of materials that have worn away.

escarpment steep cliff formed by erosion or faulting

evapotranspiration the movement of water into the atmosphere by evaporation from the soil and by transpiration from plants

export product or service produced in one country for sale in another country

extensive farming type of farming in which small amounts of labour, machinery, and fertilizers are used on large farms. Yields per hectare are small. Most agricultural activities in Canada are of this kind.

fair earthshare measurement of productive land in the world divided by number of people in the world. This is how much of the productive land each person would be entitled to, if all of the world's productive land was shared equally.

false colours colours artificially added to satellite images of Earth, to make patterns more obvious. These colours would not actually be seen from space.

family immigrant category of Canadian immigrant in which family members and close relatives of Canadian citizens or landed immigrants can be brought to Canada

fertilizer substance, such as manure or chemical fertilizer, put on agricultural land to make it able to produce more

First Nation group of Aboriginal people who share the same culture and heritage

fjord long, narrow inlet of the sea with steep sides. Fjords were created by glaciers that scraped out valleys. When the glaciers melted, the sea flooded the valleys.

foreign aid financial assistance provided to developing countries from other countries, usually developed countries

fossil fuel any mineral that can be burned to produce energy (e.g., coal, natural gas, oil)

free trade trade without tariff barriers

frontal rainfall rainfall caused by lighter, warmer air being forced to rise over colder, denser air

frost-free period the number of days between the last frost in spring and the first frost in autumn

GDP per capita *See* gross domestic product (GDP) per capita

gemstone diamond diamond of high quality used in jewellery, prized because of its rarity and beauty

Gender Empowerment Measure (GEM) index designed to indicate the amount of economic and political power that a country's women have

general-purpose map map that contains many different types of information

genetically modified organisms (GMOs) organisms whose genetic structure has been changed to create a characteristic that is seen as desirable, e.g., resistance to a disease

geocaching hobby based on the use of a handheld GPS unit and maps to find a hidden cache (stash of items). The person who has hidden the cache places its location on the Internet so "geocachers" can search for it.

geographic information systems (GIS) integrated software package for the input, management, analysis, and display of spatial information

geographical systems various interconnected systems that shape our world, e.g., forces that cause devastating earthquakes or why nations trade with each other

geography the study of Earth's physical and human systems and the relationships among them

geologic time history of Earth from its formation to the present. Earth's history may be divided into several major time periods, called eras:

Cenozoic era (most recent 66 million years)

Mesozoic era (245 million to 66 million years ago)

Paleozoic era (570 million to 245 million years ago)

Precambrian era (4600 million to 570 million years ago)

geologist expert who studies the history, composition, and structure of Earth's crust

geomatics science and technology of gathering, analyzing, and manipulating geographic (geospatial) information

geoscience a general term used to describe a wide range of specialized scientific fields within the broad areas of geology and resource management

geospatial pertaining to the location of items that can be located on Earth's surface

geostationary orbit satellite orbiting about 36 000 km above Earth at a speed that keeps it exactly above the same place on Earth

geotechnologies new geographic technologies, such as remote sensing, GPS, and GIS, that have revolutionized the field of geography

glaciation the formation of massive ice sheets that extend from each pole to cover the land

glaciers slow-moving masses of ice

global connections economic, social, political, and geographic connections between and among countries around the world, e.g., economic connections such as buying shoes made in another country

globalization the development of an increasingly integrated world in which free movement of goods, services, and people make national borders less important

Global Positioning System (GPS) satellite navigation system that is used to compute the exact latitude and longitude position of any place on Earth

global village idea that the world is becoming like one large village because of improvements in communication

global warming rise in the world's temperatures as a result of increasing levels of carbon dioxide and other greenhouse gases in the atmosphere

GMOs *See* genetically modified organisms

Google one of the most popular search engines. The company's mission statement reads "Google's mission is to organize the world's information and make it universally accessible and useful."

graduated colour map map in which a range of colour shades is used to indicate different values

greenbelt undeveloped land protected from urban development surrounding a city. It contains farms, parks, and natural areas.

greenhouse effect absorption of heat energy by greenhouse gases and reradiation into the atmosphere

greenhouse gases (GHGs) gases, such as carbon dioxide and methane, that contribute to global warming

gross domestic product (GDP) per capita total value of the goods and services produced within a country per person, excluding transactions with other countries

gross world product (GWP) the value of the total goods and services produced annually in the world

groundfish fish, such as cod and sole, that live and feed near the bottom of the sea

groundwater water found below Earth's surface in the spaces in soil and bedrock

growing degree-days (GDDs) a measure of heat in one day. Daily GDDs over a period of a year are added together to determine the amount of heat available in a specific location. GDDs are used to determine locations in which plants can be successfully grown. They are also used to estimate the stage of development of plants and insects because the development of organisms is closely related to the accumulation of heat.

growing season the number of days when the mean daily air temperature equals or exceeds 5°C (air temperature at which most animal feed crops begin to grow). Farmers grow only those crops that will ripen within the growing season in their area.

halocarbon chemical compound composed of carbon and one or more halogens (bromine, chlorine, fluorine, or iodine)

hardwood wood produced from broad-leaved trees such as maple, oak, and elm. Hardwood is used to make furniture, sports equipment, tool handles, floors, and boats. Not all hardwoods are "hard"; for example, poplar and basswood are actually quite soft.

herbicide chemical designed to kill unwanted plants (weeds). If used improperly, a herbicide can become a pollutant.

highlands areas of high elevation containing mountains and plateaus

high-order good or service high-priced product or service that is purchased infrequently

hinterland the area around a town that trades with it. Hinterlands have fewer services and less variety in economic activities than urban areas.

hit Web page containing the word(s) entered in a search with a search engine

Human Development Index (HDI) index that includes measures of health, education, and wealth to indicate a country's level of human development

humus dark, upper layer of soil made up of partially decayed plant material

hydro-electric generating station facility that generates electricity by the movement of falling water

hydrologic cycle pathway followed by water from oceans and lakes through the atmosphere and then back to the land and waterways

immigrant person who moves to a new country with the intention of settling there

immigrate to move permanently to a country other than one's native country

immigration rate number of new Canadians who have immigrated here from another country per 1000 people of Canada's population

impervious quality of a substance that does not allow water to pass through it

import product that is brought into a country from another country

import substitution process of replacing foreign-produced goods with Canadian ones to support Canadian business, e.g., buying a Canadian-made car instead of one made in the United States, Japan, or elsewhere

independent variable (graphing) the independent variable goes on the horizontal axis of the graph and is, to a greater or lesser extent, causing or influencing the dependent variable.

index number, expressed without a unit of measurement, used to make comparisons between and among countries

Indian Act, 1876 act of the Canadian government authorizing the government to sign treaties with Native groups to give up their claim to the lands they occupied and move to reserves

indicator an occurrence or circumstance that demonstrates the existence of certain environmental conditions

indicator minerals minerals that are found with diamonds. When these minerals are traced back to their point of origin, diamonds can be located.

industrial diamond poor quality diamond used as a tool in many kinds of industries because it is the hardest known substance

industrial mineral non-metallic minerals, such as salt or asbestos, used by industry and manufacturing

Industrial Revolution time, beginning in the late 1700s in England, when the introduction of water power and steam into factories greatly increased the size and output of industries

inshore fishery commercial fishing that takes place within a few kilometres of the shoreline. Small fishing boats go out to sea and return to shore each day.

instream use use of water without removing it from its source for activities, e.g., fishing and hydro-electric power

intensive farming large amount of labour, machinery, and fertilizers used on small farms. High yields per hectare are obtained. The growing of fruit is an example of intensive farming.

intercity movement *between* cities, e.g., an intercity bus between Toronto and Montreal

Internet international network linking computers of individuals, educational and research institutions, government agencies, and businesses

interprovincial migration the relocation of individuals from one province to another

intervening obstacle event or factor that discourages people from migrating from one place to another

intracity movement *within* a city. For example, an intracity bus moves people from their home to school.

jet stream west to east movement of air in the mid-latitude flowing at speeds of up to 400 km/h at an altitude of between 8000 and 15 000 m

joule (J) metric unit used to measure energy

just-in-time (JIT) manufacturing and stock control system in which goods are produced and delivered only as they are needed

kimberlite pipe rare geologic structure that may contain diamonds; exists only in enormous masses of ancient rock called cratons

knowledge industry type of industry based on human knowledge rather than on natural resources

Kyoto Protocol 1997 treaty designed to limit the impact of global warming that was signed by 180 countries and came into effect in 2005. Developed countries agreed to reduce greenhouse gas emissions by 5.2% below 1990 levels between 2008 and 2012.

labour supply availability of workers or labour force (total number of people working and looking for work in an area)

land capability ability of land to be used for a certain purpose. For example, land capability for agriculture is based on soil quality, drainage, slope, and climate.

landform natural feature on Earth's surface

land use how urban, suburban, or rural land is and can be used (e.g., parks, housing, industry, commercial, agriculture, etc.)

large-scale map map that shows a large amount of detail of a small area, such as a map with a scale of 1:50 000

latitude distance north or south of the equator, measured in degrees. The equator is 0° and the North Pole is 90° north latitude.

leaching removal of minerals from soil by water as it moves downward through the soil. Leaching occurs in wet climates.

leeward side of a mountain or mountain range facing away from the prevailing winds

life expectancy average lifespan of a population

lignite soft, low-value coal sometimes used in thermal-electric plants

line scale line divided into units of distance (e.g., km) that represent the actual units on the ground

line symbol linear symbol used to represent features on topographic maps, e.g., roads and railway lines

literacy percentage of a population that has the ability to read and write

location factors factors such as historical head start, market, location of raw materials, power, fresh water, labour, transportation, and political situation that help explain the location of cities and industries

lock enclosed section in a canal that permits vessels to be raised or lowered to different water levels outside this compartment, either by letting water in or out of the compartment or, in a lift lock, by raising or lowering the water-filled compartment itself

longitude distance east and west of the prime meridian, measured in degrees. The prime meridian is 0° longitude.

long-grass prairie type of vegetation in the Canadian prairie provinces where higher precipitation levels cause grasses to grow longer than in drier, short-grass prairie areas

long lot settlement pattern in southern Quebec and some other areas of Canada where individual lots tend to be long and narrow and extend back from major rivers or roads

lowlands areas of low elevation containing plains and hills

low-order good or service product or service that is purchased frequently

manufacturing processing raw materials into a more finished state. For example, making lumber from logs is primary manufacturing, and making furniture from lumber is secondary manufacturing.

map representation of Earth's features drawn on a flat surface

map grid series of lines on a map that can be used to locate any place on the map

map projection method used to transfer features of the globe onto the flat surface of a map. There are hundreds of ways that this can be done and hundreds of different projections. Each projection has its strengths and weaknesses.

maritime climate climate type that is strongly influenced by the closeness of an ocean or other large water body. The annual temperature range tends to be small and precipitation is high.

market customers of a company

mechanization process whereby machinery takes over the work of humans or animals

meltwater water resulting from the melting of glacier ice and/or snow

mental map map in our mind of places we know

Mesozoic era period of geologic time from 245 million to 66 million years ago. *See* geologic time.

metallic mineral mineral that yields a metal when processed, for example, iron, gold, uranium, and silver

methane colourless, odourless, flammable gas, the simplest of the hydrocarbons

middle-order good or service product or service that people buy occasionally

milling processing ore into concentrates

mineral valuable substance taken from rocks by mining

mineral reserve known quantity of minerals in a country or area

mineral rights rights to access and profit from minerals found under the surface of land

mixed forest vegetation region that contains both coniferous and deciduous trees. It is a transition zone between the deciduous forest and the boreal forest.

mobility ability to move about

moderating effect effect that large water bodies have on the climate over nearby land areas. Winter temperatures are warmer and summer temperatures are cooler than areas located away from large water bodies. The result is a small annual temperature range.

multicultural characteristic of a society that is made up of many different cultures

multinational corporations (MNCs) corporations that have operations in countries outside their country of origin that are also known as transnational corporations

multiplier effect total effect on the economy caused by an expansion or contraction in one part of it. For example, a new mine employing 300 people may cause 900 other jobs to develop in manufacturing and services.

nationalist person who believes that English-Canadian culture is swamped with American cultural "products" and encourages independence from the United States, especially in the area of culture

natural increase rate difference between the birth rate and the death rate of a country

natural vegetation plants that would grow in an area in the absence of human influence

near-polar orbit fixed north–south orbit followed by satellites as Earth rotates below them

net exports amount by which the exports of a commodity (e.g., wheat) are greater than the imports of that commodity

net imports amount by which the imports of a commodity (e.g., stereo equipment) are greater than the exports of that commodity

net migration rate difference between people immigrating to a country and people emigrating from the same country

newly industrializing country countries in the transition stage between developing and developed countries. Newly industrializing countries typically have rapidly growing economies.

new urbanism new planning movement to combat urban and suburban sprawl. It includes:

- building communities around people instead of cars
- an identifiable downtown centre
- narrow lots and smaller houses (higher density)
- mixed-income housing
- homes designed to look like those built 50 to 100 years ago

non-basic industry industry that sells its products within the community. It does not bring money into the community.

non-basic service service that is provided within the community. It does not bring money into the community.

non-commercial forest part of a forest that has trees too small to harvest or is too far away from the market

non-governmental organization (NGO) organization that is not part of a government and provides a wide range of aid around the world

non-metallic mineral mineral that yields non-metals when processed, e.g., salt, potash, and asbestos

non-renewable resource resource that can be used only once, e.g., oil or iron ore

Northern Strategy comprehensive development strategy for Canada's North that enables northern people to achieve the best possible political, economical, and social development

northing last three figures in a map reference, giving the north–south location

nuclear-electric generating station place where energy, in the form of heat, is generated by splitting atoms of radioactive materials, then is used to generate electricity

official development assistance (ODA) government-provided foreign aid

offshore fishery ocean fishery using boats longer than 25 m. The boats stay at sea several days before returning to shore with their catch.

oil sand mixture of heavy crude oil, sand, and water

oil seed seed used in the production of oils, e.g., canola and sunflower

old growth forest area of mature forest that has never been cut down

One-Tonne Challenge a federal government program, started in 2003, to encourage Canadians to take personal actions to reduce their current emissions of greenhouse gases by one tonne per year and then to maintain that new level

open pit mining method of mining using a large hole that is dug for the purpose of extracting ore found near Earth's surface

ore rock that contains enough valuable minerals to make mining profitable

organic farming agriculture without the use of chemicals, antibiotics, hormones, or genetically modified organisms. Organic farming ensures sustainable agriculture and does not damage the environment.

outsourcing transferring a business and its jobs to another country where labour is cheaper. The term also refers to buying services or products from an outside supplier or manufacturer to cut costs.

Pacific Rim countries in the Americas, Asia, and Oceania (geographical region that includes Australia, New Zealand, and most of the smaller islands) that border the Pacific Ocean

Paleozoic era period of geologic time from 570 million to 245 million years ago. *See* geologic time.

Pangaea supercontinent that included all Earth's land masses. It existed from about 300 million to about 200 million years ago.

parent material rock from which soil is derived

parkland vegetation region that is a transition zone between Grassland and Boreal Forest

peacekeeping military assistance, usually by members of the UN, that functions as a police force or conflict mediator, where the parties in a conflict have agreed to work toward peace

peacemaking military assistance, usually by members of the UN, that may include military operations, where there has been no peace agreement

pelagic fish fish, such as salmon and tuna, that live and feed in the open ocean

permafrost ground that does not completely thaw in the summer

pesticide chemicals designed to kill harmful plants (herbicide) and harmful insects (insecticide)

phytoplankton microscopic aquatic plants found in plankton

pie graph common graph that uses sections of a circle to illustrate comparative values

piggyback system system whereby truck trailers are transported on railway cars

pipeline line of pipes for carrying gas, oil, or other liquids

plate tectonics theory that states that Earth's outer shell consists of plates that move causing earthquakes, volcanoes, mountains, and the formation of new crust

plateau elevated flat area. *See* highlands.

point symbol symbol representing features that occupy a specific point, such as bridges and buildings, on a topographic map

polar front stormy boundary between cold, dry polar air and warm, moist tropical air

political decision decision made by government that will help attract new business or, if it is not careful, that will drive investment away

population density figure calculated by dividing the population of a region by the region's area

population distribution pattern showing where people live in an area. For example, a scattered distribution along a coastline or road.

population growth rate measurement that combines both natural increase and net migration to calculate the overall growth of a country's population

population pyramid graph that depicts population distribution by age and sex

power grid system of electrical power lines that connects large generating stations to buildings where people use electricity

Precambrian era period of geologic time from the beginning of the Earth to 570 million years ago; first era in the Earth's geologic history. There were virtually no life forms at this time. *See* geologic time.

prevailing winds winds that are most commonly found in an area. For example, over most of Canada, the prevailing winds are the westerlies, which blow from west to east.

primary industry industry that deals with the production of primary products such as minerals that are mined or quarried, or an agricultural product that is harvested in its raw state

prime meridian line (meridian) of longitude on maps or globes that joins the North and South Poles and runs through Greenwich, England. Longitude is measured 180° east and 180° west from this line (0°).

proportional area graph type of graph that can be produced in many shapes, frequently circles; is often combined with pie graphs to show not just the amount of something, but also how this quantity is divided

protectionism a national policy of trying to protect certain industries by having high tariffs. It is the opposite of free trade.

pull factor factors that draw immigrants to a country, such as job opportunities, freedom of speech and religion, and lower taxes

push factor factors, such as war, absence of human rights, poor economic and educational opportunities, religious persecution, terrorism, and natural disasters, that encourage people to emigrate from their country

quaternary industry highly specialized (and usually expensive) knowledge-based technological and support services

quaternary worker person who works in an industry that involves intellectual services, such as writing software and architectural design. Other quaternary industries include the high tech industry, research and development, and information technology.

radar in remote sensing, radar sensors send out microwaves to Earth's surface and use the microwaves reflected back to create an image of human objects and natural features on Earth's surface

rain shadow area on the leeward side of mountains, receiving little precipitation

raw material something used by an industry to be processed into a more finished state. For example, iron ore (raw material) is made into steel (product), and steel (raw material) is made into an automobile (product).

refugee person who migrates to another country out of fear of cruel or inhumane treatment (or even death) in his or her own country

relative measure type of measure that considers total amounts in relation to population sizes

relief precipitation precipitation created when an air mass rises to cross a mountain barrier; also called orographic precipitation.

remote situated far from main centres of population

remote sensing study of characteristics of Earth using photographs and electronic images taken from aircraft and satellites

renew make new again

renewable resource resource that replaces itself unless badly mismanaged. For example, trees grow to replace those cut down or lost to fire or disease; polluted water is cleaned by the environment.

representative fraction scale scale on a map given as a ratio of distance on the map to distance on the ground, e.g., 1:50 000, which means 1 cm on the map represents 50 000 cm on Earth's surface

research and development (R&D) process of inventing a new product and then preparing this product for sale

reserve area of land set aside for the use of a band of status Indians

reservoir artificial lake built to store water for use in a hydro-electric generating station, for irrigation, or for flood control

residential density measure of the number of housing units per hectare

resource-based community a town that exists primarily to exploit the presence of a mineral, forest, or other resource

retail sale of goods to the public in stores

rift valley valley created when the portion of land between two faults (cracks in the earth) drops down. The St. Lawrence River valley is a rift valley.

Royal Proclamation of 1763 proclamation on land treaties by the British establishing two important principles for negotiations: (a) land ownership rights of the First Nations must be respected; (b) if a First Nation did choose to give up land, it should receive a fair payment for it

Rule of 70 in demographics, process whereby you divide 70 by the population growth rate to estimate how many years it will take for the country's population to double

run-off rain water that flows on Earth's surface rather than being absorbed by the ground

rural outside towns and cities

rural depopulation the migration of people from rural areas to urban areas

rural settlement permanent settlement of people in an area that is well removed from large urban centres

rural–urban fringe area adjacent to an urban area where there is a mixture of urban and rural land uses

satellite manufactured object that is launched by a rocket and circles Earth. Satellites are used to communicate, to study Earth's resources, and to aid the military.

saturated zone area where crevices in the rock and the spaces between the particles of soil, sand, and gravel are filled with water. The top of this zone is called the water table.

scale measurement on a map that represents an actual distance on Earth's surface. For example, a scale of 1:50 000 means that 1 cm on the map represents 50 000 cm on Earth's surface.

search engine program designed to help you find information (Web sites) on a computer system such as the World Wide Web

secondary industry industry dealing with manufacturing or construction

secondary recovery variety of methods used to remove a greater percentage of oil from deposits. Even with secondary recovery, only about 60% of the oil in most deposits can be recovered.

section system survey system in most of the prairie provinces with units of land 1.6 km by 1.6 km (1 square mile). When settlers first arrived, they were given a quarter-section of land to farm.

sediment eroded material that is deposited by water, wind, or glacial ice

selective cutting lumbering technique in which only trees of a certain type, size, and quality are cut

self-government principle that each distinct group of people has the right to control its own affairs. In Canada, this term is most often applied to First Nations.

services tertiary industries that provide functions needed by other industries and society in general. Services include retailing, education, healthcare, communications, and government. The service sector is the largest part of Canada's economy.

settlement pattern distribution of homes, farms, villages, towns, and cities in an area

shellfish molluscs and crustaceans such as oysters, shrimps, and lobsters

shelterwood logging method of forest harvesting in which up to 70% of trees are cut, leaving small patches of old growth standing to provide seeds for regeneration

shield large area of Precambrian rock that forms the core of a continent

short-grass prairie type of vegetation in the Canadian prairie provinces where very little precipitation causes grasses to be shorter than in slightly wetter long-grass prairie areas

silviculture branch of forestry dealing with the cultivation and care of forests

site refers to the characteristics of the land on which a city is built

situation refers to the relationship between a city's location and the area surrounding it

slag the impurities that are separated from molten metal and removed during smelting

small-scale map map that shows a small amount of detail of a large area, such as a map with a scale of 1:250 000

Smart Growth conservation policy intended to promote and manage growth of communities, sustain a strong economy in the region, and promote a healthy natural environment

smelting process whereby metals are removed from ore or concentrate for use in industry

smokestack industry traditional resource-based industry, such as steel-making, auto assembly, or oil refining

sod mat deep intertwined root system of the grass. This sod mat absorbs and stores moisture, and holds the soil in place.

softwood wood produced by coniferous (needle-leaved) trees

soil surface layer of Earth, composed of mineral and organic materials, air, and water

soil profile different horizons (layers) in the soil and the rock layer (bedrock) below the soil. Each horizon has different physical, biological, and chemical characteristics.

specific claim First Nation's claim based on a belief that the government did not fulfill its obligations under a treaty or other agreement related to land, money, or other assets

spreadsheet computer program designed particularly to manipulate numerical information

stacked bar graph very much like a simple bar graph, with one important difference: while each bar in a simple bar graph represents one value, a stacked bar can be used to represent several closely related values

statistical analysis studying collected data for the purposes of summarizing information to make it more usable and for making generalizations

stereo pair pair of aerial photographs that, when looked at through a stereoscope, shows a 3-dimensional image

stewardship the management of resources in a careful and sustainable way

strip mining method of mining used to recover mineral deposits located very near the surface

subsidy money given in the form of a grant or gift by a government to a private company, organization, or individual farmers to help them stay in business

suburban referring to low-density housing areas, commercial areas, etc. usually found on the outskirts of a city. Suburban is between rural and urban.

survey system pattern of land division used in an area

sustainability approach to development that meets the needs of the present without negatively affecting the ability of future generations to meet their needs

sustainable agriculture approach to agricultural production that can be maintained indefinitely without harming the environment

sustained yield forest management use of forest resources at a rate that allows the forests to renew themselves

sustained yield management use of a renewable resource at a rate that allows the resource to renew itself. For example, the number of fish caught should not be greater than the number of fish reaching maturity.

tailings waste materials left over from processing ore

tandem engineering a process whereby two or more engineering teams work on a product and the next generation of that product simultaneously to speed up the process of getting new products to market

tariff tax charged on goods imported to Canada to protect Canadian industries

telematics GPS technology that is integrated with computers and mobile communications equipment. For example, vehicle telematics can track a company's fleet vehicles, locate stolen vehicles, and collect road tolls.

temperature range subtraction of coldest average monthly temperature from warmest average monthly temperature

tertiary industry industry that provides services rather than goods

tertiary worker person who works in services. This sector of the economy includes government services, retail and wholesale, transportation, banking, entertainment, education, and utilities.

thematic map map containing information on only one topic or theme

thermoelectric generating station electrical power plant where electricity is generated from energy produced by burning fuels such as coal, oil, and natural gas

threshold population number of customers needed to make a business profitable or to allow a service, such as a post office or library, to be offered

topographic map large-scale map showing both natural and human-made features

topography natural and human features of the landscape

topsoil surface layer of soil

toxic chemical chemical that is harmful to humans or to the environment

trade process of buying and selling goods and services. International trade involves the buying and selling of goods and services between countries.

trade deficit situation in which a country has bought (imported) more in goods or services than it has sold in exports

trade surplus situation in which a country has bought (imported) less in goods or services than it has sold in exports

transect line through a community along which land use or other data are analyzed

transition zone area where the characteristics of one region gradually change into those of another

transportation movement of people and things from one place to another

transportation hub major centre for international and domestic transportation

treaty in Canada, an official agreement between the federal government and First Nations whereby the Aboriginal peoples give up their land rights except for reserves and accept treaty money and other kinds of government assistance

tree line boundary between the Tundra and the Boreal Forest zone. North of this line it is too cold for trees to grow.

tributary a small stream or river that joins a larger stream or river

tsunami a long, high sea wave caused by underwater earthquakes

tundra northernmost vegetation region, found in areas too cold for trees to grow. Bushes, grasses, mosses, and similar plants dominate.

underground mining method of mining used to recover deep mineral deposits

unit train train that carries large amounts of only one cargo along a route. For example, coal is carried from the interior of British Columbia to Vancouver for shipment to Japan.

urban towns and cities of 1000 or more people

urban growth actual number of people by which a city or town's population grows

urban renewal process of rebuilding older parts of a city

urban sprawl low-density development surrounding a city

urbanization process of changing from rural to urban

value added when materials are processed, their value increases. For example, when tomatoes are made into tomato juice, the value of the juice is greater than the value of the unprocessed tomatoes. The difference in price between the unprocessed tomatoes and the tomato juice is the value added.

variable a factor whose value changes over time, such as fertility and mortality rates, greenhouse gas emissions, and GDP per capita

water table top of the soil zone in which all pore spaces are filled with water, called the saturated zone. Above the water table, the pore spaces are filled with air.

watershed an area of high land that separates one drainage basin from another

waypoint fixed location with latitude and longitude coordinates that is stored in a GPS unit

weather combination of temperature, precipitation, cloud cover, and winds experienced daily

weathering breakdown of rock into small particles

Web pages documents that are accessible through the World Wide Web

wetlands swamp, marsh, and bog; places where the water table is at ground level

wholesale buying and selling of goods *other* than to the public. For example, sale of goods by manufacturer to distributor

wind horizontal movement of air over Earth's surface, caused by differences in air pressure

windward the side of a mountain range that faces the prevailing wind

winter-city concept idea to build cities with inside and outside environments that are livable during long, harsh winters

winter ice road roads that are built over frozen tundra, lakes, and rivers to provide vehicle access to northern communities and mining sites during the winter

withdrawal use water that is permanently removed from a river for consumption in homes, industries, agriculture, or business

World Wide Web (WWW) international network of Internet sites

x/y scattergraph simple and useful graph showing relationship between two sets of data

zoning laws, usually passed by city governments, controlling the kind and amount of development in an area

zooplankton microscopic aquatic animals found in plankton

INDEX

A

B

C

N

Credits and Sources

The publisher has made every reasonable effort to trace the ownership of extracts, data, and visuals to make full acknowledgment for their use. The publisher will be pleased to correct any errors or omissions that may have occurred, providing written notification has been received.

p. 1 C. Mayhew & R. Simmon (NASA/GSFC), NOAA/NGDC, DMSP Digital Archive; p. 2 Image provided by ORBIMAGE and the NASA SeaWiFS Project; p. 4 ORBIMAGE; p. 7 CP Photo/Geoff Howe; p. 19 left Waite Air Photos Inc.; top right Canada Centre for Remote Sensing (CCRS), with permission of the Minister of Public Works and Government Services Canada, (2005); centre right Royalty-Free/CORBIS; p. 22 left © Topographic map reproduced under licence from Her Majesty the Queen in Right of Canada, with permission of Natural Resources Canada; right © Topographic map reproduced under licence from Her Majesty the Queen in Right of Canada, with permission of Natural Resources Canada; p. 25 Nottawasaga Bay, Ontario map, 1993 © Produced under licence from Her Majesty the Queen in Right of Canada, with permission of Natural Resources Canada; p. 26 Courtesy of Google; p. 27 Courtesy of Google; p. 33 Ontario Canadian Tourism/Ministry of Transportation/Ministry of Economics, Trade & Tourism; p. 37 bottom left Courtesy of Garmin; p. 38 Courtesy of OnStar Corporation; p. 39 Courtesy of Garmin; p. 41 Bruce Clark; p. 44 left Richard Olivier CORBIS/Magma; right Dodge Viper GTS and its trade dress used under license by Revell Monogram, LLC. © Daimler Chrysler Corporation 2005; p. 60 City of Toronto Archives; p. 64 City of Toronto Archives; p. 66 Canada Centre for Remote Sensing, reproduced with permission of the Minister of Public Works and Government Services Canada, 2005; p. 69 LANDSAT 7 data 2000. RADARSAT-1 data © CSA 2005. All Rights Reserved. Processed and distributed by RADARSAT International Inc., a subsidiary of MDA; p. 71 National Oceanic and Atmospheric Administration/ Department of Commerce; p. 72 Courtesy of the Canada Centre for Remote Sensing, Natural Resources Canada; p. 74 Courtesy of www.BrazilianArtists.net; p. 85 as appeared in MACWORLD, October 1992; p. 86 Courtesy of Google; p. 87 Courtesy of Google; p. 89 Courtesy of Google; p. 90 Courtesy of Copenhagen Consensus; p. 93 left, p. 96, and p. 104 CP PHOTO/Richard Lam; p. 93 centre, p. 99, and p. 104 Courtesy of Visitor's Choice Vancouver; p. 93 right, p. 97, p.104 © Canadian Broadcasting Corporation; p. 93 bottom, p. 98, and p. 104 Data source: Pictographics, Ltd.; p. 105 © Staffan Widstrand/CORBIS; p. 106 UNESCO World Heritage Centre; p. 107 © Roger De La Harpe; Gallo Images/ CORBIS; p. 108 left CP PHOTO/Adrian Wyld; right © Kurt Stier/CORBIS; p. 109 left *The Solemn Land*, 1921 by J.E.H. MacDonald, National Gallery of Canada, purchased 1921; top right Doris McCarthy, 1910 -, *Broughton Reflections* 1984, oil on canvas, 152.4 x 213.4 cm, Gift of Gowling, Strathy & Henderson, McMichael Canadian Art Collection, 1993.18; centre right *Harvest Tones* by Dan Reid, Courtesy of the artist; bottom right *Fundy Shoreline* by Tom Ward, Private Collection; p. 111 AP Photo/Dudi Anung; p. 117 Copyright © Province of British Columbia. All rights reserved, with permission of the Province of British Columbia www.ipp.gov.bc.ca; p. 120 left Howell Williams. Image source: NOAA http://www.ngdc.noaa.gov/seg/hazard/slideset/28/28_580_slide.shtml; right © Ron Stroud/Masterfile; p. 126 *White Pine* by A.J. Casson, 1898–1992. c.1957 oil on canvas 76.0 x 101.3 cm. Gift of the Founders, Robert and Signe McMichael, McMichael Art Collection 1966.16.119; p. 127 *Hillside, Lake Alphonse*, Goodridge Roberts, 1904–1974. 1942 oil on canvas 48.5 x 74.0 cm, purchased 1984 McMichael Art Collection 1984.20; p. 128 *No Grass Grows on the Beaten Path* by William Kurelek. Courtesy of the Estate of William Kurelek and the Isaacs Gallery, Toronto; p. 129 *The Glacier* by Arthur Lismer, 1928, oil on canvas, Art Gallery of Hamilton, Gift of the Women's Committee, 1960 © Mrs. Phillip N. Bridges and Marjorie Bridges; p. 132 Victor Last/Geographical Visual Aids; p. 134 Al Harvey/The Slide Farm; p. 135 © Royalty Free/CORBIS; p. 137 Al Harvey/The Slide Farm; p. 139 Victor Last/Geographical Visual Aids; p. 140 Jerry Kobalenko; p. 141 Al Harvey/The Slide Farm; p. 142 Al Harvey/The Slide Farm; p. 152 top © Daryl Benson/Masterfile; bottom © Royalty-Free/CORBIS; p. 160 © J.A. Kraulis/Masterfile; p. 165 © Lucidio Studies, MaxxImages.com; p. 166 Victor Last/ Geographical Visual Aids; p. 167 top Victor Last/ Geographical Visual Aids; bottom Ross Fried/Visuals Unlimited; p. 168 left John D. Cunningham/Visuals Unlimited; right David Royce/Visuals Unlimited; p. 169 left William H. Weber/Visuals Unlimited; right Garth Lenz/Visuals Unlimited; p. 173 top left Victor Last/Geographical Visual Aids; top right Victor Last/ Geographical Visual Aids; bottom left Al Harvey/ The Slide Farm; bottom centre Victor Last/Geographical Visual Aids; bottom right Victor Last/ Geographical Visual Aids; p. 182 Akira-Kamio; p. 183 top Canadian Tourism Facts and Figures, 2003; centre Canadian Tourism Facts and Figures 2003; p. 184 Canadian Tourism Facts and Figures 2003; p. 185 left

O. Bierwagen/Spectrum Stock, Toronto; centre right © Alberto Biscaro/ Masterfile; bottom right © J. David Andres/Masterfile; p. 191 left Harold M. Lambert/ Lambert/Getty Images; right Dick Hemingway; p. 198 Bruce Clark; p. 200 CP PHOTO/Chuck Mitchell; p. 202 right © Gary Fiegehen/Maxximages.com; p. 206 left Courtesy of the Government of Nunavut; right © Her Majesty the Queen in Right of Canada, Natural Resources Canada; p. 209 Henry Huntington/Alaska Stock; p. 211 Visuals Unlimited/Tim Hauf Photography; p. 216 Courtesy of Karen Taylor; p. 219 Canapress/Jacques Boissinot; p. 228 © Russ Heinl Group/Maxximages.com; p. 229 © Russ Heinl Group/ Maxximages.com; p. 230 © Russ Heinl Group/Maxximages.com; p. 232 Courtesy of Town of Huntsville; p. 236 Courtesy of Blue Mountain; p. 238 CP Photo/Boris Spremo; p. 240 © Michael S. Yamashita/ CORBIS/MAGMA; p. 242 © Buddy Mays/CORBIS; p. 243 top © Barrett & MacKay Photo; p. 248 Waite Air Photos Inc.; p. 251 Waite Air Photos Inc.; p. 255 Bruce Clark; p. 258 Photo by Mark Kavanagh, ktransit.com; p. 260 Courtesy West Edmonton Mall; p. 262 Photo Rick Berry and Oak Ridges Trail Association; p. 263 © Queen's Printer for Ontario, 2005. Reproduced with permission; p. 267 Toronto Star/Dick Loek; p. 268 top CP PHOTO/Steve White; bottom David Moll/Calgary Herald; p. 269 left Rick Robinson - Canadian Pacific Railway Archives E.8203-3; top right © COMSTOCK Images; centre right Courtesy Research In Motion Limited; bottom right Todd Korol; p. 282 left A Gurmankin/Visuals Unlimited; right Gre Locke/Stray Light Pictures; p. 288 CP PHOTO/Nick Procaylo; p. 289 © Natalie Fobes/CORBIS; p. 294 © Frank Krehmer/Masterfile; p. 295 Pete Turner/Getty Images; p. 304 © Paul A. Souders/CORBIS; p. 305 AP Photo/Frank Augstein; p. 307 © Daryl Benson/ Masterfile; p. 314 Garth Lenz/Visuals Unlimited; p. 318 CP Images.ca/ Phototake; p. 320 Barrett and MacKay Photo; p. 323 © Ed Gifford/Masterfile; p. 325 Bruce Clark; p. 334 left © Mark Gibson/Maxximages.com; right © Stuart McCall Photography/ Maxximages.com; p. 335 © Kharen Hill Photography/Maxximages.com; p. 338 André P. Therrien; p. 339 Courtesy of City of Elliot Lake; p. 345 Courtesy of BHP Diamonds Inc. and Photographer Jiri Hermann; p. 346 © Courtesy of BHP Diamonds Inc. and Photographer Jiri Hermann; p. 352 This map was taken from The Atlas of Canada http://atlas.gc.ca/ © 2005. Produced under licence from Her Majesty the Queen in Right of Canada, with permission of Natural Resources Canada; p. 354 © Stewart Cohen/ Maxximages.com; p. 355 top right By permission of Petroleum Communication Foundation; centre © Images BC/Maxximages.com; p. 357 right AP Photo/Al Grillo; p. 371 Greg Locke/Stray Light Photos; p. 379 Courtesy of Alcan; p. 386 top left Courtesy of ATI Technologies Inc.; p. 388 Courtesy ATI Technologies Inc.; p. 392 left © Masterfile; right © WireImageStock/Masterfile; p. 393 Photo courtesy of The Canadian Science Centre for Human and Animal Health; p. 394 AP Photo/Rich Pedroncelli; p. 400 CP Photo/Steve White; p. 401 The Toronto Star/M. Slaughter; p. 405 © Canstock Images/ Maxximages.com; p. 406 top left John Verelast/ Library and Archives of Canada/C-092414; centre right National Archives of Canada/PA-38683; centre left © Bettman/CORBIS/MAGMA ; p. 411 Photo Madhava Enros; p. 415 © Barrett & MacKay Photo; p. 418 © Images BC/ Maxximages.com; p. 425 Nasa; p. 427 left © Barrett & MacKay; right Jeff Greenberg/Image Network Inc.; p. 428 With permission from Terms of the 70s, Slang of the Seventies, http://www.inthe70s.com; p. 431 CP Photo/ Edmonton Sun/Dave Cameron; p. 433 left Garry Briand/Firstlight.ca; top right KA2004-R103-455d, Cpl John Bradley, Canadian Forces Combat Camera, National Defence, 2004, with the permission of Minister of Public Works and Government Services, 2005; centre right CP Photo/Chuck Stoody; bottom right AP Photo/Stephen Chernin; p. 441 AP Photo/ Linda Ehrichs; p. 446 top Courtesy of Canadian Forces Photographic Unit; bottom IS2005-220a Sgt. Frank Hudec, Canadian Forces Combat Camera, National Defence, 2005, with the permission of the Minister of Public Works and Government Services, 2005; p. 448 CP PHOTO/Adrian Wyld; p. 449 courtesy of Free The Children; p. 455 top left © David Muir/Masterfile; top 2nd from left CP Photo/Peter Kneffel; top 2nd from right Stephanie Paschal/Rex Features; top right AP Photo/Carlos Osorio; bottom left Fhoto Pollex; bottom centre © Scott Tysick/Masterfile; bottom right © Cooperphoto/CORBIS; p. 459 © Roy Ooms/ Masterfile; p. 460 Photo courtesy of Bombardier Inc.; p. 461 SW Production/Maxximages.com; p. 467 Dick Hemingway; p. 470 top CP PHOTO/Frank Gunn; bottom Photo by Matt Carmichael/Getty Images; p. 473 top left NATO Photos; right IS2005-1029a, MCpl Paul MacGregor, Canadian Forces Combat Camera, National Defence, 2005, with the permission of the Minister of Public Works and Government Services Canada, 2005; bottom left IS2003-2552a, Sgt. Frank Hudec, Canadian Forces Combat Camera, National Defence, 2003, with the permission of the Minister of Public Works and Government Services Canada, 2005; p. 475 left Nick Kim; top right Photo by Matthew Simmons/Getty Images; centre right © Dale Wilson/Masterfile; bottom right © J.A. Kraulis/ Masterfile; p. 485 Photo Courtesy of City of Dawson Creek, Photographer Rod Harmon; p. 490 © Canadian Broadcasting Corporation; p. 495 CP/AP/Pavel

Rahman; p. 499 left CP PHOTO/Jacques Boissinot; p. 500 Mark E. Gibson/Visuals Unlimited; p. 504 © Damir Frkovic/Masterfile; p. 505 AP/John McConnico; p. 506 CP/Kevin Frayer; p. 508 CP/Mike Thomas; p. 510 CP/Kevin Frayer; p. 512 Pierre Verdy/AFP/Getty Images; p. 514 left © Colin Garratt; Milepost 92 ? /CORBIS; right © William Campbell/ CORBIS; p. 521 left © Canstock Images/Maxx Images.com; centre CP Photo/Larry McDougal; right © Ed Young/CORBIS; p. 528 Firstlight.ca; p. 531 © UNESCO; p. 532 Earth Day Canada - www.earthday.ca

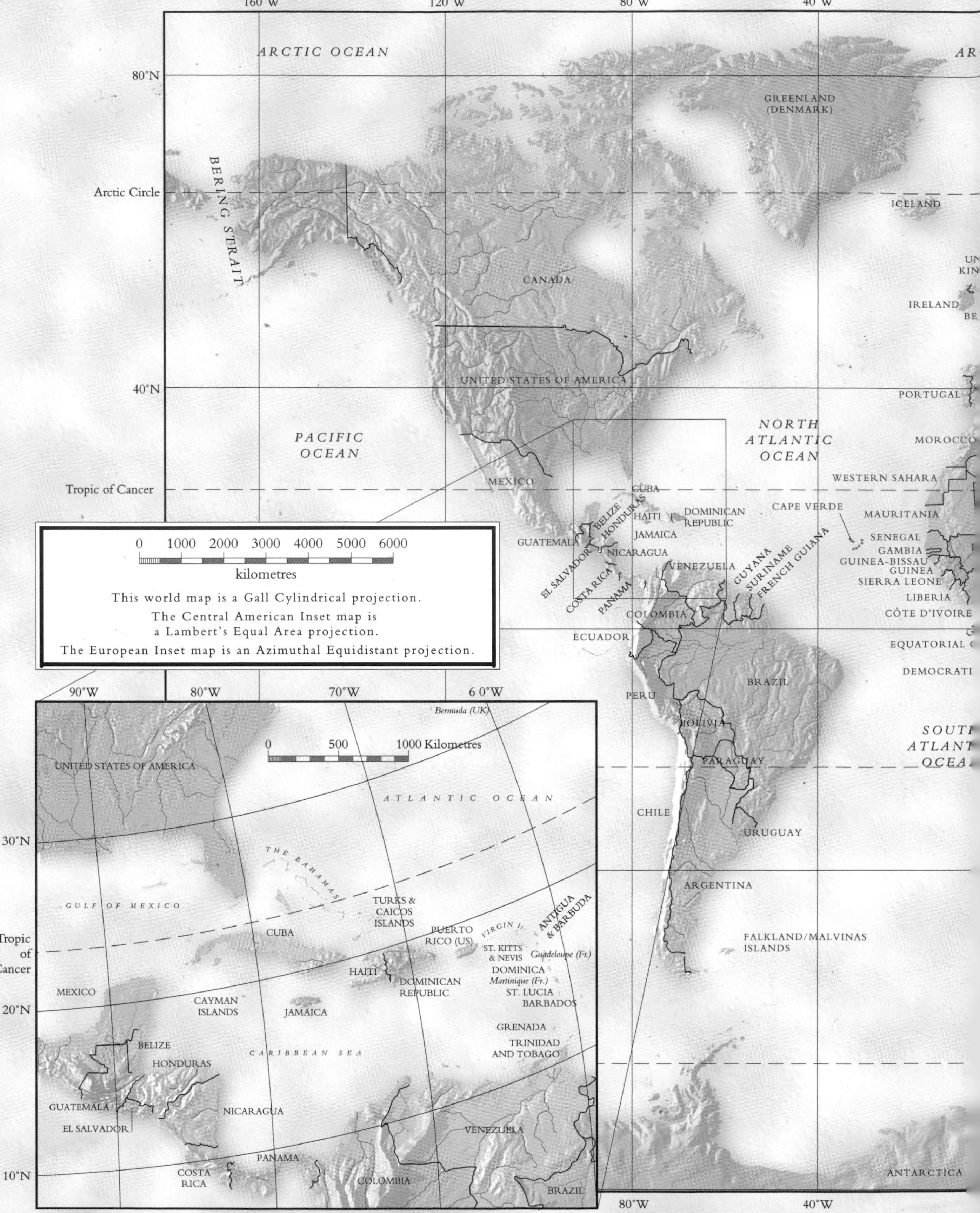

160°W
120°W
80°W
40°W
80°N
40°N
Arctic Circle
Tropic of Cancer
ARCTIC OCEAN
BERING STRAIT
GREENLAND (DENMARK)
ICELAND
CANADA
IRELAND
UNITED STATES OF AMERICA
PORTUGAL
PACIFIC OCEAN
NORTH ATLANTIC OCEAN
MOROCCO
MEXICO
WESTERN SAHARA
CUBA
CAPE VERDE
MAURITANIA
BELIZE
HONDURAS
HAITI
DOMINICAN REPUBLIC
GUATEMALA
JAMAICA
SENEGAL
GAMBIA
GUINEA-BISSAU
GUINEA
SIERRA LEONE
LIBERIA
CÔTE D'IVOIRE
EQUATORIAL
DEMOCRATI
NICARAGUA
EL SALVADOR
COSTA RICA
PANAMA
VENEZUELA
GUYANA
SURINAME
FRENCH GUIANA
COLOMBIA
ECUADOR
BRAZIL
PERU
BOLIVIA
PARAGUAY
CHILE
URUGUAY
ARGENTINA
FALKLAND/MALVINAS ISLANDS
ANTARCTICA
0 1000 2000 3000 4000 5000 6000
kilometres
This world map is a Gall Cylindrical projection.
The Central American Inset map is a Lambert's Equal Area projection.
The European Inset map is an Azimuthal Equidistant projection.
90°W
80°W
70°W
60°W
30°N
20°N
10°N
Tropic of Cancer
Bermuda (UK)
0 500 1000 Kilometres
UNITED STATES OF AMERICA
ATLANTIC OCEAN
THE BAHAMAS
GULF OF MEXICO
TURKS & CAICOS ISLANDS
ANTIGUA & BARBUDA
CUBA
PUERTO RICO (US)
VIRGIN Is.
ST. KITTS & NEVIS
Guadeloupe (Fr.)
DOMINICA
Martinique (Fr.)
HAITI
DOMINICAN REPUBLIC
MEXICO
CAYMAN ISLANDS
JAMAICA
ST. LUCIA
BARBADOS
GRENADA
TRINIDAD AND TOBAGO
BELIZE
CARIBBEAN SEA
HONDURAS
GUATEMALA
EL SALVADOR
NICARAGUA
VENEZUELA
PANAMA
COSTA RICA
COLOMBIA
BRAZIL